Ask the Authors!

We have taught math for many years. During that time, we have had students ask us a number of questions about mathematics and this course. Here you find some of the questions we have been asked most often, starting with the big one.

Dick Aufmann   **Joanne Lockwood**

Why do I have to take this course? You may have heard that *"Math is everywhere."* That is probably a slight exaggeration, but math does find its way into many disciplines. There are obvious places like engineering, science, and medicine. There are other disciplines such as business, social science, and political science where math may be less obvious but still essential. If you are going to be an artist, writer, or musician, the direct connection to math may be even less obvious. Even so, as art historians who have studied the Mona Lisa have shown, there is a connection to math. But, suppose you find these reasons not all that compelling. **There is still a reason to learn basic math skills: You will be a better consumer and be able to make better financial choices for you and your family.** For instance, is it better to buy a car or lease a car? Math can provide an answer.

I find math difficult. Why is that? It is true that some people, even very smart people, find math difficult. Some of this can be traced to previous math experiences. If your basic skills are lacking, it is more difficult to understand the math in a new math course. Some of the difficulty can be attributed to the ideas and concepts in math. They can be quite challenging to learn. Nonetheless, most of us can learn and understand the ideas in the math courses that are required for graduation. **If you want math to be less difficult, practice. When you have finished practicing, practice some more.** Ask an athlete, actor, singer, dancer, artist, doctor, skateboarder, or (name a profession) what it takes to become successful and the one common characteristic they all share is that they practiced—a lot.

Why is math important? As we mentioned earlier, math is found in many fields of study. There are, however, other reasons to take a math course. Primary among these reasons is to become a better problem solver. Math can help you learn critical thinking skills. It can help you develop a logical plan to solve a problem. Math can help you see relationships between ideas and to identify patterns. **When employers are asked what they look for in a new employee, being a problem solver is one of the highest ranked criteria.**

What do I need to do to pass this course? The most important thing you must do is to know and understand the requirements outlined by your instructor. These requirements are usually given to you in a syllabus. Once you know what is required, you can chart a course of action. Set time aside to study and do homework. If possible, choose your classes so that you have a free hour after your math class. Use this time to review your lecture notes, rework examples given by the instructor, and begin your homework. All of us eventually need help, so know where you can get assistance with this class. This means knowing your instructor's office hours, the hours of the math help center, and how to access available online resources. And finally, do not get behind. **Try to do some math EVERY day, even if it is for only 20 minutes.**

:ompleted by the specified date each

s   )e accumulated by any combination of the

f   s for each method listed further down

tl

1)   ....ivities using the code provided in packages purchased at
SMC bookstore.
2) (Fall and Spring only) Attend <u>Supplemental Instruction</u> sessions on scheduled
times and days.
3) (Fall and Spring only) Attend Faculty led workshops on scheduled times and
days.
4) Complete activity worksheets from specific activity workbooks **provided in
packages** purchased at SMC bookstore.

To accumulate hours towards your arranged hour commitment you must follow the directions correctly. Failure to follow these directions may result in hours not being accumulated on the official report and can result in a substandard grade.

Option 1.Online Hours (REQUIRES ACCESS CODE provided free in this new package) - use any computer –

1. Once your class begins, you will receive an email with your Web Assign log in credentials. You do not need to create a Web Assign account. One will be created for you. Go to webassign.net and select "Log In".

2. Upon logging into your new account, you will be asked for an access code. If you do not already have an access code, you can purchase one from the bookstore.

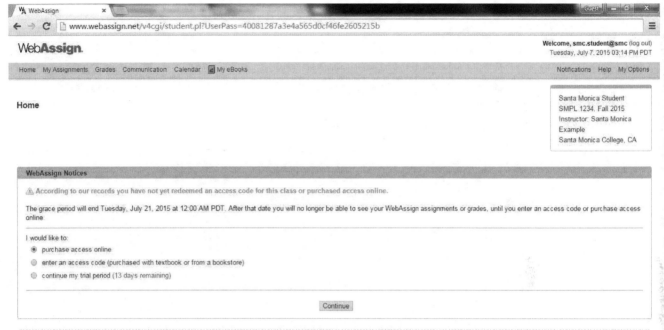

3. Once you are logged in, you will see the page below with your assignments.

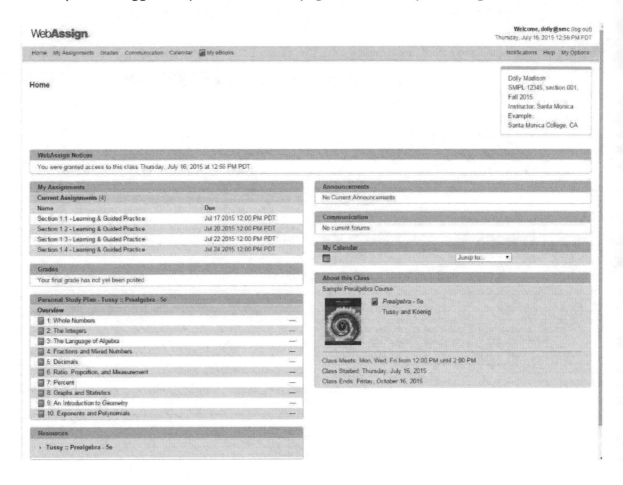

• Web Assign homework: complete assignments through the Web Assign "my assignments" tab. Students will receive 60 minutes credit toward their Arranged Hours requirement for each Homework section that is completed with a score of 70% or higher.

• Sign out: log off from the system. Assignments on homework tab with scores under 70% and completion of other material does not accumulate hours.

Option 2. Supplemental Instruction Workshops - (Spring and Fall only) see postings in MC 84 - Maximum of 2 hours per day

- Sign in: sign in on sheet provided by SI Leader, make sure to include your section number.
- Activity: participate in activities conducted by the SI Leader.
- Sign out: sign out on the sheet provided by the SI Leader. Failure to sign out results in 0 hours being accumulated.

Option 3. Faculty Led Workshops - (Spring and Fall only) see postings for times in MC 84

If the workshop takes place in MC 84, students are required to sign into the system on one of the login computers provided to help track math lab usage for budgeting and scheduling by choosing "Lab Hours", enter student id and press enter.

- Sign in on the computer next to the door
- Sign in: sign in on sheet provided by faculty Leader, make sure to include your section number.
- Activity: participate in activities conducted.
- Sign out: sign out on the sheet provided. Failure to sign out results in 0 hours being accumulated.
- Sign out on the computer next to the door as you leave the math lab.

Option 4. Activity Workbooks (REQUIRES WORKBOOKS provided free in new packages) in Math Lab - MC 84 - Maximum of 2 hours per day

Students are required to sign into the system on one of the login computers provided to help track math lab usage for budgeting and scheduling by choosing "Lab Hours", enter student id and press enter.

- Sign in on the computer next to the door
- Complete an activity of your choice found in the Learning Guide for Math 31, or workbooks at the end of the Math 81 and Math 84 packets. These books are all found in most packages sold at the bookstore.
- Take the completed activity to Judith Mosher or an Instructional Assistant and have it stamped and sign off.
- Take this stamped and signed off activity to your instructor for documentation.
- Sign out: on the computer next to the door as you leave - FYI: This computer tracks math lab usage to be used for budgeting and scheduling. It is very important to sign in and out.

How do I check my Arranged Hours?
1. Go to CC and select Enrollment
2. Choose the correct semester
3. Select "Student Records"
4. Select "Lab/Tutor Hours" icon
5. Select "Math Computer & Tutoring Lab" option from the drop down menu.

FYI: There is a time delay between online hours and SI hours when completed, and when they appear in the system.

Math 81 Essentials of Math

Santa Monica College

Revised 9th Edition

Aufmann | Lockwood

CENGAGE
Learning·

Australia • Brazil • Japan • Korea • Mexico • Singapore • Spain • United Kingdom • United States

Math 81 Essentials of Math: Santa Monica College, Revised 9th Edition

Essentials of Mathematics: An Applied Approach, 9th Edition
Richard N. Aufmann
Joanne S. Lockwood

For product information and technology assistance, contact us at
Cengage Learning Customer & Sales Support, 1-800-354-9706

For permission to use material from this text or product, submit all requests online at **cengage.com/permissions**
Further permissions questions can be emailed to
permissionrequest@cengage.com

This book contains select works from existing Cengage Learning resources and was produced by Cengage Learning Custom Solutions for collegiate use. As such, those adopting and/or contributing to this work are responsible for editorial content accuracy, continuity and completeness.

Compilation © 2015 Cengage Learning

ISBN: 9781305751248

WCN: 01-100-101

Cengage Learning
20 Channel Center Street
Boston, MA 02210
USA

Cengage Learning is a leading provider of customized learning solutions with office locations around the globe, including Singapore, the United Kingdom, Australia, Mexico, Brazil, and Japan. Locate your local office at:
www.international.cengage.com/region.

Cengage Learning products are represented in Canada by Nelson Education, Ltd.

For your lifelong learning solutions, visit **www.cengage.com/custom.**

Visit our corporate website at **www.cengage.com.**

Brief Contents

Contents

CHAPTER

2

Fractions

65

CHAPTER

3

Decimals

129

CHAPTER

4 Ratio and Proportion   177

Preface

Among the many questions we ask when we begin the process of revising a textbook, the most important is, "How can we improve the learning experience for the student?" We find answers to this question in a variety of ways, but most commonly by talking to students and instructors and by evaluating the written feedback we receive from instructors. Bearing this feedback in mind, our ultimate goal as we set out to create the ninth edition of *Essentials of Mathematics: An Applied Approach* was to provide students with more materials to help them better understand the underlying concepts presented in this course. As a result, we have made the following changes to the new edition.

New to this edition is the **Focus on Success** vignette that appears at the beginning of each chapter. **Focus on Success** offers practical tips for improving study habits and performance on tests and exams.

We now include an **Apply the Concept** box within the objectives that teach addition, subtraction, multiplication, and division. The arithmetic operation is applied to a real-world situation so that students can relate the operation to their everyday lives. For example, multiplication of whole numbers is applied to determining the total number of cans of soda in eight six-packs of soda.

The definition and key concept boxes have been enhanced in this edition; they now include examples to show how the general case translates to specific cases.

In each exercise set, the first group of exercises is now titled **Concept Check.** The **Concept Check** exercises focus on the concepts that lie behind the skills developed in the section. We consider an understanding of these concepts essential to a student's success in mastering the skills required to complete the exercises that follow.

Every chapter contains **Check Your Progress** exercises. This feature appears approximately mid-chapter and tests students' understanding of the concepts presented to that point in the chapter.

Critical Thinking exercises are included at the end of every exercise set. They may involve further exploration or analysis of the topic at hand. They may also integrate concepts introduced earlier in the text.

We trust that the new and enhanced features of the ninth edition will help students more successfully engage with the content. By narrowing the gap between the concrete and the abstract, between the real world and the theoretical, students should more plainly see that mastering the skills and topics presented is well within their reach and well worth the effort.

New to This Edition

- **Apply the Concept** boxes are provided within objectives that teach arithmetic operations.

- **Concept Check** exercises appear at the beginning of each exercise set.

- Enhanced definition/key concept boxes now provide examples that illustrate how the general case applies to specific cases.

- The **Focus on Success** feature at the beginning of each chapter offers practical guidance to help students develop positive study habits.

- **Check Your Progress** exercises appear approximately mid-chapter and test students' understanding of the concepts presented thus far in the chapter.

- **In the News** articles within the exercise sets have been updated, as have application problems throughout the text.

- **Critical Thinking** exercises appear at the end of each exercise set.

- **Projects or Group Activities** are now included at the end of each exercise set.

- **Chapter A, AIM for Success,** now appears as the first chapter of the text. This chapter describes skills used by students who have been successful in this course. Topics include how to stay motivated, making a commitment to success, time management, and how to prepare for and take tests. A guide to the textbook is included to help students use its features effectively.

- More annotations have been added to the worked Examples, to more effectively explain the steps of the solutions.

- Many of the **Chapter Summaries** have been expanded to include more entries and more descriptive explanations.

Organizational Changes

We have made the following changes in order to improve the effectiveness of the textbook and enhance the student's learning experience.

- In Chapter 1, the introductions to the four arithmetic operations were rewritten using real world applications to motivate the use of each operation.

- Section 1.5, Division of Whole Numbers, now includes additional exercises that focus on quotients and dividends that contain zero.

- Section 2.8, Order, Exponents, and the Order of Operations Agreement, was revised. Exponential notation is more fully integrated into the exercises that require the Order of Operations Agreement.

- Section 3.1 contains a new objective on comparing decimals. In the previous edition, this topic was covered later in the chapter. It was moved here to provide students with a better understanding of decimals and place value prior to the lessons on operations with decimals.

- Objective C in Section 3.6 was rewritten. There is now greater emphasis on the topic of comparing fractions and decimals.

- Section 5.1 now contains more examples of converting from a percent to a fraction or from a percent to a decimal. In Objective B of this section, students are given more practice in converting from a fraction or a decimal to a percent. The Section 5.1 exercise set was revised extensively to provide the student with a significantly improved selection of exercises.

- Section 6.1, Applications to Purchasing, was rewritten and now includes real world examples to motivate the topics of unit cost and finding the most economical purchase.

- Accompanying Chapter 6 are new and expanded compound interest rate tables as well as a new and expanded Monthly Payment Table to calculate mortgage and car loan payments.

- Section 6.4, Real Estate Expenses, was rewritten to include contemporary topics and interest rates.

Take AIM and Succeed!

An Objective-Based Approach

Essentials of Mathematics: An Applied Approach is organized around a carefully constructed hierarchy of **objectives.** This "objective-based" approach provides an integrated learning path that enables you to find resources such as assessment tools (both within the text and online), videos, tutorials, and additional exercises for each objective in the text.

1 Each Chapter Opener outlines the learning **OBJECTIVES** that appear in each section of the chapter. The list of objectives serves as a resource to guide you in your study and review of the topics.

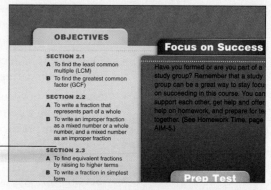

2 Taking the **PREP TEST** for each chapter will help you determine which topics you need to study more carefully and which topics you need only review. The **ANSWERS** to the **PREP TEST** provide references to the **OBJECTIVES** on which the exercises are based.

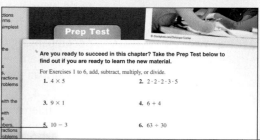

3 In every section, an **OBJECTIVE STATEMENT** introduces each new topic of discussion. Videos are available for each objective.

SECTION

2.1 The Least Common Multiple and Greatest Common Factor

OBJECTIVE A *To find the least common multiple (LCM)*

Tips for Success
Before you begin a new chapter, you should take some time to review previously learned skills.

The **multiples of a number** are the products of that number and the numbers 1, 2, 3, 4, 5, ...

$3 \times 1 = 3$
$3 \times 2 = 6$
$3 \times 3 = 9$

4 Section exercises are keyed to **OBJECTIVE STATEMENTS.**

OBJECTIVE A *To find the least common multiple (LCM)*

For Exercises 11 to 40, find the LCM.

11. 5, 8	12. 3, 6	13. 3, 8	14. 2, 5	15. 4, 6
16. 6, 8	17. 8, 12	18. 12, 16	19. 5, 12	20. 3, 16
21. 8, 14	22. 4, 10	23. 8, 32	24. 7, 21	25. 9, 36

An Objective-Based Review

This "objective-based" approach continues through the end-of-chapter review and addresses a broad range of study styles by offering a **wide variety of review tools.**

 CHECK YOUR PROGRESS exercises appear approximately mid-chapter and test your understanding of the concepts presented up to that point in the chapter.

> ✔ **CHECK YOUR PROGRESS: CHAPTER 2**
>
> 1. Graph −3 on the number line.
>   −6 −5 −4 −3 −2 −1 0 1 2 3 4 5 6
>
> 2. On the number line, which number is 5 units to the left of 2?
>
> 3. Place the correct symbol, < or >, between the two numbers.
>   −12   −16
>
> 4. Write the given numbers in order from smallest to largest.
>   −8, 7, −19, 4

At the end of each chapter, you will find a **CHAPTER SUMMARY** containing **KEY WORDS** and **ESSENTIAL RULES AND PROCEDURES** presented in the chapter. Each entry includes an objective reference and a page reference that show where in the chapter the concept was introduced. An example demonstrating the concept is also included.

> **CHAPTER**
>
> **3**   Summary
>
> **Key Words**   **Examples**
>
> A number written in decimal notation has three parts: a whole-   For the decimal 31.25, 3
> number part, a decimal point, and a decimal part. The decimal   number part and 25 is the
> part of a number represents a number less than 1. A number written in
> decimal notation is often simply called a decimal. [3.1A, p. 130]

By completing the **CHAPTER REVIEW EXERCISES,** you can practice working on problems in an order that is different from the order in which they were presented in the chapter. The **ANSWER** to each Chapter Review exercise includes a reference to the objective on which the exercise is based. This reference will help you quickly identify where to go if you need further practice with a particular concept.

> **CHAPTER**
>
> **3**   Review Exercises
>
> 1. Find the quotient of 3.6515 and 0.067.   2. Find the sum of 369.41, 88.3, 9.774,

Each **CHAPTER TEST** is designed to simulate a typical test of the concepts covered in the chapter. Each **ANSWER** includes an objective reference as well as a reference to a numbered Example, You Try It, or HOW TO in the text that is similar to the given test question.

> **CHAPTER**
>
> **3**   TEST
>
> 1. Place the correct symbol, < or >, between the two   2. Subtract: 13.027 − 8.94
>   numbers.
>   0.0068   0.000963

CUMULATIVE REVIEW EXERCISES, which appear at the end of each chapter (beginning with Chapter 2), help you maintain previously learned skills. The **ANSWERS** include references to the section objectives on which the exercises are based.

> **Cumulative Review Exercises**
>
> 1. Divide: 89)‾20,932   2. Simplify: $2^3 \cdot 4^2$
>
> 3. Simplify: $2^2 − (7 − 3) \div 2 + 1$ 4. Find the LCM of 9, 12, and 24.

Understanding the Concepts

Each of the following features is designed to give you a fuller understanding of the key concepts.

 CONCEPT CHECK exercises promote conceptual understanding. Completing these exercises will deepen your understanding of the concepts you are learning and provide the foundation you need to successfully complete the remaining exercises in the exercise set.

Definition/key concept boxes contain examples to illustrate how each definition or key concept is applied in practice.

TAKE NOTE boxes alert you to concepts that require special attention.

POINT OF INTEREST boxes, which relate to the topic under discussion, may be historical in nature or of general interest.

Application of the Concepts

The section exercises offer many opportunities to put the concepts you are learning into practice.

 APPLY THE CONCEPT boxes illustrate how an arithmetic operation is applied to a real-world situation so that you understand how the operation is used in everyday life.

OBJECTIVE A   *To multiply a number by a single digit*

Multiplication is used to find the total number of objects in several groups when each group contains the same number of objects.

APPLY THE CONCEPT ....

Sebastian purchased 8 six-packs of soda for a party. The total number of cans of soda he purchased can be found by adding 6 eight times. Sebastian purchased 48 cans of soda.

$6 + 6 + 6 + 6 + 6 + 6 + 6 + 6 = 48$

The number of cans can also be found by using multiplication.

$$6 \quad \times \quad 8 \quad = \quad 48$$

Multiplicand × Multiplier = Product

The **multiplicand** is the number of objects in each group (6 cans in each six-pack); the **multiplier** is the number of groups (8 six-packs); the **product** is the total number of objects (48 cans). Frequently we will discuss the *factors* of a product. A **factor** is one of the numbers that are multiplied to obtain a product. 6 and 8 are factors of 48.

Here is a table of basic multiplication facts. These facts should be memorized.

Basic Multiplication Facts

THINK ABOUT IT exercises promote deeper conceptual understanding. Completing these exercises will expand your understanding of the concepts being addressed.

30. $1347 - 103$ **31.** $9999 - 6794$ **32.** $1525 - 702$ **33.** $8843 - 7621$ **34.** 7806

For Exercises 35 and 36, find two whole numbers with the given difference and sum.

35. Difference = 2; sum = 8   **36.** Difference = 5; sum = 9

 CRITICAL THINKING exercises may involve further exploration or analysis of the topic at hand. They may also integrate concepts introduced earlier in the text.

Critical Thinking

80. If you roll two ordinary six-sided dice and add the two numbers that appear on top, how many different sums are possible?

81. If you add two *different* whole numbers, is the sum always greater than either one of the numbers? If not, give an example.

82. If you add two whole numbers, is the sum always greater than either one of the numbers? If not, give an example. (Compare this with Exercise 81.)

83. Make up a word problem for which the answer is the sum of 34 and 28.

84. Call a number "lucky" if it ends in a 7. How many lucky numbers are less than 100?

Working through the application exercises that contain **REAL DATA** will prepare you to answer questions and solve problems that you encounter outside of class, using facts and information that you gather on your own.

IN THE NEWS exercises help you understand the importance of mathematics in our everyday world. These application exercises are based on information taken from popular media sources such as newspapers, magazines, and the Internet.

104. **College Education**   See the news clipping at the right.
   a. Find the average cost of tuition, room, and board for 4 years at a public university.
   b. Find the average cost of tuition, room, and board for 4 years at a private university.
   c. Find the difference in the average cost of tuition, room, and board for 4 years at a private university and 4 years at a public university.

Construction   The table at the right below shows the hourly wages for four types of jobs at a small construction company. Use this table for Exercises 105 to 107.

105. The owner of this company wants to provide the electrical installation for a new house. On the basis of the architectural plans, it is estimated that the installation will require 3 electricians, each working 50 hours, to complete

In the NEWS!

Comparing Tuition Costs

The average annual cost of tuition, room, and board at a four-year public university is $15,875. At a four-year private university, the average cost is $42,841.

Source: National Center for Education Statistics

By completing the **WRITING** exercises, you will improve your communication skills while increasing your understanding of mathematical concepts.

Critical Thinking

96. A survey was conducted to determine people's favorite color from among blue, green, red, purple, and other. The surveyor claims that $\frac{1}{3}$ of the people responded blue, $\frac{1}{6}$ responded green, $\frac{1}{8}$ responded red, $\frac{1}{12}$ responded purple, and $\frac{2}{5}$ responded some other color. Is this possible? Explain your answer.

Projects or Group Activities

A **unit fraction** is a fraction with numerator 1 and denominator greater than 1. For instance, $\frac{1}{2}$ and $\frac{1}{15}$ are unit fractions.

Focus on Study Skills

An emphasis on setting a foundation of good study habits is woven into the text.

UPDATED!

CHAPTER A, AIM FOR SUCCESS, outlines study skills that are used by students who have been successful in this course. By making Chapter A the first chapter of the text, the stage is set for a successful beginning to the course.

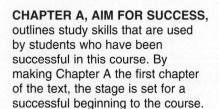

New ▶ FOCUS ON SUCCESS appears at the start of each Chapter Opener. These tips are designed to help you make the most of the text and your time as you progress through the course and prepare for tests and exams.

TIPS FOR SUCCESS boxes outline good study habits and function as reminders throughout the text.

Focus on Skills and Problem Solving

The following features exemplify the emphasis on skills and the problem-solving process.

HOW TO examples provide solutions with detailed explanations for selected topics in each section.

INTEGRATING TECHNOLOGY margin notes offer optional instruction in the use of a scientific calculator.

The **EXAMPLE/YOU TRY IT** matched pairs are designed to actively involve you in the learning process. The You Try Its are based on the Examples. These problems are paired so that you can easily refer to the steps in the Example as you work through the accompanying You Try It.

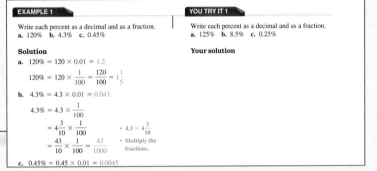

Complete, **WORKED-OUT SOLUTIONS** to the You Try Its are included in an appendix at the back of the text. Compare your solution to the solution given in the appendix to obtain immediate feedback and reinforcement of the concept you are studying.

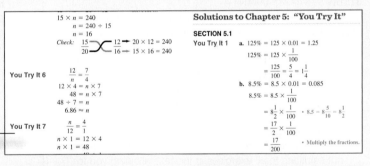

The **PROBLEM-SOLVING APPROACH** used throughout the text emphasizes the importance of problem-solving strategies. Model strategies are presented as guides for you to follow as you attempt the You Try Its that accompany the numbered Examples.

PROJECTS OR GROUP ACTIVITIES appear at the end of each exercise set. Your instructor may assign these individually, or you may be asked to work through the activities in groups.

Additional Resources —
Get More from Your Textbook!

Instructor Resources

Annotated Instructor's Edition (AIE)
(ISBN 978-1-285-09664-3)

The Annotated Instructor's Edition features answers to all of the problems in the text, as well as an appendix denoting those problems that can be found in Enhanced WebAssign.

PowerLecture with Diploma®
(ISBN 978-1-285-09462-5)

This DVD provides the instructor with dynamic media tools for teaching. Create, deliver, and customize tests (both print and online) in minutes with Diploma's Computerized Testing featuring algorithmic equations. Easily build solution sets for homework or exams using Solution Builder's online solutions manual. Quickly and easily update your syllabus with the Syllabus Creator, which was created by the authors and contains the new edition's table of contents.

Complete Solutions Manual (ISBN 978-1-285-09439-7)
Author: Carrie Green

The Complete Solutions Manual provides worked-out solutions to all of the problems in the text.

Instructor's Resource Binder with Appendix
(ISBN 978-1-285-09664-3)

Author: Maria H. Andersen, Muskegon Community College; Appendices by Richard N. Aufmann, Palomar College, and Joanne S. Lockwood, Nashua Community College

Each section of the main text is discussed in uniquely designed Teaching Guides that contain tips, examples, activities, worksheets, overheads, assessments, and solutions to all worksheets and activities.

Solution Builder

This online instructor database offers complete, worked-out solutions to all exercises in the text, allowing you to create customized, secure solutions printouts (in PDF format) matched exactly to the problems you assign in class. For more information, visit www.cengage.com/solutionbuilder.

Enhanced WebAssign® (ISBN 978-0-538-73810-1)

Exclusively from Cengage Learning, Enhanced WebAssign combines the exceptional mathematics content that you know and love with the most powerful online homework solution, WebAssign. Enhanced WebAssign engages students with immediate feedback, rich tutorial content, and interactive, fully customizable eBooks (YouBook), helping students to develop a deeper conceptual understanding of their subject matter. Online assignments can be built by selecting from thousands of text-specific problems or supplemented with problems from any Cengage Learning textbook.

Student Resources

Student Solutions Manual
(ISBN 978-1-285-09173-0)
Author: Carrie Green

Go beyond answers and improve your grade! This manual provides worked-out, step-by-step solutions to the odd-numbered problems in the text. The Student Solutions Manual gives you the information you need to truly understand how the problems are solved.

Student Workbook (ISBN 978-1-285-09466-3)
Author: Maria H. Andersen, Muskegon Community College

Get a head start. The Student Workbook contains assessments, activities, and worksheets for classroom discussions, in-class activities, and group work.

AIM for Success Student Practice Sheets
(ISBN 978-1-285-09719-0)
Author: Christine S. Verity

AIM for Success Student Practice Sheets provide additional problems to help you learn the material.

Enhanced WebAssign (ISBN 978-0-538-73810-1)

Enhanced WebAssign (assigned by the instructor) provides you with instant feedback on homework assignments. This online homework system is easy to use and includes helpful links to textbook sections, video examples, and problem-specific tutorials.

Acknowledgments

The authors would like to thank the people who have reviewed the ninth edition and provided many valuable suggestions.

Becky Bradshaw, *Lake Superior College*
Harvey Cartine, *Warren County Community College*
Jim Dawson, *College of Southern Idaho*
Cindy Dickson, *College of Southern Idaho*
Estella G. Elliott, *College of Southern Idaho*
Stephen Ester, *Saint Petersburg College*
Cassie Firth, *Northern Oklahoma College*
Lori L. Grady, *University of Wisconsin–Whitewater*
Nicholas Grener, *California State University, East Bay*
Ryan Grossman, *Ivy Tech Community College–Indiana*
Autumn Hoover, *Angelo State University*
Pat Horacek, *Pensacola State College*
Kelly Jackson, *Camden County College*
Thomas Judge, *California State University, East Bay*
Katy Koe, *Lincoln College*
William Lind, *Bryant and Stratton College*
Renee Lustig, *LeCordon Bleu College of Culinary Arts*
David Maina, *Columbia College, Chicago*
Connie Meade, *College of Southern Idaho*
Eugenia M. Moreno, *Butte Community College*
Dan Quynh Nguyen, *California State University, East Bay*
Rod Oberdick, *Delaware Technical Community College*
Scott Phelps, *University of La Verne*
David Poock, *Davenport University*
Nolan Thomas Rice, *College of Southern Idaho*
Daria Santerre, *Norwalk Community College*
Patricia Shepherd, *Ivy Tech Community College*
Darlyn Thomas, *Hennepin Technical College*
Sherri Urcavich, *University of Wisconsin–Green Bay*
Dr. Pamela D. Walker, *Northwestern College*
Donna M. Weglarz, *Westwood College–DuPage*
Lisa Williams, *College of the Abermarle*
Solomon Lee Willis, *Cleveland Community College*
Jerry Jacob Woods, *Westwood College*
Chen Zhixiong, *New Jersey City University*

Special thanks go to Jean Bermingham for copyediting the manuscript and proofreading pages, to Carrie Green for preparing the solutions manuals, and to Lauri Semarne for her work in ensuring the accuracy of the text. We would also like to thank the many people at Cengage Learning who worked to guide the manuscript for the ninth edition from development through production.

Index of Applications

AIM for Success

A

Focus on Success

This important chapter describes study skills that are used by students who have been successful in this course. Chapter A covers a wide range of topics that focus on what you need to do to succeed in this class. It includes a complete guide to the textbook and how to use its features to become a successful student.

hxdbzxy/Shutterstock.com

Prep Test

Are you ready to succeed in this course?

1. Read this chapter. Answer all of the questions. Write down your answers on paper.

2. Write down your instructor's name.

3. Write down the classroom number.

4. Write down the days and times the class meets.

5. Bring your textbook, a notebook, and a pen or pencil to every class.

6. Be an active participant, not a passive observer.

A.1 How to Succeed in This Course

Get Ready

We are committed to your success in learning mathematics and have developed many tools and resources to support you along the way.

DO YOU WANT TO EXCEL IN THIS COURSE?

Read on to learn about the skills you'll need and how best to use this book to get the results you want.

We have written this text in an *interactive* style. More about this later but, in short, this means that you are supposed to interact with the text. Do not just read the text! Work along with it. Ready? Let's begin!

WHY ARE YOU TAKING THIS COURSE?

Did you interact with the text, or did you just read the last question? Get some paper and a pencil or pen and answer the question. Really—you will have more success in math and other courses you take if you **actively participate.** Now, **interact.** Write down one reason you are taking this course.

```
┌─────────────────────────────────────────────────────────────┐
│                                                             │
│                                                             │
│                                                             │
│                                                             │
└─────────────────────────────────────────────────────────────┘
```

Of course, we have no idea what you just wrote, but experience has shown us that many of you wrote something along the lines of "I have to take it to graduate" or "It is a pre-requisite to another course I have to take" or "It is required for my major." Those reasons are perfectly fine. Every teacher has had to take courses that were not directly related to his or her major.

WHY DO YOU WANT TO SUCCEED IN THIS COURSE?

Think about why you want to succeed in this course. List the reasons here (not in your head . . . on the paper!):

```
┌─────────────────────────────────────────────────────────────┐
│                                                             │
│                                                             │
│                                                             │
└─────────────────────────────────────────────────────────────┘
```

One reason you may have listed is that math skills are important in order to be successful in your chosen career. That is certainly an important reason. Here are some other reasons.

- Math is a skill that applies across careers, which is certainly a benefit in our world of changing job requirements. A good foundation in math may enable you to more easily make a career change.
- Math can help you learn critical thinking skills, an attribute all employers want.
- Math can help you see relationships between ideas and identify patterns.

Take Note

Motivation alone won't lead to success. For example, suppose a person who cannot swim is rowed out to the middle of a lake and thrown overboard. That person has a lot of motivation to swim, but most likely will drown without some help. You'll need motivation *and* learning in order to succeed.

Motivate Yourself

You'll find many real-life problems in this book, relating to sports, money, cars, music, and more. We hope that these topics will help you understand how mathematics is used in everyday life. To learn all of the necessary skills and to understand how you can apply them to your life outside of this course, motivate yourself to learn.

One of the reasons we asked you why you are taking this course was to provide motivation for you to succeed. When there is a reason to do something, that task is easier to accomplish. We understand that you may not want to be taking this course but, to achieve your career goal, this is a necessary step. Let your career goal be your motivation for success.

MAKE THE COMMITMENT TO SUCCEED!

With practice, you will improve your math skills. Skeptical? Think about when you first learned to drive a car, ride a skateboard, dance, paint, surf, or any other talent that you now have. You may have felt self-conscious or concerned that you might fail. But with time and practice, you learned the skill.

List a situation in which you accomplished your goal by spending time practicing and perfecting your skills (such as learning to play the piano or to play basketball):

You do not get "good" at something by doing it once a week. **Practice** is the backbone of any successful endeavor—including math!

Develop a "Can Do" Attitude Toward Math

You can do math! When you first learned the skills you just listed above, you may not have done them well. With practice, you got better. With practice, you will get better at math. Stay focused, motivated, and committed to success.

We cannot emphasize enough how important it is to overcome the "I Can't Do Math" syndrome. If you listen to interviews of very successful athletes after a particularly bad performance, you will note that they focus on the positive aspects of what they did, not the negative. Sports psychologists encourage athletes always to be positive—to have a "can do" attitude. Develop this attitude toward math and you will succeed.

Change your conversation about mathematics. Do not say "I can't do math," "I hate math," or "Math is too hard." These comments just give you an excuse to fail. You don't want to fail, and we don't want you to fail. Write it down now: **I can do math!**

Strategies for Success

PREPARE TO SUCCEED

There are a number of things that may be worrisome to you as you begin a new semester. List some of those things now.

Here are some of the concerns expressed by our students.

- **Tuition**
  Will I be able to afford school?
- **Job**
  I must work. Will my employer give me a schedule that will allow me to go to school?
- **Anxiety**
  Will I succeed?
- **Child care**
  What will I do with my kids while I'm in class or when I need to study?
- **Time**
  Will I be able to find the time to attend class and study?
- **Degree goals**
  How long will it take me to finish school and earn my degree?

These are all important and valid concerns. Whatever your concerns, acknowledge them. Choose an education path that allows you to accommodate your concerns. Make sure they don't prevent you from succeeding.

SELECT A COURSE

Many schools offer math assessment tests. These tests evaluate your present math skills. They don't evaluate how smart you are, so don't worry about your score on the test. If you are unsure about where you should start in the math curriculum, these tests can show you where to begin. You are better off starting at a level that is appropriate for you than starting with a more advanced class and then dropping it because you can't keep up. Dropping a class is a waste of time and money.

If you have difficulty with math, avoid short courses that compress the class into a few weeks. If you have struggled with math in the past, this environment does not give you the time to process math concepts. Similarly, avoid classes that meet once a week. The time delay between classes makes it difficult to make connections between concepts.

Some career goals require a number of math courses. If that is true of your major, try to take a math course every semester until you complete the requirements. Think about it this way. If you take, say, French I, and then wait two semesters before taking French II, you may forget a lot of material. Math is much the same. You must keep the concepts fresh in your mind.

Time Management

One of the most important requirements in completing any task is to acknowledge the amount of time it will take to finish the job successfully. Before a construction company starts to build a skyscraper, the company spends months looking at how much time each of the phases of construction will take. This is done so that resources can be allocated when appropriate. For instance, it would not make sense to schedule the electricians to run wiring until the walls are up.

MANAGE YOUR TIME!

We know how busy you are outside of school. Do you have a full-time or a part-time job? Do you have children? Do you visit your family often? Do you play school sports or participate in the school orchestra or theater company? It can be stressful to balance all of the important activities and responsibilities in your life. Creating a time management plan will help you schedule enough time to do everything you need to do. Let's get started.

First, you need a calendar. You can use a daily planner, a calendar for a smartphone, or an online calendar, such as the ones offered by Google, MSN, or Yahoo. It is best to have a calendar on which you can fill in daily activities and be able to see a weekly or monthly view as well.

Start filling in your calendar now, even if it means stopping right here and finding a calendar. Some of the things you might include are:

- The hours each class meets
- Time for driving to and from work or school
- Leisure time, an important aspect of a healthy lifestyle
- Time for study. Plan at least one hour of study for each hour in class. This is a *minimum!*
- Time to eat
- Your work schedule
- Time for extracurricular activities such as sports, music lessons, or volunteer work
- Time for family and friends
- Time for sleep
- Time for exercise

We really hope you did this. If not, please reconsider. One of the best pathways to success is understanding how much time it takes to succeed. When you finish your calendar, if it does not allow you enough time to stay physically and emotionally healthy, rethink some of your school or work activities. We don't want you to lose your job because you have to study math. On the other hand, we don't want you to fail in math because of your job.

If math is particularly difficult for you, consider taking fewer course units during the semesters you take math. This applies equally to any other subject that you may find difficult. There is no rule that you must finish college in four years. It is a myth—discard it now.

Now extend your calendar for the entire semester. Many of the entries will repeat, such as the time a class meets. In your extended calendar, include significant events that may disrupt your normal routine. These might include holidays, family outings, birthdays, anniversaries, or special events such as a concert or a football game. In addition to these events, be sure to include the dates of tests, the date of the final exam, and dates that projects or papers are due. These are all important semester events. Having them on your calendar will remind you that you need to make time for them.

CLASS TIME

To be successful, attend class. You should consider your commitment to attend class as serious as your commitment to your job or to keeping an appointment with a dear friend. It is difficult to overstate the importance of attending class. If you miss work, you don't get paid. If you miss class, you are not getting the full benefit of your tuition dollar. You are losing money.

If, by some unavoidable situation, you cannot attend class, find out as soon as possible what was covered in class. You might:

- Ask a friend for notes and the assignment.
- Contact your instructor and get the assignment. Missing class is no excuse for not being prepared for the next class.
- Determine whether there are online resources that you can use to help you with the topics and concepts that were discussed in the class you missed.

Going to class is important. Once you are there, participate in class. Stay involved and active. When your instructor asks a question, try to at least mentally answer the question. If you have a question, ask. Your instructor expects questions and wants you to understand the concept being discussed.

HOMEWORK TIME

In addition to attending class, you must do homework. Homework is the best way to reinforce the ideas presented in class. You should plan on at least one to two hours of

Take Note

Be realistic about how much time you have. One gauge is that working 10 hours per week is approximately equivalent to taking one three-unit course. If your college considers 15 units a full load and you are working 10 hours per week, you should consider taking 12 units. The more you work, the fewer units you should take.

CandyBox Images/Shutterstock.com

homework and study for each hour you are in class. We've had many students tell us that one to two hours seems like a lot of time. That may be true, but if you want to attain your goals, you must be willing to devote the time to being successful in this math course.

You should schedule study time just as if it were class time. To do this, write down where and when you study best. For instance, do you study best at home, in the library, at the math center, under a tree, or somewhere else? Some psychologists who research successful study strategies suggest that just by varying where you study, you can increase the effectiveness of a study session. While you are considering where you prefer to study, also think about the time of day during which your study period will be most productive. Write down your thoughts.

Look at what you have written, and be sure that you can consistently be in your favorite study environment at the time you have selected. Studying and homework are extremely important. Just as you should not miss class, **do not miss study time.**

Before we leave this important topic, we have a few suggestions. If at all possible, create a study hour right after class. The material will be fresh in your mind, and the immediate review, along with your homework, will help reinforce the concepts you are learning.

If you can't study right after class, make sure that you set aside some time *on the day of the class* to review notes and begin the homework. The longer you wait, the more difficult it will be to recall some of the important points covered during class. Study math in small chunks—one hour a day (perhaps not enough for most of us), every day, is better than seven hours in one sitting. If you are studying for an extended period of time, break up your study session by studying one subject for a while and then moving on to another subject. Try to alternate between similar or related courses. For instance, study math for a while, then science, and then back to math. Or study history for a while, then political science, and then back to history.

Meet some of the people in your class and try to **put together a study group.** The group could meet two or three times a week. During those meetings, you could quiz each other, prepare for a test, try to explain a concept to someone else in the group, or get help on a topic that is difficult for you.

After reading these suggestions, you may want to rethink where and when you study best. If so, do that now. Remember, however, that it is your individual style that is important. Choose what works for *you,* and stick to it.

Habits of Successful Students

There are a number of habits that successful students use. Think about what these might be, and write them down.

What you have written is very important. The habits you have listed are probably the things you know you must do to succeed. Here is a list of some responses from successful students we have known.

- **Set priorities.** You will encounter many distractions during the semester. Do not allow them to prevent you from reaching your goal.

- **Take responsibility.** Your instructor, this textbook, tutors, math centers, and other resources are there to help you succeed. Ultimately, however, you must choose to learn. You must choose success.

- **Hang out with successful students.** Success breeds success. When you work and study with successful students, you are in an environment that will help you succeed. Seek out people who are committed to their goals.

- **Study regularly.** We have mentioned this before, but it is too important not to be repeated.

- **Self test.** Once every few days, select homework exercises from previous assignments and use them to test your understanding. Try to do these exercises without getting help from examples in the text. These self tests will help you gain confidence that you can do these types of problems on a test given in class.

- **Try different strategies.** If you read the text and are still having difficulty understanding a concept, consider going a step further. Contact the instructor or find a tutor. Many campuses have some free tutorial services. Go to the math or learning center. Consult another textbook. Be active and get the help you need.

- **Make flash cards.** This is one of the strategies that some math students do not think to try. Flash cards are a very important part of learning math. For instance, your instructor may use words or phrases such as *linear, quadratic, exponent, base, rational,* and many others. If you don't know the meanings of these words, you will not know what is being discussed.

- **Plod along.** Your education is not a race. The primary goal is to finish. Taking too many classes and then dropping some does not get you to the end any faster. Take only as many classes as you can successfully manage.

SECTION

A.2 How to Use This Text to Succeed in This Course

Get the Big Picture

One of the major resources that you will have access to the entire semester is this textbook. We have written this text with you and your success in mind. The following is a guide to the features of this text that will help you succeed.

Actually, we want you to get the *really* big picture. Take a few minutes to read the table of contents. You may feel some anxiety about all the new concepts you will be learning. Try to think of this as an exciting opportunity to learn math. Now look through the entire book. Move quickly. Don't spend more than a few seconds on each page. Scan titles, look at pictures, and notice diagrams.

Getting this "big picture" view will help you see where this course is going. To reach your goal, it's important to get an idea of the steps you will need to take along the way.

As you look through the book, find topics that interest you. What's your preference? Racing? Sailing? TV? Amusement parks? Find the Index of Applications at the front of the book, and pull out three subjects that interest you. Write those topics here.

Understand the Organization

Look again at the Table of Contents. There are six chapters in this book. You'll see that every chapter is divided into sections, and each section contains a number of learning objectives. Each learning objective is labeled with a letter from A to D. Knowing how this book is organized will help you locate important topics and concepts as you're studying.

Before you start a new objective, take a few minutes to read the Objective Statement for that objective. Then, browse through the objective material. Especially note the words or phrases in bold type—these are important concepts that you'll need to know as you move along in the course. These words are good candidates for flash cards. If possible, include an example of the concept on the flash card, as shown at the left.

You will also see important concepts and rules set off in boxes. Here is one about the Multiplication Property of One. These rules are also good candidates for flash cards.

Flash Card

Multiplication Property
of One

Multiplying a number
by 1 does not change
the number.

Examples:
8 × 1 = 8
1 × 6 = 6

Multiplication Property of One
Multiplying a number by 1 does not change the number.
EXAMPLES
1. 8 × 1 = 8   **2.** 1 × 6 = 6

Leaf through Section 1.2 of Chapter 1. Write down the words in bold and any concepts or rules that are displayed in boxes.

Use the Interactive Method

As we mentioned earlier, this textbook is based on an interactive approach. We want you to be actively involved in learning mathematics, and have given you many suggestions for getting "hands-on" with this book.

HOW TO Look on page 27. See HOW TO 2? A HOW TO introduces a concept (in this case, multiplying whole numbers) and includes a step-by-step solution of the type of exercise you will find in the homework.

HOW TO 2   Find the product of 47 and 23.

Multiply by the ones digit.	Multiply by the tens digit.	Add.

$$\begin{array}{r} 47 \\ \times\ 23 \\ \hline 141 \end{array} \ (= 47 \times 3)$$

$$\begin{array}{r} 47 \\ \times\ 23 \\ \hline 141 \\ 940 \end{array} \ (= 47 \times 20)$$

$$\begin{array}{r} 47 \\ \times\ 23 \\ \hline 141 \\ 940 \\ \hline 1081 \end{array}$$

↑
Writing the 0 keeps the columns aligned correctly.

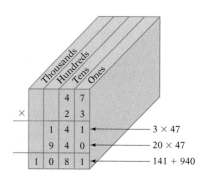

- 3 × 47
- 20 × 47
- 141 + 940

Grab paper and a pencil and work along as you're reading through the HOW TO. When you're done, get a clean sheet of paper. Write down the problem and try to complete the solution without looking at your notes or at the book. When you're done, check your answer. If you got it right, you're ready to move on.

Look through the text and find three instances of a HOW TO. Write the concept illustrated in each HOW TO here.

Example/You Try It Pair You'll need hands-on practice to succeed in mathematics. When we show you an example, work it out yourself, right beside the solution. Use the Example/You Try It pairs to get the practice you need.

Take a look at page 27. Example 2 and You Try It 2 are shown here.

EXAMPLE 2

Find 829 multiplied by 603.

Solution

$$\begin{array}{r} 829 \\ \times\ 603 \\ \hline 2487 \\ 49740 \\ \hline 499,887 \end{array}$$

- 3 × 829 = 2487
- Write a zero in the tens column for 0 × 829.
- 6 × 829 = 4974

YOU TRY IT 2

Multiply: 756 × 305

Your solution

Solution on p. S2

You'll see that each Example is fully worked out. Study the Example by carefully working through each step. Then, try to complete the You Try It. Use the solution to the Example as a model for solving the You Try It. If you get stuck, the solutions to the You Try Its are provided in the back of the book. There is a page number directly following the You Try It that shows you where you can find the completely-worked-out solution. Use the solution to get a hint for the step on which you are stuck. Then, try again!

When you've arrived at your solution, check your work against the solution in the back of the book. Turn to page S2 to see the solution for You Try It 2.

Remember that sometimes there is more than one way to solve a problem. But your answer should always match the answer we've given in the back of the book. If you have any questions about whether your method will always work, check with your instructor.

Use a Strategy to Solve Word Problems

Learning to solve word problems is one of the reasons you are studying math. This is where you combine all of the critical thinking skills you have learned to solve practical problems.

Try not to be intimidated by word problems. Basically, what you need is a strategy that will help you come up with the equation you will need to solve the problem. When you are looking at a word problem, try the following:

- **Read the problem.** This may seem pretty obvious, but we mean really read it. Don't just scan it. Read the problem slowly and carefully.

- **Write down what is known and unknown.** Now that you have read the problem, go back and write down everything that is known. Next, write down what it is you are trying to find. *Write* this—don't just think it! Be as specific as you can. For instance, if you are asked to find a distance, don't just write "I need to find the distance." Be specific and write "I need to find the distance between Earth and the moon."

- **Think of a method to find the unknown.** For instance, should you use addition, subtraction, multiplication, or division to find the unknown quantity? This is certainly the most difficult step.

- **Solve the problem.** Be careful as you solve the problem. There is no sense in getting to this point and then making a careless mistake. The unknown in most problems will include a unit such as feet, dollars, or miles per hour. When you write your answer, include a unit. An answer such as 20 doesn't mean much. Is it 20 feet, 20 dollars, 20 miles per hour, or something else?

- **Check your solution.** Now that you have an answer, go back to the problem and ask yourself whether it makes sense. This is an important step. For instance, if, according to your answer, the cost of a car is $2.51, you know that something went wrong.

In this text, the solution of every word problem is broken down into two steps, **Strategy** and **Solution.** The Strategy consists of the first three steps discussed above. The Solution is the last two steps. Here is an Example from page 28 of the text. Because you have not yet studied the concepts involved in the problem, you may not be able to solve it. However, note the detail in the Strategy. When you do the You Try It following an Example, be sure to include your own Strategy.

EXAMPLE 4

A pharmacist's assistant earns $640 for working a 40-hour week. This week the assistant also worked 7 hours of overtime at $26 an hour. Find the assistant's total pay for the week.

Strategy

To find the assistant's total pay for the week:
- Find the overtime pay by multiplying the hours of overtime (7) by the overtime rate of pay (26).
- Add the weekly salary (640) to the overtime pay.

Solution

$$\begin{array}{r} 26 \\ \times\ 7 \\ \hline 182 \end{array} \text{ overtime pay}$$

$$\begin{array}{r} 640 \\ +\ 182 \\ \hline 822 \end{array}$$

The assistant earned $822 this week.

YOU TRY IT 4

The buyer for Ross Department Store can buy 80 men's suits for $7600. Each sports jacket will cost the store $62. The manager orders 80 men's suits and 25 sports jackets. What is the total cost of the order?

Your strategy

Your solution

Solutions on p. S2

When you have finished studying a section, do the exercises your instructor has selected. Math is not a spectator sport. You must practice every day. Do the homework and do not get behind.

Ace the Test

There are a number of features in this text that will help you prepare for a test. These features will help you even more if you do just one simple thing: When you are doing your homework, go back to each previous homework assignment for the current chapter and rework two exercises. That's right—just *two* exercises. You will be surprised at how much better prepared you will be for a test by doing this.

Here are some additional aids to help you ace the test.

Chapter Summary Once you've completed a chapter, look at the Chapter Summary. The Chapter Summary is divided into two sections: Key Words and Essential Rules and Procedures. Flip to page 196 to see the Chapter Summary for Chapter 4. The summary shows all of the important topics covered in the chapter. Do you see the reference following each topic? This reference shows you the objective and page in the text where you can find more information on the concept.

Write down one Key Word and one Essential Rule or Procedure. Explain the meaning of the reference "4.1A, page 178."

_____

_____

Chapter Review Exercises Turn to page 197 to see the Chapter Review Exercises for Chapter 4. When you do the review exercises, you're giving yourself an important opportunity to test your understanding of the chapter. The answer to each review exercise is given at the back of the book, along with the objective the question relates to. When you're done with the Chapter Review Exercises, check your answers. If you had trouble with any of the questions, you can restudy the objectives and retry some of the exercises in those objectives for extra help.

Go to the Answer Section at the back of the text. Find the answers for the Chapter Review Exercises for Chapter 4. Write down the answer to Exercise 6. Explain the meaning of the reference "4.2B."

Chapter Test The Chapter Test for each chapter can be found after the Chapter Review Exercises and can be used to help you prepare for your exam. The answer to each question is given at the back of the book, along with both an objective reference and a reference to a HOW TO, Example, or You Try It that the question relates to. Think of these tests as "practice runs" for your in-class tests. Take the test in a quiet place, and try to work through it in the same amount of time that will be allowed for your actual exam.

The aids we have mentioned above will help you prepare for a test. You should begin your review *at least* two days before the test—three days is better. These aids will get you ready for the test.

Here are some suggestions to try while you are actually taking the test.

- **Try to relax.** We know that test situations make some students quite nervous or anxious. These feelings are normal. Try to stay calm and focused on what you know. If you have prepared as we have suggested, the answers will begin to come to you.
- **Scan the test.** Get a feeling for the big picture.
- **Read the directions carefully.** Make sure you answer each question fully.
- **Work the problems that are easiest for you first.** This will help you with your confidence and help reduce any nervous feelings you may have.

Ready, Set, Succeed!

It takes hard work and commitment to succeed, but we know you can do it! Doing well in mathematics is just one step you'll take on your path to success. Good luck. We wish you success.

hxdbzxy/Shutterstock.com

Whole Numbers

Focus on Success

Have you read Chapter A, AIM for Success? It describes study skills used by students who have been successful in their math courses. It gives you tips on how to stay motivated, how to manage your time, and how to prepare for exams. Chapter A also includes a complete guide to the textbook and how to use its features to be successful in this course. It starts on page AIM-1.

Andresr/Shutterstock.com

Prep Test

Are you ready to succeed in this chapter? Take the Prep Test below to find out if you are ready to learn the new material.

1. Name the number of ◆s shown below.

◆ ◆ ◆ ◆ ◆ ◆ ◆

2. Write the numbers from 1 to 10.

1 __ __ __ __ __ __ __ __ 10

3. Match the number with its word form.
a. 4	**A.** five
b. 2	**B.** one
c. 5	**C.** zero
d. 1	**D.** four
e. 3	**E.** two
f. 0	**F.** three

1.1 Introduction to Whole Numbers

OBJECTIVE A *To identify the order relation between two numbers*

The **whole numbers** are 0, 1, 2, 3, 4, 5, 6, 7, 8, 9, 10, 11, 12, 13, 14, ...

The three dots mean that the list continues on and on and that there is no largest whole number.

Just as distances are associated with the markings on the edge of a ruler, the whole numbers can be associated with points on a line. This line is called the **number line.** The arrow on the number line below indicates that there is no largest whole number.

The **graph of a whole number** is shown by placing a heavy dot directly above that number on the number line. Here is the graph of 7 on the number line:

The number line can be used to show the order of whole numbers. A number that appears to the left of a given number **is less than (<)** the given number. A number that appears to the right of a given number **is greater than (>)** the given number.

Four is less than seven.
4 < 7

Twelve is greater than seven.
12 > 7

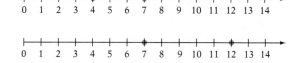

EXAMPLE 1

Graph 11 on the number line.

Solution

YOU TRY IT 1

Graph 6 on the number line.

Your solution

EXAMPLE 2

Place the correct symbol, < or >, between the two numbers.
a. 39   24
b. 0   51

Solution
a. 39 > 24
b. 0 < 51

YOU TRY IT 2

Place the correct symbol, < or >, between the two numbers.
a. 45   29
b. 27   0

Your solution
a.
b.

Solutions on p. S1

OBJECTIVE B   *To write whole numbers in words and in standard form*

When a whole number is written using the digits 0, 1, 2, 3, 4, 5, 6, 7, 8, and 9, it is said to be in **standard form.** The position of each digit in the number determines the digit's **place value.** The diagram below shows a **place-value chart** naming the first 12 place values. The number 37,462 is in standard form and has been entered in the chart.

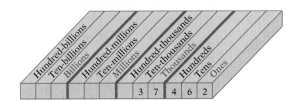

In the number 37,462, the position of the digit 3 determines that its place value is ten-thousands.

Point of Interest

The Babylonians had a place-value system based on 60. Its influence is still with us in angle measurement and time: 60 seconds in 1 minute, 60 minutes in 1 hour. It appears that the earliest record of a base-10 place-value system for natural numbers dates from the 8th century.

When a number is written in standard form, each group of digits separated from the other digits by a comma (or commas) is called a **period.** The number 3,786,451,294 has four periods. The period names are shown in red in the place-value chart above.

To write a number in words, start from the left. Name the number in each period. Then write the period name in place of the comma.

3,786,451,294 is read "three billion seven hundred eighty-six million four hundred fifty-one thousand two hundred ninety-four."

To write a whole number in standard form, write the number named in each period, and replace each period name with a comma.

Four million sixty-two thousand five hundred eighty-four is written 4,062,584. The zero is used as a place holder for the hundred-thousands place.

EXAMPLE 3

Write 25,478,083 in words.

Solution

Twenty-five million four hundred seventy-eight thousand eighty-three

YOU TRY IT 3

Write 36,462,075 in words.

Your solution

EXAMPLE 4

Write three hundred three thousand three in standard form.

Solution

303,003

YOU TRY IT 4

Write four hundred fifty-two thousand seven in standard form.

Your solution

Solutions on p. S1

OBJECTIVE C   *To write whole numbers in expanded form*

The whole number 26,429 can be written in **expanded form** as

$20,000 + 6000 + 400 + 20 + 9.$

The place-value chart can be used to find the expanded form of a number.

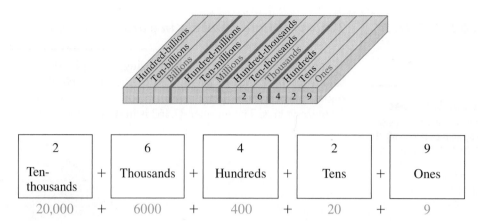

2		6		4		2		9
Ten-thousands	+	Thousands	+	Hundreds	+	Tens	+	Ones
20,000	+	6000	+	400	+	20	+	9

The number 420,806 is written in expanded form below. Note the effect of having zeros in the number.

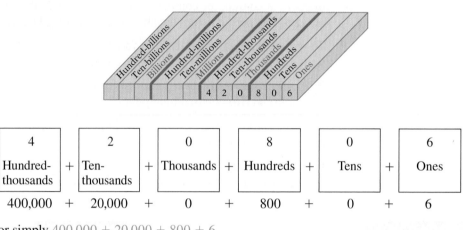

4		2		0		8		0		6
Hundred-thousands	+	Ten-thousands	+	Thousands	+	Hundreds	+	Tens	+	Ones
400,000	+	20,000	+	0	+	800	+	0	+	6

or simply 400,000 + 20,000 + 800 + 6.

EXAMPLE 5

Write 23,859 in expanded form.

Solution

20,000 + 3000 + 800 + 50 + 9

EXAMPLE 6

Write 709,542 in expanded form.

Solution

700,000 + 9000 + 500 + 40 + 2

YOU TRY IT 5

Write 68,281 in expanded form.

Your solution

YOU TRY IT 6

Write 109,207 in expanded form.

Your solution

Solutions on p. S1

OBJECTIVE D   *To round a whole number to a given place value*

When the distance to the moon is given as 240,000 miles, the number represents an approximation to the true distance. Taking an approximate value for an exact number is called **rounding.** A rounded number is always rounded to a given place value.

37 is closer to 40 than it is to 30. 37 rounded to the nearest ten is 40.

673 rounded to the nearest ten is 670. 673 rounded to the nearest hundred is 700.

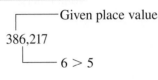

A whole number is rounded to a given place value without using the number line by looking at the first digit to the right of the given place value.

HOW TO 1   Round 13,834 to the nearest hundred.

Given place value

13,834

3 < 5

• If the digit to the right of the given place value is less than 5, that digit and all digits to the right are replaced by zeros.

13,834 rounded to the nearest hundred is 13,800.

HOW TO 2   Round 386,217 to the nearest ten-thousand.

Given place value

386,217

6 > 5

• If the digit to the right of the given place value is greater than or equal to 5, increase the digit in the given place value by 1, and replace all other digits to the right by zeros.

386,217 rounded to the nearest ten-thousand is 390,000.

EXAMPLE 7

Round 525,453 to the nearest ten-thousand.

Solution

Given place value

525,453

5 = 5

525,453 rounded to the nearest ten-thousand is 530,000.

YOU TRY IT 7

Round 368,492 to the nearest ten-thousand.

Your solution

EXAMPLE 8

Round 1972 to the nearest hundred.

Solution

Given place value

1972

7 > 5

1972 rounded to the nearest hundred is 2000.

YOU TRY IT 8

Round 3962 to the nearest hundred.

Your solution

Solutions on p. S1

1.1 EXERCISES

✔ Concept Check

1. Determine whether the statement is true or false.

   a. $23 > 48$ **b.** $0 < 14$ **c.** $15 > 0$ **d.** $47 < 74$

2. Name the place value of the digit 3 in each number.

   a. 83,479   **b.** 3,491,507   **c.** 2,634,958   **d.** 76,319,204

OBJECTIVE A   *To identify the order relation between two numbers*

For Exercises 3 to 6, graph the number on the number line.

3. 3

4. 5

5. 9

6. 0

For Exercises 7 to 14, place the correct symbol, $<$ or $>$, between the two numbers.

7. 37   49   **8.** 58   21   **9.** 101   87   **10.** 245   158

11. 2701   2071   **12.** 0   45   **13.** 107   0   **14.** 815   928

15. 🗝 Do the inequalities $21 < 30$ and $30 > 21$ express the same order relation?

OBJECTIVE B   *To write whole numbers in words and in standard form*

For Exercises 16 to 23, write the number in words.

16. 2675   **17.** 3790   **18.** 42,928   **19.** 58,473

20. 356,943   **21.** 498,512   **22.** 3,697,483   **23.** 6,842,715

For Exercises 24 to 29, write the number in standard form.

24. Eighty-five

25. Three hundred fifty-seven

26. Three thousand four hundred fifty-six

27. Sixty-three thousand seven hundred eighty

28. Six hundred nine thousand nine hundred forty-eight

29. Seven million twenty-four thousand seven hundred nine

30. What is the place value of the first digit on the left in a seven-digit whole number?

OBJECTIVE C   *To write whole numbers in expanded form*

For Exercises 31 to 38, write the number in expanded form.

31. 5287

32. 6295

33. 58,943

34. 453,921

35. 200,583

36. 301,809

37. 403,705

38. 3,000,642

39. The expanded form of a number consists of four numbers added together. Must the number be a four-digit number?

OBJECTIVE D   *To round a whole number to a given place value*

For Exercises 40 to 51, round the number to the given place value.

40. 926   Tens

41. 845   Tens

42. 1439   Hundreds

43. 3973   Hundreds

44. 43,607   Thousands

45. 52,715   Thousands

46. 389,702   Thousands

47. 629,513   Thousands

48. 647,989   Ten-thousands

49. 253,678   Ten-thousands

50. 36,702,599   Millions

51. 71,834,250   Millions

52. True or false? If a number rounded to the nearest ten is less than the original number, then the ones digit of the original number is greater than 5.

Critical Thinking

53. If 3846 is rounded to the nearest ten and then that number is rounded to the nearest hundred, is the result the same as the result you get when you round 3846 to the nearest hundred? If not, which method is correct for rounding to the nearest hundred?

Projects or Group Activities

54. The U.S. House of Representatives has 435 members. The number of representatives that each state sends to the House of Representatives is based on the population of the state. State populations are determined every 10 years by the Census Bureau. Use the Census Bureau's Internet site to determine which states gained or lost a seat in the House of Representatives after the 2010 census.

1.2 Addition of Whole Numbers

OBJECTIVE A *To add whole numbers*

Addition is the process of finding the total of two or more numbers.

APPLY THE CONCEPT

Maryka carried 4 soccer balls from her car to the soccer field. She returned to her car and carried 3 more balls to the field. By counting, the total of 4 balls and 3 balls is 7 balls. Maryka carried a total of 7 balls from her car to the field.

$$4 + 3 = 7$$

Addend + Addend = Sum

Here is a table of basic addition facts. These facts should be memorized.

Basic Addition Facts

+	1	2	3	4	5	6	7	8	9
1	1 + 1 = 2	1 + 2 = 3	1 + 3 = 4	1 + 4 = 5	1 + 5 = 6	1 + 6 = 7	1 + 7 = 8	1 + 8 = 9	1 + 9 = 10
2	2 + 1 = 3	2 + 2 = 4	2 + 3 = 5	2 + 4 = 6	2 + 5 = 7	2 + 6 = 8	2 + 7 = 9	2 + 8 = 10	2 + 9 = 11
3	3 + 1 = 4	3 + 2 = 5	3 + 3 = 6	3 + 4 = 7	3 + 5 = 8	3 + 6 = 9	3 + 7 = 10	3 + 8 = 11	3 + 9 = 12
4	4 + 1 = 5	4 + 2 = 6	4 + 3 = 7	4 + 4 = 8	4 + 5 = 9	4 + 6 = 10	4 + 7 = 11	4 + 8 = 12	4 + 9 = 13
5	5 + 1 = 6	5 + 2 = 7	5 + 3 = 8	5 + 4 = 9	5 + 5 = 10	5 + 6 = 11	5 + 7 = 12	5 + 8 = 13	5 + 9 = 14
6	6 + 1 = 7	6 + 2 = 8	6 + 3 = 9	6 + 4 = 10	6 + 5 = 11	6 + 6 = 12	6 + 7 = 13	6 + 8 = 14	6 + 9 = 15
7	7 + 1 = 8	7 + 2 = 9	7 + 3 = 10	7 + 4 = 11	7 + 5 = 12	7 + 6 = 13	7 + 7 = 14	7 + 8 = 15	7 + 9 = 16
8	8 + 1 = 9	8 + 2 = 10	8 + 3 = 11	8 + 4 = 12	8 + 5 = 13	8 + 6 = 14	8 + 7 = 15	8 + 8 = 16	8 + 9 = 17
9	9 + 1 = 10	9 + 2 = 11	9 + 3 = 12	9 + 4 = 13	9 + 5 = 14	9 + 6 = 15	9 + 7 = 16	9 + 8 = 17	9 + 9 = 18

Some special properties of addition that are used frequently are given below.

Commutative Property of Addition

Two numbers can be added in either order; the sum will be the same.

EXAMPLES

1. $4 + 8 = 8 + 4$
$12 = 12$

2. $9 + 6 = 6 + 9$
$15 = 15$

Associative Property of Addition

Grouping an addition in any order gives the same result. Parentheses are grouping symbols that mean "Do operations inside parentheses first."

EXAMPLES

1. $(3 + 2) + 4 = 3 + (2 + 4)$
$5 + 4 = 3 + 6$
$9 = 9$

2. $(3 + 6) + 2 = 3 + (6 + 2)$
$9 + 2 = 3 + 8$
$11 = 11$

Addition Property of Zero

Zero added to any number does not change the number.

EXAMPLES

1. $4 + 0 = 4$ **2.** $0 + 7 = 7$

Point of Interest

The plus sign first appeared in 1489 in *Mercantile Arithmetic*. It was used to indicate a surplus, not as the symbol for addition. That use did not occur until about 1515.

To add large numbers, begin by arranging the numbers vertically, keeping the digits of the same place value in the same column.

HOW TO 1   Add: $321 + 6472$

THOUSANDS HUNDREDS TENS ONES

$$\begin{array}{cccc} & 3 & 2 & 1 \\ + 6 & 4 & 7 & 2 \\ \hline 6 & 7 & 9 & 3 \end{array}$$

• Add the digits in each column.

There are several words or phrases in English that indicate the operation of addition. Here are some examples:

added to	3 added to 5	$5 + 3$
more than	7 more than 5	$5 + 7$
the sum of	the sum of 3 and 9	$3 + 9$
increased by	4 increased by 6	$4 + 6$
the total of	the total of 8 and 3	$8 + 3$
plus	5 plus 10	$5 + 10$

Integrating Technology

Most scientific calculators use *algebraic logic:* the add (+), subtract (−), multiply (×), and divide (÷) keys perform the indicated operation using the number in the display and the next number keyed in. For instance, for HOW TO 2 at the right, enter 24 + 71 = . The display reads 95.

When the sum of the digits in a column exceeds 9, the addition will involve **carrying.**

HOW TO 2   What is the sum of 487 and 369?

HUNDREDS TENS ONES

$$\begin{array}{ccc} & \overset{1}{} & \\ 4 & 8 & 7 \\ + 3 & 6 & 9 \\ \hline & & 6 \end{array}$$

• The phrase *the sum of* means to add.
• Add the ones column.
  $7 + 9 = 16$ (1 ten + 6 ones).
  Write the 6 in the ones column and carry the 1 ten to the tens column.

$$\begin{array}{ccc} \overset{1}{} & \overset{1}{} & \\ 4 & 8 & 7 \\ + 3 & 6 & 9 \\ \hline & 5 & 6 \end{array}$$

• Add the tens column.
  $1 + 8 + 6 = 15$ (1 hundred + 5 tens).
  Write the 5 in the tens column and carry the 1 hundred to the hundreds column.

$$\begin{array}{ccc} \overset{1}{} & \overset{1}{} & \\ 4 & 8 & 7 \\ + 3 & 6 & 9 \\ \hline 8 & 5 & 6 \end{array}$$

• Add the hundreds column.
  $1 + 4 + 3 = 8$ (8 hundreds).
  Write the 8 in the hundreds column.

The sum is 856.

EXAMPLE 1

Find the total of 17, 103, and 8.

Solution

$$\begin{array}{r} \overset{1}{17} \\ 103 \\ + 8 \\ \hline 128 \end{array}$$

• $7 + 3 + 8 = 18$
Write the 8 in the ones column. Carry the 1 to the tens column.

YOU TRY IT 1

What is 347 increased by 12,453?

Your solution

EXAMPLE 2

Find the sum of 89, 36, and 98.

Solution

$$\begin{array}{r} \overset{2}{89} \\ 36 \\ + 98 \\ \hline 223 \end{array}$$

• $9 + 6 + 8 = 23$
Write the 3 in the ones column. Carry the 2 to the tens column.

YOU TRY IT 2

Add: $95 + 88 + 67$

Your solution

EXAMPLE 3

Add: 41,395
        4,327
        497,625
      + 32,991

Solution

$$\begin{array}{r} \overset{1\,1\,2\ \,2\,1}{41,395} \\ 4,327 \\ 497,625 \\ + 32,991 \\ \hline 576,338 \end{array}$$

YOU TRY IT 3

Add: 392
         4,079
        89,035
       + 4,992

Your solution

Solutions on p. S1

Integrating Technology

This example illustrates that estimation is important when one is using a calculator.

ESTIMATION: Estimation and Calculators

At some places in the text, you will be asked to use your calculator. Effective use of a calculator requires that you estimate the answer to the problem. This helps ensure that you have entered the numbers correctly and pressed the correct keys.

For example, if you use your calculator to find $22,347 + 5896$ and the answer in the calculator's display is 131,757,912, you should realize that you have entered some part of the calculation incorrectly. In this case, you pressed ☓ instead of ➕. By estimating the answer to a problem, you can help ensure the accuracy of your calculations. There is a special symbol for **approximately equal to:** $\approx$.

For example, to estimate the answer to $22,347 + 5896$, round each number to the same place value. In this case, we will round to the nearest thousand. Then add.

$$\begin{array}{r} 22,347 \approx 22,000 \\ + 5,896 \approx + 6,000 \\ \hline 28,000 \end{array}$$

The sum $22,347 + 5896$ is approximately 28,000. Knowing this, you would know that 131,757,912 is much too large and is therefore incorrect.

To estimate the sum of two numbers, first round each number to the same place value, and then add. Compare this answer with the calculator's answer.

trekandshoot/Shutterstock.com

OBJECTIVE B   *To solve application problems*

To solve an application problem, first read the problem carefully. Devising a **strategy** involves identifying the quantity to be found and planning the steps that are necessary to find that quantity. Finding the **solution of an application problem** involves performing each operation stated in the strategy and writing the answer.

HOW TO 3

The table below displays the Walmart store count and square footage in the United States as reported in the Walmart 2011 Annual Report.

	Discount Stores	Supercenters	Sam's Clubs	Neighborhood Markets
Number of units	629	3029	611	168
Square footage (in millions)	68	560	81	7

Find the total number of Walmart discount stores and Supercenters in the United States.

Strategy   To find the total number of Walmart discount stores and Supercenters in the United States, read the table to find the number of each type of store in the United States. Then add the numbers.

Solution
```
   629
+ 3029
------
  3658
```

Walmart has a total of 3658 discount stores and Supercenters in the United States.

EXAMPLE 4

Use the table above to find the total number of Sam's Clubs and neighborhood markets that Walmart owns in the United States.

Strategy

To determine the total number of Sam's Clubs and neighborhood markets, read the table to find the number of Sam's Clubs and the number of neighborhood markets. Then add the two numbers.

Solution
```
  611
+ 168
-----
  779
```

Walmart owns a total of 779 Sam's Clubs and neighborhood markets.

YOU TRY IT 4

Use the table above to determine the total square footage of Walmart stores in the United States.

Your strategy

Your solution

Solution on p. S1

1.2 EXERCISES

✔ Concept Check

For Exercises 1 to 6, identify the property on page 8 or 9 that justifies the statement.

1. $347 + 0 = 347$

2. $6 + (8 + 1) = (6 + 8) + 1$

3. $(3 + 7) + 4 = 3 + (7 + 4)$

4. $13 + 302 = 302 + 13$

5. $(9 + 8) + 3 = (8 + 9) + 3$

6. $23 + (0 + 9) = 23 + 9$

OBJECTIVE A   *To add whole numbers*

For Exercises 7 to 36, add.

7. $\begin{array}{r} 17 \\ +\ 11 \\ \hline \end{array}$

8. $\begin{array}{r} 25 \\ +\ 63 \\ \hline \end{array}$

9. $\begin{array}{r} 83 \\ +\ 42 \\ \hline \end{array}$

10. $\begin{array}{r} 63 \\ +\ 94 \\ \hline \end{array}$

11. $\begin{array}{r} 77 \\ +\ 25 \\ \hline \end{array}$

12. $\begin{array}{r} 63 \\ +\ 49 \\ \hline \end{array}$

13. $\begin{array}{r} 56 \\ +\ 98 \\ \hline \end{array}$

14. $\begin{array}{r} 86 \\ +\ 68 \\ \hline \end{array}$

15. $\begin{array}{r} 658 \\ +\ 831 \\ \hline \end{array}$

16. $\begin{array}{r} 842 \\ +\ 936 \\ \hline \end{array}$

17. $\begin{array}{r} 735 \\ +\ 93 \\ \hline \end{array}$

18. $\begin{array}{r} 189 \\ +\ 50 \\ \hline \end{array}$

19. $\begin{array}{r} 859 \\ +\ 725 \\ \hline \end{array}$

20. $\begin{array}{r} 637 \\ +\ 829 \\ \hline \end{array}$

21. $\begin{array}{r} 36,925 \\ +\ 65,392 \\ \hline \end{array}$

22. $\begin{array}{r} 56,772 \\ +\ 51,239 \\ \hline \end{array}$

23. $\begin{array}{r} 50,873 \\ +\ 28,453 \\ \hline \end{array}$

24. $\begin{array}{r} 34,872 \\ +\ 46,079 \\ \hline \end{array}$

25. $\begin{array}{r} 878 \\ 737 \\ +\ 189 \\ \hline \end{array}$

26. $\begin{array}{r} 768 \\ 461 \\ +\ 669 \\ \hline \end{array}$

27. $\begin{array}{r} 319 \\ 348 \\ +\ 912 \\ \hline \end{array}$

28. $\begin{array}{r} 292 \\ 579 \\ +\ 315 \\ \hline \end{array}$

29. $\begin{array}{r} 9409 \\ 3253 \\ +\ 7078 \\ \hline \end{array}$

30. $\begin{array}{r} 8188 \\ 8020 \\ +\ 7104 \\ \hline \end{array}$

31. $\begin{array}{r} 2038 \\ 2243 \\ +\ 3139 \\ \hline \end{array}$

32. $\begin{array}{r} 4252 \\ 6882 \\ +\ 5235 \\ \hline \end{array}$

33. $\begin{array}{r} 67,428 \\ 32,171 \\ +\ 20,971 \\ \hline \end{array}$

34. $\begin{array}{r} 52,801 \\ 11,664 \\ +\ 89,638 \\ \hline \end{array}$

35. $\begin{array}{r} 76,290 \\ 43,761 \\ +\ 87,402 \\ \hline \end{array}$

36. $\begin{array}{r} 43,901 \\ 98,301 \\ +\ 67,943 \\ \hline \end{array}$

For Exercises 37 to 44, add.

37. 20,958 + 3218 + 42

38. 80,973 + 5168 + 29

39. 392 + 37 + 10,924 + 621

40. 694 + 62 + 70,129 + 217

41. 294 + 1029 + 7935 + 65

42. 692 + 2107 + 3196 + 92

43. 97 + 7234 + 69,532 + 276

44. 87 + 1698 + 27,317 + 727

45. What is 9874 plus 4509?

46. What is 7988 plus 5678?

47. What is 3487 increased by 5986?

48. What is 99,567 increased by 126,863?

49. What is 23,569 more than 9678?

50. What is 7894 more than 45,872?

51. What is 479 added to 4579?

52. What is 23,902 added to 23,885?

53. Find the total of 659, 55, and 1278.

54. Find the total of 4561, 56, and 2309.

55. Find the sum of 34, 329, 8, and 67,892.

56. Find the sum of 45, 1289, 7, and 32,876.

For Exercises 57 to 60, use a calculator to add. Then round the numbers to the nearest hundred, and use estimation to determine whether the sum is reasonable.

57. 1234 + 9780 + 6740

58. 919 + 3642 + 8796

59. 241 + 569 + 390 + 1672

60. 107 + 984 + 1035 + 2904

For Exercises 61 to 64, use a calculator to add. Then round the numbers to the nearest thousand, and use estimation to determine whether the sum is reasonable.

61.	32,461	**62.**	29,036	**63.**	25,432	**64.**	66,541
	9,844		22,904		62,941		29,365
	+ 59,407		+ 7,903		+ 70,390		+ 98,742

For Exercises 65 to 68, use a calculator to add. Then round the numbers to the nearest ten-thousand, and use estimation to determine whether the sum is reasonable.

65. 67,421
 82,984
 66,361
 10,792
 + 34,037

66. 21,896
 4,235
 62,544
 21,892
 + 1,334

67. 281,421
 9,874
 34,394
 526,398
 + 94,631

68. 542,698
 97,327
 7,235
 73,667
 + 173,201

69. Which property of addition (see pages 8 and 9) allows you to use either arrangement shown at the right to find the sum of 691 and 452?

 691
 + 452

 452
 + 691

OBJECTIVE B   *To solve application problems*

70. Use the table of Walmart data on page 11. What does the sum $68 + 560$ represent?

71. **Demographics** In a recent year, according to the Centers for Disease Control and Prevention, there were 138,660 twin births in this country, 5877 triplet births, 345 quadruplet deliveries, and 46 quintuplet and other higher-order multiple births. Find the total number of multiple births during the year.

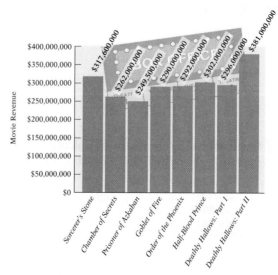

Melissa King/Shutterstock.com

72. **Demographics** The Census Bureau estimated that the U.S. population would grow by 296 million people from 2000 to 2100. Given that the U.S. population in 2000 was 281 million, find the Census Bureau's estimate of the U.S. population in 2100.

The Film Industry The graph at the right shows the domestic box-office gross income from the first eight *Harry Potter* movies. Use this information for Exercises 73 to 75.

73. Find the total gross income from the eight *Harry Potter* movies.

74. Find the total gross income from the two lowest-grossing *Harry Potter* movies.

75. Find the total gross income from the two highest-grossing *Harry Potter* movies.

(*Source:* www.the-numbers.com/movies/series/HarryPotter.php)

76. Geometry The perimeter of a triangle is the sum of the lengths of the three sides of the triangle. Find the perimeter of a triangle that has sides that measure 12 inches, 14 inches, and 17 inches.

12 in. 14 in.

17 in.

77. Travel The odometer on a moving van reads 68,692. The driver plans to drive 515 miles the first day, 492 miles the second day, and 278 miles the third day.
a. How many miles will be driven during the three days?
b. What will the odometer reading be at the end of the trip?

78. 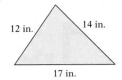 **Internet** Thirty-seven million U.S. households do not have broadband Internet access. Seventy-eight million U.S. households do have broadband Internet access. How many households are there in the United States? (*Source:* U.S. Department of Commerce)

79. ● **Energy** In a recent year, the United States produced 5,633,000 barrels of crude oil per day and imported 9,003,300 barrels of crude oil per day. Find the total number of barrels of crude oil produced and imported per day in the United States. (*Source:* Energy Information Administration)

eyeidea/Shutterstock.com

Critical Thinking

80. If you roll two ordinary six-sided dice and add the two numbers that appear on top, how many different sums are possible?

81. If you add two *different* whole numbers, is the sum always greater than either one of the numbers? If not, give an example.

82. If you add two whole numbers, is the sum always greater than either one of the numbers? If not, give an example. (Compare this with Exercise 81.)

83. Make up a word problem for which the answer is the sum of 34 and 28.

84. Call a number "lucky" if it ends in a 7. How many lucky numbers are less than 100?

Projects or Group Activities

The size, or magnitude, of a number can be represented on the number line by an arrow.

The number 3 can be represented anywhere on the number line by an arrow that is 3 units in length.

To add on the number line, place the arrows representing the addends head to tail, with the first arrow starting at zero. The sum is represented by an arrow starting at zero and stopping at the tip of the last arrow.

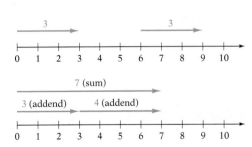

85. Represent the sum of 2 and 6 using arrows on the number line.

86. Represent the sum of 5 and 4 using arrows on the number line.

SECTION

1.3 Subtraction of Whole Numbers

OBJECTIVE A *To subtract whole numbers without borrowing*

Subtraction is the process of finding the difference between two numbers.

APPLY THE CONCEPT

A store had 7 iPads in stock. Nathan sold 3 iPads from the stock. By counting, the difference between 7 iPads and 3 iPads is 4. There are 4 iPads remaining in stock.

7 iPads

3 iPads   4 iPads

7 iPads	−	3 iPads	=	4 iPads
Minuend	**−**	**Subtrahend**	**=**	**Difference**

Subtraction can be related to addition as shown at the right. This relationship can be used to check a subtraction.

Subtrahend   3
+ Difference   + 4
= Minuend   7

 Point of Interest
The minus sign dates from the same period as the plus sign, around 1515.

To subtract large numbers, begin by arranging the numbers vertically, keeping the digits that have the same place value in the same column. Then subtract the digits in each column.

HOW TO 1 Subtract 8955 − 2432 and check.

$$
\begin{array}{r}
\text{THOUSANDS}\ \text{HUNDREDS}\ \text{TENS}\ \text{ONES} \\
8\ |\ 9\ |\ 5\ |\ 5 \\
-\ 2\ |\ 4\ |\ 3\ |\ 2 \\
\hline
6\ |\ 5\ |\ 2\ |\ 3
\end{array}
$$

Check: Subtrahend   2432
     + Difference   + 6523
     = Minuend   8955

EXAMPLE 1

Subtract 6594 − 3271 and check.

Solution

$$
\begin{array}{r}
6594 \\
-\ 3271 \\
\hline
3323
\end{array}
$$

Check:
$$
\begin{array}{r}
3271 \\
+\ 3323 \\
\hline
6594
\end{array}
$$

YOU TRY IT 1

Subtract 8925 − 6413 and check.

Your solution

EXAMPLE 2

Subtract 15,762 − 7541 and check.

Solution

$$
\begin{array}{r}
15,762 \\
-\ 7,541 \\
\hline
8,221
\end{array}
$$

Check:
$$
\begin{array}{r}
7,541 \\
+\ 8,221 \\
\hline
15,762
\end{array}
$$

YOU TRY IT 2

Subtract 17,504 − 9302 and check.

Your solution

Solutions on p. S1

OBJECTIVE B   *To subtract whole numbers with borrowing*

In all the subtraction problems in the preceding objective, for each place value, the lower digit was smaller than the upper digit. When the lower digit is larger than the upper digit, subtraction will involve **borrowing.**

HOW TO 2   Subtract: $692 - 378$

	8+1	
6	9	2
− 3	7	8

Because $8 > 2$, borrowing is necessary.
9 tens = 8 tens + 1 ten.

	8+①	10
6	9	2
− 3	7	8

Borrow 1 ten from the tens column and write 10 in the ones column.

	8	12
6	9	2
− 3	7	8

Add the borrowed 10 to 2.

	8	12
6	9	2
− 3	7	8

Subtract the digits in each column.

The phrases below are used to indicate the operation of subtraction. An example is shown at the right of each phrase.

minus	8 minus 5	$8 - 5$
less	9 less 3	$9 - 3$
less than	2 less than 7	$7 - 2$
the difference between	the difference between 8 and 2	$8 - 2$
decreased by	5 decreased by 1	$5 - 1$

Take Note

"The difference between 1234 and 485" means $1234 - 485$.

HOW TO 3   Find the difference between 1234 and 485, and check.

		2	14
1	2	3	4
−	4	8	5
			9

	1	12	14
1	2	3	4
−	4	8	5
		4	9

0	11	12	14
1	2	3	4
−	4	8	5
	7	4	9

Check:

1 1
485
+ 749
1234

Tips for Success

The HOW TO feature indicates an example with explanatory remarks. Using paper and pencil, you should work through the example. See *AIM for Success* at the front of the book.

Subtraction with a zero in the minuend involves repeated borrowing.

HOW TO 4   Subtract: $3904 - 1775$

	8	10	
3	9	0	4
− 1	7	7	5

$5 > 4$
There is a 0 in the tens column. Borrow 1 hundred (= 10 tens) from the hundreds column and write 10 in the tens column.

	8	9 10	14
3	9	0	4
− 1	7	7	5

Borrow 1 ten from the tens column and add 10 to the 4 in the ones column.

	8	9 10	14
3	9	0	4
− 1	7	7	5
2	1	2	9

Subtract the digits in each column.

EXAMPLE 3

Subtract 4392 − 678 and check.

Solution

$$
\begin{array}{r}
\overset{3}{\cancel{4}}\ \overset{13}{\cancel{3}}\ \overset{8}{\cancel{9}}\ \overset{12}{\cancel{2}} \\
-\quad 6\ 7\ 8 \\
\hline
3\ 7\ 1\ 4
\end{array}
$$

Check:
$$
\begin{array}{r}
678 \\
+\ 3714 \\
\hline
4392
\end{array}
$$

YOU TRY IT 3

Subtract 3481 − 865 and check.

Your solution

EXAMPLE 4

Find 23,954 less than 63,221 and check.

Solution

$$
\begin{array}{r}
\overset{5}{\cancel{6}}\ \overset{12}{\underset{2}{\cancel{3}}},\ \overset{11}{\underset{1}{\cancel{2}}}\ \overset{11}{\underset{1}{\cancel{2}}}\ \overset{11}{\cancel{1}} \\
-\ 2\ 3\ ,\ 9\ 5\ 4 \\
\hline
3\ 9\ ,\ 2\ 6\ 7
\end{array}
$$

Check:
$$
\begin{array}{r}
23,954 \\
+\ 39,267 \\
\hline
63,221
\end{array}
$$

YOU TRY IT 4

Find 54,562 decreased by 14,485 and check.

Your solution

EXAMPLE 5

Subtract 46,005 − 32,167 and check.

Solution

$$
\begin{array}{r}
\overset{5}{4}\ \overset{10}{\cancel{6}},\ \cancel{0}\ 0\ 5 \\
-\ 3\ 2,\ 1\ 6\ 7
\end{array}
$$

- There are two zeros in the minuend. Borrow 1 thousand from the thousands column and write 10 in the hundreds column.

$$
\begin{array}{r}
\overset{5}{4}\ \overset{9}{\cancel{6}},\ \overset{10}{\cancel{0}}\ \cancel{0}\ 5 \\
-\ 3\ 2,\ 1\ 6\ 7
\end{array}
$$

- Borrow 1 hundred from the hundreds column and write 10 in the tens column.

$$
\begin{array}{r}
\overset{5}{4}\ \overset{9}{\cancel{6}},\ \overset{9}{\cancel{0}}\ \overset{10}{\cancel{0}}\ \overset{15}{\cancel{5}} \\
-\ 3\ 2,\ 1\ 6\ 7 \\
\hline
1\ 3,\ 8\ 3\ 8
\end{array}
$$

- Borrow 1 ten from the tens column and add 10 to the 5 in the ones column.

Check:
$$
\begin{array}{r}
32,167 \\
+\ 13,838 \\
\hline
46,005
\end{array}
$$

YOU TRY IT 5

Subtract 64,003 − 54,936 and check.

Your solution

Solutions on pp. S1–S2

ESTIMATION: Estimating the Difference Between Two Whole Numbers

Calculate 323,502 − 28,912. Then use estimation to determine whether the difference is reasonable.

Subtract to find the exact difference. To estimate the difference, round each number to the same place value. Here we have rounded to the nearest ten-thousand. Then subtract. The estimated answer is 290,000, which is very close to the exact difference 294,590.

$$
\begin{array}{rcr}
323,502 & \approx & 320,000 \\
-\ 28,912 & \approx & -\ 30,000 \\
\hline
294,590 & & 290,000
\end{array}
$$

OBJECTIVE C *To solve application problems*

🌑 The table at the right shows the populations of the four regions of the United States. Use this table for Example 6 and You Try It 6.

Region	Population
Northeast	55,317,240
Midwest	66,927,001
South	114,555,744
West	71,945,553

Source: U.S. Census Bureau

EXAMPLE 6

Find the difference between the population of the most populous region and the population of the least populous region.

Strategy

To find the difference:

- Identify the most populous region (the South) and the least populous region (the Northeast).
- Subtract the population of the Northeast (55,317,240) from the population of the South (114,555,744).

Solution 114,555,744
  − 55,317,240
  59,238,504

There are 59,238,504 more people living in the South than in the Northeast.

YOU TRY IT 6

Find the difference between the population of the Midwest and the population of the Northeast.

Your strategy

Your solution

EXAMPLE 7

You had a balance of $415 on your student debit card. You then used the card, deducting $197 for books, $48 for art supplies, and $24 for theater tickets. What is your new student debit card balance?

Strategy

To find your new debit card balance:

- Add to find the total of the three deductions (197 + 48 + 24).
- Subtract the total of the three deductions from the original balance (415).

Solution

  197   415
   48   − 269
 + 24   ──────
 ────   146
  269 total deductions

Your new debit card balance is $146.

YOU TRY IT 7

Your total weekly salary is $638. Deductions of $127 for taxes, $18 for insurance, and $35 for savings are taken from your pay. Find your weekly take-home pay.

Your strategy

Your solution

Solutions on p. S2

1.3 EXERCISES

✔ Concept Check

For Exercises 1 to 4, find the difference. Then write the related addition problem using Subtrahend + Difference = Minuend.

1. $9 - 5$ **2.** $7 - 2$ **3.** $11 - 0$ **4.** $8 - 8$

OBJECTIVE A *To subtract whole numbers without borrowing*

For Exercises 5 to 34, subtract.

5. $\begin{array}{r} 12 \\ -\ 8 \end{array}$
6. $\begin{array}{r} 11 \\ -\ 4 \end{array}$
7. $\begin{array}{r} 15 \\ -\ 6 \end{array}$
8. $\begin{array}{r} 19 \\ -\ 8 \end{array}$
9. $\begin{array}{r} 25 \\ -\ 3 \end{array}$

10. $\begin{array}{r} 16 \\ -\ 7 \end{array}$
11. $\begin{array}{r} 68 \\ -\ 8 \end{array}$
12. $\begin{array}{r} 55 \\ -\ 4 \end{array}$
13. $\begin{array}{r} 89 \\ -\ 23 \end{array}$
14. $\begin{array}{r} 77 \\ -\ 3 \end{array}$

15. $\begin{array}{r} 88 \\ -\ 57 \end{array}$
16. $\begin{array}{r} 54 \\ -\ 21 \end{array}$
17. $\begin{array}{r} 1305 \\ -\ 404 \end{array}$
18. $\begin{array}{r} 1202 \\ -\ 701 \end{array}$
19. $\begin{array}{r} 1497 \\ -\ 706 \end{array}$

20. $\begin{array}{r} 1763 \\ -\ 801 \end{array}$
21. $\begin{array}{r} 2836 \\ -\ 1711 \end{array}$
22. $\begin{array}{r} 8974 \\ -\ 3972 \end{array}$
23. $\begin{array}{r} 9273 \\ -\ 6142 \end{array}$
24. $\begin{array}{r} 8976 \\ -\ 7463 \end{array}$

25. $129 - 82$ **26.** $77 - 36$ **27.** $969 - 44$ **28.** $132 - 61$ **29.** $4865 - 304$

30. $1347 - 103$ **31.** $9999 - 6794$ **32.** $1525 - 702$ **33.** $8843 - 7621$ **34.** $7806 - 3405$

For Exercises 35 and 36, find two whole numbers with the given difference and sum.

35. Difference = 2; sum = 8 **36.** Difference = 5; sum = 9

OBJECTIVE B *To subtract whole numbers with borrowing*

For Exercises 37 to 80, subtract.

37. $\begin{array}{r} 71 \\ -\ 18 \end{array}$
38. $\begin{array}{r} 93 \\ -\ 28 \end{array}$
39. $\begin{array}{r} 47 \\ -\ 18 \end{array}$
40. $\begin{array}{r} 44 \\ -\ 27 \end{array}$

41. $\begin{array}{r} 37 \\ -\ 29 \end{array}$
42. $\begin{array}{r} 50 \\ -\ 27 \end{array}$
43. $\begin{array}{r} 70 \\ -\ 33 \end{array}$
44. $\begin{array}{r} 993 \\ -\ 537 \end{array}$

45.   250
        − 192

46.   840
        − 783

47.   768
        − 194

48.   770
        − 395

49. 674 − 337

50. 3526 − 387

51. 1712 − 289

52. 4350 − 729

53. 1702 − 948

54. 1607 − 869

55. 5933 − 3754

56. 7293 − 3748

57. 9407 − 2918

58. 3706 − 2957

59. 8605 − 7716

60. 8052 − 2709

61. 80,305 − 9176

62. 70,702 − 4239

63. 10,004 − 9306

64. 80,009 − 63,419

65. 70,618 − 41,213

66. 80,053 − 27,649

67. 70,700 − 21,076

68. 80,800 − 42,023

69.   2600
        − 1972

70.   8400
        − 3762

71.   9003
        − 2471

72.   6004
        − 2392

73.   8202
        − 3916

74.   7050
        − 4137

75.   7015
        − 2973

76.   4207
        − 1624

77.   7005
        − 1796

78.   8003
        − 2735

79.   20,005
        − 9,627

80.   80,004
        − 8,237

81. Which of the following phrases represent the subtraction 673 − 571?

(i) 571 less 673   **(ii)** 571 less than 673   **(iii)** 673 decreased by 571

82. Find 10,051 less 9027.

83. Find 17,031 less 5792.

84. Find the difference between 1003 and 447.

85. What is 29,874 minus 21,392?

86. What is 29,797 less than 68,005?

87. What is 69,379 less than 70,004?

88. What is 25,432 decreased by 7994?

89. What is 86,701 decreased by 9976?

For Exercises 90 to 93, use the relationship between addition and subtraction to complete the statement.

90. ___ + 39 = 104   **91.** 67 + ___ = 90   **92.** ___ + 497 = 862   **93.** 253 + ____ = 4901

For Exercises 94 to 99, use a calculator to subtract. Then round the numbers to the nearest ten-thousand and use estimation to determine whether the difference is reasonable.

94.   80,032
    − 19,605

95.   90,765
    − 60,928

96.   32,574
    − 10,961

97.   96,430
    − 59,762

98.   567,423
    − 208,444

99.   300,712
    − 198,714

OBJECTIVE C   *To solve application problems*

100. Banking You have $304 in your checking account. If you write a check for $139, how much is left in your checking account?

101. Insects The table at the right shows the number of taste genes and the number of smell genes in the mosquito, fruit fly, and honey bee.
   a. How many more smell genes does the honey bee have than the mosquito?
   b. How many more taste genes does the mosquito have than the fruit fly?
   c. Which of these insects has the best sense of smell?
   d. Which of these insects has the worst sense of taste?

	Mosquito	Fruit Fly	Honey Bee
Taste genes	76	68	10
Smell genes	79	62	170

Source: www.sciencedaily.com
Images: mosquito, © iStockphoto.com/Henrik Larsson; fruit fly,
© iStockphoto.com/arlindo71; honey bee, © iStockphoto.com/beti gorse

102. Electric Car Sales The graph at the right shows the projected sales of electric cars in the United States from 2015 to 2020.
   a. Are sales of electric cars projected to increase for the years shown?
   b. How many more electric cars are projected to be sold in 2020 than in 2015?
   c. Between which two consecutive years is the number of electric cars sold projected to increase the most?

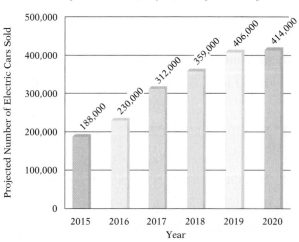

Projected Sales of Electric Cars in the United States
(*Source: An Analysis of Battery Electric Vehicle Production Projections;* Cunnigham, John; MIT, 2009)

103. **Earth Science**   Use the graph at the right to find the difference between the maximum heights to which the Great Fountain and Valentine geysers erupt.

104. ● **Earth Science**   According to the graph at the right, how much higher is the eruption of the Giant than that of Old Faithful?

105. ● **Education**   In a recent year, 775,424 women and 573,079 men earned a bachelor's degree. How many more women than men earned a bachelor's degree that year? (*Source:* The National Center for Education Statistics)

The Maximum Heights of the Eruptions of Six Geysers at Yellowstone National Park

● **Demographics**   The graph at the right shows the expected U.S. population aged 100 and over for every 2 years from 2010 to 2020. Use this information for Exercises 106 to 108.

106. What is the expected growth in the population aged 100 and over during the 10-year period?

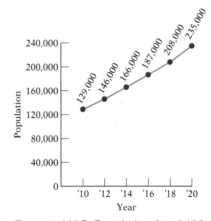

107. **a.** Which 2-year period has the smallest expected increase in the number of people aged 100 and over?
   b. Which 2-year period has the greatest expected increase?

108. What does the difference $208{,}000 - 166{,}000$ represent?

Expected U.S. Population Aged 100 and Over
Source: U.S. Census Bureau

109. **Finances**   You had a credit card balance of $409 before you used the card to purchase books for $168, CDs for $36, and a pair of shoes for $97. You then made a payment to the credit card company of $350. Find your new credit card balance.

Critical Thinking

110. Answer true or false.
   a. $9 - (5 - 3) = (9 - 5) - 3$
   b. Subtraction is an associative operation. *Hint:* See part (a) of this exercise.

111. 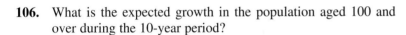 Make up a word problem for which the difference between 15 and 8 is the answer.

Projects or Group Activities

112. Write down a five-digit number in which all of the digits are different. Now reverse the order of the digits to form a new five-digit number. Subtract the smaller number from the larger one. Add the digits of the difference. If the result is a two-digit number, add the digits again. What is the result? Try this with a four-digit or six-digit number. Is the result always the same?

✓ CHECK YOUR PROGRESS: CHAPTER 1 ....

1. Graph 7 on the number line.

2. Place the correct symbol, < or >, between the two numbers.
   107   97

3. Write 82,743 in words.

4. Write 2,530,021 in words.

5. Write twenty-three thousand four hundred one in standard form.

6. Write nine hundred three thousand three in standard form.

7. Write 63,291 in expanded form.

8. Round 592,455 to the nearest thousand.

9. Round 45,962 to the nearest ten-thousand.

10. Add: 90,361 + 2955 + 750,679

11. Find the sum of 2034 and 12,598.

12. Find 40,781 increased by 156,742.

13. Subtract: 12,045 − 4987

14. Find 823 less than 9361.

15. ⬤ **National Debt** An estimate of the national debt is fourteen trillion seven hundred fifty-eight billion dollars. Round this number to the nearest hundred billion.

16. ⬤ **Waterfalls** The height of Yosemite Falls is 2425 feet, and the height of Colonial Falls is 2585 feet. How much higher is Colonial Falls than Yosemite Falls?

17. **Charity** Janice decided to donate some money to a charity. Her contributions for a six-month period were $25, $30, $13, $15, $20, and $27. Find the total amount of her contribution for the six months.

⬤ **Health Statistics** The table at the right shows the median height, in centimeters (cm), from birth to age 5 for boys and girls. Use this chart for Exercises 18 and 19. (*Source:* National Center for Health Statistics)

18. How many centimeters do boys grow from birth to age 5?

19. Between which two consecutive years do girls grow the most?

Age	Height of Girls (cm)	Height of Boys (cm)
Birth	49	50
1	74	75
2	84	87
3	95	91
4	100	102
5	108	110

20. **Sports** The scores for a professional golfer for four rounds of golf were 68, 72, 69, and 66. What was the total score for the golfer for the four rounds of golf?

SECTION

1.4 | Multiplication of Whole Numbers

OBJECTIVE A   *To multiply a number by a single digit*

Multiplication is used to find the total number of objects in several groups when each group contains the same number of objects.

APPLY THE CONCEPT

Sebastian purchased 8 six-packs of soda for a party. The total number of cans of soda he purchased can be found by adding 6 eight times. Sebastian purchased 48 cans of soda.

6 + 6 + 6 + 6 + 6 + 6 + 6 + 6 = 48

The number of cans can also be found by using multiplication.

$$6 \times 8 = 48$$

Multiplicand × Multiplier = Product

The **multiplicand** is the number of objects in each group (6 cans in each six-pack); the **multiplier** is the number of groups (8 six-packs); the **product** is the total number of objects (48 cans). Frequently we will discuss the *factors* of a product. A **factor** is one of the numbers that are multiplied to obtain a product. 6 and 8 are factors of 48.

Here is a table of basic multiplication facts. These facts should be memorized.

Basic Multiplication Facts

×	1	2	3	4	5	6	7	8	9
1	$1 \times 1 = 1$	$1 \times 2 = 2$	$1 \times 3 = 3$	$1 \times 4 = 4$	$1 \times 5 = 5$	$1 \times 6 = 6$	$1 \times 7 = 7$	$1 \times 8 = 8$	$1 \times 9 = 9$
2	$2 \times 1 = 2$	$2 \times 2 = 4$	$2 \times 3 = 6$	$2 \times 4 = 8$	$2 \times 5 = 10$	$2 \times 6 = 12$	$2 \times 7 = 14$	$2 \times 8 = 16$	$2 \times 9 = 18$
3	$3 \times 1 = 3$	$3 \times 2 = 6$	$3 \times 3 = 9$	$3 \times 4 = 12$	$3 \times 5 = 15$	$3 \times 6 = 18$	$3 \times 7 = 21$	$3 \times 8 = 24$	$3 \times 9 = 27$
4	$4 \times 1 = 4$	$4 \times 2 = 8$	$4 \times 3 = 12$	$4 \times 4 = 16$	$4 \times 5 = 20$	$4 \times 6 = 24$	$4 \times 7 = 28$	$4 \times 8 = 32$	$4 \times 9 = 36$
5	$5 \times 1 = 5$	$5 \times 2 = 10$	$5 \times 3 = 15$	$5 \times 4 = 20$	$5 \times 5 = 25$	$5 \times 6 = 30$	$5 \times 7 = 35$	$5 \times 8 = 40$	$5 \times 9 = 45$
6	$6 \times 1 = 6$	$6 \times 2 = 12$	$6 \times 3 = 18$	$6 \times 4 = 24$	$6 \times 5 = 30$	$6 \times 6 = 36$	$6 \times 7 = 42$	$6 \times 8 = 48$	$6 \times 9 = 54$
7	$7 \times 1 = 7$	$7 \times 2 = 14$	$7 \times 3 = 21$	$7 \times 4 = 28$	$7 \times 5 = 35$	$7 \times 6 = 42$	$7 \times 7 = 49$	$7 \times 8 = 56$	$7 \times 9 = 63$
8	$8 \times 1 = 8$	$8 \times 2 = 16$	$8 \times 3 = 24$	$8 \times 4 = 32$	$8 \times 5 = 40$	$8 \times 6 = 48$	$8 \times 7 = 56$	$8 \times 8 = 64$	$8 \times 9 = 72$
9	$9 \times 1 = 9$	$9 \times 2 = 18$	$9 \times 3 = 27$	$9 \times 4 = 36$	$9 \times 5 = 45$	$9 \times 6 = 54$	$9 \times 7 = 63$	$9 \times 8 = 72$	$9 \times 9 = 81$

 Tips for Success

Some students think that they can "coast" at the beginning of this course because the topic of Chapter 1 is whole numbers. However, this chapter lays the foundation for the entire course. Be sure you know and understand all of the concepts presented. For example, study the properties of multiplication presented in this lesson.

The times sign "×" is only one symbol that is used to indicate multiplication. Each of the expressions that follow represents multiplication.

$$7 \times 8 \qquad 7 \cdot 8 \qquad 7(8) \qquad (7)(8) \qquad (7)8$$

As with addition, there are some useful properties of multiplication.

Commutative Property of Multiplication

Two numbers can be multiplied in either order; the product will be the same.

EXAMPLES

1. $4 \times 3 = 3 \times 4$
   $12 = 12$

2. $9 \times 7 = 7 \times 9$
   $63 = 63$

Associative Property of Multiplication

Grouping numbers to be multiplied in any order gives the same result. Do the multiplication inside the parentheses first.

EXAMPLES

1. $(4 \times 2) \times 3 = 4 \times (2 \times 3)$
   $8 \times 3 = 4 \times 6$
   $24 = 24$

2. $3 \times (2 \times 5) = (3 \times 2) \times 5$
   $3 \times 10 = 6 \times 5$
   $30 = 30$

Multiplication Property of One

Multiplying a number by 1 does not change the number.

EXAMPLES

1. $8 \times 1 = 8$

2. $1 \times 6 = 6$

Multiplication Property of Zero

A number multiplied by zero is zero.

EXAMPLES

1. $7 \times 0 = 0$

2. $0 \times 4 = 0$

Tips for Success

One of the key instructional features of this text is the Example/You Try It pairs. Each Example is completely worked. You are to solve the You Try It problems. When you are ready, check your solution against the one given in the Solutions section. The solution for You Try It 1 below is on page S2 (see the reference at the bottom right of the You Try It). See *AIM for Success* at the front of the book.

Multiplication of larger numbers requires repeated use of the basic multiplication facts.

HOW TO 1   Multiply: 37×4

$$\overset{2}{37}$$
$$\underline{\times\ 4}$$
$$8$$

• $4 \times 7 = 28$ (2 tens + 8 ones)
Write the 8 in the ones column and carry the 2 to the tens column.

$$\overset{2}{37}$$
$$\underline{\times\ 4}$$
$$148$$

• The 3 in 37 is 3 tens.
4×3 tens =   12 tens
Add the carry digit. $\underline{+\ 2\ \text{tens}}$
       14 tens

The product is 148.

The phrases below are used to indicate the operation of multiplication. An example is shown at the right of each phrase.

times	7 times 3	$7 \cdot 3$
the product of	the product of 6 and 9	$6 \cdot 9$
multiplied by	8 multiplied by 2	$8 \cdot 2$

EXAMPLE 1

Find the product of 735 and 9.

Solution

$$\overset{3\ 4}{735}$$
$$\underline{\times\ \ 9}$$
$$6615$$

• $9 \times 5 = 45$
Write the 5 in the ones column.
Carry the 4 to the tens column.
$9 \times 3 = 27,\ 27 + 4 = 31$
$9 \times 7 = 63,\ 63 + 3 = 66$

YOU TRY IT 1

Multiply: 648×7

Your solution

Solution on p. S2

OBJECTIVE B   *To multiply larger whole numbers*

Note the pattern in the products shown at the right.

Multiply the nonzero parts of the factors.

Then attach the same number of zeros to the product as the total number of zeros in the factors.

HOW TO 2   Find the product of 47 and 23.

Multiply by the ones digit.	Multiply by the tens digit.	Add.
47	47	47
× 23	× 23	× 23
141 (= 47 × 3)	141	141
	940 (= 47 × 20)	940
		1081

Writing the 0 keeps the columns aligned correctly.

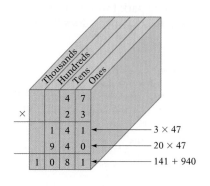

The place-value chart on the right above illustrates the placement of the products.

Note the placement of the products when multiplying by a factor that contains a zero.

HOW TO 3   Multiply: 439 × 206

```
    439
 ×  206
   2634
    000     0 × 439
    878
  90,434
```

When working the problem, we usually write only one zero. Writing this zero ensures the proper placement of the products.

```
    439
 ×  206
   2634
   8780
  90,434
```

EXAMPLE 2

Find 829 multiplied by 603.

Solution

```
    829
 ×  603
   2487
  49740
 499,887
```

• 3 × 829 = 2487
• Write a zero in the tens column for 0 × 829.
• 6 × 829 = 4974

YOU TRY IT 2

Multiply: 756 × 305

Your solution

Solution on p. S2

ESTIMATION: Estimating the Product of Two Whole Numbers

Calculate 3267 × 389. Then use estimation to determine whether the product is reasonable.

Multiply to find the exact product.   3267 × 389 = 1,270,863

To estimate the product, round each number   3267 ≈   3000
so that it has only one nonzero digit. Then multiply.   × 389 ≈   × 400
The estimated answer is 1,200,000, which is   1,200,000
very close to the exact product 1,270,863.

OBJECTIVE C *To solve application problems*

EXAMPLE 3

A state park forester receives a salary of $1050 each week. How much does the forester earn in 4 weeks?

Strategy

To find the forester's earnings for 4 weeks, multiply the weekly salary (1050) by the number of weeks (4).

Solution

```
  1050
×    4
  4200
```

The forester earns $4200 in 4 weeks.

YOU TRY IT 3

An elephant will eat approximately 150 pounds of food each day. How many pounds of food will an elephant eat in a 365-day year?

Your strategy

Your solution

EXAMPLE 4

A pharmacist's assistant earns $640 for working a 40-hour week. This week the assistant also worked 7 hours of overtime at $26 an hour. Find the assistant's total pay for the week.

Strategy

To find the assistant's total pay for the week:
• Find the overtime pay by multiplying the hours of overtime (7) by the overtime rate of pay (26).
• Add the weekly salary (640) to the overtime pay.

Solution

```
   26              640
×   7            + 182
  182  overtime pay   822
```

The assistant earned $822 this week.

YOU TRY IT 4

The buyer for Ross Department Store can buy 80 men's suits for $7600. Each sports jacket will cost the store $62. The manager orders 80 men's suits and 25 sports jackets. What is the total cost of the order?

Your strategy

Your solution

1.4 EXERCISES

✔ Concept Check

For Exercises 1 to 4, write the expression as a product.

1. $2 + 2 + 2 + 2 + 2 + 2$ **2.** $4 + 4 + 4 + 4 + 4$ **3.** $7 + 7 + 7 + 7$ **4.** $18 + 18 + 18$

For Exercises 5 to 8, identify the property on pages 25–26 that justifies the statement.

5. $1 \times 23 = 23$ **6.** $(9 \times 5) \times 7 = 9 \times (5 \times 7)$ **7.** $8 \times 12 = 12 \times 8$ **8.** $(9 \times 5) \times 7 = (5 \times 9) \times 7$

OBJECTIVE A   *To multiply a number by a single digit*

For Exercises 9 to 43, multiply.

9. $\begin{array}{r} 3 \\ \times\, 4 \\ \hline \end{array}$ **10.** $\begin{array}{r} 2 \\ \times\, 8 \\ \hline \end{array}$ **11.** $\begin{array}{r} 5 \\ \times\, 7 \\ \hline \end{array}$ **12.** $\begin{array}{r} 6 \\ \times\, 4 \\ \hline \end{array}$ **13.** $\begin{array}{r} 5 \\ \times\, 5 \\ \hline \end{array}$

14. $\begin{array}{r} 7 \\ \times\, 7 \\ \hline \end{array}$ **15.** $\begin{array}{r} 0 \\ \times\, 7 \\ \hline \end{array}$ **16.** $\begin{array}{r} 8 \\ \times\, 0 \\ \hline \end{array}$ **17.** $\begin{array}{r} 8 \\ \times\, 9 \\ \hline \end{array}$ **18.** $\begin{array}{r} 7 \\ \times\, 6 \\ \hline \end{array}$

19. $\begin{array}{r} 66 \\ \times\, 3 \\ \hline \end{array}$ **20.** $\begin{array}{r} 70 \\ \times\, 4 \\ \hline \end{array}$ **21.** $\begin{array}{r} 67 \\ \times\, 5 \\ \hline \end{array}$ **22.** $\begin{array}{r} 127 \\ \times\, 9 \\ \hline \end{array}$ **23.** $\begin{array}{r} 623 \\ \times\, 4 \\ \hline \end{array}$

24. $\begin{array}{r} 802 \\ \times\, 5 \\ \hline \end{array}$ **25.** $\begin{array}{r} 607 \\ \times\, 9 \\ \hline \end{array}$ **26.** $\begin{array}{r} 300 \\ \times\, 5 \\ \hline \end{array}$ **27.** $\begin{array}{r} 600 \\ \times\, 7 \\ \hline \end{array}$ **28.** $\begin{array}{r} 906 \\ \times\, 8 \\ \hline \end{array}$

29. $\begin{array}{r} 703 \\ \times\, 9 \\ \hline \end{array}$ **30.** $\begin{array}{r} 127 \\ \times\, 5 \\ \hline \end{array}$ **31.** $\begin{array}{r} 632 \\ \times\, 3 \\ \hline \end{array}$ **32.** $\begin{array}{r} 559 \\ \times\, 4 \\ \hline \end{array}$ **33.** $\begin{array}{r} 632 \\ \times\, 8 \\ \hline \end{array}$

34. $\begin{array}{r} 524 \\ \times\, 4 \\ \hline \end{array}$ **35.** $\begin{array}{r} 337 \\ \times\, 5 \\ \hline \end{array}$ **36.** $\begin{array}{r} 841 \\ \times\, 6 \\ \hline \end{array}$ **37.** $\begin{array}{r} 6709 \\ \times\, 7 \\ \hline \end{array}$ **38.** $\begin{array}{r} 3608 \\ \times\, 5 \\ \hline \end{array}$

39. $\begin{array}{r} 8568 \\ \times\, 7 \\ \hline \end{array}$ **40.** $\begin{array}{r} 5495 \\ \times\, 4 \\ \hline \end{array}$ **41.** $\begin{array}{r} 4780 \\ \times\, 4 \\ \hline \end{array}$ **42.** $\begin{array}{r} 3690 \\ \times\, 5 \\ \hline \end{array}$ **43.** $\begin{array}{r} 9895 \\ \times\, 2 \\ \hline \end{array}$

44. True or false? The product of two one-digit whole numbers must be a two-digit whole number.

45. Find the product of 5, 7, and 4.

46. Find the product of 6, 2, and 9.

47. What is 3208 multiplied by 7?

48. What is 5009 multiplied by 4?

49. What is 3105 times 6?

50. What is 8957 times 8?

OBJECTIVE B *To multiply larger whole numbers*

For Exercises 51 to 82, multiply.

51.   16
× 21

52.   18
× 24

53.   35
× 26

54.   27
× 72

55.   693
× 91

56.   581
× 72

57.   419
× 80

58.   727
× 60

59.   8279
×   46

60.   9577
×   35

61.   6938
×   78

62.   8875
×   67

63.   7035
×   57

64.   6702
×   48

65.   3009
×   35

66.   6003
×   57

67.   809
× 530

68.   607
× 460

69.   800
× 325

70.   700
× 274

71.   987
× 349

72.   688
× 674

73.   312
× 134

74.   423
× 427

75.   379
× 500

76.   684
× 700

77.   985
× 408

78.   758
× 209

79.   3407
×   309

80.   5207
×   902

81.   4258
×   986

82.   6327
×   876

83. Find a one-digit number and a two-digit number whose product is a number that ends in two zeros.

84. What is 5763 times 45?

85. What is 7349 times 27?

86. Find the product of 2, 19, and 34.

87. Find the product of 6, 73, and 43.

88. What is 376 multiplied by 402?

89. What is 842 multiplied by 309?

For Exercises 90 to 97, use a calculator to multiply. Then use estimation to determine whether the product is reasonable.

90.   8745
      $\times$ 63

91.   4732
      $\times$ 93

92.   2937
      $\times$ 206

93.   8941
      $\times$ 726

94.   3097
      $\times$ 1025

95.   6379
      $\times$ 2936

96. 32,508
      $\times$ 591

97. 62,504
      $\times$ 923

OBJECTIVE C   *To solve application problems*

98. Geometry The perimeter of a square is equal to four times the length of a side of the square. Find the perimeter of the square herb box garden shown at the right.

8 ft

99. Geometry The area of a rectangle is equal to the product of the length and the width. Find the area of the rectangular tennis court shown at the right.

36 ft

100. The price of grapes is $3 per pound, and the price of cherries is $5 per pound. Which of the following represents the price of 4 pounds of grapes and 2 pounds of cherries?
   (i) $(4 \times 3) + (4 \times 5)$ **(ii)** $(2 \times 3) + (4 \times 5)$
   (iii) $5 \times (3 + 5)$ **(iv)** $(4 \times 3) + (2 \times 5)$

78 ft

101. Fuel Efficiency Rob Hill owns a compact car that averages 43 miles on 1 gallon of gas. How many miles could the car travel on 12 gallons of gas?

In the NEWS!

Find Your Match Online

eHarmony, the online matchmaking service, boasts marriages among its members at the rate of 542 a day.

Source: www.eharmony.com

102. Fuel Efficiency A plane flying from Los Angeles to Boston uses 865 gallons of jet fuel each hour. How many gallons of jet fuel were used on a 6-hour flight?

103. ● **Matchmaking Services** See the news clipping at the right.
   a. How many marriages occur between eHarmony members each week?
   b. How many marriages occur each year? Use a 365-day year.

104. 🔵 **College Education** See the news clipping at the right.
   a. Find the average cost of tuition, room, and board for 4 years at a public university.
   b. Find the average cost of tuition, room, and board for 4 years at a private university.
   c. Find the difference in the average cost of tuition, room, and board for 4 years at a private university and 4 years at a public university.

> **In the NEWS!**
>
> **Comparing Tuition Costs**
>
> The average annual cost of tuition, room, and board at a four-year public university is $15,875. At a four-year private university, the average cost is $42,841.
> *Source:* National Center for Education Statistics

Construction The table at the right below shows the hourly wages for four types of jobs at a small construction company. Use this table for Exercises 105 to 107.

105. The owner of this company wants to provide the electrical installation for a new house. On the basis of the architectural plans, it is estimated that the installation will require 3 electricians, each working 50 hours, to complete the job. What is the estimated cost for the electricians' labor?

Type of Work	Wage per Hour
Electrician	$34
Plumber	$30
Clerk	$16
Bookkeeper	$20

106. Carlos Vasquez, a plumbing contractor, hires 4 plumbers from this company at the hourly wage given in the table. If each plumber works 23 hours, what are the total wages paid by Carlos?

107. The owner of this company estimates that a kitchen remodel will require 1 electrician working 30 hours and 1 plumber working 33 hours. This project also requires 3 hours of clerical work and 4 hours of bookkeeping. What is the total cost for these four components of the remodel?

Critical Thinking

108. Determine whether each statement is always true, sometimes true, or never true.
   a. A whole number times zero is zero.
   b. A whole number times 1 is the whole number.
   c. The product of two whole numbers is greater than either of the numbers.

109. 🔵 **Safety** According to the National Safety Council, in a recent year, a death resulting from an accident occurred at the rate of 1 every 5 minutes. At this rate, how many accidental deaths occurred each hour? Each day? Throughout the year? Explain how you arrived at your answers.

110. 🔵 **Demographics** According to the Population Reference Bureau, in the world today, 267 people are born every minute and 108 people die every minute. Using this statistic, what is the increase in the world's population every hour? Every day? Every week? Every year? Use a 365-day year. Explain how you arrived at your answers.

Projects or Group Activities

111. What multiplication problem is shown at the right? The letters S, T, R, A, and W stand for five different digits.

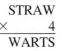

$$\begin{array}{r} \text{STRAW} \\ \times \qquad 4 \\ \hline \text{WARTS} \end{array}$$

SECTION

1.5 | Division of Whole Numbers

OBJECTIVE A   *To divide by a single digit with no remainder in the quotient*

Division is used to separate objects into equal groups.

APPLY THE CONCEPT ···

Four friends want to share equally in the cost of a $24 birthday present for their friend Bianca. From the diagram below, each friend's share of the cost is $6.

Cost of the present
$24

Gina's share   Jason's share   Michelle's share   Isaiah's share
$6 $6 $6 $6

The solution of this division problem is written as follows:

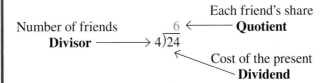

Note that the quotient multiplied by the divisor equals the dividend.

$\dfrac{6}{4\overline{)24}}$ because $\boxed{\underset{\text{Quotient}}{6}} \times \boxed{\underset{\text{Divisor}}{4}} = \boxed{\underset{\text{Dividend}}{24}}$

$\dfrac{6}{9\overline{)54}}$ because   6   ×   9   =   54

$\dfrac{5}{8\overline{)40}}$ because   5   ×   8   =   40

Property of One in Division

Any whole number, except zero, divided by itself is 1.

EXAMPLES

1. $\dfrac{1}{8\overline{)8}}$ 2. $\dfrac{1}{14\overline{)14}}$

Property of Zero in Division

Zero divided by any whole number other than zero is zero.

EXAMPLES

1. $\dfrac{0}{7\overline{)0}}$ 2. $\dfrac{0}{13\overline{)0}}$

Note that the Property of Zero in Division states that zero divided by any whole number *other than zero* is zero. Division by zero is not allowed. Here is an example of why this is so.

Integrating Technology

Enter 8 ÷ 0 = on your calculator. An error message is displayed because division by zero is not allowed.

Suppose we try to divide 0 into 8, and write $0\overline{)8}^{?}$. The quotient—the number that replaces the question mark—times the divisor, 0, must equal the dividend, 8. In other words, $\boxed{?} \times 0$ would have to be 8. However, any number times zero is zero. There is no number whose product with 0 is 8, and therefore no number that can replace the question mark to make a true statement.

When the dividend is a larger whole number, the digits in the quotient are found in steps.

HOW TO 1   Divide $4\overline{)3192}$ and check.

$$\begin{array}{r} 7 \\ 4\overline{)\,3192} \\ -28 \\ \hline 39 \end{array}$$

- Think $4\overline{)31}^{\,7}$. Place 7 in the quotient.
- Multiply 7×4.
- Subtract: $31 - 28 = 3$. Bring down the 9.

$$\begin{array}{r} 79 \\ 4\overline{)\,3192} \\ -28 \\ \hline 39 \\ -36 \\ \hline 32 \end{array}$$

- Think $4\overline{)39}^{\,9}$. Place 9 in the quotient.
- Multiply 9×4.
- Subtract: $39 - 36 = 3$. Bring down the 2.

$$\begin{array}{r} 798 \\ 4\overline{)\,3192} \\ -28 \\ \hline 39 \\ -36 \\ \hline 32 \\ -32 \\ \hline 0 \end{array}$$

- Think $4\overline{)32}^{\,8}$. Place 8 in the quotient.
- Multiply 8×4.
- Subtract: $32 - 32 = 0$.

Check:
$$\begin{array}{r} 798 \\ \times \quad 4 \\ \hline 3192 \end{array}$$

The place-value chart can be used to show why this method works.

$$\begin{array}{r} \text{HUNDREDS} \;\; \text{TENS} \;\; \text{ONES} \\ 7 \;\; 9 \;\; 8 \\ 4\overline{)\;3\;1\;9\;2} \\ -\;2\;8\;0\;0 \quad \text{7 hundreds} \times 4 \\ \hline 3\;9\;2 \\ -\;3\;6\;0 \quad \text{9 tens} \times 4 \\ \hline 3\;2 \\ -\;3\;2 \quad \text{8 ones} \times 4 \\ \hline 0 \end{array}$$

There are other ways of expressing division.

54 divided by 9 equals 6.

54   ÷   9 equals 6.

$\dfrac{54}{9}$ equals 6.

EXAMPLE 1

Divide $7\overline{)56}$ and check.

Solution

$7\overline{)56}^{\,8}$

Check: $8 \times 7 = 56$

YOU TRY IT 1

Divide $9\overline{)63}$ and check.

Your solution

EXAMPLE 2

Divide $2808 \div 8$ and check.

Solution

$$
\begin{array}{r}
351 \\
8\overline{)\,2808} \\
-24 \\
\hline
40 \\
-40 \\
\hline
08 \\
-\,8 \\
\hline
0
\end{array}
$$

Check: $351 \times 8 = 2808$

YOU TRY IT 2

Divide $4077 \div 9$ and check.

Your solution

EXAMPLE 3

Divide $7\overline{)2856}$ and check.

Solution

$$
\begin{array}{r}
408 \\
7\overline{)\,2856} \\
-28 \\
\hline
05 \\
-0 \\
\hline
56 \\
-56 \\
\hline
0
\end{array}
$$

- Think $7\overline{)5}^{\,0}$. Place 0 in the quotient.
- Multiply 0×7.
- Subtract: $5 - 0 = 5$. Bring down the 6.

Check: $408 \times 7 = 2856$

YOU TRY IT 3

Divide $9\overline{)6345}$ and check.

Your solution

Solutions on pp. S2–S3

OBJECTIVE B   *To divide by a single digit with a remainder in the quotient*

Sometimes it is not possible to separate objects into a whole number of equal groups.

APPLY THE CONCEPT ···

A baker has 14 muffins to pack into 3 boxes. Each box holds 4 muffins. From the diagram, we see that after the baker places 4 muffins in each box, there are 2 left over. The 2 leftover muffins represent the **remainder.**

The baker's division problem can be written as follows.

$$
\begin{array}{r}
\text{Quotient} \\
4 \leftarrow \text{(Number in each box)} \\
\text{Divisor} \longrightarrow 3\overline{)\,14} \leftarrow \text{Dividend} \\
\text{(Number of boxes)} \quad -12 \quad \text{(Total number of muffins)} \\
2 \leftarrow \text{Remainder} \\
\text{(Number left over)}
\end{array}
$$

The answer to a division problem with a remainder is frequently written

$$3\overline{)14}^{\,4\ r2}$$

Note that
$$\boxed{\begin{array}{c}4\\ \text{Quotient}\end{array}} \times \boxed{\begin{array}{c}3\\ \text{Divisor}\end{array}} + \boxed{\begin{array}{c}2\\ \text{Remainder}\end{array}} = \boxed{\begin{array}{c}14\\ \text{Dividend}\end{array}}.$$

···

EXAMPLE 4

Divide $4\overline{)2522}$ and check.

Solution

$$
\begin{array}{r}
630 \text{ r2} \\
4\overline{)\,2522} \\
-24 \\
\hline
12 \\
-12 \\
\hline
02 \\
-0 \\
\hline
2
\end{array}
$$

• Think $4\overline{)2}$. Place 0 in the quotient.
• Multiply 0×4.
• Subtract: $2 - 0 = 2$.

Check: $(630 \times 4) + 2 =$
$\qquad 2520 \quad + 2 = 2522$

YOU TRY IT 4

Divide $6\overline{)5225}$ and check.

Your solution

EXAMPLE 5

Divide $9\overline{)27{,}438}$ and check.

Solution

$$
\begin{array}{r}
3{,}048 \ \text{r6} \\
9\overline{)\ 27{,}438} \\
-27 \\
\hline
0\ 4 \\
-0 \\
\hline
43 \\
-36 \\
\hline
78 \\
-72 \\
\hline
6
\end{array}
$$

- Think $9\overline{)4}$. Place 0 in the quotient.
- Multiply 0×9.
- Subtract: $4 - 0 = 4$. Bring down the 3.

Check: $(3048 \times 9) + 6 =$
$\qquad 27{,}432 \ \ + 6 = 27{,}438$

YOU TRY IT 5

Divide $7\overline{)21{,}409}$ and check.

Your solution

Solution on p. S3

OBJECTIVE C *To divide by larger whole numbers*

When the divisor has more than one digit, estimate at each step by using the first digit of the divisor. If that product is too large, lower the guess by 1 and try again.

HOW TO 2 Divide $34\overline{)1598}$ and check.

$$
\begin{array}{r}
5 \\
34\overline{)\ 1598} \\
-170 \\
\end{array}
$$

- Think $3\overline{)15}$.
- Multiply 5×34.

170 is too large. Lower the guess by 1 and try again.

$$
\begin{array}{r}
4 \\
34\overline{)\ 1598} \\
-136 \\
\hline
238
\end{array}
$$

- Multiply 4×34.
- Subtract $159 - 136 = 23$. Bring down the 8.

$$
\begin{array}{r}
47 \\
34\overline{)\ 1598} \\
-136 \\
\hline
238 \\
-238 \\
\hline
0
\end{array}
$$

- Think $3\overline{)23}$.
- Multiply 7×34.
- Subtract.

Check:
$$
\begin{array}{r}
47 \\
\times 34 \\
\hline
188 \\
141 \\
\hline
1598
\end{array}
$$

The phrases below are used to indicate the operation of division. An example is shown at the right of each phrase.

the quotient of	the quotient of 9 and 3	$9 \div 3$
divided by	6 divided by 2	$6 \div 2$

EXAMPLE 6

Find 7077 divided by 34 and check.

Solution

```
        208 r5
34) 7077
   −68
     27        • Think 34)27⁰. Place 0 in the quotient.
    −0         • Multiply 0 × 34.
    277        • Subtract: 27 − 0 = 27. Bring down the 7.
   −272
      5
```

Check: (208 × 34) + 5 =
      7072   + 5 = 7077

YOU TRY IT 6

Divide 4578 ÷ 42 and check.

Your solution

EXAMPLE 7

Find the quotient of 21,312 and 56, and check.

Solution

```
        380 r32
56) 21,312        • Think 5)21⁴. 4 × 56 is too large.
  −16 8             Try 3.
    4 51
   −4 48
      32
     −0
      32
```

Check: (380 × 56) + 32 =
      21,280   + 32 = 21,312

YOU TRY IT 7

Divide 18,359 ÷ 39 and check.

Your solution

EXAMPLE 8

Divide 427)24,782 and check.

Solution

```
         58 r16
427) 24,782
   −21 35
     3 432
    −3 416
        16
```

Check: (58 × 427) + 16 =
      24,766   + 16 = 24,782

YOU TRY IT 8

Divide 534)33,219 and check.

Your solution

EXAMPLE 9

Divide $386\overline{)206{,}149}$ and check.

Solution

$$
\begin{array}{r}
534 \text{ r}25 \\
386\overline{)\,206{,}149} \\
-193\,0 \\
\hline
13\,14 \\
-11\,58 \\
\hline
1\,569 \\
-1\,544 \\
\hline
25
\end{array}
$$

Check: $(534 \times 386) + 25 =$
$ 206{,}124 \;+\; 25 = 206{,}149$

YOU TRY IT 9

Divide $515\overline{)216{,}848}$ and check.

Your solution

Solution on p. S3

ESTIMATION: Estimating the Quotient of Two Whole Numbers

Calculate $38{,}772 \div 54$. Then use estimation to determine whether the quotient is reasonable.

Divide to find the exact quotient.

$38{,}772 \;\boxed{\div}\; 54 \;\boxed{=}\; 718$

To estimate the quotient, round each number so that it contains one nonzero digit. Then divide. The estimated answer is 800, which is close to the exact quotient 718.

$38{,}772 \div 54 \approx$
$40{,}000 \div 50 = 800$

OBJECTIVE D *To solve application problems*

The **average** of several numbers is the sum of all the numbers divided by the number of those numbers.

A student has six test grades in a Spanish class. They are 81, 87, 80, 85, 79, and 86. To find the student's average of test score, divide the sum of the six test scores by 6.

$$\text{Average test score} = \frac{81 + 87 + 80 + 85 + 79 + 86}{6} = \frac{498}{6} = 83$$

The student's average test score in the Spanish class is 83.

HOW TO 3

🥧 The table below shows how much a median-income family can expect to spend raising a child to the age of 17 years. Find the average amount spent each year. Round to the nearest dollar.

Expenses to Raise a Child	
Housing	$70,020
Food	$35,970
Transportation	$28,590
Child care/education	$37,740
Clothing	$13,260
Health care	$17,760
Other	$19,030

Source: Department of Agriculture,
Expenditures on Children by Families

Strategy

To find the average amount spent each year:

- Add all the numbers in the table to find the total amount spent during the 17 years.
- Divide the sum by 17.

Solution

$$
\begin{array}{r}
70,020 \\
35,970 \\
28,590 \\
37,740 \\
13,260 \\
17,760 \\
+\quad 19,030 \\
\hline
222,370
\end{array}
$$

• Sum of all the costs

$$
\begin{array}{r}
13{,}080 \text{ r}10 \\
17 \overline{)\; 222{,}370} \\
-17 \\
\hline
52 \\
-51 \\
\hline
1\,3 \\
-\;\;0 \\
\hline
1\,37 \\
-1\,36 \\
\hline
10 \\
-\;\;0 \\
\hline
10
\end{array}
$$

• When rounding to the nearest whole number, compare twice the remainder to the divisor. If twice the remainder is less than the divisor, drop the remainder. If twice the remainder is greater than or equal to the divisor, add 1 to the units digit of the quotient and drop the remainder.

• Twice the remainder is 2 × 10 = 20. Because 20 > 17, add 1 to the units digit of the quotient.

The average amount spent each year to raise a child to the age of 17 is $13,081.

EXAMPLE 10

Ngan Hui, a freight supervisor, shipped 35,640 bushels of wheat in 9 railroad cars. Find the amount of wheat shipped in each car.

Strategy

To find the amount of wheat shipped in each car, divide the number of bushels (35,640) by the number of cars (9).

Solution

$$
\begin{array}{r}
3\,960 \\
9\overline{)\,35{,}640} \\
-27 \\
\hline
86 \\
-81 \\
\hline
54 \\
-54 \\
\hline
0
\end{array}
$$

Each car carried 3960 bushels of wheat.

YOU TRY IT 10

Suppose a Michelin retail outlet can store 270 tires on 15 shelves. How many tires can be stored on each shelf?

Your strategy

Your solution

EXAMPLE 11

The used car you are buying costs $11,216. A down payment of $2000 is required. The remaining balance is paid in 48 equal monthly payments. What is the monthly payment?

Strategy

To find the monthly payment:

- Find the remaining balance by subtracting the down payment (2000) from the total cost of the car (11,216).
- Divide the remaining balance by the number of equal monthly payments (48).

Solution

$$
\begin{array}{r}
11{,}216 \\
-\ 2{,}000 \\
\hline
9{,}216
\end{array}
$$

• **Remaining balance**

$$
\begin{array}{r}
192 \\
48\overline{)\,9216} \\
-48 \\
\hline
441 \\
-432 \\
\hline
96 \\
-96 \\
\hline
0
\end{array}
$$

The monthly payment is $192.

YOU TRY IT 11

A soft-drink manufacturer produces 12,600 cans of soft drink each hour. Cans are packed 24 to a case. How many cases of soft drink are produced in 8 hours?

Your strategy

Your solution

Solutions on pp. S3–S4

1.5 EXERCISES

✔ Concept Check

For Exercises 1 to 4, find the quotient. Then write the related multiplication problem using Quotient × Divisor = Dividend.

1. $4\overline{)8}$ **2.** $3\overline{)12}$ **3.** $5\overline{)30}$ **4.** $9\overline{)63}$

For Exercises 5 to 8, use the relationship between multiplication and division to complete the multiplication problem.

5. __ × 9 = 54   **6.** 12 × __ = 60   **7.** 8 × __ = 96   **8.** __ × 15 = 90

OBJECTIVE A   *To divide by a single digit with no remainder in the quotient*

For Exercises 9 to 24, divide.

9. $7\overline{)49}$ **10.** $5\overline{)80}$ **11.** $6\overline{)96}$ **12.** $6\overline{)480}$

13. $4\overline{)840}$ **14.** $3\overline{)690}$ **15.** $7\overline{)308}$ **16.** $7\overline{)203}$

17. $9\overline{)6327}$ **18.** $4\overline{)2120}$ **19.** $8\overline{)7280}$ **20.** $9\overline{)8118}$

21. $7\overline{)35,042}$ **22.** $4\overline{)28,032}$ **23.** $9\overline{)54,450}$ **24.** $8\overline{)25,632}$

25. What is 7525 divided by 7?   **26.** What is 32,364 divided by 4?

27. 🔖 If the dividend and the divisor in a division problem are the same number, what is the quotient?

OBJECTIVE B   *To divide by a single digit with a remainder in the quotient*

For Exercises 28 to 50, divide.

28. $4\overline{)9}$ **29.** $2\overline{)7}$ **30.** $5\overline{)27}$ **31.** $9\overline{)88}$ **32.** $3\overline{)40}$

33. $6\overline{)97}$ **34.** $8\overline{)83}$ **35.** $5\overline{)54}$ **36.** $7\overline{)632}$ **37.** $4\overline{)363}$

38. $4\overline{)921}$ **39.** $7\overline{)845}$ **40.** $8\overline{)1635}$ **41.** $5\overline{)1548}$ **42.** $7\overline{)9432}$

43. $7\overline{)8124}$ **44.** $3\overline{)5162}$ **45.** $5\overline{)3542}$ **46.** $8\overline{)3274}$

47. $4\overline{)15{,}301}$ **48.** $7\overline{)43{,}500}$ **49.** $6\overline{)34{,}263}$ **50.** $7\overline{)21{,}495}$

51. What is 45,738 divided by 4? Round to the nearest ten.

52. What is 37,896 divided by 9? Round to the nearest hundred.

53. What is 3572 divided by 7? Round to the nearest ten.

54. What is 78,345 divided by 4? Round to the nearest hundred.

55. True or false? When a three-digit number is divided by a one-digit number, the quotient can be a one-digit number.

OBJECTIVE C   *To divide by larger whole numbers*

For Exercises 56 to 83, divide.

56. $27\overline{)96}$ **57.** $44\overline{)82}$ **58.** $42\overline{)87}$ **59.** $67\overline{)93}$

60. $41\overline{)897}$ **61.** $32\overline{)693}$ **62.** $23\overline{)784}$ **63.** $25\overline{)772}$

64. $74\overline{)600}$ **65.** $92\overline{)500}$ **66.** $70\overline{)329}$ **67.** $50\overline{)467}$

68. $36\overline{)7225}$ **69.** $44\overline{)8821}$ **70.** $19\overline{)3859}$ **71.** $32\overline{)9697}$

72. $88\overline{)3127}$ **73.** $92\overline{)6177}$ **74.** $29\overline{)14{,}721}$ **75.** $63\overline{)44{,}653}$

76. $22\overline{)98{,}654}$ **77.** $77\overline{)83{,}629}$ **78.** $57\overline{)114{,}545}$ **79.** $73\overline{)365{,}566}$

80. $206\overline{)3097}$ **81.** $504\overline{)6504}$ **82.** $654\overline{)1217}$ **83.** $546\overline{)2344}$

84. Find the quotient of 5432 and 21.

85. Find the quotient of 8507 and 53.

86. What is 37,294 divided by 72?

87. What is 76,788 divided by 46?

88. Find 23,457 divided by 43. Round to the nearest hundred.

89. Find 341,781 divided by 43. Round to the nearest ten.

90. True or false? If the remainder of a division problem is 210, then the divisor was less than 210.

For Exercises 91 to 102, use a calculator to divide. Then use estimation to determine whether the quotient is reasonable.

91. $76\overline{)389{,}804}$

92. $53\overline{)117{,}925}$

93. $29\overline{)637{,}072}$

94. $67\overline{)738{,}072}$

95. $38\overline{)934{,}648}$

96. $34\overline{)906{,}304}$

97. $309\overline{)876{,}324}$

98. $642\overline{)323{,}568}$

99. $209\overline{)632{,}016}$

100. $614\overline{)332{,}174}$

101. $179\overline{)5{,}734{,}444}$

102. $374\overline{)7{,}712{,}254}$

OBJECTIVE D   *To solve application problems*

103. Salaries Melissa's annual starting salary as a chemical engineer is $69,048. What is her monthly salary?

104. Cooking A chef is making 120 meatballs from 6 pounds of hamburger. Six pounds of hamburger contain 7200 calories.
a. How many calories are in one meatball?
b. How many calories are in one pound of hamburger?

105. Jewelry A jeweler is making 15 identical gold necklaces from 30 ounces of a gold alloy that costs $375 per ounce. What is the cost of the gold alloy in each necklace?

106. Manufacturing It costs a manufacturer of the energy drink Z-ENG $126,000 to make 63,000 bottles of the drink. The manufacturer packages the Z-ENG in cartons of four bottles. What is the cost of a carton of four bottles of Z-ENG?

107. Education A nursing student received scores of 86, 94, 79, and 93 on four anatomy exams. What was the nursing student's average score for the four exams?

108. Education To receive an A grade in a Spanish course, a professor requires a minimum score of 450 points on the five semester exams. If Richard receives a score of 82 on the first exam, what average score must Richard receive on the remaining four tests to achieve the minimum total of 450 points?

109. Electronics The cost of a 3D television that you are purchasing is $3180. If you make a down payment of $1620 and agree to pay off the remaining balance in 12 equal monthly payments, what is the monthly payment?

110. Wages A sales associate earns $440 for working a 40-hour week. Last week, the associate worked an additional 9 hours at $13 an hour. What is the difference between the associate's hourly overtime pay rate and the regular hourly pay rate?

● **Insurance** The table at the right shows the sources of insurance claims for losses of laptop computers in a recent year. Claims have been rounded to the nearest ten thousand dollars. Use this information for Exercises 111 and 112.

Source	Claims
Accidents	$560,000
Theft	$300,000
Power surge	$80,000
Lightning	$50,000
Transit	$20,000
Water/flood	$20,000
Other	$110,000

Source: Safeware, The Insurance Company

111. What was the average monthly claim for theft?

112. For all sources combined, find the average claim per month.

● **Work Hours** The table at the right shows, for different countries, the average numbers of hours per year that employees work. Use this information for Exercises 113 to 115. Use a 50-week year. Round answers to the nearest whole number.

Country	Annual Number of Hours Worked
France	1554
Germany	1390
Greece	2119
United Kingdom	1646
United States	1768

Source: Organization for Economic Cooperation and Development

113. What is the average number of hours worked per week by employees in the United Kingdom?

114. On average, how many more hours per week do employees in the United States work than employees in France?

115. On average, how many more hours per week do employees work in the country with the most hours worked per year than in the country with the least hours worked per year?

116. ● **Weather** The daily low temperatures, in degrees Fahrenheit, for 9 consecutive summer days in Fargo, North Dakota, were 66, 55, 55, 61, 62, 66, 65, 52, and 58. What was the average low temperature for those 9 days?

117. ● **U.S. Postal Service** Use the information in the news clipping at the right to determine, on average, how many pieces of mail the U.S. Postal Service processed per day this year. Assume there are 300 working days in a year.

> ## In the NEWS!
>
> **Decline in USPS Mail Volume**
>
> This year, the U.S. Postal Service processed 117 billion pieces of mail. This is a decline of 6 billion pieces from last year.
> *Source:* www.usps.com

118. 🗒 Which problems below require division to solve?

   (i) Four friends want to share a restaurant bill of $48 equally. Find the amount that each friend should pay.

   (ii) On average, Sam spends $30 a week on gas. Find Sam's average yearly expenditure for gas.

   (iii) Emma's 12 phone bills for last year totaled $660. Find Emma's average monthly phone bill.

Critical Thinking

119. Payroll Deductions Your paycheck shows deductions of $225 for savings, $98 for taxes, and $27 for insurance. Find the total of the three deductions.

Dairy Products   The topic of the graph at the right is the eggs produced in the United States during a recent year. It shows where the eggs that were produced went or how they were used. Use this graph for Exercises 120 and 121.

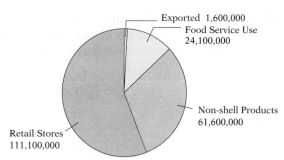

120. Use the graph to determine the total number of cases of eggs produced during the year.

121. How many more cases of eggs were sold by retail stores than were used for non-shell products?

Exported 1,600,000
Food Service Use 24,100,000
Non-shell Products 61,600,000
Retail Stores 111,100,000

Eggs Produced in the United States (in cases)
Source: American Egg Board

 Finances   The graph at the right shows the annual expenditures, for a recent year, of an average household in the United States. Use this information for Exercises 122 to 124. Round answers to the nearest whole number.

122. What is the total amount spent annually by an average household in the United States?

123. What is the average monthly expense for housing?

124. What is the difference between the average monthly expense for food and the average monthly expense for health care?

125. Finances   You purchase a used car with a down payment of $2500 and monthly payments of $195 for 48 months. Find the total amount paid for the car.

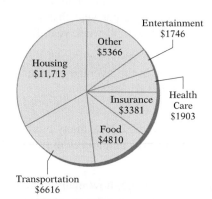

Entertainment $1746
Other $5366
Housing $11,713
Insurance $3381
Health Care $1903
Food $4810
Transportation $6616

Average Annual Household Expenses
Source: Bureau of Labor Statistics Consumer Expenditure Survey

Projects or Group Activities

126. A **factor** of a given number is a number that divides the given number evenly. For instance, 6 is a factor of 54 but 8 is not a factor of 54.
  a. Find all the factors of 48.
  b. Find all the factors of 144.
  c. Find all the factors of 97.

For Exercises 127 to 130, state which operation—addition, subtraction, multiplication, or division—you would use to solve the problem. Do not solve.

127. Mary and Jose are building a brick walkway. They have 35 bricks, 7 of which are unusable. How many usable bricks do they have?

128. Mary and Jose are building a brick walkway. They want to have a walkway that has 7 bricks in each row and 35 rows. How many bricks do they need?

129. Mary and Jose are building a brick walkway. They have 35 bricks and want a walkway that is 7 bricks wide. How many rows of bricks can they make?

130. Mary and Jose are building a brick walkway. They have 7 bricks and purchase 35 more bricks. How many bricks do they now have?

1.6 Exponential Notation and the Order of Operations Agreement

OBJECTIVE A   *To simplify expressions that contain exponents*

Repeated multiplication of the same factor can be written in two ways:

$$3 \cdot 3 \cdot 3 \cdot 3 \cdot 3 \quad \text{or} \quad 3^5 \leftarrow \textbf{Exponent}$$

The **exponent** indicates how many times the factor occurs in the multiplication. The expression 3^5 is in **exponential notation.**

It is important to be able to read numbers written in exponential notation.

$6 = 6^1$ is read "six to the first power" or just "six." Usually the exponent 1 is not written.

$6 \cdot 6 = 6^2$ is read "six squared" or "six to the second power."

$6 \cdot 6 \cdot 6 = 6^3$ is read "six cubed" or "six to the third power."

$6 \cdot 6 \cdot 6 \cdot 6 = 6^4$ is read "six to the fourth power."

$6 \cdot 6 \cdot 6 \cdot 6 \cdot 6 = 6^5$ is read "six to the fifth power."

Each place value in the place-value chart can be expressed as a power of 10.

Ten =	10	=	10	$= 10^1$
Hundred =	100	=	$10 \cdot 10$	$= 10^2$
Thousand =	1000	=	$10 \cdot 10 \cdot 10$	$= 10^3$
Ten-thousand =	10,000	=	$10 \cdot 10 \cdot 10 \cdot 10$	$= 10^4$
Hundred-thousand =	100,000	=	$10 \cdot 10 \cdot 10 \cdot 10 \cdot 10$	$= 10^5$
Million =	1,000,000	=	$10 \cdot 10 \cdot 10 \cdot 10 \cdot 10 \cdot 10$	$= 10^6$

Integrating Technology

A calculator can be used to evaluate an exponential expression. The y^x key (or, on some calculators, an x^y or $\wedge$ key) is used to enter the exponent. For instance, for the example at the right, enter 4 y^x 3 $=$. The display reads 64.

To simplify a numerical expression containing exponents, write each factor as many times as indicated by the exponent, and then carry out the indicated multiplication.

$$4^3 = 4 \cdot 4 \cdot 4 = 64$$

$$2^2 \cdot 3^4 = (2 \cdot 2) \cdot (3 \cdot 3 \cdot 3 \cdot 3) = 4 \cdot 81 = 324$$

EXAMPLE 1

Write $3 \cdot 3 \cdot 3 \cdot 5 \cdot 5$ in exponential notation.

Solution

$3 \cdot 3 \cdot 3 \cdot 5 \cdot 5 = 3^3 \cdot 5^2$

YOU TRY IT 1

Write $2 \cdot 2 \cdot 2 \cdot 2 \cdot 3 \cdot 3 \cdot 3$ in exponential notation.

Your solution

Solution on p. S4

EXAMPLE 2

Write as a power of 10: $10 \cdot 10 \cdot 10 \cdot 10$

Solution

$10 \cdot 10 \cdot 10 \cdot 10 = 10^4$

YOU TRY IT 2

Write as a power of 10: $10 \cdot 10 \cdot 10 \cdot 10 \cdot 10 \cdot 10 \cdot 10$

Your solution

EXAMPLE 3

Simplify $3^2 \cdot 5^3$.

Solution

$$3^2 \cdot 5^3 = (3 \cdot 3) \cdot (5 \cdot 5 \cdot 5)$$
$$= 9 \cdot 125$$
$$= 1125$$

YOU TRY IT 3

Simplify $2^3 \cdot 5^2$.

Your solution

Solutions on p. S4

OBJECTIVE B   *To use the Order of Operations Agreement to simplify expressions*

More than one operation may occur in a numerical expression. The answer may be different depending on the order in which the operations are performed. For example, consider $3 + 4 \times 5$.

Multiply first, then add.

$$3 + \underbrace{4 \times 5}$$
$$\underbrace{3 + 20}$$
$$23$$

Add first, then multiply.

$$\underbrace{3 + 4} \times 5$$
$$\underbrace{7 \times 5}$$
$$35$$

An Order of Operations Agreement is used so that only one answer is possible.

Order of Operations Agreement

Step 1. Perform operations inside grouping symbols such as parentheses.
Step 2. Simplify exponential expressions.
Step 3. Do multiplication and division as they occur from left to right.
Step 4. Do addition and subtraction as they occur from left to right.

EXAMPLES

1. $3(7 - 2) = 3(5)$ • Perform operations inside grouping symbols. [Step 1]
         $= 15$ • Multiply. [Step 3]

2. $5 \cdot 4^2 = 5 \cdot 16$ • Simplify exponential expressions. [Step 2]
         $= 80$ • Multiply. [Step 3]

3. $18 \div 9 \cdot 4 = 2 \cdot 4$ • Do multiplication and division from left to right. [Step 3]
         $= 8$

4. $12 - 2 \cdot 4 = 12 - 8$ • Do multiplication and division from left to right. [Step 3]
         $= 4$ • Do addition and subtraction from left to right. [Step 4]

Integrating Technology

Many scientific calculators have an x^2 key. This key is used to square the displayed number. For example, after the user presses 4 x^2 $=$, the display reads 16.

HOW TO 1 Simplify: $3 \times (2 + 1) - 2^2 + 4 \div 2$

Use the Order of Operations Agreement.

$$3 \times \underbrace{(2 + 1)} - 2^2 + 4 \div 2$$

$$3 \times 3 - \underbrace{2^2} + 4 \div 2 \qquad \textbf{1.} \quad \text{Perform operations inside parentheses.}$$

$$\underbrace{3 \times 3} - 4 + 4 \div 2 \qquad \textbf{2.} \quad \text{Simplify expressions with exponents.}$$

$$9 - 4 + \underbrace{4 \div 2} \qquad \textbf{3.} \quad \text{Do multiplication and division as they occur from left to right.}$$

$$\underbrace{9 - 4} + 2$$

$$\underbrace{5 + 2} \qquad \textbf{4.} \quad \text{Do addition and subtraction as they occur from left to right.}$$

$$7$$

One or more of the steps of the Order of Operations Agreement may not be needed to simplify an expression. In that case, proceed to the next step in the Order of Operations Agreement.

HOW TO 2 Simplify $5 + 8 \div 2$.

There are no parentheses or exponents, so Steps 1 and 2 of the Order of Operations Agreement are not needed. Proceed to Step 3 of the agreement.

$$5 + \underbrace{8 \div 2}$$

$$\underbrace{5 + 4} \qquad \textbf{3.} \quad \text{Do multiplication or division.}$$

$$9 \qquad \textbf{4.} \quad \text{Do addition or subtraction.}$$

EXAMPLE 4

Simplify: $64 \div (8 - 4)^2 \cdot 9 - 5^2$

Solution

$64 \div (8 - 4)^2 \cdot 9 - 5^2$

$= 64 \div 4^2 \cdot 9 - 5^2$ • **Parentheses**

$= 64 \div 16 \cdot 9 - 25$ • **Exponents**

$= 4 \cdot 9 - 25$ • **Division and multiplication**

$= 36 - 25$

$= 11$ • **Subtraction**

YOU TRY IT 4

Simplify: $5 \cdot (8 - 4)^2 \div 4 - 2$

Your solution

Solution on p. S4

1.6 EXERCISES

✔ Concept Check

1. How many times does 7 occur as a factor in the expression 7^5?

2. Using the Order of Operations Agreement, does $8 \cdot (4 \cdot 2) = (8 \cdot 4) \cdot 2$? If so, what Property of Multiplication does this show? See pages 25 and 26 for the Properties of Multiplication.

3. Which expressions below have the same value?
   (i) $8 \div 4 \div 2$ **(ii)** $8 \div (4 \div 2)$ **(iii)** $(8 \div 4) \div 2$?

4. Which expressions below have the same value?
   (i) $8 - 4 - 2$ **(ii)** $(8 - 4) - 2$ **(iii)** $8 - (4 - 2)$

OBJECTIVE A   *To simplify expressions that contain exponents*

For Exercises 5 to 16, write the number in exponential notation.

5. $2 \cdot 2 \cdot 2$

6. $7 \cdot 7 \cdot 7 \cdot 7 \cdot 7$

7. $6 \cdot 6 \cdot 6 \cdot 7 \cdot 7 \cdot 7 \cdot 7$

8. $6 \cdot 6 \cdot 9 \cdot 9 \cdot 9 \cdot 9$

9. $2 \cdot 2 \cdot 2 \cdot 3 \cdot 3 \cdot 3$

10. $3 \cdot 3 \cdot 10 \cdot 10$

11. $5 \cdot 7 \cdot 7 \cdot 7 \cdot 7 \cdot 7$

12. $4 \cdot 4 \cdot 4 \cdot 5 \cdot 5 \cdot 5$

13. $3 \cdot 3 \cdot 3 \cdot 6 \cdot 6 \cdot 6 \cdot 6$

14. $2 \cdot 2 \cdot 5 \cdot 5 \cdot 5 \cdot 8$

15. $3 \cdot 3 \cdot 3 \cdot 5 \cdot 9 \cdot 9 \cdot 9$

16. $2 \cdot 2 \cdot 2 \cdot 4 \cdot 7 \cdot 7 \cdot 7$

For Exercises 17 to 41, simplify.

17. 2^3

18. 2^6

19. $2^4 \cdot 5^2$

20. $2^6 \cdot 3^2$

21. $3^2 \cdot 10^2$

22. $2^3 \cdot 10^4$

23. $6^2 \cdot 3^3$

24. $4^3 \cdot 5^2$

25. $5 \cdot 2^3 \cdot 3$

26. $6 \cdot 3^2 \cdot 4$

27. $2^2 \cdot 3^2 \cdot 10$

28. $3^2 \cdot 5^2 \cdot 10$

29. $0^2 \cdot 4^3$

30. $6^2 \cdot 0^3$

31. $3^2 \cdot 10^4$

32. $5^3 \cdot 10^3$ **33.** $2^2 \cdot 3^3 \cdot 5$ **34.** $5^2 \cdot 7^3 \cdot 2$ **35.** $2 \cdot 3^4 \cdot 5^2$ **36.** $6 \cdot 2^6 \cdot 7^2$

37. $5^2 \cdot 3^2 \cdot 7^2$ **38.** $4^2 \cdot 9^2 \cdot 6^2$ **39.** $3^4 \cdot 2^6 \cdot 5$ **40.** $4^3 \cdot 6^3 \cdot 7$ **41.** $4^2 \cdot 3^3 \cdot 10^4$

42. Rewrite the expression using the numbers 3 and 5 exactly once. Then simplify the expression.
   a. $3 + 3 + 3 + 3 + 3$
   b. $3 \cdot 3 \cdot 3 \cdot 3 \cdot 3$

OBJECTIVE B   *To use the Order of Operations Agreement to simplify expressions*

For Exercises 43 to 81, simplify by using the Order of Operations Agreement.

43. $4 - 2 + 3$ **44.** $6 - 3 + 2$ **45.** $6 \cdot 3 + 5$

46. $5 \cdot 9 + 2$ **47.** $14 - 2 \cdot 4$ **48.** $12 + 3 \cdot 5$

49. $3 + 6 \div 3$ **50.** $12 + 8 \div 4$ **51.** $2 \cdot 3^2$

52. $5 \cdot 2^3$ **53.** $4 \cdot (5 - 3) + 2$ **54.** $3 + (4 + 2) \div 3$

55. $5 + (8 + 4) \div 6$ **56.** $8 - 2^2 + 4$ **57.** $16 \cdot (3 + 2) \div 10$

58. $12 \cdot (1 + 5) \div 12$ **59.** $10 - 2^3 + 4$ **60.** $5 \cdot 3^2 + 8$

61. $16 + 4 \cdot 3^2$ **62.** $12 + 4 \cdot 2^3$ **63.** $16 + (8 - 3) \cdot 2$

64. $7 + (9 - 5) \cdot 3$ **65.** $2^2 + 3 \cdot (6 - 2)^2$ **66.** $3^3 + 5 \cdot (8 - 6)^3$

67. $2^2 \cdot 3^2 + 2 \cdot 3$ **68.** $4 \cdot 6 + 3^2 \cdot 4^2$ **69.** $3 \cdot (6 - 2) + 4$

70. $5 \cdot (8 - 4) - 6$

71. $8 - (8 - 2) \div 3$

72. $12 - (12 - 4) \div 4$

73. $8 + 2 - 3 \cdot 2 \div 3$

74. $10 + 1 - 5 \cdot 2 \div 5$

75. $3 \cdot (4 + 2) \div 6$

76. $(7 - 3)^2 \div 2 - 4 + 8$

77. $20 - 4 \div 2 \cdot (3 - 1)^3$

78. $12 \div 3 \cdot 2^2 + (7 - 3)^2$

79. $(4 - 2) \cdot 6 \div 3 + (5 - 2)^2$

80. $18 - 2 \cdot 3 + (4 - 1)^3$

81. $100 \div (2 + 3)^2 - 8 \div 2$

By placing parentheses at various places in the expression $2 \cdot 3 + 8 \cdot 4 - 2$, it is possible to change the value of the expression. For Exercises 82 to 85, insert parentheses in the above expression so that the value is the given number.

82. 22

83. 54

84. 44

85. 66

Critical Thinking

For Exercises 86 to 89, determine whether the two expressions are equal.

86. $(2 + 3)^5$ and $2^5 + 3^5$

87. $(2 + 3)^5$ and $2^5 + 3^5$

88. $(12 \div 3)^4$ and $12^4 \div 3^4$

89. $(6 - 4)^4$ and $6^4 - 4^4$

Projects or Group Activities

90. Recall that the Associative Property of Addition states that grouping an addition in any order gives the same result.
   a. Is subtraction an associative operation? Explain your answer.
   b. Is division an associative operation? Explain your answer.

91. Evaluate **a.** $(3^4)^2$ and **b.** $3^{(4^2)}$.
   c. According to the Order of Operations Agreement, what is the value of 3^{4^2}?

SECTION

1.7 Prime Numbers and Factoring

OBJECTIVE A *To factor numbers*

Whole-number **factors** of a number divide that number evenly (there is no remainder).

1, 2, 3, and 6 are whole-number factors of 6 because they divide 6 evenly.

$$\frac{6}{1\overline{)6}} \quad \frac{3}{2\overline{)6}} \quad \frac{2}{3\overline{)6}} \quad \frac{1}{6\overline{)6}}$$

Note that both the divisor and the quotient are factors of the dividend.

To find the factors of a number, try dividing the number by 1, 2, 3, 4, 5, ... Those numbers that divide the number evenly are its factors. Continue this process until the factors start to repeat.

HOW TO 1 Find all the factors of 42.

$42 \div 1 = 42$ 1 and 42 are factors.
$42 \div 2 = 21$ 2 and 21 are factors.
$42 \div 3 = 14$ 3 and 14 are factors.
$42 \div 4$ Will not divide evenly
$42 \div 5$ Will not divide evenly
$42 \div 6 = 7$ 6 and 7 are factors.   } Factors are repeating; all the
$42 \div 7 = 6$ 7 and 6 are factors.   factors of 42 have been found.

1, 2, 3, 6, 7, 14, 21, and 42 are the factors of 42.

The following rules are helpful in finding the factors of a number.

2 is a factor of a number if the last digit of the number is 0, 2, 4, 6, or 8.

436 ends in 6; therefore, 2 is a factor of 436. (436 ÷ 2 = 218)

3 is a factor of a number if the sum of the digits of the number is divisible by 3.

The sum of the digits of 489 is 4 + 8 + 9 = 21. 21 is divisible by 3. Therefore, 3 is a factor of 489. (489 ÷ 3 = 163)

5 is a factor of a number if the last digit of the number is 0 or 5.

520 ends in 0; therefore, 5 is a factor of 520. (520 ÷ 5 = 104)

EXAMPLE 1

Find all the factors of 30.

Solution

$30 \div 1 = 30$
$30 \div 2 = 15$
$30 \div 3 = 10$
$30 \div 4$ • Will not divide evenly
$30 \div 5 = 6$
$30 \div 6 = 5$ • Factors are repeating.

1, 2, 3, 5, 6, 10, 15, and 30 are the factors of 30.

YOU TRY IT 1

Find all the factors of 40.

Your solution

Solution on p. S4

To find the prime factorization of a number

A number is a **prime number** if its only whole-number factors are 1 and itself. 7 is prime because its only factors are 1 and 7. If a number is not prime, it is called a **composite number.** Because 6 has factors of 2 and 3, 6 is a composite number. The number 1 is not considered a prime number; therefore, it is not included in the following list of prime numbers less than 50.

$$2, 3, 5, 7, 11, 13, 17, 19, 23, 29, 31, 37, 41, 43, 47$$

The **prime factorization** of a number is the expression of the number as a product of its prime factors. In the example below, we use a "T-diagram" to find the prime factors of 60. Begin with the smallest prime number as a trial divisor, and continue with prime numbers as trial divisors until the final quotient is 1.

$$
\begin{array}{c|c}
\multicolumn{2}{c}{60} \\
\hline
2 & 30 \\
2 & 15 \\
3 & 5 \\
5 & 1 \\
\end{array}
\qquad
\begin{aligned}
60 \div 2 &= 30 \\
30 \div 2 &= 15 \\
15 \div 3 &= 5 \\
5 \div 5 &= 1 \\
\end{aligned}
$$

The prime factorization of 60 is $2 \cdot 2 \cdot 3 \cdot 5$.

Finding the prime factorization of larger numbers can be more difficult. Try each prime number as a trial divisor. Stop when the square of the trial divisor is greater than the number being factored.

HOW TO 2 Find the prime factorization of 106.

$$
\begin{array}{c|c}
\multicolumn{2}{c}{106} \\
\hline
2 & 53 \\
53 & 1 \\
\end{array}
$$

• 53 cannot be divided evenly by 2, 3, 5, 7, or 11. Prime numbers greater than 11 need not be tested because 11^2 is greater than 53.

The prime factorization of 106 is $2 \cdot 53$.

EXAMPLE 2

Find the prime factorization of 315.

Solution

$$
\begin{array}{c|c}
\multicolumn{2}{c}{315} \\
\hline
3 & 105 \\
3 & 35 \\
5 & 7 \\
7 & 1 \\
\end{array}
$$

• $315 \div 3 = 105$
• $105 \div 3 = 35$
• $35 \div 5 = 7$
• $7 \div 7 = 1$

$315 = 3 \cdot 3 \cdot 5 \cdot 7$

YOU TRY IT 2

Find the prime factorization of 44.

Your solution

EXAMPLE 3

Find the prime factorization of 201.

Solution

$$
\begin{array}{c|c}
\multicolumn{2}{c}{201} \\
\hline
3 & 67 \\
67 & 1 \\
\end{array}
$$

• Try only 2, 3, 5, 7, and 11, because $11^2 > 67$.

$201 = 3 \cdot 67$

YOU TRY IT 3

Find the prime factorization of 177.

Your solution

Solutions on p. S4

1.7 EXERCISES

✔ Concept Check

1. Which of the following numbers are factors of 72?
    (i) 0   **(ii)** 1   **(iii)** 9   **(iv)** 14   **(v)** 24   **(vi)** 72

2. Which of the following numbers are prime factors of 210?
    (i) 2   **(ii)** 5   **(iii)** 7   **(iv)** 11   **(v)** 30   **(vi)** 35

OBJECTIVE A   *To factor numbers*

For Exercises 3 to 42, find all the factors of the number.

3. 4   **4.** 6   **5.** 10   **6.** 20   **7.** 7

8. 12   **9.** 9   **10.** 8   **11.** 13   **12.** 17

13. 18   **14.** 24   **15.** 56   **16.** 36   **17.** 45

18. 28   **19.** 29   **20.** 33   **21.** 22   **22.** 26

23. 52   **24.** 49   **25.** 82   **26.** 37   **27.** 57

28. 69   **29.** 48   **30.** 64   **31.** 95   **32.** 46

33. 54   **34.** 50   **35.** 66   **36.** 77   **37.** 80

38. 100   **39.** 96   **40.** 85   **41.** 90   **42.** 101

43. True or false? A number can have an odd number of factors.

44. True or false? If a number has exactly four factors, then the product of those four factors must be the number.

OBJECTIVE B   *To find the prime factorization of a number*

For Exercises 45 to 88, find the prime factorization.

45. 6   **46.** 14   **47.** 17   **48.** 83

49. 24 **50.** 12 **51.** 27 **52.** 9

53. 36 **54.** 40 **55.** 19 **56.** 37

57. 90 **58.** 65 **59.** 115 **60.** 80

61. 18 **62.** 26 **63.** 28 **64.** 49

65. 31 **66.** 42 **67.** 62 **68.** 81

69. 22 **70.** 39 **71.** 101 **72.** 89

73. 66 **74.** 86 **75.** 74 **76.** 95

77. 67 **78.** 78 **79.** 55 **80.** 46

81. 120 **82.** 144 **83.** 160 **84.** 175

85. 216 **86.** 400 **87.** 625 **88.** 225

89. True or false? The prime factorization of 102 is $2 \cdot 51$.

Critical Thinking

90. All prime numbers greater than 10 end in one of four digits. What are these digits?

91. Not every number that ends in one of the digits you found in Exercise 90 is a prime number. Give examples of numbers that end in each of these digits but are not prime numbers.

92. There are three digits such that any two of them will form a two-digit prime number. What are these three digits? Give an example of a prime number that uses all three digits. Give an example of a number that uses all three digits but is not a prime number.

Projects or Group Activities

93. What is the Sieve of Eratosthenes? Use this method to find all prime numbers less than 100.

Key Words	Examples
The **whole numbers** are 0, 1, 2, 3, 4, 5, 6, 7, 8, 9, 10, ... [1.1A, p. 2]	
The **graph of a whole number** is shown by placing a heavy dot directly above that number on the number line. [1.1A, p. 2]	This is the graph of 4 on the number line. 0 1 2 3 4 5 6 7 8 9 10 11 12
The symbol for **is less than** is $<$. The symbol for **is greater than** is $>$. These symbols are used to show the order relation between two numbers. [1.1A, p. 2]	$3 < 7$ $9 > 2$
When a whole number is written using the digits 0, 1, 2, 3, 4, 5, 6, 7, 8, and 9, it is said to be in **standard form.** The position of each digit in the number determines the digit's **place value.** The place values are used to write the expanded form of a number. [1.1B, p. 3]	The number 598,317 is in standard form. The digit 8 is in the thousands place. The number 598,317 is written in expanded form as $500,000 + 90,000 + 8000 + 300 + 10 + 7.$
Addition is the process of finding the total of two or more numbers. The numbers being added are called **addends.** The result is the **sum.** [1.2A, p. 8]	$\begin{array}{r} \overset{1\ \ 11}{8,762} \\ +\ 1,359 \\ \hline 10,121 \end{array}$
Subtraction is the process of finding the difference between two numbers. The **minuend** minus the **subtrahend** equals the **difference.** [1.3A, p. 16]	$\begin{array}{r} 52,173 \\ -\ 34,968 \\ \hline 17,205 \end{array}$

Multiplication is repeated addition of the same number. The numbers that are multiplied are called **factors**. The result is the **product.** [1.4A, p. 25]

$$\begin{array}{r} \overset{4\ 5}{358} \\ \times\ \ \ 7 \\ \hline 2506 \end{array}$$

Division is used to separate objects into equal groups. The **dividend** divided by the **divisor** equals the **quotient.** [1.5A, p. 33]

For any division problem,
(**quotient · divisor**) + **remainder** = **dividend.** [1.5B, p. 36]

$$\begin{array}{r} 93\ \text{r}3 \\ 7\overline{)\ 654} \\ -63 \\ \hline 24 \\ -21 \\ \hline 3 \end{array}$$

Check: $(7 \cdot 93) + 3 = 651 + 3 = 654$

The expression 4^3 is in **exponential notation. The exponent,** 3, indicates how many times 4 occurs as a factor in the multiplication. [1.6A, p. 47]

$5^4 = 5 \cdot 5 \cdot 5 \cdot 5 = 625$

Whole-number **factors** of a number divide that number evenly (there is no remainder). [1.7A, p. 53]

$18 \div 1 = 18$
$18 \div 2 = 9$
$18 \div 3 = 6$
$18 \div 4$ 4 does not divide 18 evenly.
$18 \div 5$ 5 does not divide 18 evenly.
$18 \div 6 = 3$ The factors are repeating.

The factors of 18 are 1, 2, 3, 6, 9, and 18.

A number greater than 1 is a **prime number** if its only whole-number factors are 1 and itself. If a number is not prime, it is a **composite number.** [1.7B, p. 54]

The prime numbers less than 20 are 2, 3, 5, 7, 11, 13, 17, and 19.
The composite numbers less than 20 are 4, 6, 8, 9, 10, 12, 14, 15, 16, and 18.

The **prime factorization** of a number is the expression of the number as a product of its prime factors. [1.7B, p. 54]

$$\begin{array}{r} 42 \\ \hline 2\ |\ 21 \\ 3\ |\ \ 7 \\ 7\ |\ \ 1 \end{array}$$

The prime factorization of 42 is $2 \cdot 3 \cdot 7$.

Essential Rules and Procedures	**Examples**
To round a number to a given place value: If the digit to the right of the given place value is less than 5, replace that digit and all digits to the right by zeros. If the digit to the right of the given place value is greater than or equal to 5, increase the digit in the given place value by 1, and replace all other digits to the right by zeros. [1.1D, p. 4]	36,178 rounded to the nearest thousand is 36,000. 4592 rounded to the nearest thousand is 5000.
Properties of Addition [1.2A, p. 8]	
Commutative Property of Addition Two numbers can be added in either order; the sum will be the same.	$8 + 3 = 3 + 8$
Associative Property of Addition Grouping an addition in any order gives the same result.	$(2 + 4) + 6 = 2 + (4 + 6)$
Addition Property of Zero Zero added to a number does not change the number.	$7 + 0 = 7$
To estimate the answer to an addition calculation: Round each number to the same place value. Perform the calculation using the rounded numbers. [1.2A, p. 10]	$\begin{array}{rr} 39,471 & 40,000 \\ 12,586 & +\,10,000 \\ \hline & 50,000 \end{array}$ 50,000 is an estimate of the sum of 39,471 and 12,586.
Properties of Multiplication [1.4A, pp. 25–26]	
Commutative Property of Multiplication Two numbers can be multiplied in either order; the product will be the same.	$2 \cdot 8 = 8 \cdot 2$
Associative Property of Multiplication Grouping numbers to be multiplied in any order gives the same result.	$(2 \cdot 4) \cdot 6 = 2 \cdot (4 \cdot 6)$
Multiplication Property of Zero A number multiplied by zero is zero.	$3 \cdot 0 = 0$
Multiplication Property of One Multiplying a number by 1 does not change the number.	$6 \cdot 1 = 6$
Division Properties of Zero and One [1.5A, p. 33] Any whole number, except zero, divided by itself is 1. Zero divided by any whole number other than zero is zero.	$3 \div 3 = 1$ $0 \div 3 = 0$

Order of Operations Agreement [1.6B, p. 48]

Step 1. Perform operations inside grouping symbols such as parentheses.

Step 2. Simplify exponential expressions.

Step 3. Do multiplication and division as they occur from left to right.

Step 4. Do addition and subtraction as they occur from left to right.

$$5^2 - 3(2 + 4) = 5^2 - 3(6)$$
$$= 25 - 3(6)$$
$$= 25 - 18$$
$$= 7$$

1. Simplify: $3 \cdot 2^3 \cdot 5^2$

2. Write 10,327 in expanded form.

3. Find all the factors of 18.

4. Find the sum of 5894, 6301, and 298.

5. Subtract: $\begin{array}{r} 4926 \\ -\ 3177 \\ \hline \end{array}$

6. Divide: $7\overline{)14{,}945}$

7. Place the correct symbol, $<$ or $>$, between the two numbers: 101   87

8. Write $5 \cdot 5 \cdot 7 \cdot 7 \cdot 7 \cdot 7 \cdot 7$ in exponential notation.

9. What is 2019 multiplied by 307?

10. What is 10,134 decreased by 4725?

11. Add: $\begin{array}{r} 298 \\ 461 \\ +\ 322 \\ \hline \end{array}$

12. Simplify: $2^3 - 3 \cdot 2$

13. Round 45,672 to the nearest hundred.

14. Write 276,057 in words.

15. Find the quotient of 109,763 and 84.

16. Write two million eleven thousand forty-four in standard form.

17. What is 3906 divided by 8?

18. Simplify: $3^2 + 2^2 \cdot (5 - 3)$

19. Simplify: $8 \cdot (6 - 2)^2 \div 4$

20. Find the prime factorization of 72.

21. What is 3895 minus 1762?

22. Multiply: $\begin{array}{r} 843 \\ \times\ 27 \\ \hline \end{array}$

23. **Wages**   Vincent Meyers, a sales assistant, earns $480 for working a 40-hour week. Last week, Vincent worked an additional 12 hours at $24 an hour. Find Vincent's total pay for last week's work.

24. **Fuel Efficiency**   Louis Reyes, a sales executive, drove a car 351 miles on 13 gallons of gas. Find the number of miles driven per gallon of gasoline.

25. **Consumerism**   A car is purchased for $29,880, with a down payment of $3000. The balance is paid in 48 equal monthly payments. Find the monthly car payment.

26. **Compensation**   An insurance account executive received commissions of $723, $544, $812, and $488 during a 4-week period. Find the total income from commissions for the 4 weeks.

27. **Banking**   You had a balance of $516 in your checking account before making deposits of $88 and $213. Find the total amount deposited, and determine your new account balance.

28. **Car Payments**   You have a car payment of $246 per month. What is the total of the car payments over a 12-month period?

College Enrollment   The table at the right shows the approximate numbers of males and females enrolled in U.S. colleges in 2005 and 2009. Use this information for Exercises 29 to 32.

29. In which year, 2005 or 2009, were more males enrolled in U.S. colleges?

Year	Males	Females
2005	7,455,925	10,031,550
2009	8,769,504	11,658,207

Source: National Center for Education Statistics

30. What is the difference between the number of males and the number of females enrolled in U.S. colleges in 2005?

31. Find the increase in the number of males enrolled in U.S. colleges from 2005 to 2009.

32. How many more students were enrolled in U.S. colleges in 2009 than in 2005?

CHAPTER

1 | TEST

1. Simplify: $3^3 \cdot 4^2$

2. Write 207,068 in words.

3. Subtract: $\begin{array}{r} 23{,}006 \\ -\ 7{,}937 \end{array}$

4. Find all the factors of 20.

5. Multiply: $\begin{array}{r} 9736 \\ \times\ 704 \end{array}$

6. Simplify: $4^2 \cdot (4 - 2) \div 8 + 5$

7. Write 906,378 in expanded form.

8. Round 74,965 to the nearest hundred.

9. Divide: $97\overline{)108{,}764}$

10. Write $3 \cdot 3 \cdot 3 \cdot 7 \cdot 7$ in exponential form.

11. Find the sum of 8756, 9094, and 37,065.

12. Find the prime factorization of 84.

13. Simplify: $16 \div 4 \cdot 2 - (7 - 5)^2$

14. Find the product of 8 and 90,763.

15. Write one million two hundred four thousand six in standard form.

16. Divide: $7\overline{)60{,}972}$

17. Place the correct symbol, < or >, between the two numbers: 21   19

18. Find the quotient of 5624 and 8.

19. Add: 25,492
             +71,306

20. Find the difference between 29,736 and 9814.

Education   The table at the right shows the projected enrollment in public and private elementary and secondary schools for the fall of 2013 and the fall of 2016. Use this information for Exercises 21 and 22.

Year	Pre-Kindergarten through Grade 8	Grades 9 through 12
2013	41,873,000	16,000,000
2016	43,097,000	16,684,000

Source: The National Center for Education Statistics

21. Find the difference between the projected total enrollment in 2016 and in 2013.

22. In 2016, how many students are projected to be enrolled in pre-kindergarten through grade 12?

23. Farming   A farmer harvested 48,290 pounds of lemons from one grove and 23,710 pounds of lemons from another grove. The lemons were packed in boxes with 24 pounds of lemons in each box. How many boxes were needed to pack the lemons?

24. Biology   A hummingbird beats its wings approximately 52 times per second. How many times will a hummingbird beat its wings in 900 seconds (15 minutes)?

25. Traffic   A radar detector was set up on a highway to determine the average speed of motorists on a certain segment of the highway. The recorded speeds, in miles per hour, for 12 cars were 68, 73, 59, 77, 65, 52, 71, 68, 76, 64, 59, and 60. What was the average speed for these 12 cars?

Fractions

Focus on Success

Have you formed or are you part of a study group? Remember that a study group can be a great way to stay focused on succeeding in this course. You can support each other, get help and offer help on homework, and prepare for tests together. (See Homework Time, page AIM-5.)

© iStockphoto.com/Christoper Futcher

Prep Test

Are you ready to succeed in this chapter? Take the Prep Test below to find out if you are ready to learn the new material.

For Exercises 1 to 6, add, subtract, multiply, or divide.

1. 4×5

2. $2 \cdot 2 \cdot 2 \cdot 3 \cdot 5$

3. 9×1

4. $6 + 4$

5. $10 - 3$

6. $63 \div 30$

7. Which of the following numbers divide evenly into 12?
   1 2 3 4 5 6 7 8 9 10 11 12

8. Simplify: $8 \times 7 + 3$

9. Complete: $8 = ? + 1$

10. Place the correct symbol, $<$ or $>$, between the two numbers.
    44   48

2.1

The Least Common Multiple and Greatest Common Factor

OBJECTIVE A   *To find the least common multiple (LCM)*

 Tips for Success

Before you begin a new chapter, you should take some time to review previously learned skills. One way to do this is to complete the Prep Test. See page 65. This test focuses on the particular skills that will be required for the new chapter.

The **multiples of a number** are the products of that number and the numbers 1, 2, 3, 4, 5, ...

$$3 \times 1 = 3$$
$$3 \times 2 = 6$$
$$3 \times 3 = 9$$
$$3 \times 4 = 12$$ The multiples of 3 are 3, 6, 9, 12, 15, ...
$$3 \times 5 = 15$$
.
.
.

A number that is a multiple of two or more numbers is a **common multiple** of those numbers.

The multiples of 4 are 4, 8, 12, 16, 20, 24, 28, 32, 36, ...
The multiples of 6 are 6, 12, 18, 24, 30, 36, 42, ...
Some common multiples of 4 and 6 are 12, 24, and 36.

The **least common multiple (LCM)** is the smallest common multiple of two or more numbers.

The least common multiple of 4 and 6 is 12.

Listing the multiples of each number is one way to find the LCM. Another way to find the LCM uses the prime factorization of each number.

To find the LCM of 450 and 600, find the prime factorization of each number and write the factorization of each number in a table. Circle the greatest product in each column. The LCM is the product of the circled numbers.

	2	3	5
450 =	2	(3 · 3)	(5 · 5)
600 =	(2 · 2 · 2)	3	5 · 5

• In the column headed by 5, the products are equal. Circle just one product.

The LCM is the product of the circled numbers.
The LCM $= 2 \cdot 2 \cdot 2 \cdot 3 \cdot 3 \cdot 5 \cdot 5 = 1800$.

EXAMPLE 1

Find the LCM of 24, 36, and 50.

Solution

	2	3	5
24 =	(2 · 2 · 2)	3	
36 =	2 · 2	(3 · 3)	
50 =	2		(5 · 5)

The LCM $= 2 \cdot 2 \cdot 2 \cdot 3 \cdot 3 \cdot 5 \cdot 5 = 1800$.

YOU TRY IT 1

Find the LCM of 12, 27, and 50.

Your solution

Solution on p. S4

OBJECTIVE B   *To find the greatest common factor (GCF)*

Recall that a number that divides another number evenly is a factor of that number. The number 64 can be evenly divided by 1, 2, 4, 8, 16, 32, and 64, so the numbers 1, 2, 4, 8, 16, 32, and 64 are factors of 64.

A number that is a factor of two or more numbers is a **common factor** of those numbers.

The factors of 30 are 1, 2, 3, 5, 6, 10, 15, and 30.

The factors of 105 are 1, 3, 5, 7, 15, 21, 35, and 105.

The common factors of 30 and 105 are 1, 3, 5, and 15.

The **greatest common factor (GCF)** is the largest common factor of two or more numbers.

The greatest common factor of 30 and 105 is 15.

Listing the factors of each number is one way of finding the GCF. Another way to find the GCF is to use the prime factorization of each number.

To find the GCF of 126 and 180, find the prime factorization of each number and write the factorization of each number in a table. Circle the least product in each column that does not have a blank. The GCF is the product of the circled numbers.

	2	3	5	7
126 =	(2)	(3 · 3)		7
180 =	2 · 2	3 · 3	5	

• In the column headed by 3, the products are equal. Circle just one product. Columns 5 and 7 have a blank, so 5 and 7 are not common factors of 126 and 180. Do not circle any number in these columns.

The GCF is the product of the circled numbers.
The GCF = $2 \cdot 3 \cdot 3 = 18$.

EXAMPLE 2

Find the GCF of 90, 168, and 420.

Solution

	2	3	5	7
90 =	(2)	3 · 3	5	
168 =	2 · 2 · 2	(3)		7
420 =	2 · 2	3	5	7

The GCF = $2 \cdot 3 = 6$.

YOU TRY IT 2

Find the GCF of 36, 60, and 72.

Your solution

EXAMPLE 3

Find the GCF of 7, 12, and 20.

Solution

	2	3	5	7
7 =				7
12 =	2 · 2	3		
20 =	2 · 2		5	

Because no numbers are circled, the GCF = 1.

YOU TRY IT 3

Find the GCF of 11, 24, and 30.

Your solution

Solutions on p. S4

2.1 EXERCISES

✔ **Concept Check**

For Exercises 1 to 4, list the first four multiples of the given number.

1. 5   **2.** 7   **3.** 10   **4.** 15

5. List the first ten multiples of 6 and the first ten multiples of 8. What are the common multiples of 6 and 8 in the lists? What is the least common multiple of 6 and 8?

For Exercises 6 to 9, list the factors of the given number.

6. 12   **7.** 20   **8.** 23   **9.** 28

10. List the factors of 18 and the factors of 24. What are the common factors of 18 and 24? What is the greatest common factor of 18 and 24?

OBJECTIVE A   *To find the least common multiple (LCM)*

For Exercises 11 to 40, find the LCM.

11. 5, 8	**12.** 3, 6	**13.** 3, 8	**14.** 2, 5	**15.** 4, 6
16. 6, 8	**17.** 8, 12	**18.** 12, 16	**19.** 5, 12	**20.** 3, 16
21. 8, 14	**22.** 4, 10	**23.** 8, 32	**24.** 7, 21	**25.** 9, 36
26. 14, 42	**27.** 44, 60	**28.** 120, 160	**29.** 102, 184	**30.** 123, 234
31. 4, 8, 12	**32.** 5, 10, 15	**33.** 3, 5, 10	**34.** 2, 5, 8	**35.** 3, 8, 12
36. 5, 12, 18	**37.** 9, 36, 64	**38.** 18, 54, 63	**39.** 3, 7, 20	**40.** 4, 9, 35

41. 🔖 True or false? If two numbers have no common factors, then the LCM of the two numbers is their product.

42. 🔖 True or false? If one number is a multiple of a second number, then the LCM of the two numbers is the second number.

OBJECTIVE B *To find the greatest common factor (GCF)*

For Exercises 43 to 72, find the GCF.

43. 3, 5   **44.** 5, 7   **45.** 6, 9   **46.** 18, 24   **47.** 15, 25

48. 14, 49   **49.** 25, 100   **50.** 16, 80   **51.** 32, 51   **52.** 21, 44

53. 12, 80   **54.** 8, 36   **55.** 16, 140   **56.** 48, 144   **57.** 44, 96

58. 18, 32   **59.** 3, 5, 11   **60.** 6, 8, 10   **61.** 7, 14, 49   **62.** 6, 15, 36

63. 10, 15, 20   **64.** 12, 18, 20   **65.** 24, 40, 72   **66.** 3, 17, 51   **67.** 17, 31, 81

68. 14, 42, 84   **69.** 25, 125, 625   **70.** 12, 68, 92   **71.** 32, 56, 72   **72.** 24, 36, 48

73. True or false? If two numbers have a GCF of 1, then the LCM of the two numbers is their product.

74. True or false? If the LCM of two numbers is one of the two numbers, then the GCF of the numbers is the other of the two numbers.

Critical Thinking

75. Work Schedules Joe Salvo, a lifeguard, works 3 days and then has a day off. Joe's friend Raya works 5 days and then has a day off. How many days after Joe and Raya have a day off together will they have another day off together?

76. Find the LCM of each of the following pairs of prime numbers: 2 and 3, 5 and 7, and 11 and 19. Based on these examples, what is the LCM of two prime numbers?

77. Find the GCF of each of the following pairs of prime numbers: 3 and 5, 7 and 11, and 29 and 43. Based on these examples, what is the GCF of two prime numbers?

Projects or Group Activities

78. Using the pattern for the first two triangles shown below, determine the center number of the last triangle.

79. Two numbers are called *coprime* if the GCF of the two numbers is 1. Determine whether each pair of numbers is coprime.

    a. 48, 50   **b.** 25, 36   **c.** 22, 27   **d.** 71, 73

2.2 Introduction to Fractions

OBJECTIVE A   *To write a fraction that represents part of a whole*

 Take Note

The *fraction bar* separates the numerator from the denominator. The *numerator* is the part of the fraction that appears above the fraction bar. The *denominator* is the part of the fraction that appears below the fraction bar.

A **fraction** can represent the number of equal parts of a whole.

The shaded portion of the circle is represented by the fraction $\frac{4}{7}$. Four of the seven equal parts of the circle (that is, four-sevenths of it) are shaded.

Each part of a fraction has a name.

Fraction bar $\rightarrow \dfrac{4 \leftarrow \textbf{Numerator}}{7 \leftarrow \textbf{Denominator}}$

Point of Interest

The fraction bar was first used in 1050 by al-Hassar. It is also called a vinculum.

A **proper fraction** is a fraction less than 1. The numerator of a proper fraction is smaller than the denominator. The shaded portion of the circle can be represented by the proper fraction $\frac{3}{4}$.

A **mixed number** is a number greater than 1 with a whole-number part and a fractional part. The shaded portion of the circles can be represented by the mixed number $2\frac{1}{4}$.

An **improper fraction** is a fraction greater than or equal to 1. The numerator of an improper fraction is greater than or equal to the denominator. The shaded portion of the circles can be represented by the improper fraction $\frac{9}{4}$. The shaded portion of the square can be represented by $\frac{4}{4}$.

EXAMPLE 1

Express the shaded portion of the circles as a mixed number.

Solution $3\frac{2}{5}$

YOU TRY IT 1

Express the shaded portion of the circles as a mixed number.

Your solution

EXAMPLE 2

Express the shaded portion of the circles as an improper fraction.

Solution $\dfrac{17}{5}$

YOU TRY IT 2

Express the shaded portion of the circles as an improper fraction.

Your solution

Solutions on p. S4

OBJECTIVE B *To write an improper fraction as a mixed number or a whole number, and a mixed number as an improper fraction*

Point of Interest

Archimedes (c. 287–212 B.C.) is the person who calculated that $\pi \approx 3\frac{1}{7}$. He actually showed that $3\frac{10}{71} < \pi < 3\frac{1}{7}$. The approximation $3\frac{10}{71}$ is more accurate but more difficult to use.

Note from the diagram that the mixed number $2\frac{3}{5}$ and the improper fraction $\frac{13}{5}$ both represent the shaded portion of the circles, so $2\frac{3}{5} = \frac{13}{5}$.

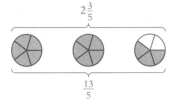

An improper fraction can be written as a mixed number or a whole number.

HOW TO 1   Write $\frac{13}{5}$ as a mixed number.

Divide the numerator by the denominator.	To write the fractional part of the mixed number, write the remainder over the divisor.	Write the answer.
$\begin{array}{r} 2 \\ 5\overline{)\ 13} \\ -10 \\ \hline 3 \end{array}$	$\begin{array}{r} 2\frac{3}{5} \\ 5\overline{)\ 13} \\ -10 \\ \hline 3 \end{array}$	$\dfrac{13}{5} = 2\dfrac{3}{5}$

To write a mixed number as an improper fraction, multiply the denominator of the fractional part by the whole-number part. The sum of this product and the numerator of the fractional part is the numerator of the improper fraction. The denominator remains the same.

HOW TO 2   Write $7\frac{3}{8}$ as an improper fraction.

$$7\frac{3}{8} = \frac{(8 \times 7) + 3}{8} = \frac{56 + 3}{8} = \frac{59}{8} \qquad 7\frac{3}{8} = \frac{59}{8}$$

EXAMPLE 3

Write $\frac{21}{4}$ as a mixed number.

Solution
$$\begin{array}{r} 5 \\ 4\overline{)\ 21} \\ -20 \\ \hline 1 \end{array} \qquad \frac{21}{4} = 5\frac{1}{4}$$

YOU TRY IT 3

Write $\frac{22}{5}$ as a mixed number.

Your solution

EXAMPLE 4

Write $\frac{18}{6}$ as a whole number.

Solution
$$\frac{18}{6} = 18 \div 6 = 3$$

YOU TRY IT 4

Write $\frac{28}{7}$ as a whole number.

Your solution

EXAMPLE 5

Write $21\frac{3}{4}$ as an improper fraction.

Solution
$$21\frac{3}{4} = \frac{84 + 3}{4} = \frac{87}{4}$$

YOU TRY IT 5

Write $14\frac{5}{8}$ as an improper fraction.

Your solution

Solutions on pp. S4–S5

2.2 EXERCISES

✔ Concept Check

For Exercises 1 to 4, identify the fraction as a proper fraction, an improper fraction, or a mixed number. State whether the fraction is less than 1, equal to 1, or greater than 1.

1. $\dfrac{12}{7}$ **2.** $5\dfrac{2}{11}$ **3.** $\dfrac{29}{40}$ **4.** $\dfrac{13}{13}$

OBJECTIVE A   *To write a fraction that represents part of a whole*

For Exercises 5 to 8, express the shaded portion of the circle as a fraction.

5.   **6.**   **7.**   **8.**

For Exercises 9 to 14, express the shaded portion of the circles as a mixed number.

9.   **10.**

11.   **12.**

13.   **14.**

For Exercises 15 to 20, express the shaded portion of the circles as an improper fraction.

15.   **16.**

17.   **18.**

19.   **20.**

21. Shade $1\dfrac{2}{5}$ of   **22.** Shade $1\dfrac{3}{4}$ of

23. Shade $\dfrac{6}{5}$ of   **24.** Shade $\dfrac{7}{3}$ of

25. 🖋 True or false? The fractional part of a mixed number is an improper fraction.

OBJECTIVE B *To write an improper fraction as a mixed number or a whole number, and a mixed number as an improper fraction*

For Exercises 26 to 49, write the improper fraction as a mixed number or a whole number.

26. $\dfrac{11}{4}$ **27.** $\dfrac{16}{3}$ **28.** $\dfrac{20}{4}$ **29.** $\dfrac{18}{9}$ **30.** $\dfrac{9}{8}$ **31.** $\dfrac{13}{4}$

32. $\dfrac{23}{10}$ **33.** $\dfrac{29}{2}$ **34.** $\dfrac{48}{16}$ **35.** $\dfrac{51}{3}$ **36.** $\dfrac{8}{7}$ **37.** $\dfrac{16}{9}$

38. $\dfrac{7}{3}$ **39.** $\dfrac{9}{5}$ **40.** $\dfrac{16}{1}$ **41.** $\dfrac{23}{1}$ **42.** $\dfrac{17}{8}$ **43.** $\dfrac{31}{16}$

44. $\dfrac{12}{5}$ **45.** $\dfrac{19}{3}$ **46.** $\dfrac{9}{9}$ **47.** $\dfrac{40}{8}$ **48.** $\dfrac{72}{8}$ **49.** $\dfrac{3}{3}$

For Exercises 50 to 73, write the mixed number as an improper fraction.

50. $2\dfrac{1}{3}$ **51.** $4\dfrac{2}{3}$ **52.** $6\dfrac{1}{2}$ **53.** $8\dfrac{2}{3}$ **54.** $6\dfrac{5}{6}$ **55.** $7\dfrac{3}{8}$

56. $9\dfrac{1}{4}$ **57.** $6\dfrac{1}{4}$ **58.** $10\dfrac{1}{2}$ **59.** $15\dfrac{1}{8}$ **60.** $8\dfrac{1}{9}$ **61.** $3\dfrac{5}{12}$

62. $5\dfrac{3}{11}$ **63.** $3\dfrac{7}{9}$ **64.** $2\dfrac{5}{8}$ **65.** $12\dfrac{2}{3}$ **66.** $1\dfrac{5}{8}$ **67.** $5\dfrac{3}{7}$

68. $11\dfrac{1}{9}$ **69.** $12\dfrac{3}{5}$ **70.** $3\dfrac{3}{8}$ **71.** $4\dfrac{5}{9}$ **72.** $6\dfrac{7}{13}$ **73.** $8\dfrac{5}{14}$

74. True or false? If an improper fraction is equivalent to 1, then the numerator and the denominator are the same number.

Critical Thinking

75. Name three situations in which fractions are used. Provide an example of a fraction that is used in each situation.

Projects or Group Activities

76. Using a denominator of 5, write improper fractions that represent the numbers 1, 2, 3, and 4.

77. Using a denominator of 8, write an improper fraction that represents a number greater than 2 but less than 3. *Hint*: There is more than one answer.

2.3 Writing Equivalent Fractions

OBJECTIVE A *To find equivalent fractions by raising to higher terms*

Equal fractions with different denominators are called **equivalent fractions.**

$\frac{4}{6}$ is equivalent to $\frac{2}{3}$.

Remember that the Multiplication Property of One states that the product of a number and 1 is the number. This is true for fractions as well as whole numbers. This property can be used to write equivalent fractions.

$$\frac{2}{3} \times 1 = \frac{2}{3} \times \frac{1}{1} = \frac{2 \cdot 1}{3 \cdot 1} = \frac{2}{3}$$

$$\frac{2}{3} \times 1 = \frac{2}{3} \times \boxed{\frac{2}{2}} = \frac{2 \cdot 2}{3 \cdot 2} = \frac{4}{6} \qquad \frac{4}{6} \text{ is equivalent to } \frac{2}{3}.$$

$$\frac{2}{3} \times 1 = \frac{2}{3} \times \boxed{\frac{4}{4}} = \frac{2 \cdot 4}{3 \cdot 4} = \frac{8}{12} \qquad \frac{8}{12} \text{ is equivalent to } \frac{2}{3}.$$

$\frac{2}{3}$ was rewritten as the equivalent fractions $\frac{4}{6}$ and $\frac{8}{12}$.

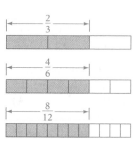

HOW TO 1 Write a fraction that is equivalent to $\frac{5}{8}$ and has a denominator of 32.

$32 \div 8 = 4$

$\frac{5}{8} = \frac{5 \cdot 4}{8 \cdot 4} = \frac{20}{32}$

$\frac{20}{32}$ is equivalent to $\frac{5}{8}$.

- Divide the larger denominator by the smaller.
- Multiply the numerator and denominator of the given fraction by the quotient (4).

EXAMPLE 1

Write $\frac{2}{3}$ as an equivalent fraction that has a denominator of 42.

Solution $42 \div 3 = 14, \frac{2}{3} = \frac{2 \cdot 14}{3 \cdot 14} = \frac{28}{42}$

$\frac{28}{42}$ is equivalent to $\frac{2}{3}$.

YOU TRY IT 1

Write $\frac{3}{5}$ as an equivalent fraction that has a denominator of 45.

Your solution

EXAMPLE 2

Write 4 as a fraction that has a denominator of 12.

Solution Write 4 as $\frac{4}{1}$.

$12 \div 1 = 12, 4 = \frac{4 \cdot 12}{1 \cdot 12} = \frac{48}{12}$

$\frac{48}{12}$ is equivalent to 4.

YOU TRY IT 2

Write 6 as a fraction that has a denominator of 18.

Your solution

Solutions on p. S5

OBJECTIVE B *To write a fraction in simplest form*

Writing the **simplest form of a fraction** means writing it so that the numerator and denominator have no common factors other than 1.

The fractions $\frac{4}{6}$ and $\frac{2}{3}$ are equivalent fractions.

$\frac{4}{6}$ has been written in simplest form as $\frac{2}{3}$.

The Multiplication Property of One can be used to write fractions in simplest form. Write the numerator and denominator of the given fraction as a product of factors. Write factors common to both the numerator and denominator as an improper fraction equivalent to 1.

$$\frac{4}{6} = \frac{2 \cdot 2}{2 \cdot 3} = \frac{2}{2} \cdot \frac{2}{3} = \frac{2}{2} \cdot \frac{2}{3} = 1 \cdot \frac{2}{3} = \frac{2}{3}$$

The process of eliminating common factors is displayed with slashes through the common factors as shown at the right.

To write a fraction in simplest form, eliminate the common factors.

An improper fraction can be changed to a mixed number.

$$\frac{4}{6} = \frac{2 \cdot \overset{1}{\cancel{2}}}{2 \cdot 3} = \frac{2}{3}$$

$$\frac{18}{30} = \frac{\overset{1}{\cancel{2}} \cdot \overset{1}{\cancel{3}} \cdot 3}{\underset{1}{\cancel{2}} \cdot \underset{1}{\cancel{3}} \cdot 5} = \frac{3}{5}$$

$$\frac{22}{6} = \frac{\overset{1}{\cancel{2}} \cdot 11}{\underset{1}{\cancel{2}} \cdot 3} = \frac{11}{3} = 3\frac{2}{3}$$

EXAMPLE 3

Write $\frac{15}{40}$ in simplest form.

Solution
$$\frac{15}{40} = \frac{3 \cdot \overset{1}{\cancel{5}}}{2 \cdot 2 \cdot 2 \cdot \underset{1}{\cancel{5}}} = \frac{3}{8}$$

YOU TRY IT 3

Write $\frac{16}{24}$ in simplest form.

Your solution

EXAMPLE 4

Write $\frac{6}{42}$ in simplest form.

Solution
$$\frac{6}{42} = \frac{\overset{1}{\cancel{2}} \cdot \overset{1}{\cancel{3}}}{\underset{1}{\cancel{2}} \cdot \underset{1}{\cancel{3}} \cdot 7} = \frac{1}{7}$$

YOU TRY IT 4

Write $\frac{8}{56}$ in simplest form.

Your solution

EXAMPLE 5

Write $\frac{8}{9}$ in simplest form.

Solution
$$\frac{8}{9} = \frac{2 \cdot 2 \cdot 2}{3 \cdot 3} = \frac{8}{9}$$

$\frac{8}{9}$ is already in simplest form because there are no common factors in the numerator and denominator.

YOU TRY IT 5

Write $\frac{15}{32}$ in simplest form.

Your solution

EXAMPLE 6

Write $\frac{30}{12}$ in simplest form.

Solution
$$\frac{30}{12} = \frac{\overset{1}{\cancel{2}} \cdot \overset{1}{\cancel{3}} \cdot 5}{\underset{1}{\cancel{2}} \cdot 2 \cdot \underset{1}{\cancel{3}}} = \frac{5}{2} = 2\frac{1}{2}$$

YOU TRY IT 6

Write $\frac{48}{36}$ in simplest form.

Your solution

Solutions on p. S5

2.3 EXERCISES

✔ Concept Check

1. Is there a fraction equivalent to $\frac{3}{5}$ with a denominator of 7? Explain.

2. If a fraction is in simplest form, what is the GCF of the numerator and denominator of the fraction?

OBJECTIVE A *To find equivalent fractions by raising to higher terms*

For Exercises 3 to 37, write an equivalent fraction with the given denominator.

3. $\dfrac{1}{2} = \dfrac{}{10}$

4. $\dfrac{1}{4} = \dfrac{}{16}$

5. $\dfrac{3}{16} = \dfrac{}{48}$

6. $\dfrac{5}{9} = \dfrac{}{81}$

7. $\dfrac{3}{8} = \dfrac{}{32}$

8. $\dfrac{7}{11} = \dfrac{}{33}$

9. $\dfrac{3}{17} = \dfrac{}{51}$

10. $\dfrac{7}{10} = \dfrac{}{90}$

11. $\dfrac{3}{4} = \dfrac{}{16}$

12. $\dfrac{5}{8} = \dfrac{}{32}$

13. $3 = \dfrac{}{9}$

14. $5 = \dfrac{}{25}$

15. $\dfrac{1}{3} = \dfrac{}{60}$

16. $\dfrac{1}{16} = \dfrac{}{48}$

17. $\dfrac{11}{15} = \dfrac{}{60}$

18. $\dfrac{3}{50} = \dfrac{}{300}$

19. $\dfrac{2}{3} = \dfrac{}{18}$

20. $\dfrac{5}{9} = \dfrac{}{36}$

21. $\dfrac{5}{7} = \dfrac{}{49}$

22. $\dfrac{7}{8} = \dfrac{}{32}$

23. $\dfrac{5}{9} = \dfrac{}{18}$

24. $\dfrac{11}{12} = \dfrac{}{36}$

25. $7 = \dfrac{}{3}$

26. $9 = \dfrac{}{4}$

27. $\dfrac{7}{9} = \dfrac{}{45}$

28. $\dfrac{5}{6} = \dfrac{}{42}$

29. $\dfrac{15}{16} = \dfrac{}{64}$

30. $\dfrac{11}{18} = \dfrac{}{54}$

31. $\dfrac{3}{14} = \dfrac{}{98}$

32. $\dfrac{5}{6} = \dfrac{}{144}$

33. $\dfrac{5}{8} = \dfrac{}{48}$

34. $\dfrac{7}{12} = \dfrac{}{96}$

35. $\dfrac{5}{14} = \dfrac{}{42}$

36. $\dfrac{2}{3} = \dfrac{}{42}$

37. $\dfrac{17}{24} = \dfrac{}{144}$

38. 🖹 When you multiply the numerator and denominator of a fraction by the same number, you are actually multiplying the fraction by the number _____.

OBJECTIVE B *To write a fraction in simplest form*

For Exercises 39 to 73, write the fraction in simplest form.

39. $\dfrac{4}{12}$

40. $\dfrac{8}{22}$

41. $\dfrac{22}{44}$

42. $\dfrac{2}{14}$

43. $\dfrac{2}{12}$

44. $\dfrac{50}{75}$ **45.** $\dfrac{40}{36}$ **46.** $\dfrac{12}{8}$ **47.** $\dfrac{0}{30}$ **48.** $\dfrac{10}{10}$

49. $\dfrac{9}{22}$ **50.** $\dfrac{14}{35}$ **51.** $\dfrac{75}{25}$ **52.** $\dfrac{8}{60}$ **53.** $\dfrac{16}{84}$

54. $\dfrac{20}{44}$ **55.** $\dfrac{12}{35}$ **56.** $\dfrac{8}{36}$ **57.** $\dfrac{28}{44}$ **58.** $\dfrac{12}{16}$

59. $\dfrac{16}{12}$ **60.** $\dfrac{24}{18}$ **61.** $\dfrac{24}{40}$ **62.** $\dfrac{44}{60}$ **63.** $\dfrac{8}{88}$

64. $\dfrac{9}{90}$ **65.** $\dfrac{144}{36}$ **66.** $\dfrac{140}{297}$ **67.** $\dfrac{48}{144}$ **68.** $\dfrac{32}{120}$

69. $\dfrac{60}{100}$ **70.** $\dfrac{33}{110}$ **71.** $\dfrac{36}{16}$ **72.** $\dfrac{80}{45}$ **73.** $\dfrac{32}{160}$

74. Suppose the denominator of a fraction is a multiple of the numerator. When the fraction is written in simplest form, what number is its numerator?

Critical Thinking

75. Make a list of five different fractions that are equivalent to $\frac{2}{3}$.

76. Show that $\frac{15}{24} = \frac{5}{8}$ by using a diagram.

Projects or Group Activities

77. Geography **a.** What fraction of the states in the United States of America have names that begin with the letter M?
b. What fraction of the states have names that begin and end with a vowel?

2.4　Addition of Fractions and Mixed Numbers

OBJECTIVE A　*To add fractions with the same denominator*

Addition of Fractions with the Same Denominator

To add fractions with the same denominator, add the numerators and place the sum over the common denominator.

EXAMPLES

1. $\dfrac{2}{7} + \dfrac{3}{7} = \dfrac{2+3}{7} = \dfrac{5}{7}$

2. $\dfrac{1}{8} + \dfrac{5}{8} = \dfrac{1+5}{8} = \dfrac{6}{8} = \dfrac{3}{4}$

📝 **Take Note**

In Example 2 at the right, note that the answer is reduced to simplest form. Always write your answer in simplest form.

EXAMPLE 1

Add: $\dfrac{5}{18} + \dfrac{7}{18}$

Solution

$\dfrac{5}{18} + \dfrac{7}{18} = \dfrac{5+7}{18} = \dfrac{12}{18}$

$= \dfrac{2}{3}$

• The denominators are the same. Add the numerators. Place the sum over the common denominator.
• Write the answer in simplest form.

YOU TRY IT 1

Add: $\dfrac{3}{8} + \dfrac{7}{8}$

Your solution

Solution on p. S5

OBJECTIVE B　*To add fractions with different denominators*

Addition of Fractions with Different Denominators

To add fractions with different denominators, first rewrite the fractions as equivalent fractions with a common denominator. Then add the numerators and place the sum over the common denominator. The LCM of the denominators of the fractions is the **least common denominator (LCD).**

EXAMPLE

Add: $\dfrac{1}{2} + \dfrac{1}{3}$

The LCM of the denominators 2 and 3 is 6.

$\dfrac{1}{2} + \dfrac{1}{3} = \dfrac{3}{6} + \dfrac{2}{6}$　• Write equivalent fractions with 6 as the denominator.

$= \dfrac{3+2}{6} = \dfrac{5}{6}$　• Add the numerators.

📱 **Integrating Technology**

Some scientific calculators have a fraction key, $a^{b/c}$. It is used to perform operations on fractions. To use this key to simplify the expression at the right, enter

$1 \; \boxed{a^{b/c}} \; 2 + 1 \; \boxed{a^{b/c}} \; 3 \; \boxed{=}$
$\underbrace{}_{\frac{1}{2}} \qquad \underbrace{}_{\frac{1}{3}}$

EXAMPLE 2

Add: $\dfrac{5}{8} + \dfrac{7}{9}$

Solution

Write equivalent fractions using 72 (the LCM of the denominators) as the common denominator. Then add.

$$\dfrac{5}{8} + \dfrac{7}{9} = \dfrac{45}{72} + \dfrac{56}{72} = \dfrac{45 + 56}{72} = \dfrac{101}{72} = 1\dfrac{29}{72}$$

YOU TRY IT 2

Add: $\dfrac{7}{9} + \dfrac{11}{15}$

Your solution

EXAMPLE 3

Find $\dfrac{7}{12}$ more than $\dfrac{3}{8}$.

Solution

Write equivalent fractions using 24 (the LCM of the denominators) as the common denominator. Then add.

$$\dfrac{3}{8} + \dfrac{7}{12} = \dfrac{9}{24} + \dfrac{14}{24} = \dfrac{9 + 14}{24} = \dfrac{23}{24}$$

YOU TRY IT 3

Find the sum of $\dfrac{5}{12}$ and $\dfrac{9}{16}$.

Your solution

EXAMPLE 4

Add: $\dfrac{2}{3} + \dfrac{3}{5} + \dfrac{5}{6}$

Solution

Write equivalent fractions using 30 (the LCM of the denominators) as the common denominator. Then add.

$$\dfrac{2}{3} + \dfrac{3}{5} + \dfrac{5}{6} = \dfrac{20}{30} + \dfrac{18}{30} + \dfrac{25}{30} = \dfrac{20 + 18 + 25}{30}$$

$$= \dfrac{63}{30} = 2\dfrac{3}{30} = 2\dfrac{1}{10}$$

YOU TRY IT 4

Add: $\dfrac{3}{4} + \dfrac{4}{5} + \dfrac{5}{8}$

Your solution

Solutions on p. S5

OBJECTIVE C *To add whole numbers, mixed numbers, and fractions*

The sum of a whole number and a fraction is a mixed number.

Take Note

The procedure at the right illustrates why $2 + \dfrac{2}{3} = 2\dfrac{2}{3}$.

You do not need to show these steps when adding a whole number and a fraction. Here are two more examples:

$$7 + \dfrac{1}{5} = 7\dfrac{1}{5}$$

$$6 + \dfrac{3}{4} = 6\dfrac{3}{4}$$

HOW TO 1 Add: $2 + \dfrac{2}{3}$

$$2 + \dfrac{2}{3} = \dfrac{6}{3} + \dfrac{2}{3} = \dfrac{8}{3} = 2\dfrac{2}{3}$$

To add a whole number and a mixed number, write the fraction and then add the whole numbers.

HOW TO 2 Add: $7\dfrac{2}{5} + 4$

Write the fraction.

$$\begin{array}{r} 7\dfrac{2}{5} \\ + 4 \\ \hline \dfrac{2}{5} \end{array}$$

Add the whole numbers.

$$\begin{array}{r} 7\dfrac{2}{5} \\ + 4 \\ \hline 11\dfrac{2}{5} \end{array}$$

To add two mixed numbers, add the fractional parts and then add the whole numbers. Remember to reduce the sum to simplest form.

Integrating Technology

Use the fraction key on a calculator to enter mixed numbers. For the example at the right, enter

5 $a^{b/c}$ 4 $a^{b/c}$ 9 +

$$5\frac{4}{9}$$

6 $a^{b/c}$ 14 $a^{b/c}$ 15 =

$$6\frac{14}{15}$$

HOW TO 3   What is $6\frac{14}{15}$ added to $5\frac{4}{9}$?

The LCM of the denominators 9 and 15 is 45.

Add the fractional parts.

$$5\frac{4}{9} = 5\frac{20}{45}$$
$$+6\frac{14}{15} = 6\frac{42}{45}$$
$$\frac{62}{45}$$

Add the whole numbers.

$$5\frac{4}{9} = 5\frac{20}{45}$$
$$+6\frac{14}{15} = 6\frac{42}{45}$$
$$11\frac{62}{45} = 11 + \frac{62}{45} = 11 + 1\frac{17}{45} = 12\frac{17}{45}$$

APPLY THE CONCEPT

A pastry chef is making a blueberry cake that requires $1\frac{1}{3}$ cups of flour for the streusel topping and $1\frac{1}{4}$ cups of flour for the cake. To find the total amount of flour the chef needs, add $1\frac{1}{3}$ and $1\frac{1}{4}$.

$$1\frac{1}{3} + 1\frac{1}{4} = 1\frac{4}{12} + 1\frac{3}{12} = 2\frac{7}{12}$$

The chef needs $2\frac{7}{12}$ cups of flour.

EXAMPLE 5

Add: $5 + \frac{3}{8}$

Solution $5 + \frac{3}{8} = 5\frac{3}{8}$

YOU TRY IT 5

What is 7 added to $\frac{6}{11}$?

Your solution

EXAMPLE 6

Find 17 increased by $3\frac{3}{8}$.

Solution $17 + 3\frac{3}{8} = 20\frac{3}{8}$

YOU TRY IT 6

Find the sum of 29 and $17\frac{5}{12}$.

Your solution

EXAMPLE 7

Add: $5\frac{2}{3} + 11\frac{5}{6} + 12\frac{7}{9}$

Solution $5\frac{2}{3} = 5\frac{12}{18}$ • LCD = 18

$$11\frac{5}{6} = 11\frac{15}{18}$$
$$+ 12\frac{7}{9} = 12\frac{14}{18}$$
$$28\frac{41}{18} = 30\frac{5}{18}$$

YOU TRY IT 7

Add: $7\frac{4}{5} + 6\frac{7}{10} + 13\frac{11}{15}$

Your solution

Solutions on p. S5

OBJECTIVE D   *To solve application problems*

EXAMPLE 8

The lengths of the luff, leech, and foot of the jib for a sailboat are shown at the right. Find the perimeter of the sail. (Perimeter is the distance around an object.)

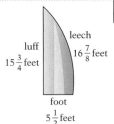

luff $15\frac{3}{4}$ feet

leech $16\frac{7}{8}$ feet

foot $5\frac{1}{2}$ feet

Strategy

To find the perimeter, add the lengths of the luff, leech, and foot ($15\frac{3}{4}$, $16\frac{7}{8}$, and $5\frac{1}{2}$).

Solution

$$15\frac{3}{4} + 16\frac{7}{8} + 5\frac{1}{2} = 15\frac{6}{8} + 16\frac{7}{8} + 5\frac{4}{8}$$

$$= 36\frac{17}{8} = 38\frac{1}{8}$$

The perimeter of the sail is $38\frac{1}{8}$ feet.

YOU TRY IT 8

On Monday, you spent $4\frac{1}{2}$ hours in class, $3\frac{3}{4}$ hours studying, and $1\frac{1}{3}$ hours driving. Find the total number of hours spent on these three activities.

Your strategy

Your solution

EXAMPLE 9

This week, Barbara Walsh worked 4 hours on Tuesday, $2\frac{1}{3}$ hours on Wednesday, and $5\frac{2}{3}$ hours on Friday at a part-time job. Barbara is paid $9 an hour. How much did she earn this week?

Strategy

To find how much Barbara earned:
- Find the total number of hours worked.
- Multiply the total number of hours worked by the hourly wage (9).

Solution

$$\begin{array}{r} 4 \\ 2\frac{1}{3} \\ + 5\frac{2}{3} \\ \hline 11\frac{3}{3} = 12 \text{ hours worked} \end{array}$$

$$\begin{array}{r} 12 \\ \times \ 9 \\ \hline 108 \end{array}$$

Barbara earned $108 this week.

YOU TRY IT 9

Jeff Sapone, a carpenter, worked $1\frac{2}{3}$ hours of overtime on Monday, $3\frac{1}{3}$ hours of overtime on Tuesday, and 2 hours of overtime on Wednesday. At an overtime hourly rate of $36, find Jeff's overtime pay for the 3 days.

Your strategy

Your solution

Solutions on pp. S5–S6

2.4 EXERCISES

✔ Concept Check

For Exercises 1 and 2, replace the question marks to make a true statement.

1. $\dfrac{2}{9} + \dfrac{5}{9} = \dfrac{? + ?}{9} = \dfrac{?}{9}$

2. $\dfrac{1}{8} + \dfrac{3}{8} = \dfrac{? + ?}{8} = \dfrac{?}{8} = ?$

For Exercises 3 to 6, find the LCD of the fractions.

3. $\dfrac{1}{4}, \dfrac{3}{8}$

4. $\dfrac{2}{3}, \dfrac{3}{4}$

5. $\dfrac{5}{6}, \dfrac{4}{9}$

6. $\dfrac{1}{2}, \dfrac{3}{5}, \dfrac{3}{14}$

OBJECTIVE A *To add fractions with the same denominator*

For Exercises 7 to 22, add.

7. $\dfrac{2}{7} + \dfrac{1}{7}$

8. $\dfrac{3}{11} + \dfrac{5}{11}$

9. $\dfrac{2}{9} + \dfrac{4}{9}$

10. $\dfrac{5}{8} + \dfrac{1}{8}$

11. $\dfrac{3}{14} + \dfrac{5}{14}$

12. $\dfrac{3}{20} + \dfrac{9}{20}$

13. $\dfrac{1}{2} + \dfrac{1}{2}$

14. $\dfrac{1}{3} + \dfrac{2}{3}$

15. $\dfrac{8}{11} + \dfrac{7}{11}$

16. $\dfrac{9}{13} + \dfrac{7}{13}$

17. $\dfrac{8}{5} + \dfrac{9}{5}$

18. $\dfrac{5}{3} + \dfrac{7}{3}$

19. $\dfrac{3}{8} + \dfrac{7}{8} + \dfrac{1}{8}$

20. $\dfrac{5}{12} + \dfrac{7}{12} + \dfrac{1}{12}$

21. $\dfrac{4}{15} + \dfrac{7}{15} + \dfrac{11}{15}$

22. $\dfrac{5}{7} + \dfrac{4}{7} + \dfrac{5}{7}$

23. Find the sum of $\frac{5}{12}$, $\frac{1}{12}$, and $\frac{11}{12}$.

24. Find the total of $\frac{5}{8}$, $\frac{3}{8}$, and $\frac{7}{8}$.

For Exercises 25 to 28, each statement concerns a pair of fractions that have the same denominator. State whether the sum of the fractions is a proper fraction, the number 1, a mixed number, or a whole number other than 1.

25. The sum of the numerators is a multiple of the denominator.

26. The sum of the numerators is one more than the denominator.

27. The sum of the numerators is the denominator.

28. The sum of the numerators is smaller than the denominator.

OBJECTIVE B   *To add fractions with different denominators*

For Exercises 29 to 48, add.

29. $\dfrac{1}{2} + \dfrac{2}{3}$

30. $\dfrac{2}{3} + \dfrac{1}{4}$

31. $\dfrac{3}{14} + \dfrac{5}{7}$

32. $\dfrac{3}{5} + \dfrac{7}{10}$

33. $\dfrac{8}{15} + \dfrac{7}{20}$

34. $\dfrac{1}{6} + \dfrac{7}{9}$

35. $\dfrac{3}{8} + \dfrac{9}{14}$

36. $\dfrac{5}{12} + \dfrac{5}{16}$

37. $\dfrac{3}{20} + \dfrac{7}{30}$

38. $\dfrac{5}{12} + \dfrac{7}{30}$

39. $\dfrac{1}{3} + \dfrac{5}{6} + \dfrac{7}{9}$

40. $\dfrac{2}{3} + \dfrac{5}{6} + \dfrac{7}{12}$

41. $\dfrac{5}{6} + \dfrac{1}{12} + \dfrac{5}{16}$

42. $\dfrac{2}{9} + \dfrac{7}{15} + \dfrac{4}{21}$

43. $\dfrac{2}{3} + \dfrac{1}{5} + \dfrac{7}{12}$

44. $\dfrac{3}{4} + \dfrac{4}{5} + \dfrac{7}{12}$

45. $\dfrac{2}{3} + \dfrac{3}{5} + \dfrac{7}{8}$

46. $\dfrac{3}{10} + \dfrac{14}{15} + \dfrac{9}{25}$

47. $\dfrac{2}{3} + \dfrac{5}{8} + \dfrac{7}{9}$

48. $\dfrac{1}{3} + \dfrac{2}{9} + \dfrac{7}{8}$

49. What is $\dfrac{3}{8}$ added to $\dfrac{3}{5}$?

50. What is $\dfrac{5}{9}$ added to $\dfrac{7}{12}$?

51. Find the sum of $\dfrac{3}{8}$, $\dfrac{5}{6}$, and $\dfrac{7}{12}$.

52. Find the total of $\dfrac{1}{2}$, $\dfrac{5}{8}$, and $\dfrac{7}{9}$.

53. Which statement describes a pair of fractions for which the least common denominator is the product of the denominators?
   (i) The denominator of one fraction is a multiple of the denominator of the second fraction.
   (ii) The denominators of the two fractions have no common factors.

OBJECTIVE C   *To add whole numbers, mixed numbers, and fractions*

For Exercises 54 to 75, add.

54. $2\dfrac{2}{5}$
    $+\,3\dfrac{3}{10}$

55. $4\dfrac{1}{2}$
    $+\,5\dfrac{7}{12}$

56. $3\dfrac{3}{8}$
    $+\,2\dfrac{5}{16}$

57. 4
    $+\,5\dfrac{2}{7}$

58. $6\dfrac{8}{9}$
    $+\,12$

59. $7\dfrac{5}{12} + 2\dfrac{9}{16}$

60. $9\dfrac{1}{2} + 3\dfrac{3}{11}$

61. $6 + 2\dfrac{3}{13}$

62. $8\dfrac{21}{40} + 6$

63. $8\dfrac{29}{30} + 7\dfrac{11}{40}$

64. $17\dfrac{5}{16} + 3\dfrac{11}{24}$

65. $17\dfrac{3}{8} + 7\dfrac{7}{20}$

66. $14\dfrac{7}{12} + 29\dfrac{13}{21}$

67. $5\dfrac{7}{8} + 27\dfrac{5}{12}$

68. $7\dfrac{5}{6} + 3\dfrac{5}{9}$

69. $7\dfrac{5}{9} + 2\dfrac{7}{12}$

70. $3\dfrac{1}{2} + 2\dfrac{3}{4} + 1\dfrac{5}{6}$

71. $2\dfrac{1}{2} + 3\dfrac{2}{3} + 4\dfrac{1}{4}$

72. $3\dfrac{1}{3} + 7\dfrac{1}{5} + 2\dfrac{1}{7}$

73. $3\dfrac{1}{2} + 3\dfrac{1}{5} + 8\dfrac{1}{9}$

74. $6\dfrac{5}{9} + 6\dfrac{5}{12} + 2\dfrac{5}{18}$

75. $2\dfrac{3}{8} + 4\dfrac{7}{12} + 3\dfrac{5}{16}$

76. Carpentry   For the bookcase shown at the right, what is the distance from the top of the bottom shelf to the top of the next shelf?

77. Building Maintenance   A pole $6\dfrac{3}{8}$ feet long is used to change light bulbs in ceiling fixtures. The pole comes with an extension that is $3\dfrac{1}{2}$ feet long. What is the length of the pole with the extension in place?

$\dfrac{3}{4}$ in.

$11\dfrac{1}{2}$ in.

78. Find the sum of $2\frac{4}{9}$ and $5\frac{7}{12}$.

79. Find $5\frac{5}{6}$ more than $3\frac{3}{8}$.

80. What is $4\frac{3}{4}$ added to $9\frac{1}{3}$?

81. What is $4\frac{8}{9}$ added to $9\frac{1}{6}$?

82. Find the total of 2, $4\frac{5}{8}$, and $2\frac{2}{9}$.

83. Find the total of $1\frac{5}{8}$, 3, and $7\frac{7}{24}$.

For Exercises 84 and 85, state whether the given sum can be a whole number. Answer *yes* or *no*.

84. The sum of two mixed numbers

85. The sum of a mixed number and a whole number

OBJECTIVE D *To solve application problems*

86. Mechanics Find the length of the shaft.

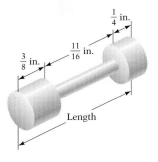

$\frac{1}{4}$ in.

$\frac{11}{16}$ in.

$\frac{3}{8}$ in.

Length

87. Mechanics Find the length of the shaft.

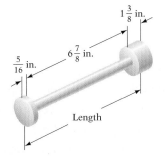

$1\frac{3}{8}$ in.

$6\frac{7}{8}$ in.

$\frac{5}{16}$ in.

Length

88. Carpentry A table 30 inches high has a top that is $1\frac{1}{8}$ inches thick. Find the total thickness of the table top after a $\frac{3}{16}$-inch veneer is applied.

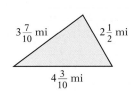

Veneer

$\frac{3}{16}$ in.

$1\frac{1}{8}$ in.

30 in.

89. For the table pictured at the right, what does the sum $30 + 1\frac{1}{8} + \frac{3}{16}$ represent?

90. Wages You are working a part-time job that pays $11 an hour. You worked 5, $3\frac{3}{4}$, $2\frac{1}{3}$, $1\frac{1}{4}$, and $7\frac{2}{3}$ hours during the last five days.

a. Find the total number of hours you worked during the last five days.
b. Find your total wages for the five days.

91. Sports The course of a yachting race is in the shape of a triangle with sides that measure $4\frac{3}{10}$ miles, $3\frac{7}{10}$ miles, and $2\frac{1}{2}$ miles. Find the total length of the course.

$3\frac{7}{10}$ mi

$2\frac{1}{2}$ mi

$4\frac{3}{10}$ mi

Construction The size of an interior door frame is determined by the width of the wall into which it is installed. The width of the wall is determined by the width of the stud in the wall and the thickness of the sheets of drywall installed on each side of the wall. A 2×4 stud is $3\frac{5}{8}$ inches thick. A 2×6 stud is $5\frac{5}{8}$ inches thick. Use this information for Exercises 92 to 94.

92. Find the thickness of a wall constructed with 2×4 studs and drywall that is $\frac{1}{2}$ inch thick.

93. Find the thickness of a wall constructed with 2×6 studs and drywall that is $\frac{1}{2}$ inch thick.

94. A fire wall is a physical barrier in a building designed to limit the spread of fire. Suppose a fire wall is built between the garage and the kitchen of a house. Find the width of the fire wall if it is constructed using 2×4 studs and drywall that is $\frac{5}{8}$ inch thick.

95. Construction Two pieces of wood must be bolted together. One piece of wood is $\frac{1}{2}$ inch thick. The second piece is $\frac{5}{8}$ inch thick. A washer will be placed on each of the outer side of the top piece of wood. The washer is $\frac{1}{16}$ inch thick. The nut is $\frac{3}{16}$ inch thick. Find the minimum length of bolt needed to bolt the two pieces of wood together.

Critical Thinking

96. ◣ A survey was conducted to determine people's favorite color from among blue, green, red, purple, and other. The surveyor claims that $\frac{1}{3}$ of the people responded blue, $\frac{1}{6}$ responded green, $\frac{1}{8}$ responded red, $\frac{1}{12}$ responded purple, and $\frac{2}{5}$ responded some other color. Is this possible? Explain your answer.

Projects or Group Activities

A **unit fraction** is a fraction with numerator 1 and denominator greater than 1. For instance, $\frac{1}{5}$ and $\frac{1}{12}$ are unit fractions.

97. List the three largest unit fractions.

98. ◣ Is there a smallest unit fraction? Explain.

Early Egyptians expressed nonunit fractions as the sums of unit fractions. For instance, $\frac{3}{10}$ would be represented as $\frac{1}{5} + \frac{1}{10}$ because $\frac{3}{10} = \frac{1}{5} + \frac{1}{10}$. For Exercises 99 to 101, represent the given fraction as the sum of two unit fractions.

99. $\frac{7}{12}$

100. $\frac{11}{24}$

101. $\frac{5}{12}$

SECTION

2.5 | Subtraction of Fractions and Mixed Numbers

OBJECTIVE A   *To subtract fractions with the same denominator*

Subtraction of Fractions with the Same Denominator

To subtract fractions with the same denominator, subtract the numerators and place the difference over the common denominator.

EXAMPLE

$$\frac{6}{7} - \frac{2}{7} = \frac{6-2}{7} = \frac{4}{7}$$

EXAMPLE 1

Subtract: $\dfrac{11}{18} - \dfrac{7}{18}$

Solution

$$\frac{11}{18} - \frac{7}{18} = \frac{11-7}{18}$$ • The denominators are the same. Subtract the numerators.

$$= \frac{4}{18}$$ • Place the difference over the common denominator.

$$= \frac{2}{9}$$ • Write the answer in simplest form.

YOU TRY IT 1

Find the difference between $\dfrac{16}{27}$ and $\dfrac{7}{27}$.

Your solution

Solution on p. S6

OBJECTIVE B   *To subtract fractions with different denominators*

Subtraction of Fractions with Different Denominators

To subtract fractions with different denominators, first rewrite the fractions as equivalent fractions with a common denominator. Then subtract the numerators and place the difference over the common denominator.

EXAMPLE

Subtract: $\dfrac{5}{6} - \dfrac{1}{4}$

The LCD of the denominators 6 and 4 is 12.

$$\frac{5}{6} - \frac{1}{4} = \frac{10}{12} - \frac{3}{12}$$ • Rewrite each fraction as an equivalent fraction with 12 as the denominator.

$$= \frac{10-3}{12} = \frac{7}{12}$$ • Subtract the numerators and place the difference over the common denominator.

EXAMPLE 2

Subtract: $\dfrac{11}{16} - \dfrac{5}{12}$

Solution

The LCD of the denominators 16 and 12 is 48. Write equivalent fractions using 48 as the common denominator. Then subtract the fractions.

$$\dfrac{11}{16} - \dfrac{5}{12} = \dfrac{33}{48} - \dfrac{20}{48} = \dfrac{33 - 20}{48} = \dfrac{13}{48}$$

YOU TRY IT 2

Subtract: $\dfrac{13}{18} - \dfrac{7}{24}$

Your solution

EXAMPLE 3

Find the difference between $\dfrac{7}{8}$ and $\dfrac{5}{12}$.

Solution

The LCD of the denominators 8 and 12 is 24. Write equivalent fractions using 24 as the common denominator. Then subtract the fractions.

$$\dfrac{7}{8} - \dfrac{5}{12} = \dfrac{21}{24} - \dfrac{10}{24} = \dfrac{21 - 10}{24} = \dfrac{11}{24}$$

YOU TRY IT 3

Find $\dfrac{5}{6}$ less than $\dfrac{8}{9}$.

Your solution

Solutions on p. S6

OBJECTIVE C *To subtract whole numbers, mixed numbers, and fractions*

To subtract mixed numbers without borrowing, subtract the fractional parts and then subtract the whole numbers.

HOW TO 1 Subtract: $5\dfrac{5}{6} - 2\dfrac{3}{4}$

Subtract the fractional parts.

$$5\dfrac{5}{6} = 5\dfrac{10}{12}$$
$$-2\dfrac{3}{4} = 2\dfrac{9}{12}$$
$$\overline{\dfrac{1}{12}}$$

• The LCD of the denominators 6 and 4 is 12.

Subtract the whole numbers.

$$5\dfrac{5}{6} = 5\dfrac{10}{12}$$
$$-2\dfrac{3}{4} = 2\dfrac{9}{12}$$
$$\overline{3\dfrac{1}{12}}$$

The difference is $3\dfrac{1}{12}$.

Subtraction of mixed numbers sometimes involves borrowing.

HOW TO 2   Subtract: $7\dfrac{1}{6} - 2\dfrac{5}{8}$

Write equivalent fractions using the LCD.

$$7\dfrac{1}{6} = 7\dfrac{4}{24}$$
$$-2\dfrac{5}{8} = 2\dfrac{15}{24}$$

Borrow 1 from 7. Add the 1 to $\dfrac{4}{24}$. Write $1\dfrac{4}{24}$ as $\dfrac{28}{24}$.

$$7\dfrac{1}{6} = \overset{6}{\cancel{7}}1\dfrac{4}{24} = 6\dfrac{28}{24}$$
$$-2\dfrac{5}{8} = \quad 2\dfrac{15}{24} = 2\dfrac{15}{24}$$

Subtract the mixed numbers.

$$7\dfrac{1}{6} = 6\dfrac{28}{24}$$
$$-2\dfrac{5}{8} = 2\dfrac{15}{24}$$
$$\rule{3cm}{0.4pt}$$
$$4\dfrac{13}{24}$$

The difference is $4\dfrac{13}{24}$.

HOW TO 3   Subtract: $5 - 2\dfrac{5}{8}$

Borrow 1 from 5.

$$5 \; = \overset{4}{\cancel{5}}\,1$$
$$-2\dfrac{5}{8} = 2\dfrac{5}{8}$$

Write 1 as a fraction so that the fractions have the same denominators.

$$5 \; = 4\dfrac{8}{8}$$
$$-2\dfrac{5}{8} = 2\dfrac{5}{8}$$

Subtract the mixed numbers.

$$5 \;\; = 4\dfrac{8}{8}$$
$$-2\dfrac{5}{8} = 2\dfrac{5}{8}$$
$$\rule{3cm}{0.4pt}$$
$$2\dfrac{3}{8}$$

The difference is $2\dfrac{3}{8}$.

APPLY THE CONCEPT ···

The inseam of a pant leg is $30\dfrac{1}{2}$ inches long. What is the length of the inseam after a tailor cuts $\dfrac{3}{4}$ inch from the pant leg?

To find the length of the inseam, subtract $\dfrac{3}{4}$ from $30\dfrac{1}{2}$.

$$30\dfrac{1}{2} - \dfrac{3}{4} = 30\dfrac{2}{4} - \dfrac{3}{4} = 29\dfrac{6}{4} - \dfrac{3}{4} = 29\dfrac{3}{4}$$

The length of the inseam is $29\dfrac{3}{4}$ inches.

Find $11\frac{5}{12}$ decreased by $2\frac{11}{16}$.

Solution

$$11\frac{5}{12} = 11\frac{20}{48} = 10\frac{68}{48} \quad \bullet \text{ LCD} = 48$$

$$-2\frac{11}{16} = 2\frac{33}{48} = 2\frac{33}{48}$$

$$\overline{\phantom{-2\frac{11}{16}}\, 8\frac{35}{48}}$$

What is $21\frac{7}{9}$ minus $7\frac{11}{12}$?

Your solution

Subtract: $9 - 4\frac{3}{11}$

Solution

$$9 \quad = 8\frac{11}{11} \quad \bullet \text{ LCD} = 11$$

$$-4\frac{3}{11} = 4\frac{3}{11}$$

$$\overline{\phantom{-4\frac{3}{11}}\, 4\frac{8}{11}}$$

Subtract: $8 - 2\frac{4}{13}$

Your solution

Solutions on p. S6

OBJECTIVE D *To solve application problems*

Outside Diameter

Inside Diameter

HOW TO 4 The outside diameter of a bushing is $3\frac{3}{8}$ inches, and the wall thickness is $\frac{1}{4}$ inch. Find the inside diameter of the bushing.

$$\frac{1}{4} + \frac{1}{4} = \frac{2}{4} = \frac{1}{2} \qquad \bullet \text{ Add } \frac{1}{4} \text{ and } \frac{1}{4} \text{ to find the total thickness of the two walls.}$$

$$3\frac{3}{8} = 3\frac{3}{8} = 2\frac{11}{8} \qquad \bullet \text{ Subtract the total thickness of the two walls from the outside diameter to find the inside diameter.}$$

$$-\frac{1}{2} = \frac{4}{8} = \frac{4}{8}$$

$$\overline{\phantom{-\frac{1}{2}}\, 2\frac{7}{8}}$$

The inside diameter of the bushing is $2\frac{7}{8}$ inches.

EXAMPLE 6

A $2\frac{2}{3}$-inch piece is cut from a $6\frac{5}{8}$-inch board. How much of the board is left?

Strategy

To find the length remaining, subtract the length of the piece cut from the total length of the board.

Solution

$$6\frac{5}{8} = 6\frac{15}{24} = 5\frac{39}{24}$$
$$-2\frac{2}{3} = 2\frac{16}{24} = 2\frac{16}{24}$$
$$\overline{\qquad\qquad\quad 3\frac{23}{24}}$$

$3\frac{23}{24}$ inches of the board are left.

YOU TRY IT 6

A flight from New York to Los Angeles takes $5\frac{1}{2}$ hours. After the plane has been in the air for $2\frac{3}{4}$ hours, how much flight time remains?

Your strategy

Your solution

EXAMPLE 7

Two painters are staining a house. In one day, one painter stained $\frac{1}{3}$ of the house and the other stained $\frac{1}{4}$ of the house. How much of the job remains to be done?

Strategy

To find how much of the job remains:
• Find the total amount of the house already stained $\left(\frac{1}{3} + \frac{1}{4}\right)$.
• Subtract the amount already stained from 1, which represents the complete job.

Solution

$$\frac{1}{3} = \frac{4}{12} \qquad\qquad 1 = \frac{12}{12}$$
$$+\frac{1}{4} = \frac{3}{12} \qquad\qquad -\frac{7}{12} = \frac{7}{12}$$
$$\overline{\quad\frac{7}{12}\quad} \qquad\qquad \overline{\quad\frac{5}{12}\quad}$$

$\frac{5}{12}$ of the house remains to be stained.

YOU TRY IT 7

A patient is put on a diet to lose 24 pounds in 3 months. The patient lost $7\frac{1}{2}$ pounds the first month and $5\frac{3}{4}$ pounds the second month. How much weight must be lost during the third month to achieve the goal?

Your strategy

Your solution

Solutions on p. S6

2.5 EXERCISES

✔ Concept Check

For Exercises 1 and 2, replace each question mark to make a true statement.

1. $\dfrac{5}{11} - \dfrac{3}{11} = \dfrac{?-?}{11} = \dfrac{?}{11}$

2. $\dfrac{7}{9} - \dfrac{4}{9} = \dfrac{?-?}{9} = \dfrac{?}{9} = ?$

For Exercises 3 and 4, answer the question without doing any calculations.

3. If $\dfrac{11}{18} - \dfrac{7}{12} = \dfrac{1}{36}$, what is the sum of $\dfrac{1}{36}$ and $\dfrac{7}{12}$?

4. If $\dfrac{9}{16} + \dfrac{1}{3} = \dfrac{43}{48}$, what is the difference between $\dfrac{43}{48}$ and $\dfrac{9}{16}$?

OBJECTIVE A　*To subtract fractions with the same denominator*

For Exercises 5 to 14, subtract.

5. $\dfrac{9}{17} - \dfrac{7}{17}$　　**6.** $\dfrac{11}{15} - \dfrac{3}{15}$　　**7.** $\dfrac{11}{12} - \dfrac{7}{12}$　　**8.** $\dfrac{13}{15} - \dfrac{4}{15}$　　**9.** $\dfrac{9}{20} - \dfrac{7}{20}$

10. $\dfrac{48}{55} - \dfrac{13}{55}$　　**11.** $\dfrac{42}{65} - \dfrac{17}{65}$　　**12.** $\dfrac{11}{24} - \dfrac{5}{24}$　　**13.** $\dfrac{23}{30} - \dfrac{13}{30}$　　**14.** $\dfrac{17}{42} - \dfrac{5}{42}$

15. What is $\dfrac{5}{14}$ less than $\dfrac{13}{14}$?　　　　　　　**16.** Find the difference between $\dfrac{7}{8}$ and $\dfrac{5}{8}$.

17. Find $\dfrac{17}{24}$ decreased by $\dfrac{11}{24}$.　　　　　　**18.** What is $\dfrac{19}{30}$ minus $\dfrac{11}{30}$?

For Exercises 19 and 20, each statement describes the difference between a pair of fractions that have the same denominator. State whether the difference of the fractions will need to be rewritten in order to be in simplest form. Answer *yes* or *no*.

19. The difference between the numerators is a factor of the denominator.

20. The difference between the numerators is 1.

OBJECTIVE B　*To subtract fractions with different denominators*

For Exercises 21 to 30, subtract.

21. $\dfrac{2}{3} - \dfrac{1}{6}$　　**22.** $\dfrac{7}{8} - \dfrac{5}{16}$　　**23.** $\dfrac{5}{8} - \dfrac{2}{7}$　　**24.** $\dfrac{5}{6} - \dfrac{3}{7}$　　**25.** $\dfrac{5}{7} - \dfrac{3}{14}$

26. $\dfrac{5}{9} - \dfrac{7}{15}$　　**27.** $\dfrac{8}{15} - \dfrac{7}{20}$　　**28.** $\dfrac{7}{9} - \dfrac{1}{6}$　　**29.** $\dfrac{9}{16} - \dfrac{17}{32}$　　**30.** $\dfrac{29}{60} - \dfrac{3}{40}$

31. What is $\frac{3}{5}$ less than $\frac{11}{12}$?

32. What is $\frac{5}{9}$ less than $\frac{11}{15}$?

33. Find the difference between $\frac{11}{24}$ and $\frac{7}{18}$.

34. Find the difference between $\frac{9}{14}$ and $\frac{5}{42}$.

35. Find $\frac{11}{12}$ decreased by $\frac{11}{15}$.

36. Find $\frac{17}{20}$ decreased by $\frac{7}{15}$.

37. What is $\frac{13}{20}$ minus $\frac{1}{6}$?

38. What is $\frac{5}{6}$ minus $\frac{7}{9}$?

39. 🐢 Which statement describes a pair of fractions for which the least common denominator is one of the denominators?
  (i) The denominator of one fraction is a factor of the denominator of the second fraction.
  (ii) The denominators of the two fractions have no common factors.

OBJECTIVE C   *To subtract whole numbers, mixed numbers, and fractions*

For Exercises 40 to 54, subtract.

40. $5\frac{7}{12}$ $-2\frac{5}{12}$

41. $16\frac{11}{15}$ $-11\frac{8}{15}$

42. $6\frac{1}{3}$ -2

43. $5\frac{7}{8}$ -1

44. 10 $-6\frac{1}{3}$

45. 3 $-2\frac{5}{21}$

46. $6\frac{2}{5}$ $-4\frac{4}{5}$

47. $16\frac{3}{8}$ $-10\frac{7}{8}$

48. $16\frac{2}{5}$ $-8\frac{4}{9}$

49. $23\frac{7}{8}$ $-16\frac{2}{3}$

50. 17 $-7\frac{8}{13}$

51. 6 $-4\frac{3}{5}$

52. $23\frac{1}{6}$ $-15\frac{3}{8}$

53. $40\frac{4}{9}$ $-24\frac{5}{6}$

54. $12\frac{5}{18}$ $-11\frac{11}{27}$

55. **Interior Design**   An interior decorator places a picture hook on a wall $29\frac{1}{2}$ inches down from the ceiling. If the support wire for the picture is $7\frac{3}{4}$ inches from the top of the picture as shown at the right, what is the distance from the ceiling to the top of the picture?

$7\frac{3}{4}$ in.

56. **Storage Space**   A laser printer $19\frac{3}{8}$ inches tall is placed on a shelf that is $23\frac{1}{4}$ inches below another shelf. Find the distance between the top of the printer and the bottom of the higher shelf.

57. What is $7\frac{3}{5}$ less than $23\frac{3}{20}$?

58. Find the difference between $12\frac{3}{8}$ and $7\frac{5}{12}$.

59. What is $10\frac{5}{9}$ minus $5\frac{11}{15}$?

60. Find $6\frac{1}{3}$ decreased by $3\frac{3}{5}$.

61. 🖼 Can the difference between a whole number and a mixed number ever be a whole number?

OBJECTIVE D   *To solve application problems*

62. **Mechanics**   Find the missing dimension.

$7\frac{7}{8}$ ft

?

$16\frac{2}{3}$ ft

63. **Mechanics**   Find the missing dimension.

$2\frac{7}{8}$ in.

?

$12\frac{3}{8}$ in.

64. ● **Sports**   In the Kentucky Derby the horses run $1\frac{1}{4}$ miles. In the Belmont Stakes they run $1\frac{1}{2}$ miles, and in the Preakness Stakes they run $1\frac{3}{16}$ miles. How much farther do the horses run in the Kentucky Derby than in the Preakness Stakes? How much farther do they run in the Belmont Stakes than in the Preakness Stakes?

Cheryl Ann Quigley/Shutterstock.com

65. **Carpentry**   The standard height of a desk is $29\frac{1}{2}$ inches. A writer is building a desk that is $28\frac{3}{4}$ inches high. How much shorter is this desk than a desk of standard height?

66. **Fundraising**   A 12-mile walkathon has three checkpoints. The first checkpoint is $3\frac{3}{8}$ miles from the starting point. The second checkpoint is $4\frac{1}{3}$ miles from the first.

   a.   How many miles is it from the starting point to the second checkpoint?
   b.   How many miles is it from the second checkpoint to the finish line?

67. **Hiking**   Two hikers plan a 3-day, $27\frac{1}{2}$-mile backpack trip carrying a total of 80 pounds. The hikers plan to travel $7\frac{3}{8}$ miles the first day and $10\frac{1}{3}$ miles the second day.

   a.   How many total miles do the hikers plan to travel the first two days?
   b.   How many miles will be left to travel on the third day?

For Exercises 68 and 69, refer to Exercise 67. Describe what each difference represents.

68. $27\frac{1}{2} - 7\frac{3}{8}$

69. $10\frac{1}{3} - 7\frac{3}{8}$

70. **Health**   A patient with high blood pressure who weighs 225 pounds is put on a diet to lose 25 pounds in 3 months. The patient loses $8\frac{3}{4}$ pounds the first month and $11\frac{5}{8}$ pounds the second month. How much weight must be lost during the third month for the goal to be achieved?

71. **Sports**   A wrestler is entered in the 172-pound weight class in the conference finals coming up in 3 weeks. The wrestler needs to lose $12\frac{3}{4}$ pounds. The wrestler loses $5\frac{1}{4}$ pounds the first week and $4\frac{1}{4}$ pounds the second week.

   a.   Without doing the calculations, determine whether the wrestler can reach his weight class by losing less in the third week than in the second week.
   b.   How many pounds must be lost in the third week to reach the desired weight?

72. **Construction**   Find the difference in thickness between a fire wall constructed with 2 × 6 studs and drywall that is $\frac{1}{2}$ inch thick and a fire wall constructed with 2 × 4 studs and drywall that is $\frac{5}{8}$ inch thick. See Exercises 92 to 94 on page 86.

73. **Finances**   If $\frac{4}{15}$ of an electrician's income is spent on housing, what fraction of the electrician's income is not spent on housing?

Critical Thinking

74. Fill in the square to produce a true statement: $5\frac{1}{3} - \boxed{} = 2\frac{1}{2}$

75. Fill in the square to produce a true statement: $\boxed{} - 4\frac{1}{2} = 1\frac{5}{8}$

Projects or Group Activities

76. Fill in the blank squares at the right so that the sum of the numbers is the same along any row, column, or diagonal. The resulting square is called a magic square.

		$\dfrac{3}{4}$
1	$\dfrac{5}{8}$	
$\dfrac{1}{2}$		$\dfrac{7}{8}$

✔ # CHECK YOUR PROGRESS: CHAPTER 2

For Exercises 1 to 4, find the LCM of the numbers.

1. 12, 18   **2.** 6, 9, 18   **3.** 2, 5, 7   **4.** 28, 36

For Exercises 5 to 8, find the GCF of the numbers.

5. 18, 24   **6.** 27, 54   **7.** 3, 6, 14   **8.** 30, 70, 105

For Exercises 9 to 12, write the fraction in simplest form.

9. $\dfrac{36}{45}$ **10.** $\dfrac{17}{51}$ **11.** $\dfrac{25}{36}$ **12.** $\dfrac{36}{4}$

For Exercises 13 to 28, add or subtract.

13. $\dfrac{2}{9} + \dfrac{4}{9}$ **14.** $\dfrac{17}{24} - \dfrac{5}{24}$ **15.** $\dfrac{7}{9} - \dfrac{7}{18}$ **16.** $\dfrac{7}{20} + \dfrac{1}{4}$

17. $\dfrac{5}{6} + \dfrac{11}{16}$ **18.** $\dfrac{3}{4} - \dfrac{9}{26}$ **19.** $\dfrac{2}{3} - \dfrac{3}{16}$ **20.** $\dfrac{3}{5} + \dfrac{1}{4}$

21. $2\dfrac{1}{10} + 7\dfrac{1}{15}$ **22.** $11\dfrac{4}{9} + 7\dfrac{1}{6}$ **23.** $7\dfrac{6}{7} - 1\dfrac{1}{2}$ **24.** $3\dfrac{13}{28} - 1\dfrac{1}{8}$

25. $5\dfrac{8}{9} + 7\dfrac{5}{6}$ **26.** $9\dfrac{3}{4} + 7\dfrac{3}{10}$ **27.** $9 - 5\dfrac{3}{4}$ **28.** $8\dfrac{1}{4} - 5\dfrac{5}{6}$

SECTION

2.6 Multiplication of Fractions and Mixed Numbers

OBJECTIVE A   *To multiply fractions*

Multiplication of Fractions

The product of two fractions is the product of the numerators over the product of the denominators.

EXAMPLE

Multiply: $\dfrac{2}{3} \times \dfrac{4}{5}$

$\dfrac{2}{3} \times \dfrac{4}{5} = \dfrac{2 \cdot 4}{3 \cdot 5} = \dfrac{8}{15}$

- Multiply the numerators.
- Multiply the denominators.

The product $\dfrac{2}{3} \times \dfrac{4}{5}$ can be read "$\dfrac{2}{3}$ times $\dfrac{4}{5}$" or "$\dfrac{2}{3}$ of $\dfrac{4}{5}$." Reading the times sign as "of" is useful in application problems.

$\dfrac{4}{5}$ of the bar is shaded.

Shade $\dfrac{2}{3}$ of the $\dfrac{4}{5}$ already shaded.

$\dfrac{8}{15}$ of the bar is then shaded dark yellow.

$\dfrac{2}{3}$ of $\dfrac{4}{5} = \dfrac{2}{3} \times \dfrac{4}{5} = \dfrac{8}{15}$

After multiplying two fractions, write the product in simplest form.

HOW TO 1   Multiply: $\dfrac{3}{4} \times \dfrac{14}{15}$

$\dfrac{3}{4} \times \dfrac{14}{15} = \dfrac{3 \cdot 14}{4 \cdot 15}$

- Multiply the numerators.
- Multiply the denominators.

$= \dfrac{3 \cdot 2 \cdot 7}{2 \cdot 2 \cdot 3 \cdot 5}$

- Write the prime factorization of each number.

$= \dfrac{\overset{1}{\cancel{3}} \cdot 2 \cdot 7}{2 \cdot 2 \cdot \underset{1}{\cancel{3}} \cdot 5} = \dfrac{7}{10}$

- Eliminate the common factors. Then multiply the remaining factors in the numerator and denominator.

This example could also be worked by using the GCF.

$\dfrac{3}{4} \times \dfrac{14}{15} = \dfrac{42}{60}$

- Multiply the numerators.
- Multiply the denominators.

$= \dfrac{6 \cdot 7}{6 \cdot 10}$

- The GCF of 42 and 60 is 6. Factor 6 from 42 and 60.

$= \dfrac{\overset{1}{\cancel{6}} \cdot 7}{\underset{1}{\cancel{6}} \cdot 10} = \dfrac{7}{10}$

- Eliminate the GCF.

EXAMPLE 1

Multiply: $\dfrac{4}{15} \times \dfrac{5}{28}$

Solution

$$\frac{4}{15} \times \frac{5}{28} = \frac{4 \cdot 5}{15 \cdot 28} = \frac{\overset{1}{2} \cdot \overset{1}{2} \cdot \overset{1}{\cancel{5}}}{3 \cdot \cancel{5} \cdot \underset{1}{2} \cdot \underset{1}{2} \cdot 7} = \frac{1}{21}$$

YOU TRY IT 1

Multiply: $\dfrac{4}{21} \times \dfrac{7}{44}$

Your solution

EXAMPLE 2

Find the product of $\frac{5}{8}$ and $\frac{7}{9}$.

Solution

$$\frac{5}{8} \times \frac{7}{9} = \frac{5 \cdot 7}{8 \cdot 9} = \frac{5 \cdot 7}{2 \cdot 2 \cdot 2 \cdot 3 \cdot 3} = \frac{35}{72}$$

YOU TRY IT 2

Find the product of $\frac{7}{12}$ and $\frac{5}{6}$.

Your solution

EXAMPLE 3

What is $\frac{9}{14}$ times $\frac{7}{12}$?

Solution

$$\frac{9}{14} \times \frac{7}{12} = \frac{9 \cdot 7}{14 \cdot 12} = \frac{3 \cdot \overset{1}{\cancel{3}} \cdot \overset{1}{\cancel{7}}}{2 \cdot \underset{1}{\cancel{7}} \cdot 2 \cdot 2 \cdot \underset{1}{\cancel{3}}} = \frac{3}{8}$$

YOU TRY IT 3

What is $\frac{5}{16}$ times $\frac{12}{25}$?

Your solution

Solutions on pp. S6–S7

OBJECTIVE B *To multiply whole numbers, mixed numbers, and fractions*

When one or more of the factors in a product is a mixed number, write each mixed number as an improper fraction before multiplying.

HOW TO 2 Multiply: $2\dfrac{2}{3} \times 4\dfrac{1}{4}$

Write each mixed number as an improper fraction; then multiply the fractions.

$$2\frac{2}{3} \times 4\frac{1}{4} = \frac{8}{3} \times \frac{17}{4}$$

$$= \frac{8 \cdot 17}{3 \cdot 4} = \frac{\overset{1}{\cancel{2}} \cdot \overset{1}{\cancel{2}} \cdot 2 \cdot 17}{3 \cdot \underset{1}{\cancel{2}} \cdot \underset{1}{\cancel{2}}} = \frac{34}{3} = 11\frac{1}{3}$$

To multiply a whole number by a fraction or a mixed number, write the whole number as a fraction with a denominator of 1.

HOW TO 3 Multiply: $3\dfrac{3}{8} \times 4$

Write the mixed number as an improper fraction. Write 4 with a denominator of 1. Then multiply the fractions.

$$3\frac{3}{8} \times 4 = \frac{27}{8} \times \frac{4}{1}$$

$$= \frac{27 \cdot 4}{8 \cdot 1} = \frac{3 \cdot 3 \cdot 3 \cdot \overset{1}{\cancel{2}} \cdot \overset{1}{\cancel{2}}}{2 \cdot \underset{1}{\cancel{2}} \cdot \underset{1}{\cancel{2}}} = \frac{27}{2} = 13\frac{1}{2}$$

APPLY THE CONCEPT ···

A hexagonal paving stone measures $5\frac{3}{4}$ inches on each side. Find the total distance around the paving stone.

To find the total distance around the paving stone, multiply $5\frac{3}{4}$ by the number of sides, 6.

$$5\frac{3}{4} \times 6 = \frac{23}{4} \times \frac{6}{1} = \frac{23 \cdot 6}{4 \cdot 1} = \frac{23 \cdot \overset{1}{2} \cdot 3}{2 \cdot 2 \cdot 1} = \frac{69}{2} = 34\frac{1}{2}$$

The total distance around the paving stone is $34\frac{1}{2}$ inches.

$5\frac{3}{4}$ in.

EXAMPLE 4

Multiply: $4\frac{5}{6} \times \frac{12}{13}$

Solution

$$4\frac{5}{6} \times \frac{12}{13} = \frac{29}{6} \times \frac{12}{13} = \frac{29 \cdot 12}{6 \cdot 13}$$

$$= \frac{29 \cdot \overset{1}{2} \cdot 2 \cdot \overset{1}{3}}{\underset{1}{2} \cdot \underset{1}{3} \cdot 13} = \frac{58}{13} = 4\frac{6}{13}$$

YOU TRY IT 4

Multiply: $5\frac{2}{5} \times \frac{5}{9}$

Your solution

EXAMPLE 5

Find $5\frac{2}{3}$ times $4\frac{1}{2}$.

Solution

$$5\frac{2}{3} \times 4\frac{1}{2} = \frac{17}{3} \times \frac{9}{2} = \frac{17 \cdot 9}{3 \cdot 2}$$

$$= \frac{17 \cdot \overset{1}{3} \cdot 3}{\underset{1}{3} \cdot 2} = \frac{51}{2} = 25\frac{1}{2}$$

YOU TRY IT 5

Find the product of $3\frac{2}{5}$ and $6\frac{1}{4}$.

Your solution

Solutions on p. S7

OBJECTIVE C *To solve application problems*

Length (ft)	Weight (lb/ft)
$6\frac{1}{2}$	$\frac{3}{8}$
$8\frac{5}{8}$	$1\frac{1}{4}$
$10\frac{3}{4}$	$2\frac{1}{2}$
$12\frac{7}{12}$	$4\frac{1}{3}$

The table at the left lists the lengths of several steel rods and their corresponding weights per foot. The weight per foot is measured in pounds per foot of rod and is abbreviated as lb/ft.

HOW TO 4 Find the weight of the steel rod that is $10\frac{3}{4}$ feet long.

Strategy

To find the weight of the steel rod, multiply its length by its weight per foot.

Solution

$$10\frac{3}{4} \times 2\frac{1}{2} = \frac{43}{4} \times \frac{5}{2} = \frac{43 \cdot 5}{4 \cdot 2} = \frac{215}{8} = 26\frac{7}{8}$$

The weight of the $10\frac{3}{4}$-foot rod is $26\frac{7}{8}$ pounds.

EXAMPLE 6

An electrician earns $206 for each day worked. What are the electrician's earnings for working $4\frac{1}{2}$ days?

Strategy

To find the electrician's total earnings, multiply the daily earnings (206) by the number of days worked $\left(4\frac{1}{2}\right)$.

Solution

$$206 \times 4\frac{1}{2} = \frac{206}{1} \times \frac{9}{2}$$

$$= \frac{206 \cdot 9}{1 \cdot 2}$$

$$= 927$$

The electrician's earnings are $927.

YOU TRY IT 6

Over the last 10 years, a house increased in value by $2\frac{1}{2}$ times. The price of the house 10 years ago was $170,000. What is the value of the house today?

Your strategy

Your solution

EXAMPLE 7

The total value of a small office building and the land on which it is built is $290,000. The value of the land is $\frac{1}{4}$ the total value. What is the dollar value of the building?

Strategy

To find the dollar value of the building:

• Find the value of the land $\left(\frac{1}{4} \times 290,000\right)$.
• Subtract the value of the land from the total value (290,000).

Solution

$$\frac{1}{4} \times 290,000 = \frac{290,000}{4}$$

$$= 72,500 \qquad \bullet \text{ Value of the land}$$

$$290,000 - 72,500 = 217,500$$

The dollar value of the building is $217,500.

YOU TRY IT 7

A paint company bought a drying chamber and an air compressor for spray painting. The total cost of the two items was $160,000. The drying chamber's cost was $\frac{4}{5}$ of the total cost. What was the cost of the air compressor?

Your strategy

Your solution

2.6 EXERCISES

✔ Concept Check

For Exercises 1 and 2, replace each question mark to make a true statement.

1. $\dfrac{5}{9} \times \dfrac{2}{3} = \dfrac{5 \cdot ?}{? \cdot 3} = ?$

2. $\dfrac{6}{9} \times 4 = \dfrac{6 \cdot ?}{7 \cdot ?} = \dfrac{?}{?} = ?$

3. 🐭 Is the product of two proper fractions always a proper fraction?

4. 🐭 Is the product of a proper fraction and a whole number less than the whole number or greater than the whole number?

OBJECTIVE A   *To multiply fractions*

For Exercises 5 to 36, multiply.

5. $\dfrac{2}{3} \times \dfrac{7}{8}$

6. $\dfrac{1}{2} \times \dfrac{2}{3}$

7. $\dfrac{5}{16} \times \dfrac{7}{15}$

8. $\dfrac{3}{8} \times \dfrac{6}{7}$

9. $\dfrac{1}{6} \times \dfrac{1}{8}$

10. $\dfrac{2}{5} \times \dfrac{5}{6}$

11. $\dfrac{11}{12} \times \dfrac{6}{7}$

12. $\dfrac{11}{12} \times \dfrac{3}{5}$

13. $\dfrac{8}{9} \times \dfrac{27}{4}$

14. $\dfrac{3}{5} \times \dfrac{3}{10}$

15. $\dfrac{5}{6} \times \dfrac{1}{2}$

16. $\dfrac{3}{8} \times \dfrac{5}{12}$

17. $\dfrac{16}{9} \times \dfrac{27}{8}$

18. $\dfrac{5}{8} \times \dfrac{16}{15}$

19. $\dfrac{3}{2} \times \dfrac{4}{9}$

20. $\dfrac{5}{3} \times \dfrac{3}{7}$

21. $\dfrac{7}{8} \times \dfrac{3}{14}$

22. $\dfrac{2}{9} \times \dfrac{4}{5}$

23. $\dfrac{7}{10} \times \dfrac{3}{8}$

24. $\dfrac{5}{12} \times \dfrac{6}{7}$

25. $\dfrac{15}{8} \times \dfrac{16}{3}$

26. $\dfrac{5}{6} \times \dfrac{4}{15}$

27. $\dfrac{1}{2} \times \dfrac{2}{15}$

28. $\dfrac{3}{8} \times \dfrac{5}{16}$

29. $\dfrac{5}{7} \times \dfrac{14}{15}$

30. $\dfrac{3}{8} \times \dfrac{36}{41}$

31. $\dfrac{5}{12} \times \dfrac{42}{65}$

32. $\dfrac{16}{33} \times \dfrac{55}{72}$

33. $\dfrac{12}{5} \times \dfrac{5}{3}$

34. $\dfrac{17}{9} \times \dfrac{81}{17}$

35. $\dfrac{10}{21} \times \dfrac{14}{15}$

36. $\dfrac{19}{64} \times \dfrac{48}{95}$

37. 🐭 Give an example of a proper and an improper fraction whose product is 1.

38. Multiply $\frac{7}{12}$ and $\frac{15}{42}$.

39. Multiply $\frac{32}{9}$ and $\frac{3}{8}$.

40. Find the product of $\frac{5}{9}$ and $\frac{3}{20}$.

41. Find the product of $\frac{7}{3}$ and $\frac{15}{14}$.

42. What is $\frac{1}{2}$ times $\frac{8}{15}$?

43. What is $\frac{3}{8}$ times $\frac{12}{17}$?

OBJECTIVE B   *To multiply whole numbers, mixed numbers, and fractions*

For Exercises 44 to 71, multiply.

44. $4 \times \frac{3}{8}$

45. $14 \times \frac{5}{7}$

46. $\frac{2}{3} \times 6$

47. $\frac{5}{12} \times 40$

48. $\frac{1}{3} \times 1\frac{1}{3}$

49. $\frac{2}{5} \times 2\frac{1}{2}$

50. $1\frac{7}{8} \times \frac{4}{15}$

51. $2\frac{1}{5} \times \frac{5}{22}$

52. $4 \times 2\frac{1}{2}$

53. $9 \times 3\frac{1}{3}$

54. $2\frac{1}{7} \times 3$

55. $5\frac{1}{4} \times 8$

56. $3\frac{2}{3} \times 5$

57. $4\frac{2}{9} \times 3$

58. $\frac{1}{2} \times 3\frac{3}{7}$

59. $\frac{3}{8} \times 4\frac{4}{5}$

60. $6\frac{1}{8} \times \frac{4}{7}$

61. $5\frac{1}{3} \times \frac{5}{16}$

62. $\frac{3}{8} \times 4\frac{1}{2}$

63. $\frac{5}{7} \times 2\frac{1}{3}$

64. $0 \times 2\frac{2}{3}$

65. $6\frac{1}{8} \times 0$

66. $2\frac{5}{8} \times 3\frac{2}{5}$

67. $5\frac{3}{16} \times 5\frac{1}{3}$

68. $5\frac{1}{5} \times 3\frac{1}{13}$

69. $3\frac{3}{4} \times 2\frac{3}{20}$

70. $12\frac{3}{5} \times 1\frac{3}{7}$

71. $6\frac{1}{2} \times 1\frac{3}{13}$

72. Computer Graphics A drawing software program allows an artist to scale (reduce or enlarge) a drawing on the computer screen. If the current height of a drawing on the screen is $4\frac{3}{8}$ inches, what is the height after the artist scales the drawing to $\frac{4}{5}$ of its current height?

73. Geometry The distance around a square, called its perimeter, is 4 times the length of one side. Find the distance around the square patio slab shown at the right.

$13\frac{1}{2}$ feet

74. True or false? If the product of a whole number and a fraction is a whole number, then the denominator of the fraction is a factor of the original whole number.

75. Multiply $2\frac{1}{2}$ and $3\frac{3}{5}$.

76. Multiply $4\frac{3}{8}$ and $3\frac{3}{5}$.

77. Find the product of $2\frac{1}{8}$ and $\frac{5}{17}$.

78. Find the product of $12\frac{2}{5}$ and $3\frac{7}{31}$.

79. What is $1\frac{3}{8}$ times $2\frac{1}{5}$?

80. What is $3\frac{1}{8}$ times $2\frac{4}{7}$?

OBJECTIVE C   *To solve application problems*

For Exercises 81 and 82, give your answer without actually doing a calculation.

81. Read Exercise 83. Will the requested cost be greater than or less than $12?

82. Read Exercise 85. Will the requested length be greater than or less than 4 feet?

83. Consumerism Salmon costs $4 per pound. Find the cost of $2\frac{3}{4}$ pounds of salmon.

84. Exercise Maria Rivera can walk $3\frac{1}{2}$ miles in 1 hour. At this rate, how far can Maria walk in $\frac{1}{3}$ hour?

$3\frac{1}{2}$ mi

1 h

?

$\frac{1}{3}$ h

85. Carpentry A board that costs $6 is $9\frac{1}{4}$ feet long. One-third of the board is cut off. What is the length of the piece cut off?

86. Geometry The perimeter of a square is equal to four times the length of a side of the square. Find the perimeter of a square whose side measures $16\frac{3}{4}$ inches.

$16\frac{3}{4}$ in.

87. Geometry To find the area of a square, multiply the length of one side of the square times itself. What is the area of a square whose side measures $5\frac{1}{4}$ feet? The area of the square will be in square feet.

88. Geometry The area of a rectangle is equal to the product of the length of the rectangle times its width. Find the area of a rectangle that has a length of $4\frac{2}{5}$ miles and a width of $3\frac{3}{10}$ miles. The area will be in square miles.

$4\frac{2}{5}$ mi

$3\frac{3}{10}$ mi

89. **Biofuels** See the news clipping at the right. About how many acres of corn planted in the United States each year are turned into ethanol?

Measurement For Exercises 90 to 92, use the table on page 99 that shows the lengths of steel rods and their corresponding weights per foot.

90. Find the weight of the $6\frac{1}{2}$-foot steel rod.

91. Find the weight of the $12\frac{7}{12}$-foot steel rod.

92. Find the total weight of the $8\frac{5}{8}$-foot and the $10\frac{3}{4}$-foot steel rods.

93. **Sewing** The Booster Club is making 22 capes for the members of the high school marching band. Each cape is made from $1\frac{3}{8}$ yards of material at a cost of $12 per yard. Find the total cost of the material.

94. **Construction** On an architectural drawing of a kitchen, the front face of the cabinet below the sink is $23\frac{1}{2}$ inches from the back wall. Before the cabinet is installed, a plumber must install a drain in the floor halfway between the wall and the front face of the cabinet. Find the required distance from the wall to the center of the drain.

Critical Thinking

95. The product of 1 and a number is $\frac{1}{2}$. Find the number.

96. **Time** Our calendar is based on the solar year, which is $365\frac{1}{4}$ days. Use this fact to explain leap years.

97. Which of the labeled points on the number line at the right could be the graph of the product of B and C?

```
├─●──●──●─┼──●───┼────●──┤
0  A  B  C  1  D   2   E   3
```

Projects or Group Activities

98. Fill in the red circles at the right with the fractions $\frac{1}{6}$, $\frac{5}{18}$, $\frac{4}{9}$, $\frac{5}{9}$, $\frac{2}{3}$, $\frac{3}{4}$, $1\frac{1}{9}$, $1\frac{1}{2}$, and $2\frac{1}{4}$ so that the product of any row is equal to $\frac{5}{18}$. (*Note:* More than one answer is possible.)

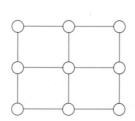

© iStockphoto.com/Janice Richard

2.7 Division of Fractions and Mixed Numbers

OBJECTIVE A *To divide fractions*

The **reciprocal of a fraction** is the fraction with the numerator and denominator interchanged.

The reciprocal of $\frac{2}{3}$ is $\frac{3}{2}$.

The process of interchanging the numerator and denominator is called **inverting a fraction.**

To find the reciprocal of a whole number, first write the whole number as a fraction with a denominator of 1. Then find the reciprocal of the fraction.

The reciprocal of 5 is $\frac{1}{5}$. $\left(\text{Think } 5 = \frac{5}{1}.\right)$

Reciprocals are used to rewrite division problems as related multiplication problems. Look at the following two problems:

$$8 \div 2 = 4 \qquad\qquad 8 \times \frac{1}{2} = 4$$

8 divided by 2 is 4. 8 times the reciprocal of 2 is 4.

"Divided by" means the same as "times the reciprocal of." Thus "÷ 2" can be replaced with "× $\frac{1}{2}$," and the answer will be the same. Fractions are divided by making this replacement.

HOW TO 1 Divide: $\dfrac{2}{3} \div \dfrac{3}{4}$

$$\frac{2}{3} \div \frac{3}{4} = \frac{2}{3} \times \frac{4}{3} = \frac{2 \cdot 4}{3 \cdot 3} = \frac{2 \cdot 2 \cdot 2}{3 \cdot 3} = \frac{8}{9}$$

- **Multiply the first fraction by the reciprocal of the second fraction.**

EXAMPLE 1

Divide: $\dfrac{5}{8} \div \dfrac{4}{9}$

Solution

$$\frac{5}{8} \div \frac{4}{9} = \frac{5}{8} \times \frac{9}{4} = \frac{5 \cdot 9}{8 \cdot 4}$$

$$= \frac{5 \cdot 3 \cdot 3}{2 \cdot 2 \cdot 2 \cdot 2 \cdot 2} = \frac{45}{32} = 1\frac{13}{32}$$

YOU TRY IT 1

Divide: $\dfrac{3}{7} \div \dfrac{2}{3}$

Your solution

EXAMPLE 2

Divide: $\dfrac{3}{5} \div \dfrac{12}{25}$

Solution

$$\frac{3}{5} \div \frac{12}{25} = \frac{3}{5} \times \frac{25}{12} = \frac{3 \cdot 25}{5 \cdot 12}$$

$$= \frac{\overset{1}{\cancel{3}} \cdot \overset{1}{\cancel{5}} \cdot 5}{\underset{1}{\cancel{5}} \cdot 2 \cdot 2 \cdot \underset{1}{\cancel{3}}} = \frac{5}{4} = 1\frac{1}{4}$$

YOU TRY IT 2

Divide: $\dfrac{3}{4} \div \dfrac{9}{10}$

Your solution

Solutions on p. S7

OBJECTIVE B *To divide whole numbers, mixed numbers, and fractions*

To divide a fraction and a whole number, first write the whole number as a fraction with a denominator of 1.

HOW TO 2 Divide: $\dfrac{3}{7} \div 5$

$$\dfrac{3}{7} \div \boxed{5} = \dfrac{3}{7} \div \boxed{\dfrac{5}{1}} = \dfrac{3}{7} \times \dfrac{1}{5} = \dfrac{3 \cdot 1}{7 \cdot 5} = \dfrac{3}{35}$$

• Write 5 with a denominator of 1. Then divide the fractions.

When a number in a quotient is a mixed number, write the mixed number as an improper fraction before dividing.

HOW TO 3 Divide: $1\dfrac{13}{15} \div 4\dfrac{4}{5}$

Write the mixed numbers as improper fractions. Then divide the fractions.

$$1\dfrac{13}{15} \div 4\dfrac{4}{5} = \dfrac{28}{15} \div \dfrac{24}{5} = \dfrac{28}{15} \times \dfrac{5}{24} = \dfrac{28 \cdot 5}{15 \cdot 24} = \dfrac{\overset{1}{2} \cdot \overset{1}{2} \cdot 7 \cdot \overset{1}{5}}{3 \cdot \underset{1}{5} \cdot \underset{1}{2} \cdot \underset{1}{2} \cdot 2 \cdot 3} = \dfrac{7}{18}$$

EXAMPLE 3

Divide $\dfrac{4}{9}$ by 6.

Solution

$$\dfrac{4}{9} \div 6 = \dfrac{4}{9} \div \dfrac{6}{1} = \dfrac{4}{9} \times \dfrac{1}{6}$$

$$= \dfrac{4 \cdot 1}{9 \cdot 6} = \dfrac{\overset{1}{2} \cdot 2}{3 \cdot 3 \cdot 2 \cdot 3} = \dfrac{2}{27}$$

YOU TRY IT 3

Divide $\dfrac{5}{7}$ by 6.

Your solution

EXAMPLE 4

Find the quotient of $\dfrac{3}{8}$ and $2\dfrac{1}{10}$.

Solution

$$\dfrac{3}{8} \div 2\dfrac{1}{10} = \dfrac{3}{8} \div \dfrac{21}{10} = \dfrac{3}{8} \times \dfrac{10}{21}$$

$$= \dfrac{3 \cdot 10}{8 \cdot 21} = \dfrac{\overset{1}{3} \cdot \overset{1}{2} \cdot 5}{2 \cdot 2 \cdot 2 \cdot \underset{1}{3} \cdot 7} = \dfrac{5}{28}$$

YOU TRY IT 4

Find the quotient of $12\dfrac{3}{5}$ and 7.

Your solution

EXAMPLE 5

Divide: $2\dfrac{3}{4} \div 1\dfrac{5}{7}$

Solution

$$2\dfrac{3}{4} \div 1\dfrac{5}{7} = \dfrac{11}{4} \div \dfrac{12}{7} = \dfrac{11}{4} \times \dfrac{7}{12} = \dfrac{11 \cdot 7}{4 \cdot 12}$$

$$= \dfrac{11 \cdot 7}{2 \cdot 2 \cdot 2 \cdot 2 \cdot 3} = \dfrac{77}{48} = 1\dfrac{29}{48}$$

YOU TRY IT 5

Divide: $3\dfrac{2}{3} \div 2\dfrac{2}{5}$

Your solution

Solutions on p. S7

EXAMPLE 6

Divide: $1\frac{13}{15} \div 4\frac{1}{5}$

Solution

$$1\frac{13}{15} \div 4\frac{1}{5} = \frac{28}{15} \div \frac{21}{5} = \frac{28}{15} \times \frac{5}{21} = \frac{28 \cdot 5}{15 \cdot 21}$$

$$= \frac{2 \cdot 2 \cdot \overset{1}{\cancel{7}} \cdot \overset{1}{\cancel{5}}}{3 \cdot \cancel{5} \cdot 3 \cdot \underset{1}{\cancel{7}}} = \frac{4}{9}$$

YOU TRY IT 6

Divide: $2\frac{5}{6} \div 8\frac{1}{2}$

Your solution

EXAMPLE 7

Divide: $4\frac{3}{8} \div 7$

Solution

$$4\frac{3}{8} \div 7 = \frac{35}{8} \div \frac{7}{1} = \frac{35}{8} \times \frac{1}{7}$$

$$= \frac{35 \cdot 1}{8 \cdot 7} = \frac{5 \cdot \overset{1}{\cancel{7}}}{2 \cdot 2 \cdot 2 \cdot \underset{1}{\cancel{7}}} = \frac{5}{8}$$

YOU TRY IT 7

Divide: $6\frac{2}{5} \div 4$

Your solution

Solutions on p. S7

OBJECTIVE C *To solve application problems*

EXAMPLE 8

A car used $15\frac{1}{2}$ gallons of gasoline on a 310-mile trip. How many miles can this car travel on 1 gallon of gasoline?

Strategy

To find the number of miles, divide the number of miles traveled by the number of gallons of gasoline used.

Solution

$$310 \div 15\frac{1}{2} = \frac{310}{1} \div \frac{31}{2}$$

$$= \frac{310}{1} \times \frac{2}{31} = \frac{310 \cdot 2}{1 \cdot 31}$$

$$= \frac{2 \cdot 5 \cdot \overset{1}{\cancel{31}} \cdot 2}{1 \cdot \underset{1}{\cancel{31}}} = \frac{20}{1} = 20$$

The car travels 20 miles on 1 gallon of gasoline.

YOU TRY IT 8

A factory worker can assemble a product in $7\frac{1}{2}$ minutes. How many products can the worker assemble in 1 hour?

Your strategy

Your solution

Solution on p. S8

EXAMPLE 9

A 12-foot board is cut into pieces $2\frac{1}{4}$ feet long for use as bookshelves. What is the length of the remaining piece after as many shelves as possible have been cut?

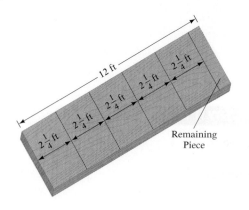

Strategy

To find the length of the remaining piece:

- Divide the total length of the board (12) by the length of each shelf $\left(2\frac{1}{4}\right)$. This will give you the number of shelves cut, with a certain fraction of a shelf left over.
- Multiply the fractional part of the result in step 1 by the length of one shelf to determine the length of the remaining piece.

Solution

$$12 \div 2\frac{1}{4} = \frac{12}{1} \div \frac{9}{4} = \frac{12}{1} \times \frac{4}{9}$$

$$= \frac{12 \cdot 4}{1 \cdot 9} = \frac{16}{3} = 5\frac{1}{3}$$

There are 5 pieces that are each $2\frac{1}{4}$ feet long.

There is 1 piece that is $\frac{1}{3}$ of $2\frac{1}{4}$ feet long.

$$\frac{1}{3} \times 2\frac{1}{4} = \frac{1}{3} \times \frac{9}{4} = \frac{1 \cdot 9}{3 \cdot 4} = \frac{3}{4}$$

The length of the piece remaining is $\frac{3}{4}$ foot.

A 16-foot board is cut into pieces $3\frac{1}{3}$ feet long for shelves for a bookcase. What is the length of the remaining piece after as many shelves as possible have been cut?

Your strategy

Your solution

2.7 EXERCISES

✔ Concept Check

For Exercises 1 to 4, find the reciprocal of the given number.

1. $\dfrac{3}{7}$ **2.** 7   **3.** $\dfrac{4}{5}$ **4.** $\dfrac{1}{6}$

5. Replace the question marks to make a true statement.

$$\frac{3}{8} \div \frac{4}{9} = \frac{3}{8} \times \frac{?}{?} = ?$$

6. Is the quotient of two proper fractions always a proper fraction?

OBJECTIVE A   *To divide fractions*

For Exercises 7 to 34, divide.

7. $\dfrac{1}{3} \div \dfrac{2}{5}$ **8.** $\dfrac{3}{7} \div \dfrac{3}{2}$ **9.** $\dfrac{3}{7} \div \dfrac{3}{7}$ **10.** $0 \div \dfrac{1}{2}$

11. $0 \div \dfrac{3}{4}$ **12.** $\dfrac{16}{33} \div \dfrac{4}{11}$ **13.** $\dfrac{5}{24} \div \dfrac{15}{36}$ **14.** $\dfrac{11}{15} \div \dfrac{1}{12}$

15. $\dfrac{1}{9} \div \dfrac{2}{3}$ **16.** $\dfrac{10}{21} \div \dfrac{5}{7}$ **17.** $\dfrac{2}{5} \div \dfrac{4}{7}$ **18.** $\dfrac{3}{8} \div \dfrac{5}{12}$

19. $\dfrac{1}{2} \div \dfrac{1}{4}$ **20.** $\dfrac{1}{3} \div \dfrac{1}{9}$ **21.** $\dfrac{1}{5} \div \dfrac{1}{10}$ **22.** $\dfrac{4}{15} \div \dfrac{2}{5}$

23. $\dfrac{7}{15} \div \dfrac{14}{5}$ **24.** $\dfrac{5}{8} \div \dfrac{15}{2}$ **25.** $\dfrac{14}{3} \div \dfrac{7}{9}$ **26.** $\dfrac{7}{4} \div \dfrac{9}{2}$

27. $\dfrac{5}{9} \div \dfrac{25}{3}$ **28.** $\dfrac{5}{16} \div \dfrac{3}{8}$ **29.** $\dfrac{2}{3} \div \dfrac{1}{3}$ **30.** $\dfrac{4}{9} \div \dfrac{1}{9}$

31. $\dfrac{5}{7} \div \dfrac{2}{7}$ **32.** $\dfrac{5}{6} \div \dfrac{1}{9}$ **33.** $\dfrac{2}{3} \div \dfrac{2}{9}$ **34.** $\dfrac{5}{12} \div \dfrac{5}{6}$

35. Divide $\dfrac{7}{8}$ by $\dfrac{3}{4}$.

36. Divide $\dfrac{7}{12}$ by $\dfrac{3}{4}$.

37. Find the quotient of $\dfrac{5}{7}$ and $\dfrac{3}{14}$.

38. Find the quotient of $\dfrac{6}{11}$ and $\dfrac{9}{32}$.

39. 📷 True or false? If a fraction has a numerator of 1, then the reciprocal of the fraction is a whole number.

40. 📷 True or false? The reciprocal of an improper fraction that is not equal to 1 is a proper fraction.

OBJECTIVE B	*To divide whole numbers, mixed numbers, and fractions*

For Exercises 41 to 79, divide.

41. $4 \div \dfrac{2}{3}$

42. $\dfrac{2}{3} \div 4$

43. $\dfrac{3}{2} \div 3$

44. $3 \div \dfrac{3}{2}$

45. $\dfrac{5}{6} \div 25$

46. $22 \div \dfrac{3}{11}$

47. $6 \div 3\dfrac{1}{3}$

48. $5\dfrac{1}{2} \div 11$

49. $6\dfrac{1}{2} \div \dfrac{1}{2}$

50. $\dfrac{3}{8} \div 2\dfrac{1}{4}$

51. $8\dfrac{1}{4} \div 2\dfrac{3}{4}$

52. $3\dfrac{5}{9} \div 32$

53. $4\dfrac{1}{5} \div 21$

54. $6\dfrac{8}{9} \div \dfrac{31}{36}$

55. $\dfrac{11}{12} \div 2\dfrac{1}{3}$

56. $\dfrac{7}{8} \div 3\dfrac{1}{4}$

57. $35 \div \dfrac{7}{24}$

58. $\dfrac{3}{8} \div 2\dfrac{3}{4}$

59. $\dfrac{11}{18} \div 2\dfrac{2}{9}$

60. $\dfrac{21}{40} \div 3\dfrac{3}{10}$

61. $2\dfrac{1}{16} \div 2\dfrac{1}{2}$

62. $7\dfrac{3}{5} \div 1\dfrac{7}{12}$

63. $1\dfrac{2}{3} \div \dfrac{3}{8}$

64. $16 \div \dfrac{2}{3}$

65. $1\dfrac{5}{8} \div 4$

66. $13\dfrac{3}{8} \div \dfrac{1}{4}$

67. $16 \div 1\dfrac{1}{2}$

68. $9 \div \dfrac{7}{8}$

69. $1\dfrac{1}{3} \div 5\dfrac{8}{9}$

70. $13\dfrac{2}{3} \div 0$

71. $82\dfrac{3}{5} \div 19\dfrac{1}{10}$

72. $45\dfrac{3}{5} \div 15$

73. $102 \div 1\dfrac{1}{2}$

74. $0 \div 3\dfrac{1}{2}$

75. $8\dfrac{2}{7} \div 1$

76. $6\dfrac{9}{16} \div 1\dfrac{3}{32}$

77. $8\dfrac{8}{9} \div 2\dfrac{13}{18}$

78. $10\dfrac{1}{5} \div 1\dfrac{7}{10}$

79. $7\dfrac{3}{8} \div 1\dfrac{27}{32}$

80. Divide $7\dfrac{7}{9}$ by $5\dfrac{5}{6}$.

81. Divide $2\dfrac{3}{4}$ by $1\dfrac{23}{32}$.

82. Find the quotient of $8\dfrac{1}{4}$ and $1\dfrac{5}{11}$.

83. Find the quotient of $\dfrac{14}{17}$ and $3\dfrac{1}{9}$.

84. True or false? The reciprocal of a mixed number is an improper fraction.

85. True or false? A fraction divided by its reciprocal is 1.

OBJECTIVE C *To solve application problems*

For Exercises 86 and 87, give your answer without actually doing a calculation.

86. Read Exercise 88. Will the requested number of boxes be greater than or less than 600?

87. Read Exercise 89. Will the requested number of servings be greater than or less than 16?

88. Consumerism Individual cereal boxes contain $\dfrac{3}{4}$ ounce of cereal. How many boxes can be filled with 600 ounces of cereal?

89. Consumerism A box of Post's Great Grains cereal costing $4 contains 16 ounces of cereal. How many $1\dfrac{1}{3}$-ounce servings are in this box?

90. Gemology A $\dfrac{5}{8}$-karat diamond was purchased for $1200. What would a similar diamond weighing 1 karat cost?

91. Real Estate The Inverness Investor Group bought $8\dfrac{1}{3}$ acres of land for $200,000. What was the cost of each acre?

92. Fuel Efficiency A car used $12\dfrac{1}{2}$ gallons of gasoline on a 275-mile trip. How many miles can the car travel on 1 gallon of gasoline?

93. Mechanics A nut moves $\dfrac{5}{32}$ inch for each turn. Find the number of turns it will take for the nut to move $1\dfrac{7}{8}$ inches.

94. Real Estate   The Hammond Company purchased $9\frac{3}{4}$ acres of land for a housing project. One and one-half acres were set aside for a park.

    a. How many acres are available for housing?

    b. How many $\frac{1}{4}$-acre parcels of land can be sold after the land for the park is set aside?

95. The Food Industry   A chef purchased a roast that weighed $10\frac{3}{4}$ pounds. After the fat was trimmed and the bone removed, the roast weighed $9\frac{1}{3}$ pounds.

    a. What was the total weight of the fat and bone?

    b. How many $\frac{1}{3}$-pound servings can be cut from the trimmed roast?

96. Carpentry   A 15-foot board is cut into pieces $3\frac{1}{2}$ feet long for a bookcase. What is the length of the piece remaining after as many shelves as possible have been cut?

97. Construction   The railing of a stairway extends onto a landing. The distance between the end posts of the railing on the landing is $22\frac{3}{4}$ inches. Five posts are to be inserted, evenly spaced, between the end posts. Each post has a square base that measures $1\frac{1}{4}$ inches. Find the distance between each pair of posts.

98. Construction   The railing of a stairway extends onto a landing. The distance between the end posts of the railing on the landing is $42\frac{1}{2}$ inches. Ten posts are to be inserted, evenly spaced, between the end posts. Each post has a square base that measures $1\frac{1}{2}$ inches. Find the distance between each pair of posts.

Critical Thinking

For Exercises 99 to 106, fill in the box to make a true statement.

99. $\dfrac{2}{3} - \square = \dfrac{1}{6}$ **100.** $\square - \dfrac{5}{8} = \dfrac{5}{24}$ **101.** $\square + \dfrac{3}{5} = 1\dfrac{1}{10}$ **102.** $\dfrac{5}{9} + \square = \dfrac{13}{18}$

103. $\dfrac{3}{4} \cdot \square = \dfrac{1}{2}$ **104.** $\square \cdot \dfrac{2}{3} = 1\dfrac{3}{4}$ **105.** $\square \div \dfrac{3}{4} = \dfrac{8}{9}$ **106.** $\dfrac{3}{4} \div \square = \dfrac{2}{3}$

107. Finances   A bank recommends that the maximum monthly payment for a home be $\frac{1}{3}$ of the owner's total monthly income. Your monthly income is \$4500. What would the bank recommend as your maximum monthly house payment?

108. ● **Sports** Researchers at Oregon State University studied the effect of grass height on the distance a struck golf ball would roll on the grass putting surface of a golf course green. For the study, plots of grass were mowed to a height of $\frac{3}{20}$ inch. This is higher than the more common heights of $\frac{1}{10}$ inch or $\frac{1}{8}$ inch used in professional golf tournaments. How much higher than the standard heights did the researchers mow the grass?

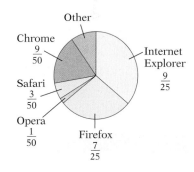

109. Board Games A wooden travel game board has hinges that allow the board to be folded in half. If the dimensions of the open board are 14 inches by 14 inches by $\frac{7}{8}$ inch, what are the dimensions of the board when it is closed?

110. Maps On a map, two cities are $4\frac{5}{8}$ inches apart. If $\frac{3}{8}$ inch on the map represents 60 miles, what is the number of miles between the two cities?

111. Publishing A page of type in a certain textbook is $7\frac{1}{2}$ inches wide. If the page is divided into three equal columns, with $\frac{3}{8}$ inch between columns, how wide is each column?

Projects or Group Activities

● **Browser Usage** The graph at the right, based on data from W3Counter, shows the market share of several Internet browsers. Use this graph for Exercises 112 to 115.

112. What total fraction of the market is represented by Internet Explorer, Firefox, and Chrome?

113. How many times more people use Safari than use Opera?

114. In 2011, there were approximately 2 billion people worldwide using the Internet. According to the graph, approximately how many people were using the Chrome browser?

115. What fraction of the world browser market do the unnamed browsers represent?

SECTION

2.8 Order, Exponents, and the Order of Operations Agreement

OBJECTIVE A *To identify the order relation between two fractions*

Point of Interest

Leonardo of Pisa, who was also called Fibonacci (c. 1175–1250), is credited with bringing the Hindu-Arabic number system to the Western world and promoting its use in place of the cumbersome Roman numeral system.

He was also influential in promoting the idea of the fraction bar. His notation, however, was very different from the notation we use today.

For instance, he wrote $\dfrac{3\ 5}{4\ 7}$ to mean $\dfrac{5}{7} + \dfrac{3}{7 \cdot 4}$, which equals $\dfrac{23}{28}$.

Recall that whole numbers can be graphed as points on the number line. Fractions can also be graphed as points on the number line.

The graph of $\frac{3}{4}$ on the number line

The number line can be used to determine the order relation between two fractions. A fraction that appears to the left of a given fraction is less than the given fraction. A fraction that appears to the right of a given fraction is greater than the given fraction.

$$\frac{1}{8} < \frac{3}{8} \qquad \frac{6}{8} > \frac{3}{8}$$

To find the order relation between two fractions with the same denominator, compare the numerators. The fraction that has the smaller numerator is the smaller fraction. When the denominators are different, begin by writing equivalent fractions with a common denominator; then compare the numerators.

HOW TO 1 Find the order relation between $\frac{11}{18}$ and $\frac{5}{8}$.

The LCD of the fractions is 72.

$$\frac{11}{18} = \frac{44}{72} \leftarrow \text{Smaller numerator}$$

$$\frac{5}{8} = \frac{45}{72} \leftarrow \text{Larger numerator}$$

$$\frac{11}{18} < \frac{5}{8} \quad \text{or} \quad \frac{5}{8} > \frac{11}{18}$$

EXAMPLE 1

Place the correct symbol, $<$ or $>$, between the two numbers.

$$\frac{5}{12} \qquad \frac{7}{18}$$

Solution

$$\frac{5}{12} = \frac{15}{36} \qquad \frac{7}{18} = \frac{14}{36}$$

$$\frac{5}{12} > \frac{7}{18}$$

YOU TRY IT 1

Place the correct symbol, $<$ or $>$, between the two numbers.

$$\frac{9}{14} \qquad \frac{13}{21}$$

Your solution

Solution on p. S8

OBJECTIVE B *To use the Order of Operations Agreement to simplify expressions*

Recall that repeated multiplication of the same number is written using an exponent.

$$\left(\frac{2}{3}\right)^4 = \frac{2}{3} \cdot \frac{2}{3} \cdot \frac{2}{3} \cdot \frac{2}{3} = \frac{2 \cdot 2 \cdot 2 \cdot 2}{3 \cdot 3 \cdot 3 \cdot 3} = \frac{16}{81}$$

The exponent 4 indicates the number of times to multiply $\frac{2}{3}$. The expression $\left(\frac{2}{3}\right)^4$ is an **exponential expression.**

The Order of Operations Agreement is used to simplify expressions containing parentheses, exponents, multiplication, division, addition, or subtraction.

Order of Operations Agreement

Step 1. Perform operations inside grouping symbols such as parentheses and fraction bars.

Step 2. Simplify exponential expressions.

Step 3. Do multiplications and divisions as they occur from left to right.

Step 4. Do additions and subtractions as they occur from left to right.

EXAMPLES

1. $\dfrac{1}{2} \cdot \left(\dfrac{4}{5} - \dfrac{1}{5}\right) = \dfrac{1}{2} \cdot \left(\dfrac{3}{5}\right)$ • Perform operations inside grouping symbols. [Step 1]

$= \dfrac{3}{10}$ • Multiply. [Step 3]

2. $\dfrac{2}{3} \cdot \left(\dfrac{3}{5}\right)^2 = \dfrac{2}{3} \cdot \dfrac{9}{25}$ • Simplify exponential expressions. [Step 2]

$= \dfrac{6}{25}$ • Multiply. [Step 3]

3. $\dfrac{1}{4} \div \dfrac{2}{5} \cdot \dfrac{2}{3} = \dfrac{1}{4} \cdot \dfrac{5}{2} \cdot \dfrac{2}{3}$ • Do multiplications and divisions from left to right. [Step 3]

$= \dfrac{5}{8} \cdot \dfrac{2}{3}$

$= \dfrac{5}{12}$

4. $\dfrac{3}{4} - \dfrac{2}{3} \cdot \dfrac{1}{2} = \dfrac{3}{4} - \dfrac{1}{3}$ • Do multiplications and divisions from left to right. [Step 3]

$= \dfrac{5}{12}$ • Do additions and subtractions from left to right. [Step 4]

HOW TO 2 Simplify: $\dfrac{14}{15} - \left(\dfrac{1}{2}\right)^2 \times \left(\dfrac{2}{3} + \dfrac{4}{5}\right)$

$\dfrac{14}{15} - \left(\dfrac{1}{2}\right)^2 \times \underbrace{\left(\dfrac{2}{3} + \dfrac{4}{5}\right)}$

1. Perform operations in parentheses.

$\dfrac{14}{15} - \underbrace{\left(\dfrac{1}{2}\right)^2} \times \dfrac{22}{15}$

2. Simplify exponential expressions.

$\dfrac{14}{15} - \underbrace{\dfrac{1}{4} \times \dfrac{22}{15}}$

3. Do multiplications and divisions as they occur from left to right.

$\underbrace{\dfrac{14}{15} - \dfrac{11}{30}}$

4. Do additions and subtractions as they occur from left to right.

$\dfrac{17}{30}$

One or more of the steps of the Order of Operations Agreement may not be needed to simplify an expression. In that case, proceed to the next step in the Order of Operations Agreement.

EXAMPLE 2

Simplify: $\left(\dfrac{3}{4}\right)^2 \div \left(\dfrac{3}{8} - \dfrac{1}{12}\right)$

Solution

$\left(\dfrac{3}{4}\right)^2 \div \left(\dfrac{3}{8} - \dfrac{1}{12}\right) = \left(\dfrac{3}{4}\right)^2 \div \left(\dfrac{7}{24}\right)$

$= \dfrac{9}{16} \div \dfrac{7}{24}$

$= \dfrac{9}{16} \cdot \dfrac{24}{7}$

$= \dfrac{27}{14}$

$= 1\dfrac{13}{14}$

YOU TRY IT 2

Simplify: $\left(\dfrac{1}{13}\right)^2 \cdot \left(\dfrac{1}{4} + \dfrac{1}{6}\right) \div \dfrac{5}{13}$

Your solution

Solution on p. S8

2.8 EXERCISES

✔ Concept Check

For Exercises 1 to 3, determine whether the shaded portion of the first figure is less than, equal to, or greater than the shaded portion of the second figure.

1.

2.

3.

4. Which expression below is equivalent to $\frac{3}{4} - \frac{1}{4} \cdot \frac{2}{3}$?

   (i) $\left(\frac{3}{4} - \frac{1}{4} \right) \cdot \frac{2}{3}$

   (ii) $\frac{3}{4} - \left(\frac{1}{4} \cdot \frac{2}{3} \right)$

OBJECTIVE A   *To identify the order relation between two fractions*

For Exercises 5 to 16, place the correct symbol, $<$ or $>$, between the two numbers.

5. $\dfrac{11}{40}$ $\dfrac{19}{40}$

6. $\dfrac{92}{103}$ $\dfrac{19}{103}$

7. $\dfrac{2}{3}$ $\dfrac{5}{7}$

8. $\dfrac{2}{5}$ $\dfrac{3}{8}$

9. $\dfrac{5}{8}$ $\dfrac{7}{12}$

10. $\dfrac{11}{16}$ $\dfrac{17}{24}$

11. $\dfrac{7}{9}$ $\dfrac{11}{12}$

12. $\dfrac{5}{12}$ $\dfrac{7}{15}$

13. $\dfrac{13}{14}$ $\dfrac{19}{21}$

14. $\dfrac{13}{18}$ $\dfrac{7}{12}$

15. $\dfrac{7}{24}$ $\dfrac{11}{30}$

16. $\dfrac{13}{36}$ $\dfrac{19}{48}$

17. 🖊 Without writing the fractions $\frac{4}{5}$ and $\frac{1}{7}$ with a common denominator, decide which fraction is larger.

OBJECTIVE B   *To use the Order of Operations Agreement to simplify expressions*

For Exercises 18 to 55, simplify.

18. $\left(\dfrac{3}{8}\right)^2$ **19.** $\left(\dfrac{5}{12}\right)^2$ **20.** $\left(\dfrac{2}{9}\right)^3$ **21.** $\left(\dfrac{1}{2}\right) \cdot \left(\dfrac{2}{3}\right)^2$

22. $\left(\dfrac{2}{3}\right) \cdot \left(\dfrac{1}{2}\right)^4$ **23.** $\left(\dfrac{1}{3}\right)^2 \cdot \left(\dfrac{3}{5}\right)^3$ **24.** $\left(\dfrac{2}{5}\right)^3 \cdot \left(\dfrac{5}{7}\right)^2$ **25.** $\left(\dfrac{5}{9}\right)^3 \cdot \left(\dfrac{18}{25}\right)^2$

26. $\dfrac{1}{2} - \dfrac{1}{3} + \dfrac{2}{3}$ **27.** $\dfrac{2}{5} + \dfrac{3}{10} - \dfrac{2}{3}$ **28.** $\dfrac{1}{3} \div \dfrac{1}{2} + \dfrac{3}{4}$

29. $\dfrac{3}{7} \cdot \dfrac{14}{15} + \dfrac{4}{5}$ **30.** $\dfrac{7}{9} - \dfrac{2}{3} \cdot \dfrac{4}{5}$ **31.** $\dfrac{5}{8} + \dfrac{1}{8} \cdot \dfrac{2}{3}$

32. $\dfrac{3}{4} \cdot \dfrac{4}{5} - \dfrac{1}{2} \cdot \dfrac{2}{3}$ **33.** $\dfrac{5}{6} \div \dfrac{2}{3} - \dfrac{3}{4} \cdot \dfrac{1}{2}$ **34.** $\dfrac{1}{3} + \dfrac{3}{5} \cdot \dfrac{4}{9} - \dfrac{1}{2}$

35. $\dfrac{7}{8} - \dfrac{2}{3} \cdot \dfrac{1}{2} + \dfrac{5}{6}$ **36.** $\dfrac{8}{9} - \dfrac{3}{4} \div \dfrac{9}{10} + \dfrac{4}{9}$ **37.** $\dfrac{5}{6} + \dfrac{1}{2} \div \dfrac{3}{4} - \dfrac{5}{8}$

38. $\left(\dfrac{3}{4}\right)^2 - \dfrac{5}{12}$ **39.** $\left(\dfrac{3}{5}\right)^3 - \dfrac{3}{25}$ **40.** $\dfrac{5}{6} \cdot \left(\dfrac{2}{3} - \dfrac{1}{6}\right) + \dfrac{7}{18}$

41. $\dfrac{3}{4} \cdot \left(\dfrac{11}{12} - \dfrac{7}{8}\right) + \dfrac{5}{16}$ **42.** $\dfrac{7}{12} - \left(\dfrac{2}{3}\right)^2 + \dfrac{5}{8}$ **43.** $\dfrac{11}{16} - \left(\dfrac{3}{4}\right)^2 + \dfrac{7}{12}$

44. $\dfrac{3}{4} \cdot \left(\dfrac{4}{9}\right)^2 + \dfrac{1}{2}$ **45.** $\dfrac{9}{10} \cdot \left(\dfrac{2}{3}\right)^3 + \dfrac{2}{3}$ **46.** $\left(\dfrac{1}{2} + \dfrac{3}{4}\right) \div \dfrac{5}{8}$

47. $\left(\dfrac{2}{3} + \dfrac{5}{6}\right) \div \dfrac{5}{9}$

48. $\dfrac{3}{8} \div \left(\dfrac{5}{12} + \dfrac{3}{8}\right)$

49. $\dfrac{7}{12} \div \left(\dfrac{2}{3} + \dfrac{5}{9}\right)$

50. $\left(\dfrac{3}{8}\right)^2 \div \left(\dfrac{3}{7} + \dfrac{3}{14}\right)$

51. $\left(\dfrac{5}{6}\right)^2 \div \left(\dfrac{5}{12} + \dfrac{2}{3}\right)$

52. $\dfrac{2}{5} \div \dfrac{3}{8} \cdot \dfrac{4}{5}$

53. $\left(\dfrac{1}{6} + \dfrac{1}{2}\right)^2 + \dfrac{2}{3}$

54. $\left(\dfrac{7}{8} - \dfrac{1}{2}\right)^2 - \dfrac{1}{16}$

55. $\dfrac{5}{6} + \left(\dfrac{3}{4} - \dfrac{1}{2}\right)^2$

56. 🔲 Insert parentheses into the expression $\dfrac{2}{9} \cdot \dfrac{5}{6} + \dfrac{3}{4} \div \dfrac{3}{5}$ so that **a.** the first operation to be performed is addition and **b.** the first operation to be performed is division.

Critical Thinking

57. ⬤ **The Food Industry** The table at the right shows the results of a survey that asked fast-food patrons their criteria for choosing where to go for fast food. For example, 3 out of every 25 people surveyed said that speed of service was most important in choosing a fast-food restaurant.
  a. According to the survey, do more people choose a fast-food restaurant on the basis of location or quality of the food?
  b. Which criterion was cited by the most people?

Fast-Food Patrons' Top Criteria for Choosing Fast-Food Restaurants	
Food quality	$\dfrac{1}{4}$
Location	$\dfrac{13}{50}$
Menu	$\dfrac{4}{25}$
Price	$\dfrac{2}{25}$
Speed	$\dfrac{3}{25}$
Other	$\dfrac{13}{100}$

Source: Maritz Marketing Research, Inc.

Projects or Group Activities

For Exercises 58 to 60, insert parentheses into the expression $\dfrac{7}{8} + \dfrac{2}{3} \cdot \dfrac{1}{2} + \dfrac{5}{6}$ so the value of the expression is the given number.

58. $1\dfrac{55}{72}$

59. $1\dfrac{29}{48}$

60. $2\dfrac{1}{24}$

CHAPTER

2   Summary

Key Words

A number that is a multiple of two or more numbers is a **common multiple** of those numbers. The **least common multiple (LCM)** of two or more numbers is the smallest common multiple of the numbers. [2.1A, p. 66]	

Examples

12, 24, 36, 48, . . . are common multiples of 4 and 6.

The LCM of 4 and 6 is 12.

A number that is a factor of two or more numbers is a **common factor** of those numbers. The **greatest common factor (GCF)** of two or more numbers is the largest common factor of the numbers. [2.1B, p. 67]

The common factors of 12 and 16 are 1, 2, and 4.

The GCF of 12 and 16 is 4.

A **fraction** can represent the number of equal parts of a whole. In a fraction, the **fraction bar** separates the **numerator** and the **denominator**. [2.2A, p. 70]

In the fraction $\frac{3}{4}$, the numerator is 3 and the denominator is 4.

In a **proper fraction,** the numerator is smaller than the denominator; a proper fraction is a number less than 1. In an **improper fraction,** the numerator is greater than or equal to the denominator; an improper fraction is a number greater than or equal to 1. A **mixed number** is a number greater than 1 with a whole-number part and a fractional part. [2.2A, p. 70]

$\frac{2}{5}$ is proper fraction.

$\frac{7}{6}$ is an improper fraction.

$4\frac{1}{10}$ is a mixed number; 4 is the whole-number part and $\frac{1}{10}$ is the fractional part.

Equal fractions with different denominators are called **equivalent fractions.** [2.3A, p. 74]

$\frac{3}{4}$ and $\frac{6}{8}$ are equivalent fractions.

A fraction is in **simplest form** when the numerator and denominator have no common factors other than 1. [2.3B, p. 75]

The fraction $\frac{11}{12}$ is in simplest form.

The **reciprocal** of a fraction is the fraction with the numerator and denominator interchanged. [2.7A, p. 105]

The reciprocal of $\frac{3}{8}$ is $\frac{8}{3}$.

The reciprocal of 5 is $\frac{1}{5}$.

Essential Rules and Procedures

To find the LCM of two or more numbers, find the prime factorization of each number and write the factorization of each number in a table. Circle the greatest product in each column. The LCM is the product of the circled numbers. [2.1A, p. 66]

Examples

	2	3
12 =	$2 \cdot 2$	3
18 =	2	$3 \cdot 3$

The LCM of 12 and 18 is
$2 \cdot 2 \cdot 3 \cdot 3 = 36$.

To find the GCF of two or more numbers, find the prime factorization of each number and write the factorization of each number in a table. Circle the least product in each column that does not have a blank. The GCF is the product of the circled numbers. [2.1B, p. 67]

	2	3
$12 =$	$2 \cdot 2$	③
$18 =$	②	$3 \cdot 3$

The GCF of 12 and 18 is $2 \cdot 3 = 6$.

To write an improper fraction as a mixed number or a whole number, divide the numerator by the denominator. [2.2B, p. 71]

$$\frac{29}{6} = 29 \div 6 = 4\frac{5}{6}$$

To write a mixed number as an improper fraction, multiply the denominator of the fractional part of the mixed number by the whole-number part. Add this product and the numerator of the fractional part. The sum is the numerator of the improper fraction. The denominator remains the same. [2.2B, p. 71]

$$3\frac{2}{5} = \frac{5 \times 3 + 2}{5} = \frac{17}{5}$$

To find equivalent fractions by raising to higher terms, multiply the numerator and denominator of the fraction by the same number. [2.3A, p. 74]

$$\frac{3}{4} = \frac{3 \cdot 5}{4 \cdot 5} = \frac{15}{20}$$

$\frac{3}{4}$ and $\frac{15}{20}$ are equivalent fractions.

To write a fraction in simplest form, write the prime factorization of the numerator and denominator of the fraction; then eliminate the common factors. [2.3B, p. 75]

$$\frac{30}{45} = \frac{2 \cdot \overset{1}{\cancel{3}} \cdot \overset{1}{\cancel{5}}}{\underset{1}{\cancel{3}} \cdot 3 \cdot \underset{1}{\cancel{5}}} = \frac{2}{3}$$

To add fractions with the same denominator, add the numerators and place the sum over the common denominator. [2.4A, p. 78]

$$\frac{5}{12} + \frac{11}{12} = \frac{16}{12} = 1\frac{4}{12} = 1\frac{1}{3}$$

To add fractions with different denominators, first rewrite the fractions as equivalent fractions with a common denominator. (The least common denominator is the LCM of the denominators of the fractions.) Then add the fractions. [2.4B, p. 78]

$$\frac{1}{4} + \frac{2}{5} = \frac{5}{20} + \frac{8}{20} = \frac{13}{20}$$

To subtract fractions with the same denominator, subtract the numerators and place the difference over the common denominator. [2.5A, p. 87]

$$\frac{9}{16} - \frac{5}{16} = \frac{4}{16} = \frac{1}{4}$$

To subtract fractions with different denominators, first rewrite the fractions as equivalent fractions with a common denominator. (The least common denominator is the LCM of the denominators of the fractions.) Then subtract the fractions. [2.5B, p. 87]

$$\frac{2}{3} - \frac{7}{16} = \frac{32}{48} - \frac{21}{48} = \frac{11}{48}$$

To multiply two fractions, multiply the numerators; this is the numerator of the product. Multiply the denominators; this is the denominator of the product. [2.6A, p. 97]

$$\frac{3}{4} \cdot \frac{2}{9} = \frac{3 \cdot 2}{4 \cdot 9} = \frac{\overset{1}{\cancel{3}} \cdot \overset{1}{\cancel{2}}}{2 \cdot 2 \cdot \underset{1}{\cancel{3}} \cdot 3} = \frac{1}{6}$$

To divide two fractions, multiply the first fraction by the reciprocal of the second fraction. [2.7A, p. 105]

$$\frac{8}{15} \div \frac{4}{5} = \frac{8}{15} \cdot \frac{5}{4} = \frac{8 \cdot 5}{15 \cdot 4}$$

$$= \frac{2 \cdot 2 \cdot 2 \cdot \overset{1}{\cancel{5}}}{3 \cdot \underset{1}{\cancel{5}} \cdot \underset{1}{\cancel{2}} \cdot \underset{1}{\cancel{2}}} = \frac{2}{3}$$

To find the order relation between two fractions with the same denominator, compare the numerators. The fraction that has the smaller numerator is the smaller fraction. [2.8A, p. 114]

$$\frac{17}{25} \leftarrow \text{Smaller numerator}$$

$$\frac{19}{25} \leftarrow \text{Larger numerator}$$

$$\frac{17}{25} < \frac{19}{25}$$

To find the order relation between two fractions with different denominators, first rewrite the fractions with a common denominator. The fraction that has the smaller numerator is the smaller fraction. [2.8A, p. 114]

$$\frac{3}{5} = \frac{24}{40} \qquad \frac{5}{8} = \frac{25}{40}$$

$$\frac{24}{40} < \frac{25}{40}$$

$$\frac{3}{5} < \frac{5}{8}$$

Order of Operations Agreement [2.8B, p. 115]

Step 1. Perform operations inside grouping symbols.
Step 2. Simplify exponential expressions.
Step 3. Do multiplications and divisions as they occur from left to right.
Step 4. Do additions and subtractions as they occur from left to right.

$$\left(\frac{1}{3}\right)^2 + \left(\frac{5}{6} - \frac{7}{12}\right) \cdot (4)$$

$$= \left(\frac{1}{3}\right)^2 + \left(\frac{1}{4}\right) \cdot (4)$$

$$= \frac{1}{9} + \left(\frac{1}{4}\right) \cdot (4)$$

$$= \frac{1}{9} + 1 = 1\frac{1}{9}$$

CHAPTER

2   Review Exercises

1. Write $\frac{30}{45}$ in simplest form.

2. Simplify: $\left(\frac{3}{4}\right)^3 \cdot \frac{20}{27} - \frac{1}{8}$

3. Express the shaded portion of the circles as an improper fraction.

4. Write an equivalent fraction with the given denominator.

$$\frac{8}{11} = \frac{}{44}$$

5. Place the correct symbol, $<$ or $>$, between the two numbers.

$$\frac{11}{18} \qquad \frac{17}{24}$$

6. Subtract: $\begin{aligned} & 18\frac{1}{6} \\ -&3\frac{5}{7} \\ \hline \end{aligned}$

7. Simplify: $\frac{2}{7}\left(\frac{5}{8} - \frac{1}{3}\right) \div \frac{3}{5}$

8. Multiply: $2\frac{1}{3} \times 3\frac{7}{8}$

9. Divide: $1\frac{1}{3} \div \frac{2}{3}$

10. Find $\frac{17}{24}$ decreased by $\frac{3}{16}$.

11. Divide: $8\frac{2}{3} \div 2\frac{3}{5}$

12. Find the GCF of 20 and 48.

13. Write an equivalent fraction with the given denominator.

$$\frac{2}{3} = \frac{}{36}$$

14. What is $\frac{15}{28}$ divided by $\frac{5}{7}$?

15. Find the total of $\frac{2}{3}$, $\frac{5}{6}$, and $\frac{2}{9}$.

16. Multiply: $2\frac{1}{4} \times 7\frac{1}{3}$

17. Find the LCM of 18 and 12.

18. Write $\frac{16}{44}$ in simplest form.

19. Add: $\dfrac{3}{8} + \dfrac{5}{8} + \dfrac{1}{8}$

20. What is $\dfrac{11}{50}$ multiplied by $\dfrac{25}{44}$?

21. Add: $4\dfrac{4}{9} + 2\dfrac{1}{6} + 11\dfrac{17}{27}$

22. Find the GCF of 15 and 25.

23. Write $\dfrac{17}{5}$ as a mixed number.

24. Simplify: $\left(\dfrac{4}{5} - \dfrac{2}{3}\right)^2 \div \dfrac{4}{15}$

25. Add: $\dfrac{3}{8} + 1\dfrac{2}{3} + 3\dfrac{5}{6}$

26. Find the LCM of 18 and 27.

27. Subtract: $\dfrac{11}{18} - \dfrac{5}{18}$

28. Write $2\dfrac{5}{7}$ as an improper fraction.

29. Divide: $\dfrac{5}{6} \div \dfrac{5}{12}$

30. Multiply: $\dfrac{5}{12} \times \dfrac{4}{25}$

31. Subtract: $\begin{array}{r} 16 \\ -\ 5\dfrac{7}{8} \\ \hline \end{array}$

32. Express the shaded portion of the circles as a mixed number.

33. **Meteorology** During 3 months of the rainy season, $5\dfrac{7}{8}$, $6\dfrac{2}{3}$, and $8\dfrac{3}{4}$ inches of rain fell. Find the total rainfall for the 3 months.

34. **Real Estate** A home building contractor bought $4\dfrac{2}{3}$ acres of land for $168,000. What was the cost of each acre?

35. **Sports** A 15-mile race has three checkpoints. The first checkpoint is $4\dfrac{1}{2}$ miles from the starting point. The second checkpoint is $5\dfrac{3}{4}$ miles from the first checkpoint. How many miles is the second checkpoint from the finish line?

36. **Fuel Efficiency** A compact car gets 36 miles on each gallon of gasoline. How many miles can the car travel on $6\dfrac{3}{4}$ gallons of gasoline?

CHAPTER

2   TEST

1. Multiply: $\dfrac{9}{11} \times \dfrac{44}{81}$

2. Find the GCF of 24 and 80.

3. Divide: $\dfrac{5}{9} \div \dfrac{7}{18}$

4. Simplify: $\left(\dfrac{3}{4}\right)^2 \div \left(\dfrac{2}{3} + \dfrac{5}{6}\right) - \dfrac{1}{12}$

5. Write $9\dfrac{4}{5}$ as an improper fraction.

6. What is $5\dfrac{2}{3}$ multiplied by $1\dfrac{7}{17}$?

7. Write $\dfrac{40}{64}$ in simplest form.

8. Place the correct symbol, $<$ or $>$, between the two numbers.
$$\dfrac{3}{8} \qquad \dfrac{5}{12}$$

9. Simplify: $\left(\dfrac{1}{4}\right)^3 \div \left(\dfrac{1}{8}\right)^2 - \dfrac{1}{6}$

10. Find the LCM of 24 and 40.

11. Subtract: $\dfrac{17}{24} - \dfrac{11}{24}$

12. Write $\dfrac{18}{5}$ as a mixed number.

13. Find the quotient of $6\dfrac{2}{3}$ and $3\dfrac{1}{6}$.

14. Write an equivalent fraction with the given denominator.
$$\dfrac{5}{8} = \dfrac{}{72}$$

15. Add: $\dfrac{5}{6}$
$\dfrac{7}{9}$
$+\dfrac{1}{15}$
_____

16. Subtract: $23\dfrac{1}{8}$
$-\;9\dfrac{9}{44}$
_____

17. What is $\dfrac{9}{16}$ minus $\dfrac{5}{12}$?

18. Simplify: $\left(\dfrac{2}{3}\right)^{4}\cdot\dfrac{27}{32}+\dfrac{1}{32}$

19. Add: $\dfrac{7}{12}+\dfrac{11}{12}+\dfrac{5}{12}$

20. What is $12\dfrac{5}{12}$ more than $9\dfrac{17}{20}$?

21. Express the shaded portion of the circles as an improper fraction.

22. Compensation   An electrician earns $240 for each day worked. What is the total of the electrician's earnings for working $3\dfrac{1}{2}$ days?

23. Real Estate   Grant Miura bought $7\dfrac{1}{4}$ acres of land for a housing project. One and three-fourths acres were set aside for a park, and the remaining land was developed into $\dfrac{1}{2}$-acre lots. How many lots were available for sale?

24. Architecture   A scale of $\dfrac{1}{2}$ inch to 1 foot is used to draw the plans for a house. The scale measurements for three walls are given in the table at the right. Complete the table to determine the actual wall lengths for the three walls A, B, and C.

Wall	Scale	Actual Wall Length
A	$6\dfrac{1}{4}$ in.	?
B	9 in.	?
C	$7\dfrac{7}{8}$ in.	?

25. Meteorology   In 3 successive months, the rainfall measured $11\dfrac{1}{2}$ inches, $7\dfrac{5}{8}$ inches, and $2\dfrac{1}{3}$ inches. Find the total rainfall for the 3 months.

Cumulative Review Exercises

1. Round 290,496 to the nearest thousand.

2. Subtract:
$$390,047 - 98,769$$

3. Find the product of 926 and 79.

4. Divide: $57\overline{)30,792}$

5. Simplify: $4 \cdot (6 - 3) \div 6 - 1$

6. Find the prime factorization of 44.

7. Find the LCM of 30 and 42.

8. Find the GCF of 60 and 80.

9. Write $7\frac{2}{3}$ as an improper fraction.

10. Write $\frac{25}{4}$ as a mixed number.

11. Write an equivalent fraction with the given denominator.
$$\frac{5}{16} = \frac{}{48}$$

12. Write $\frac{24}{60}$ in simplest form.

13. What is $\frac{9}{16}$ more than $\frac{7}{12}$?

14. Add:
$$3\frac{7}{8}$$
$$7\frac{5}{12}$$
$$+ 2\frac{15}{16}$$

15. Find $\frac{3}{8}$ less than $\frac{11}{12}$.

16. Subtract:
$$5\frac{1}{6}$$
$$-3\frac{7}{18}$$

17. Multiply: $\dfrac{3}{8} \times \dfrac{14}{15}$

18. Multiply: $3\dfrac{1}{8} \times 2\dfrac{2}{5}$

19. Divide: $\dfrac{7}{16} \div \dfrac{5}{12}$

20. Find the quotient of $6\dfrac{1}{8}$ and $2\dfrac{1}{3}$.

21. Simplify: $\left(\dfrac{1}{2}\right)^{3} \cdot \dfrac{8}{9}$

22. Simplify: $\left(\dfrac{1}{2} + \dfrac{1}{3}\right) \div \left(\dfrac{2}{5}\right)^{2}$

23. Banking Molly O'Brien had $1359 in a checking account. During the week, Molly wrote checks for $128, $54, and $315. Find the amount in the checking account at the end of the week.

24. Entertainment The tickets for a movie were $10 for an adult and $4 for a student. Find the total income from the sale of 87 adult tickets and 135 student tickets.

25. Measurement Find the total weight of three packages that weigh $1\dfrac{1}{2}$ pounds, $7\dfrac{7}{8}$ pounds, and $2\dfrac{2}{3}$ pounds.

26. Carpentry A board $2\dfrac{5}{8}$ feet long is cut from a board $7\dfrac{1}{3}$ feet long. What is the length of the remaining piece?

27. Fuel Efficiency A car travels 27 miles on each gallon of gasoline. How many miles can the car travel on $8\dfrac{1}{3}$ gallons of gasoline?

28. Real Estate Jimmy Santos purchased $10\dfrac{1}{3}$ acres of land to build a housing development. Jimmy donated 2 acres for a park. How many $\dfrac{1}{3}$-acre parcels can be sold from the remaining land?

Decimals

Focus on Success

Do you have trouble with word problems? Word problems show the variety of ways in which math can be used. The solution of every word problem can be broken down into two steps: Strategy and Solution. The Strategy consists of reading the problem, writing down what is known and unknown, and devising a plan to find the unknown. The Solution often consists of performing a calculation and checking the solution. (See Word Problems, page AIM–10).

© iStockphoto.com/Francesco Ridolfi

Prep Test

Are you ready to succeed in this chapter? Take the Prep Test below to find out if you are ready to learn the new material.

1. Express the shaded portion of the rectangle as a fraction.

2. Round 36,852 to the nearest hundred.

3. Write 4791 in words.

4. Write six thousand eight hundred forty-two in standard form.

For Exercises 5 to 8, add, subtract, multiply, or divide.

5. $37 + 8892 + 465$

6. $2403 - 765$

7. 844×91

8. $23\overline{)6412}$

3.1 Introduction to Decimals

OBJECTIVE A *To write decimals in standard form and in words*

Take Note

In decimal notation, the part of the number that appears to the left of the decimal point is the **whole-number part.** The part of the number that appears to the right of the decimal point is the **decimal part. The decimal point** separates the whole-number part from the decimal part.

Point of Interest

The decimal point did not make its appearance until the early 1600s. The original notation used subscripts with circles around them after each digit: 0 for ones, 1 for tenths (called "primes"), 2 for hundredths (called "seconds"), 3 for thousandths ("thirds"), and so on. For example, 1.375 would have been written

1   3   7   5
⓪ ① ② ③

The price tag on a sweater reads $61.88. The number 61.88 is in **decimal notation.** A number written in decimal notation is often called simply a **decimal.**

A number written in decimal notation has three parts.

61	.	88
Whole-number part	**Decimal point**	**Decimal part**

The decimal part of the number represents a number less than 1. For example, $.88 is less than $1. The decimal point (.) separates the whole-number part from the decimal part.

The position of a digit in a decimal determines the digit's place value. The place-value chart is extended to the right to show the place values of digits to the right of a decimal point.

In the decimal 458.302719, the position of the digit 7 determines that its place value is ten-thousandths.

To write a decimal in words, write the decimal part of the number as though it were a whole number, and then name the place value of the last digit.

0.9684   Nine thousand six hundred eighty-four ten-thousandths

The decimal point in a decimal is read as "and."

372.516   Three hundred seventy-two and five hundred sixteen thousandths

To write a decimal in standard form when it is written in words, write the whole-number part, replace the word *and* with a decimal point, and write the decimal part so that the last digit is in the given place-value position.

Four and twenty-three <u>hundredths</u>
3 is in the hundredths place.   4.2<u>3</u>

When writing a decimal in standard form, you may need to insert zeros after the decimal point so that the last digit is in the given place-value position.

Ninety-one and eight <u>thousandths</u>

8 is in the thousandths place.

Insert two zeros so that the 8 is in the thousandths place.

91.00<u>8</u>

Sixty-five <u>ten-thousandths</u>

5 is in the ten-thousandths place.

Insert two zeros so that the 5 is in the ten-thousandths place.

0.006<u>5</u>

EXAMPLE 1

Name the place value of the digit 8 in the number 45.687.

Solution

The digit 8 is in the hundredths place.

YOU TRY IT 1

Name the place value of the digit 4 in the number 907.1342.

Your solution

EXAMPLE 2

Write 293.50816 in words.

Solution

Two hundred ninety-three and fifty thousand eight hundred sixteen hundred-thousandths

YOU TRY IT 2

Write 55.6083 in words.

Your solution

EXAMPLE 3

Write twenty-three and two hundred forty-seven millionths in standard form.

Solution

23.000247 • **7 is in the millionths place.**

YOU TRY IT 3

Write eight hundred six and four hundred ninety-one hundred-thousandths in standard form.

Your solution

Solutions on p. S8

OBJECTIVE B   *To round a decimal to a given place value*

In general, rounding decimals is similar to rounding whole numbers except that the digits to the right of the given place value are dropped instead of being replaced by zeros.

If the digit to the right of the given place value is less than 5, that digit and all digits to the right are dropped.

Round 6.9237 to the nearest hundredth.

```
        ┌── Given place value (hundredths)
6.9237
          └── 3 < 5   Drop the digits 3 and 7.
```

6.9237 rounded to the nearest hundredth is 6.92.

If the digit to the right of the given place value is greater than or equal to 5, increase the digit in the given place value by 1, and drop all digits to its right.

Round 12.385 to the nearest tenth.

```
        ┌── Given place value (tenths)
12.385
          └── 8 > 5   Increase 3 by 1 and drop all
                      digits to the right of 3.
```

12.385 rounded to the nearest tenth is 12.4.

HOW TO 1   Round 0.46972 to the nearest thousandth.

```
      ┌── Given place value (thousandths)
0.46972
        └── 7 > 5   Round up by adding 1 to the 9 (9 + 1 = 10).
                    Carry the 1 to the hundredths place (6 + 1 = 7).
```

0.46972 rounded to the nearest thousandth is 0.470.

EXAMPLE 4

Round 0.9375 to the nearest thousandth.

Solution

```
        ┌── Given place value
0.9375
          └── 5 = 5
```

0.9375 rounded to the nearest thousandth is 0.938.

EXAMPLE 5

Round 2.5963 to the nearest hundredth.

Solution

```
        ┌── Given place value
2.5963
          └── 6 > 5
```

2.5963 rounded to the nearest hundredth is 2.60.

YOU TRY IT 4

Round 3.675849 to the nearest ten-thousandth.

Your solution

YOU TRY IT 5

Round 48.907 to the nearest tenth.

Your solution

Solutions on p. S8

EXAMPLE 6

Round 72.416 to the nearest whole number.

Solution   ┌─ Given place value

72.416

        └─ 4 < 5

72.416 rounded to the nearest whole number is 72.

YOU TRY IT 6

Round 31.8652 to the nearest whole number.

Your solution

Solution on p. S8

OBJECTIVE C   *To compare decimals*

Point of Interest
The idea that all fractions
should be represented
using decimals was first
suggested in 1585 in Simon
Stevin's publication *De
Thiende.* Stevin claimed that
such a system would make
calculations much easier for
merchants and scientists.

There is a relationship between numbers written in decimal notation and fractions.

7 tenths	59 hundredths	19 thousandths	27 ten-thousandths
$0.7 = \dfrac{7}{10}$	$0.59 = \dfrac{59}{100}$	$0.019 = \dfrac{19}{1000}$	$0.0027 = \dfrac{27}{10,000}$

This relationship can be used to compare two decimals.

HOW TO 2   Place the correct symbol, < or >, between the numbers.
0.037   0.04

	0.037	0.04
Write the numbers as fractions.	$\dfrac{37}{1000}$	$\dfrac{4}{100}$
Write the fractions with a common denominator.	$\dfrac{37}{1000}$	$\dfrac{40}{1000}$
Compare the fractions.	$\dfrac{37}{1000} <$	$\dfrac{40}{1000}$

0.037   <   0.04

EXAMPLE 7

Place the correct symbol, < or >, between the
numbers.
0.02   0.0135

Solution

0.02	0.0135	
$\dfrac{2}{100}$	$\dfrac{135}{10,000}$	• **Write the numbers as fractions.**
$\dfrac{200}{10,000}$	$\dfrac{135}{10,000}$	• **Write the fractions with a common denominator.**
$\dfrac{200}{10,000} >$	$\dfrac{135}{10,000}$	• **Compare the fractions.**

0.02   >   0.0135

YOU TRY IT 7

Place the correct symbol, < or >, between the
numbers.
0.15   0.107

Your solution

Solution on p. S8

3.1 EXERCISES

✔ Concept Check

For Exercises 1 to 4, name the place value of the digit 5.

1. 76.31587 **2.** 291.508 **3.** 432.09157 **4.** 0.0000853

For Exercises 5 to 7, write the fraction as a decimal.

5. $\dfrac{3}{10}$ **6.** $\dfrac{87}{100}$ **7.** $\dfrac{853}{1000}$

For Exercises 8 to 10, write the decimal as a fraction.

8. 0.1 **9.** 0.59 **10.** 0.601

OBJECTIVE A   *To write decimals in standard form and in words*

For Exercises 11 to 19, write the number in words.

11. 0.37 **12.** 25.6 **13.** 9.4

14. 1.004 **15.** 0.0053 **16.** 41.108

17. 0.045 **18.** 3.157 **19.** 26.04

For Exercises 20 to 27, write the number in standard form.

20. Six hundred seventy-two thousandths

21. Three and eight hundred six ten-thousandths

22. Nine and four hundred seven ten-thousandths

23. Four hundred seven and three hundredths

24. Six hundred twelve and seven hundred four thousandths

25. Two hundred forty-six and twenty-four thousandths

26. Two thousand sixty-seven and nine thousand two ten-thousandths

27. Seventy-three and two thousand six hundred eighty-four hundred-thousandths

28. Suppose the first nonzero digit to the right of the decimal point in a decimal number is in the hundredths place. If the number has three consecutive nonzero digits to the right of the decimal point, and all other digits are zero, what place value names the number?

OBJECTIVE B   *To round a decimal to a given place value*

For Exercises 29 to 46, round the number to the given place value.

29. 6.249   Tenths

30. 5.398   Tenths

31. 21.007   Tenths

32. 30.0092   Tenths

33. 18.40937   Hundredths

34. 413.5972   Hundredths

35. 72.4983   Hundredths

36. 6.061745   Thousandths

37. 936.2905   Thousandths

38. 96.8027   Whole number

39. 47.3192   Whole number

40. 5439.83   Whole number

41. 7014.96   Whole number

42. 0.023591   Ten-thousandths

43. 2.975268   Hundred-thousandths

44. 57.964   Tenths

45. 699.723   Whole number

46. 20.99693   Hundredths

47. **Measurement**   A nickel weighs about 0.1763668 ounce. Find the weight of a nickel to the nearest hundredth of an ounce.

48. **Science**   The weight of a gallon of water varies as the temperature of the water changes. At 212°F, a gallon of water weighs 7.9957 pounds. What is the weight of this gallon of water to the nearest tenth of a pound?

49. **Sports**   Runners in the Boston Marathon run a distance of 26.21875 miles. To the nearest tenth of a mile, find the distance that an entrant who completes the Boston Marathon runs.

John Kropewnicki/Shutterstock.com

For Exercises 50 and 51, give an example of a decimal number that satisfies the given condition.

50. The number rounded to the nearest hundredth is equal to the number rounded to the nearest thousandth.

51. The number rounded to the nearest tenth is greater than the number rounded to the nearest hundredth.

OBJECTIVE C   *To compare decimals*

Place the correct symbol, $<$ or $>$, between the two numbers.

52. 0.107   0.124

53. 0.278   0.203

54. 0.004   0.003

55. 0.045   0.038

56. 0.045   0.1

57. 0.037   0.13

58. 0.078   0.0095

59. 0.031   0.00987

60. 0.00765   0.0997

61. 0.02883   0.0305

62. 0.1008   0.09673

63. 0.0072   0.0008294

Critical Thinking

64. Indicate which digits of the number, if any, need not be entered on a calculator.
a. 1.500   **b.** 0.908   **c.** 60.07   **d.** 0.0032

65. Find a number between each pair of numbers.
a. Between 0.1 and 0.2
b. Between 1 and 1.1
c. Between 0 and 0.005

Projects or Group Activities

66. The time it takes a computer to add two numbers and the time it takes some atomic events in physics to occur are small fractions of a second. Find the meaning of a *nanosecond* and a *picosecond*. Tell which is the shorter period of time. Give examples of events that occur in nanoseconds and in picoseconds.

3.2   Addition of Decimals

OBJECTIVE A   *To add decimals*

To add decimals, write the numbers so that the decimal points are on a vertical line. As shown in the place value chart below, this keeps like place values in the same column. Add as for whole numbers, and write the decimal point in the sum directly below the decimal points in the addends.

HOW TO 1   Add: 0.237 + 4.9 + 27.32

Note that by placing the decimal points on a vertical line, we make sure that digits of the same place value are added.

0.237 + 4.9 + 27.32 = 32.457

EXAMPLE 1

Find the sum of 42.3, 162.903, and 65.0729.

Solution

$$
\begin{array}{r}
\overset{1\,1\,1}{42.3} \\
162.903 \\
+\ 65.0729 \\
\hline
270.2759
\end{array}
$$

• **Place the decimal points on a vertical line.**

YOU TRY IT 1

Find the sum of 4.62, 27.9, and 0.62054.

Your solution

EXAMPLE 2

Add: 0.83 + 7.942 + 15

Solution

$$
\begin{array}{r}
\overset{1\,1}{0.83} \\
7.942 \\
+\ 15. \\
\hline
23.772
\end{array}
$$

YOU TRY IT 2

Add: 6.05 + 12 + 0.374

Your solution

Solutions on p. S9

ESTIMATION: Estimating the Sum of Two or More Decimals

Calculate 23.037 + 16.7892. Then use estimation to determine whether the sum is reasonable.

Add to find the exact sum.

To estimate the sum, round each number to the same place value. Here we have rounded to the nearest whole number. Then add. The estimated answer is 40, which is very close to the exact sum, 39.8262.

23.037 **+** 16.7892 **=** 39.8262

$$
\begin{array}{r}
23.037 \approx\ \ 23 \\
+16.7892 \approx +17 \\
\hline
40
\end{array}
$$

OBJECTIVE B *To solve application problems*

🌑 During a recent month, U.S. Internet users watched an average of 889.1 minutes (14.8 hours) of video on the Internet. The table at the right shows how much video content was watched per viewer on some popular Internet sites during that month. Use this table for Example 3 and You Try It 3.

Online Video Content Viewing	
Internet Site	Minutes Watched per Viewer
Google	275.6
AOL	39.2
Yahoo! sites	42.1
Facebook	19.2
Hulu	215.5
Microsoft	47.2

Source: comScore

EXAMPLE 3

What is the total number of minutes watched per viewer for the three most-watched Internet sites listed in the table?

Strategy

To find the total number of minutes:
• Read the table to determine the three largest numbers.
• Add the numbers.

Solution

The three largest numbers are 275.6, 215.5, and 47.2. The sum of the numbers is

$$275.6 + 215.5 + 47.2 = 538.3$$

The total number of minutes watched per viewer for the three sites is 538.3 minutes.

YOU TRY IT 3

Determine the total number of minutes watched per viewer by Internet users on Facebook.com and Hulu.

Your strategy

Your solution

EXAMPLE 4

Dan Burhoe earned a salary of $210.48 for working 3 days this week as a food server. He also received $82.75, $75.80, and $99.25 in tips during the 3 days. Find his total income for the 3 days of work.

Strategy

To find the total income, add the tips (82.75, 75.80, and 99.25) to the salary (210.48).

Solution

$210.48 + 82.75 + 75.80 + 99.25 = 468.28$

Dan's total income for the 3 days of work was $468.28.

YOU TRY IT 4

Anita Khavari earns a monthly salary of $875 as an insurance agent. During the past month, she received commissions of $985.80, $791.46, $829.75, and $635.42. Find her total income for the past month.

Your strategy

Your solution

Solutions on p. S9

3.2 EXERCISES

✔ Concept Check

1. ▧ When adding decimals, why is it necessary to write the numbers so that the decimal points line up?

2. Without adding, determine whether the following sums are equal.

   $3.450 + 29.000 + 126.008$ $3.45 + 29 + 126.008$

OBJECTIVE A   *To add decimals*

For Exercises 3 to 14, add.

3. $16.008 + 2.0385 + 132.06$

4. $17.32 + 1.0579 + 16.5$

5. $1.792 + 67 + 27.0526$

6. $8.772 + 1.09 + 26.5027$

7. $3.02 + 62.7 + 3.924$

8. $9.06 + 4.976 + 59.6$

9. $82.006 + 9.95 + 0.927$

10. $0.826 + 8.76 + 79.005$

11. $4.307 + 99.82 + 9.078$

12. $4.9257 + 27.05 + 9.0063$

13. $8.72 + 99.073 + 2.9736$

14. $62.4 + 9.827 + 692.44$

15. Find the sum of $0.0944 + 1.5522$.

16. What is the total of 0.4117 and 5.355?

17. Find 99.552 more than 8.09.

18. Find the sum of 22.877 and 0.001776.

▦ For Exercises 19 to 22, use a calculator to add. Then round the numbers to the nearest whole number and use estimation to determine whether your sum is reasonable.

19.	**20.**	**21.**	**22.**
219.9	342.42	678.92	823.9
0.872	89.625	97.6	82.65
+ 13.42	+ 176.2	+ 5.423	+ 46.923

23. ▧ If none of the addends of a decimal addition problem is a whole number, is it possible for the sum to be a whole number?

OBJECTIVE B   *To solve application problems*

24. Mechanics   Find the length of the shaft.

2.15 in.

1.87 in.

1.63 in.

Length

25. Mechanics   Find the length of the shaft.

1.52 ft

0.53 ft

2.3 ft

Length

0.55 m

1.36 m

1.12 m

0.5 m

26. **Banking** You have $2143.57 in your checking account. You make deposits of $210.98, $45.32, $1236.34, and $27.99. Find the amount in your checking account after you have made the deposits if no money has been withdrawn.

27. **Geometry** One side of a garden window is in the shape of a trapezoid, as shown outlined in red. The perimeter of the trapezoid is the sum of the lengths of the four sides. Find the perimeter of the trapezoid that has sides measuring 1.36 meters, 0.55 meter, 1.12 meters, and 0.5 meter.

28. ⬤ **Demography** The world's population in 2050 is expected to be 8.9 billion people. It is projected that in that year, Asia's population will be 5.3 billion and Africa's population will be 1.8 billion. What are the expected combined populations of Asia and Africa in 2050? (*Source:* United Nations Population Division, World Population Prospects)

29. ⬤ **TV Viewership** The table at the right shows the average number of viewers per day, in millions, of three network news programs for the week of September 12 to September 16, 2011. Calculate the total average number of viewers per day for these three news programs that week.

Network News Programs
September 12–16, 2011

Source: TV by the Numbers

30. ⬤ **The Stock Market** On September 26, 2011, the Dow Jones Industrial Average climbed 272.38 points after starting the day at 10,771.48. Find the value of the Dow Jones Industrial Average at the end of the trading day on September 26, 2011.

31. 🖼 **Measurement** Can a piece of rope 4 feet long be wrapped all the way around the box shown at the right?

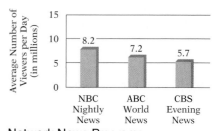

1.4 ft
1.4 ft
1.4 ft

Critical Thinking

Consumerism The table at the right gives the prices for selected products in a grocery store. Use this table for Exercises 32 and 33.

32. Does a customer with $10 have enough money to purchase raisin bran, bread, milk, and butter?

33. Name three items that would cost more than $8 but less than $9. (There is more than one answer.)

Product	Cost
Raisin bran	$3.29
Butter	$2.79
Bread	$1.99
Popcorn	$2.19
Potatoes	$3.49
Mayonnaise	$3.99
Lunch meat	$3.39
Milk	$2.59

Projects or Group Activities

Recall that a decimal number can be represented as a fraction. For instance, $0.27 = \frac{27}{100}$. For Exercises 34 to 37, write each decimal as a fraction and then add.

34. $0.29 + 0.7$ 35. $0.079 + 0.13$

36. $0.003 + 0.7 + 0.17$ 37. $0.053 + 0.09 + 0.1077$

38. 🖼 Read the Point of Interest on page 133. Do you agree with Stevin's claim that working with decimals is easier than working with fractions? Explain.

3.3 | Subtraction of Decimals

OBJECTIVE A   *To subtract decimals*

To subtract decimals, write the numbers so that the decimal points are on a vertical line. Subtract as for whole numbers, and write the decimal point in the difference directly below the decimal point in the subtrahend.

HOW TO 1   Subtract 21.532 − 9.875 and check.

Placing the decimal points on a vertical line ensures that digits of the same place value are subtracted.
21.532 − 9.875 = 11.657

Check:	Subtrahend	9.875
	+ Difference	+ 11.657
	= Minuend	21.532

HOW TO 2   Subtract 4.3 − 1.7942 and check.

$$\begin{array}{r} \overset{3\ \ \ 12\ 9\ 9\ 10}{4.3000} \\ -\ 1.7942 \\ \hline 2.5058 \end{array}$$

If necessary, insert zeros in the minuend before subtracting.

$$\begin{array}{r} Check: \quad \overset{1\ \ 1\ 1\ 1}{1.7942} \\ +\ 2.5058 \\ \hline 4.3000 \end{array}$$

EXAMPLE 1

Subtract 39.047 − 7.96 and check.

Solution
$$\begin{array}{r} \overset{8\ \ \ 9\ 14}{39.047} \\ -\ 7.96 \\ \hline 31.087 \end{array} \qquad Check: \begin{array}{r} \overset{1\ 1}{7.96} \\ +\ 31.087 \\ \hline 39.047 \end{array}$$

YOU TRY IT 1

Subtract 72.039 − 8.47 and check.

Your solution

EXAMPLE 2

Find 9.23 less than 29 and check.

Solution
$$\begin{array}{r} \overset{1\ 18\ \ \ 9\ 10}{29.00} \\ -\ 9.23 \\ \hline 19.77 \end{array} \qquad Check: \begin{array}{r} \overset{11\ \ 1}{9.23} \\ +\ 19.77 \\ \hline 29.00 \end{array}$$

YOU TRY IT 2

Find 9.67 less than 35 and check.

Your solution

EXAMPLE 3

Subtract 27.35 − 9.6793 and check.

Solution
$$\begin{array}{r} \overset{1\ 16\ \ 12\ 14\ 9\ 10}{27.3500} \\ -\ 9.6793 \\ \hline 17.6707 \end{array} \qquad Check: \begin{array}{r} \overset{11\ 111}{9.6793} \\ +\ 17.6707 \\ \hline 27.3500 \end{array}$$

YOU TRY IT 3

Subtract 3.7 − 1.9715 and check.

Your solution

Solutions on p. S9

ESTIMATION: Estimating the Difference Between Two Decimals

Calculate $820.23 - 475.748$. Then use estimation to determine whether the difference is reasonable.

Subtract to find the exact difference.

$$820.23 \; \boxed{-} \; 475.748 \; \boxed{=} \; 344.482$$

To estimate the difference, round each number to the same place value. Here we have rounded to the nearest ten. Then subtract. The estimated answer is 340, which is very close to the exact difference, 344.482.

$$
\begin{array}{r}
820.23 \approx 820 \\
- \; 475.748 \approx - \; 480 \\
\hline
340
\end{array}
$$

OBJECTIVE B   *To solve application problems*

EXAMPLE 4

You bought a book for $15.87. How much change did you receive from a $20 bill?

Strategy

To find the amount of change, subtract the cost of the book (15.87) from $20.

Solution

$$
\begin{array}{r}
20.00 \\
-15.87 \\
\hline
4.13
\end{array}
$$

You received $4.13 in change.

YOU TRY IT 4

Your breakfast cost $6.85. How much change did you receive from a $10 bill?

Your strategy

Your solution

EXAMPLE 5

You had a balance of $87.93 on your student debit card. You then used the card, deducting $15.99 for a CD, $6.85 for lunch, and $28.50 for a ticket to a football game. What is your new student debit card balance?

Strategy

To find your new debit card balance:
- Add to find the total of the three deductions (15.99 + 6.85 + 28.50).
- Subtract the total of the three deductions from the old balance (87.93).

Solution

$$
\begin{array}{r}
15.99 \\
6.85 \\
+ \; 28.50 \\
\hline
51.34
\end{array}
\text{ total of deductions}
\qquad
\begin{array}{r}
87.93 \\
- \; 51.34 \\
\hline
36.59
\end{array}
$$

Your new debit card balance is $36.59.

YOU TRY IT 5

You had a balance of $2472.69 in your checking account. You then wrote checks for $1025.60, $79.85, and $162.47. Find the new balance in your checking account.

Your strategy

Your solution

Solutions on p. S9

3.3 EXERCISES

✔ Concept Check

For Exercises 1 to 4, use the given subtraction statement to help you complete the addition statement.

1. 9.37 − 6.19 = 3.18
9.37 = _____ + 3.18

2. 81.1 − 73.43 = 7.67
7.67 + 73.43 = _____

3. 0.03 − 0.0095 = 0.0205
0.0205 + _____ = 0.03

4. 0.005 − 0.00067 = 0.00433
0.00067 + _____ = 0.005

OBJECTIVE A   *To subtract decimals*

For Exercises 5 to 28, subtract and check.

5. 24.037 − 18.41

6. 26.029 − 19.31

7. 123.07 − 9.4273

8. 214 − 7.143

9. 16.5 − 9.7902

10. 13.2 − 8.6205

11. 235.79 − 20.093

12. 463.27 − 40.095

13. 63.005 − 9.1274

14. 23.004 − 7.2175

15. 92 − 19.2909

16. 41.2405 − 25.2709

17. 0.32 − 0.0058

18. 0.78 − 0.0073

19. 3.005 − 1.982

20. 6.007 − 2.734

21. 352.16 − 90.994

22. 872 − 80.753

23. 724.32 − 69

24. 625.46 − 77.509

25. 362.394 − 19.4672

26. 421.385 − 17.5293

27. 19 − 10.372

28. 23.4 − 0.921

29. Find 97.732 less than 282.46.

30. Find 0.6206 less than 2.244.

31. What is the difference between 0.3145 and 0.03852?

32. What is the difference between 621.94 and 9.8482?

For Exercises 33 to 35, use the relationship between addition and subtraction to write the subtraction problem you would use to find the missing addend.

33. _____ + 2.325 = 7.01   **34.** 5.392 + _____ = 8.07   **35.** _____ + 8.967 = 19.35

For Exercises 36 to 39, use a calculator to subtract. Then round the numbers to the nearest whole number and use estimation to determine whether the difference you calculated is reasonable.

36.   93.079256
    − 66.09249

37.   3.7529
    − 1.00784

38.   76.53902
    − 45.73005

39.   9.07325
    − 1.924

OBJECTIVE B   *To solve application problems*

40. Mechanics   Find the missing dimension.

6.79 in.

?

14.34 in.

41. Mechanics   Find the missing dimension.

1.72 ft

?

4.31 ft

42. Business   The manager of the Edgewater Cafe takes a reading of the cash register tape each hour. At 1:00 P.M., the cash register tape read $967.54. At 2:00 P.M., the tape read $1437.15. Find the amount of sales between 1:00 P.M. and 2:00 P.M.

43. ● **Moviegoing**   The graph at the right shows the average price of a movie theater ticket for theaters in the United States. By how much did the average price of a ticket increase between 2007 and 2009?

44. ● **Coal**   In a recent year, 1.163 billion tons of coal were produced in the United States. In the same year, U.S. consumption of coal was 1.112 billion tons. (*Source:* Department of Energy) How many more million tons of coal were produced than were consumed that year?

45. ● **Super Bowl**   Super Bowl XLII was watched on the Fox network by 97.4 million people. On the same network, 63.9 million people watched the Super Bowl post-game show. (*Source:* Nielsen Network Research) How many more people watched Super Bowl XLII than watched the Super Bowl post-game show?

46.   You have $30 to spend, and you make purchases that cost $6.74 and $13.68. Which expressions correctly represent the amount of money you have left?

(**i**)   30 − 6.74 + 13.68   (**ii**)   (6.74 + 13.68) − 30
(**iii**) 30 − (6.74 + 13.68)   (**iv**) 30 − 6.74 − 13.68

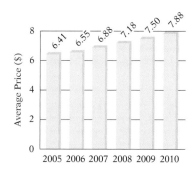

Average Price ($)

6.41   6.55   6.88   7.18   7.50   7.88

2005 2006 2007 2008 2009 2010

Average Price of a Movie Theater Ticket

Source: National Association of Theatre Owners

Jeff Gross/Getty Images

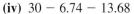

Critical Thinking

47. Find the largest amount by which the estimate of the sum of two decimals rounded to the given place value could differ from the exact sum.
  a. Tenths   **b.** Hundredths   **c.** Thousandths

Projects or Group Activities

In HOW TO 2, we suggested that you insert zeros in the minuend before subtracting. This ensures that numbers of the same place value will be subtracted. For Exercises 48–51, first write each decimal as a fraction and then subtract the fractions. This may help you see why zeros are inserted in the minuend.

48. $0.9 - 0.51$ **49.** $0.87 - 0.531$ **50.** $0.71 - 0.1633$ **51.** $0.097 - 0.069531$

✔ CHECK YOUR PROGRESS: CHAPTER 3

For Exercises 1 to 4, write the decimal as a fraction.

1. 0.7   **2.** 0.017   **3.** 0.93   **4.** 0.00087

5. Write 23.045 in words.

6. Write three hundred five and fifty-seven ten-thousandths in standard form.

7. Round 357.79645 to the nearest hundredth.

For Exercises 8 to 10, place the correct symbol, $<$ or $>$, between the numbers.

8. 0.357   0.4   **9.** 0.056   0.0107   **10.** 0.00319   0.005

For Exercises 11 to 16, perform the indicated operation.

11. $9.03 + 1.15 + 6$ **12.** $27.47 - 9.5$ **13.** $308.7 - 192.483$

14. $7.306 + 82.9912 + 0.1$ **15.** $96.54 + 749.453 + 154.007$ **16.** $72.107 - 53.9562$

SECTION

3.4 Multiplication of Decimals

OBJECTIVE A *To multiply decimals*

Point of Interest

Benjamin Banneker (1731–1806) was the first African American to earn distinction as a mathematician and scientist. He was on the survey team that determined the boundaries of Washington, D.C. The mathematics of surveying requires extensive use of decimals.

Decimals are multiplied as though they are whole numbers. Then the decimal point is placed in the product. Writing the decimals as fractions shows where to write the decimal point in the product.

$$0.\underline{3} \times 5 = \frac{3}{10} \times \frac{5}{1} = \frac{15}{10} = 1.\underline{5}$$

1 decimal place   1 decimal place

$$0.\underline{3} \times 0.\underline{5} = \frac{3}{10} \times \frac{5}{10} = \frac{15}{100} = 0.\underline{15}$$

1 decimal place   1 decimal place   2 decimal places

$$0.\underline{3} \times 0.\underline{05} = \frac{3}{10} \times \frac{5}{100} = \frac{15}{1000} = 0.\underline{015}$$

1 decimal place   2 decimal places   3 decimal places

To multiply decimals, multiply as with whole numbers. Write the decimal point in the product so that the number of decimal places in the product is the sum of the numbers of decimal places in the factors.

Integrating Technology

Scientific calculators have a floating decimal point. This means that the decimal point is automatically placed in the answer. For example, for the product at the right, enter

The display reads 7.704, with the decimal point in the correct position.

HOW TO 1 Multiply: 21.4×0.36

$$
\begin{array}{r}
21.4 \\
\times\ 0.36 \\
\hline
1284 \\
642 \\
\hline
7.704
\end{array}
$$

1 decimal place
2 decimal places

3 decimal places

HOW TO 2 Multiply: 0.037×0.08

$$
\begin{array}{r}
0.037 \\
\times\ \ 0.08 \\
\hline
0.00296
\end{array}
$$

3 decimal places
2 decimal places
5 decimal places

• Two zeros must be inserted between the 2 and the decimal point so that there are 5 decimal places in the product.

APPLY THE CONCEPT

The cost, including tax, of one adult admission to a theme park is $53.46. What is the total cost of 4 adult tickets to this theme park?

To find the total cost, multiply the admission price ($53.46) by the number of tickets (4).

$$
\begin{array}{r}
53.46 \\
\times\ \ \ \ 4 \\
\hline
213.84
\end{array}
$$

The total cost is $213.84.

To multiply a decimal by a power of 10 (10, 100, 1000, . . .), move the decimal point to the right the same number of places as there are zeros in the power of 10.

$3.892 \times 10 = 38.92$
1 zero   1 decimal place

$3.892 \times 100 = 389.2$
2 zeros   2 decimal places

$3.892 \times 1000 = 3892.$
3 zeros   3 decimal places

$3.892 \times 10,000 = 38,920.$
4 zeros   4 decimal places

• **Note that a zero must be inserted before the decimal point.**

Note that if the power of 10 is written in exponential notation, the exponent indicates how many places to move the decimal point.

$3.892 \times 10^1 = 38.92$
1 decimal place

$3.892 \times 10^2 = 389.2$
2 decimal places

$3.892 \times 10^3 = 3892.$
3 decimal places

$3.892 \times 10^4 = 38,920.$
4 decimal places

EXAMPLE 1

Multiply: 920×3.7

Solution

$$
\begin{array}{r}
920 \\
\times\ \ 3.7 \\
\hline
644\ 0 \\
2760\ \ \\
\hline
3404.0
\end{array}
$$

• **1 decimal place**

• **1 decimal place**

YOU TRY IT 1

Multiply: 870×4.6

Your solution

EXAMPLE 2

Find 0.00079 multiplied by 0.025.

Solution

$$
\begin{array}{r}
0.00079 \\
\times\ \ \ 0.025 \\
\hline
395 \\
158\ \ \\
\hline
0.00001975
\end{array}
$$

• **5 decimal places**
• **3 decimal places**

• **8 decimal places**

YOU TRY IT 2

Find 0.000086 multiplied by 0.057.

Your solution

EXAMPLE 3

Find the product of 3.69 and 2.07.

Solution

$$
\begin{array}{r}
3.69 \\
\times\ \ 2.07 \\
\hline
2583 \\
7380\ \ \\
\hline
7.6383
\end{array}
$$

• **2 decimal places**
• **2 decimal places**

• **4 decimal places**

YOU TRY IT 3

Find the product of 4.68 and 6.03.

Your solution

Solutions on p. S9

EXAMPLE 4

Multiply: $42.07 \times 10,000$

Solution

$42.07 \times 10,000 = 420,700$

YOU TRY IT 4

Multiply: 6.9×1000

Your solution

EXAMPLE 5

Find 3.01 times 10^3.

Solution

$3.01 \times 10^3 = 3010$

YOU TRY IT 5

Find 4.0273 times 10^2.

Your solution

Solutions on p. S9

ESTIMATION: Estimating the Product of Two Decimals

Calculate 28.259×0.029. Then use estimation to determine whether the product is reasonable.

Multiply to find the exact product.

$28.259 \boxed{\times} 0.029 \boxed{=} 0.819511$

To estimate the product, round each number so that it contains one nonzero digit. Then multiply. The estimated answer is 0.90, which is very close to the exact product, 0.819511.

$$28.259 \approx 30$$
$$\times 0.029 \approx \times 0.03$$
$$0.90$$

OBJECTIVE B *To solve application problems*

The tables that follow list water rates and meter fees for a city. These tables are used for Example 6 and You Try It 6.

Water Charges	
Commercial	$1.39/1000 gal
Comm Restaurant	$1.39/1000 gal
Industrial	$1.39/1000 gal
Institutional	$1.39/1000 gal
Res—No Sewer	
Residential—SF	
>0 <200 gal per day	$1.15/1000 gal
>200 <1500 gal per day	$1.39/1000 gal
>1500 gal per day	$1.54/1000 gal

Meter Charges	
Meter	Meter Fee
5/8" & 3/4"	$13.50
1"	$21.80
1-1/2"	$42.50
2"	$67.20
3"	$133.70
4"	$208.20
6"	$415.10
8"	$663.70

EXAMPLE 6

Use the tables on page 148. Find the total bill for an industrial water user with a 6-inch meter that used 152,000 gallons of water for July and August.

Strategy

To find the total cost of water:

- Find the cost of water by multiplying the cost per 1000 gallons (1.39) by the number of 1000-gallon units used.
- Add the cost of the water to the meter fee (415.10).

Solution

Cost of water $= \dfrac{152,000}{1000} \cdot 1.39 = 211.28$

Total cost $= 211.28 + 415.10 = 626.38$

The total cost is $626.38.

YOU TRY IT 6

Use the tables on page 148. Find the total bill for a commercial user that used 5000 gallons of water per day for July and August. The user has a 3-inch meter.

Your strategy

Your solution

EXAMPLE 7

It costs $.036 an hour to operate an electric motor. How much does it cost to operate the motor for 120 hours?

Strategy

To find the cost of running the motor for 120 hours, multiply the hourly cost (0.036) by the number of hours the motor is run (120).

Solution

Total cost $= 0.036 \times 120 = 4.320$

The cost of running the motor for 120 hours is $4.32.

YOU TRY IT 7

The cost of electricity to run a freezer for 1 hour is $.035. This month the freezer has run for 210 hours. Find the total cost of running the freezer this month.

Your strategy

Your solution

EXAMPLE 8

Jason Ng earns a salary of $440 for a 40-hour workweek. This week he worked 12 hours of overtime at a rate of $16.50 for each hour of overtime worked. Find his total income for the week.

Strategy

To find Jason's total income for the week:

- Find the overtime pay by multiplying the hourly overtime rate (16.50) by the number of hours of overtime worked (12).
- Add the overtime pay to the weekly salary (440).

Solution

Overtime pay $= 16.50 \times 12 = 198.00$

Total income $= 440.00 + 198.00 = 638.00$

Jason's total income for the week is $638.00.

YOU TRY IT 8

You make a down payment of $175 on an electronic drum kit and agree to make payments of $37.18 per month for the next 18 months to repay the remaining balance. Find the total cost of the electronic drum kit.

Your strategy

Your solution

Solutions on pp. S9–S10

3.4 EXERCISES

✔ Concept Check

For Exercises 1 to 3, write the number in exponential notation.

1. 100   **2.** 100,000   **3.** 1,000,000

For Exercises 4 to 6, simplify the exponential expression.

4. 10^3 **5.** 10^7 **6.** 10^4

For Exercises 7 to 10, without actually multiplying the numbers, state the number of decimal places in the product of the numbers.

7. 0.98×0.3 **8.** 12.304×96.0017 **9.** 0.09×3.009 **10.** 28.17×0.59

OBJECTIVE A   *To multiply decimals*

For Exercises 11 to 60, multiply.

11.   0.9
    × 0.4

12.   0.7
    × 0.9

13.   0.5
    × 0.5

14.   0.7
    × 0.7

15.   7.7
    × 0.9

16.   3.4
    × 0.4

17.   9.2
    × 0.2

18.   2.6
    × 0.7

19.   7.4
    × 0.1

20.   3.8
    × 0.1

21.   7.9
    ×   5

22.   9.3
    ×   7

23.   0.68
    ×   4

24.   0.83
    ×   9

25.   0.67
    ×   0.9

26.   0.84
    ×   0.3

27.   2.5
    × 5.4

28.   3.9
    × 1.9

29.   0.83
    ×   5.2

30.   0.24
    ×   2.7

31.   1.47
    × 0.09

32.   6.37
    × 0.05

33.   8.92
    × 0.004

34.   6.75
    × 0.007

35.   0.49
    × 0.16

36.   0.38
    × 0.21

37.   7.6
    × 0.01

38.   5.1
    × 0.01

39.   8.62
    ×   4

40.   5.83
    ×   7

41.   64.5
    ×   9

42.   37.8
    ×   8

43.   2.19
    × 9.2

44.   1.25
    × 5.6

45.   1.85
    × 0.023

46.   37.8
    × 0.052

47.   0.478
    ×   0.37

48.   0.526
    ×   0.22

49.   48.3
    × 0.0041

50.   67.2
    × 0.0086

51. 4.29×0.1 **52.** 6.78×0.1 **53.** 5.29×0.4 **54.** 6.78×0.5 **55.** 0.68×0.7

56. 0.56×0.9 **57.** 1.4×0.73 **58.** 6.3×0.37 **59.** 3.8×0.61 **60.** 7.2×0.72

61. Sports One meter is approximately 3.2808 feet. What is the height, in feet, of a diving board that is 3 meters above the water?

62. Cooking A pastry chef buys fine chocolate for $23.45 per pound. How much will 2.5 pounds of chocolate cost? Round to the nearest cent.

For Exercises 63 to 78, multiply.

63. 0.32×10 **64.** 6.93×10 **65.** 0.065×100 **66.** 0.039×100

67. 6.2856×1000 **68.** 3.2954×1000 **69.** $3.57 \times 10,000$ **70.** $0.006 \times 10,000$

71. 0.63×10^1 **72.** 8.52×10^1 **73.** 0.039×10^2 **74.** 82.9×10^2

75. 4.9×10^4 **76.** 6.8×10^3 **77.** 0.067×10^2 **78.** 6.83×10^4

79. Find the product of 0.0035 and 3.45. **80.** Find the product of 237 and 0.34.

81. Multiply 3.005 by 0.00392. **82.** Multiply 20.34 by 1.008.

83. Multiply 1.348 by 0.23. **84.** Multiply 0.000358 by 3.56.

85. Find the product of 23.67 and 0.0035. **86.** Find the product of 0.00346 and 23.1.

87. Find the product of 5, 0.45, and 2.3. **88.** Find the product of 0.03, 23, and 9.45.

For Exercises 89 to 100, use a calculator to multiply. Then use estimation to determine whether the product you calculated is reasonable.

89. 28.5 $\times$ 3.2 **90.** 86.3 $\times$ 4.4 **91.** 2.38 $\times$ 0.44 **92.** 9.82 $\times$ 0.77

93. 0.866 $\times$ 4.5 **94.** 0.239 $\times$ 8.2 **95.** 4.34 $\times$ 2.59 **96.** 6.87 $\times$ 9.98

97. 8.434 $\times$ 0.044 **98.** 7.037 $\times$ 0.094 **99.** 28.44 $\times$ 1.12 **100.** 86.57 $\times$ 7.33

OBJECTIVE B *To solve application problems*

101. Recycling Four hundred empty soft drink cans weigh 18.75 pounds. A recycling center pays $.75 per pound for the cans. Find the amount received for the 400 cans. Round to the nearest cent.

102. Recycling A recycling center pays $.045 per pound for newspapers.
   a. Estimate the payment for recycling 520 pounds of newspapers.
   b. Find the actual amount received from recycling the newspapers.

103. **Electricity** In the United States, the average residential monthly bill for electricity is $103.67. (*Source:* U.S. Energy Information Administration) What is a U.S. homeowner's average annual cost of electricity?

104. **Transportation** A long-haul truck driver earns $.43 for each mile driven. How much will a truck driver earn for driving 1507 miles from Boston to Miami?

Taxes For tax purposes, the Internal Revenue Service (IRS) allows a deduction on tax returns if the taxpayer uses a car for business, charitable work, medical needs, or relocating. The allowable amounts for 2011 are given in the table at the right. Use this table for Exercises 105 to 108.

IRS Mileage Deduction Table	
Business	$.50 per mile
Charitable work	$.14 per mile
Medical needs	$.165 per mile
Relocating	$.165 per mile

Source: Internal Revenue Service

105. During 2011, an accountant drove 1843 miles while doing charitable work for a college scholarship program. What is the accountant's mileage deduction for charitable work in 2011?

106. A welder specializing in electron beam welding relocated from Denver, Colorado, to Boston, Massachusetts, a distance of 1971 miles. What is the welder's mileage deduction for relocating in 2011? Round to the nearest cent.

107. Describe what the numerical expression 2374 × 0.50 represents.

108. Is the mileage deduction for medical needs less than or greater than the mileage deduction for charitable work?

109. **Taxes** The tax per gallon of gasoline in California is $.477. (*Source:* Tax Foundation) If you fill your gasoline tank with 12.5 gallons of gasoline in California, how much will you pay in taxes? Round to the nearest cent.

110. **Geometry** The perimeter of a square is equal to four times the length of a side of the square. Find the perimeter of a square whose side measures 2.8 meters.

2.8 m

3.5 ft

6.75 ft

111. **Geometry** The area of a rectangle is equal to the product of the length of the rectangle times its width. Find the area of a rectangle that has a length of 6.75 feet and a width of 3.5 feet. The area will be in square feet.

112. **Finance** You bought a car for $5000 down and made payments of $499.50 each month for 36 months.
   a. Find the amount of the payments over the 36 months.
   b. Find the total cost of the car.

113. **Compensation** A certified nurse anesthetist (CRNA) earns a salary of $3440 for a 40-hour work week. This week the CRNA worked 15 hours of overtime at a rate of $149.35 for each hour of overtime worked.
   a. Find the CRNA's overtime pay.
   b. Find the CRNA's total income for the week.

114. **Consumerism** Bay Area Rental Cars charges $25 a day and $.25 per mile for renting a car. You rented a car for 3 days and drove 235 miles. Find the total cost of renting the car.

115. **Social Security** Use the information in the news clipping at the right. If the federal government issued about 136 million checks during its last year of issuing paper checks, how much money would have been saved that year by eliminating the paper check option?

In the NEWS!

No More Paper Checks

With a paper check now costing $0.92 more to issue than an electronic payment, the federal government has eliminated the paper check option for Social Security recipients.
Source: usnews.com

116. Transportation   A taxi costs $2.50 and $.20 for each $\frac{1}{8}$ mile driven. Find the cost of hiring a taxi to get from the airport to the hotel, a distance of $5\frac{1}{2}$ miles.

117. Business   The table at the right lists three pieces of steel required for a repair project.
  a. Find the total cost of grade 1.
  b. Find the total cost of grade 2.
  c. Find the total cost of grade 3.
  d. Find the total cost of the three pieces of steel.

Grade of Steel	Weight (pounds per foot)	Required Number of Feet	Cost per Pound
1	2.2	8	$3.20
2	3.4	6.5	$3.35
3	6.75	15.4	$3.94

118. Business   A confectioner ships holiday packs of candy and nuts anywhere in the United States. At the left below is a price list for nuts and candy, and at the right below is a table of shipping charges to zones in the United States.

Code	Description	Price
112	Almonds 16 oz	$6.75
116	Cashews 8 oz	$5.90
117	Cashews 16 oz	$8.50
130	Macadamias 7 oz	$7.25
131	Macadamias 16 oz	$11.95
149	Pecan halves 8 oz	$8.25
155	Mixed nuts 8 oz	$6.80
160	Cashew brittle 8 oz	$5.95
182	Pecan roll 8 oz	$6.70
199	Chocolate peanuts 8 oz	$5.90

Pounds	Zone 1	Zone 2	Zone 3	Zone 4
1–3	$7.55	$7.85	$8.25	$8.75
4–6	$8.10	$8.40	$8.80	$9.30
7–9	$8.50	$8.80	$9.20	$9.70
10–12	$8.90	$9.20	$9.60	$10.10

Corbis/Jupiter Images

Use the information in the tables above to find the cost of sending each of the following orders to the given mail zone. For any fraction of a pound, use the next higher weight. Sixteen ounces (16 oz) is equal to 1 pound.

a.

Code	Quantity
116	2
130	1
149	3
182	4

Mail to zone 4.

b.

Code	Quantity
112	1
117	4
131	2
160	3
182	5

Mail to zone 3.

c.

Code	Quantity
117	3
131	1
155	2
160	4
182	1
199	3

Mail to zone 2.

Critical Thinking

119. Show how the decimal is placed in the product of 1.3×2.31 by first writing each number as a fraction and then multiplying. Then change the product back to decimal notation.

120. ◼ Explain how the decimal point is placed when a number is multiplied by 10, 100, 1000, 10,000, etc.

121. ◼ Explain how the decimal point is placed in the product of two decimals.

Projects or Group Activities

122. Automotive Repair Chris works at B & W Garage as an auto mechanic and has just completed an engine overhaul for a customer. To determine the cost of the repair job, Chris keeps a list of times worked and parts used. A parts list and a list of the times worked are shown below.

Parts Used		Time Spent	
Item	Quantity	Day	Hours
Gasket set	1	Monday	7.0
Ring set	1	Tuesday	7.5
Valves	8	Wednesday	6.5
Wrist pins	8	Thursday	8.5
Valve springs	16	Friday	9.0
Rod bearings	8		
Main bearings	5		
Valve seals	16		
Timing chain	1		

Price List		
Item Number	Description	Unit Price
27345	Valve spring	$9.25
41257	Main bearing	$17.49
54678	Valve	$16.99
29753	Ring set	$169.99
45837	Gasket set	$174.90
23751	Timing chain	$50.49
23765	Fuel pump	$229.99
28632	Wrist pin	$23.55
34922	Rod bearing	$13.69
2871	Valve seal	$1.69

a. Organize a table of data showing the parts used, the unit price for each part, and the price of the quantity used. *Hint:* Use the following headings for the table.

Quantity   Item Number   Description   Unit Price   Total

b. Add up the numbers in the "Total" column to find the total cost of the parts.

c. If the charge for labor is $46.75 per hour, compute the cost of labor.

d. What is the total cost for parts and labor?

3.5

Division of Decimals

To divide decimals

Tips for Success

To learn mathematics, you must be an active participant. Listening and watching your professor do mathematics are not enough. Take notes in class, mentally think through every question your instructor asks, and try to answer it even if you are not called on to do so. Ask questions when you have them. See *AIM for Success* at the front of the book for other ways to be an active learner.

To divide decimals, move the decimal point in the divisor to the right to make the divisor a whole number. Move the decimal point in the dividend the same number of places to the right. Place the decimal point in the quotient directly above the decimal point in the dividend, and then divide as with whole numbers.

HOW TO 1 Divide: $3.25\overline{)15.275}$

$$3.25.\overline{)15.27.5}$$

- **Move the decimal point 2 places to the right in the divisor and then in the dividend. Place the decimal point in the quotient.**

$$\begin{array}{r} 4.7 \\ 325.\overline{)\ 1527.5} \\ -1300 \\ \hline 227\ 5 \\ -227\ 5 \\ \hline 0 \end{array}$$

- **Divide as with whole numbers.**

Moving the decimal point the same number of decimal places in the divisor and dividend does not change the value of the quotient, because this process is the same as multiplying the numerator and denominator of a fraction by the same number. In HOW TO 1 above,

$$3.25\overline{)15.275} = \frac{15.275}{3.25} = \frac{15.275 \times 100}{3.25 \times 100} = \frac{1527.5}{325} = 325\overline{)1527.5}$$

When dividing decimals, we usually round the quotient off to a specified place value, rather than writing the quotient with a remainder.

HOW TO 2 Divide: $0.3\overline{)0.56}$

Round to the nearest hundredth.

$$\begin{array}{r} 1.866 \approx 1.87 \\ 0.3.\overline{)\ 0.5.600} \\ -\ 3 \\ \hline 2\ 6 \\ -2\ 4 \\ \hline 20 \\ -18 \\ \hline 20 \\ -18 \\ \hline \end{array}$$

We must carry the division to the thousandths place to round the quotient to the nearest hundredth. Therefore, zeros must be inserted in the dividend so that the quotient has a digit in the thousandths place.

Integrating Technology

A calculator displays the quotient to the limit of the calculator's display. Enter

to determine the number of places your calculator displays.

HOW TO 3 Find the quotient of 5.793 and 3.24. Round to the nearest thousandth.

$$
\begin{array}{r}
1.7879 \approx 1.788 \\
3.24\overline{)\ 5.79.3000} \\
-32\ 4 \\
\hline
25\ 53 \\
-22\ 68 \\
\hline
2\ 85\ 0 \\
-2\ 59\ 2 \\
\hline
25\ 80 \\
-22\ 68 \\
\hline
3\ 120 \\
-2\ 916 \\
\hline
2040 \\
-1944 \\
\hline
\end{array}
$$

Zeros must be inserted in the dividend so that the quotient has a digit in the ten-thousandths place.

APPLY THE CONCEPT

Three friends decide to share equally in the cost of lunch. If the total bill for lunch is $38.19, what amount is owed by each person?

To find the amount owed by each person, divide the total bill ($38.19) by the number of friends (3).

$$
\begin{array}{r}
12.73 \\
3\overline{)38.19}
\end{array}
$$

The amount owed by each person is $12.73.

To divide a decimal by a power of 10 (10, 100, 1000, . . .), move the decimal point to the left the same number of places as there are zeros in the power of 10.

$34.65 \div 1\underline{0} = 3.465$
1 zero   1 decimal place

$34.65 \div 1\underline{00} = 0.3465$
2 zeros   2 decimal places

$34.65 \div 1\underline{000} = 0.03465$
3 zeros   3 decimal places
- Note that a zero must be inserted between the 3 and the decimal point.

$34.65 \div 1\underline{0,000} = 0.003465$
4 zeros   4 decimal places
- Note that two zeros must be inserted between the 3 and the decimal point.

If the power of 10 is written in exponential notation, the exponent indicates how many places to move the decimal point.

$34.65 \div 10^1 = 3.465$ 1 decimal place $34.65 \div 10^3 = 0.03465$ 3 decimal places

$34.65 \div 10^2 = 0.3465$ 2 decimal places $34.65 \div 10^4 = 0.003465$ 4 decimal places

---

EXAMPLE 1

Divide: $0.1344 \div 0.032$

Solution

$$
\begin{array}{r}
4.2 \\
0.032\overline{)\ 0.134.4} \\
-128 \\
\hline
6\ 4 \\
-6\ 4 \\
\hline
0
\end{array}
$$

- Move the decimal point 3 places to the right in the divisor and the dividend.

YOU TRY IT 1

Divide: $0.1404 \div 0.052$

Your solution

Solution on p. S10

EXAMPLE 2

Divide: $58.092 \div 82$
Round to the nearest thousandth.

Solution

$$
\begin{array}{r}
0.7084 \approx 0.708 \\
82{\overline{\smash{\big)}\,58.0920}} \\
-57\,4 \\
\hline
69 \\
-0 \\
\hline
692 \\
-656 \\
\hline
360 \\
-328 \\
\hline
\end{array}
$$

YOU TRY IT 2

Divide: $37.042 \div 76$
Round to the nearest thousandth.

Your solution

EXAMPLE 3

Find the quotient of 420.9 and 7.06.
Round to the nearest tenth.

Solution

$$
\begin{array}{r}
59.61 \approx 59.6 \\
7.06{,}{\overline{\smash{\big)}\,420.90{,}00}} \\
-353\,0 \\
\hline
67\,90 \\
-63\,54 \\
\hline
4\,36\,0 \\
-4\,23\,6 \\
\hline
12\,40 \\
-7\,06 \\
\hline
\end{array}
$$

YOU TRY IT 3

Find the quotient of 370.2 and 5.09.
Round to the nearest tenth.

Your solution

EXAMPLE 4

Divide: $402.75 \div 1000$

Solution $402.75 \div 1000 = 0.40275$

YOU TRY IT 4

Divide: $309.21 \div 10{,}000$

Your solution

EXAMPLE 5

What is 0.625 divided by 10^2?

Solution $0.625 \div 10^2 = 0.00625$

YOU TRY IT 5

What is 42.93 divided by 10^4?

Your solution

Solutions on p. S10

ESTIMATION: Estimating the Quotient of Two Decimals

Calculate $282.18 \div 0.48$. Then use estimation to determine whether the quotient is reasonable.

Divide to find the exact quotient. $282.18 \;\boxed{\div}\; 0.48 \;\boxed{=}\; 587.875$

To estimate the quotient, round each number
so that it contains one nonzero digit. Then
divide. The estimated answer is 600, which
is very close to the exact quotient, 587.875.

$$282.18 \div 0.48 \approx 300 \div 0.5$$
$$= 600$$

OBJECTIVE B   *To solve application problems*

The graph at the right shows average hourly earnings in the United States for selected years. Use this table for Example 6 and You Try It 6.

Average Hourly Earnings in the U.S.

Source: Bureau of Labor Statistics

EXAMPLE 6

How many times greater were the average hourly earnings in 2000 than in 1980? Round to the nearest whole number.

Strategy

To find how many times greater the average hourly earnings were, divide the 2000 average hourly earnings (14.02) by the 1980 average hourly earnings (6.85).

Solution

$14.02 \div 6.85 \approx 2$

The average hourly earnings in 2000 were about 2 times greater than in 1980.

YOU TRY IT 6

How many times greater were the average hourly earnings in 2010 than in 1980? Round to the nearest tenth.

Your strategy

Your solution

EXAMPLE 7

You purchased a car for $15,317.28 and made a down payment of $3000. The balance was paid in 48 monthly payments. Find the monthly car payment.

Strategy

To find the monthly car payment:

• Subtract the down payment (3000) from the purchase price (15,317.28). This is the amount financed.
• Divide the amount financed by 48.

Solution

$$\begin{array}{r} 15{,}317.28 \\ -\ 3000.00 \\ \hline 12{,}317.28 \end{array}$$ amount financed

$$\begin{array}{r} 256.61 \\ 48\overline{)12{,}317.28} \end{array}$$

The monthly car payment was $256.61.

YOU TRY IT 7

A Nielsen survey of the average number of people (in millions) who watch television each day of the week is given in the table below.

Mon.	Tues.	Wed.	Thu.	Fri.	Sat.	Sun.
91.9	89.8	90.6	93.9	78.0	77.1	87.7

Find the average number of people who watch television per day.

Your strategy

Your solution

Solutions on p. S10

3.5 EXERCISES

✔ Concept Check

For Exercises 1 and 2, fill in the blanks to complete the sentences.

1. To determine the placement of the decimal point in the quotient of two decimals, move the decimal point in the divisor to the _____ to make the divisor a _____ number. Move the decimal point in the dividend the same number of places to the _____ . Place the decimal point in the quotient directly above the decimal point in the _____ .

2. When dividing by a power of 10, move the decimal point to the _____ the same number of places as the _____ on 10.

OBJECTIVE A   *To divide decimals*

For Exercises 3 to 22, divide.

3. $3\overline{)2.46}$

4. $7\overline{)3.71}$

5. $0.8\overline{)3.84}$

6. $0.9\overline{)6.93}$

7. $0.7\overline{)62.3}$

8. $0.4\overline{)52.8}$

9. $0.4\overline{)24}$

10. $0.5\overline{)65}$

11. $0.7\overline{)59.01}$

12. $0.9\overline{)8.721}$

13. $0.5\overline{)16.15}$

14. $0.8\overline{)77.6}$

15. $0.7\overline{)3.542}$

16. $0.6\overline{)2.436}$

17. $6.3\overline{)8.19}$

18. $3.2\overline{)7.04}$

19. $3.6\overline{)0.396}$

20. $2.7\overline{)0.648}$

21. $6.9\overline{)26.22}$

22. $1.7\overline{)84.66}$

For Exercises 23 to 30, divide. Round to the nearest tenth.

23. $55.62 \div 8.8$

24. $25.43 \div 5.4$

25. $5.427 \div 9.5$

26. $1.837 \div 1.4$

27. $18.4 \div 7.3$

28. $52.9 \div 8.1$

29. $0.183 \div 0.17$

30. $0.381 \div 0.47$

For Exercises 31 to 38, divide. Round to the nearest hundredth.

31. $6.467 \div 8$

32. $4.817 \div 16$

33. $0.0647 \div 0.72$

34. $0.0418 \div 0.53$

35. $38.665 \div 0.95$

36. $7 \div 0.55$

37. $27.738 \div 60.8$

38. $3.171 \div 45.6$

For Exercises 39 to 46, divide. Round to the nearest thousandth.

39. $1.028 \div 54$

40. $6.729 \div 27$

41. $34.31 \div 95.3$

42. $75.469 \div 77.8$

43. $0.4871 \div 4.72$

44. $0.2695 \div 2.67$

45. $0.2307 \div 26.7$

46. $0.1142 \div 17.2$

For Exercises 47 to 54, divide. Round to the nearest whole number.

47. $89.76 \div 90$

48. $16.5 \div 4$

49. $1.0478 \div 0.413$

50. $2.148 \div 0.519$

51. $0.79 \div 0.778$

52. $3.092 \div 0.075$

53. $392 \div 6.9$

54. $8.729 \div 0.075$

55. Geometry   A square has four sides of equal length. If the total distance around a square, called its perimeter, is 4.15 meters, what is the length of one side of the square?

56. Fuel Cost   The cost of 16.5 gallons of gasoline is $62.37. What is the cost of 1 gallon of gasoline?

For Exercises 57 to 72, divide.

57. $4.07 \div 10$

58. $0.039 \div 10$

59. $42.67 \div 10$

60. $389.7 \div 100$

61. $1.037 \div 100$

62. $237.835 \div 100$

63. $8.295 \div 1000$

64. $82,547 \div 1000$

65. $0.32 \div 10^1$

66. $87.65 \div 10^1$

67. $23.627 \div 10^2$

68. $2.954 \div 10^2$

69. $0.0053 \div 10^2$

70. $289.32 \div 10^3$

71. $1.8932 \div 10^3$

72. $0.139 \div 10^3$

73. Divide 44.208 by 2.4.

74. Divide 0.04664 by 0.44.

75. Find the quotient of 723.15 and 45.

76. Find the quotient of 3.3463 and 3.07.

77. Divide 13.5 by 10^3.

78. Divide 0.045 by 10^5.

79. Find the quotient of 23.678 and 1000.

80. Find the quotient of 7.005 and 10,000.

81. What is 0.0056 divided by 0.05?

82. What is 123.8 divided by 0.02?

For Exercises 83 to 91, use a calculator to divide. Round to the nearest ten-thousandth. Then use estimation to determine whether the quotient you calculated is reasonable.

83. $42.42 \div 3.8$

84. $69.8 \div 7.2$

85. $389 \div 0.44$

86. $642 \div 0.83$

87. $6.394 \div 3.5$

88. $8.429 \div 4.2$

89. $1.235 \div 0.021$

90. $7.456 \div 0.072$

91. $95.443 \div 1.32$

92. A four-digit whole number is divided by 1000. Is the quotient less than 1 or greater than 1?

OBJECTIVE B *To solve application problems*

93. A 12-pack of bottled spring water sells for $3.85. State whether to use *multiplication* or *division* to find the specified amount.
   a. The cost of one bottle of spring water
   b. The cost of four 12-packs of spring water

94. A city school district spends $8754 per student, and the school district in a nearby suburb spends $10,296 per student. Which expression represents how many times greater the amount spent per student by the suburban schools is than the amount spent per student by the city schools?
   (i) $10,296 - 8754$ (ii) $10,296 \div 8754$
   (iii) $8754 \div 10,296$ (iv) $10,296 \times 8754$

95. **Transportation** A truck driver is paid by the number of miles driven. If a truck driver earns $.46 per mile, how many miles must the trucker drive in 1 hour to earn $16.00 per hour? Round to the nearest mile.

96. **Tourism** See the news clipping at the right. Find the average amount spent by each visitor to Washington, D.C. Round to the nearest cent.

97. **Sports** Ramon, a high school football player, gained 162 yards on 26 carries in a high school football game. Find the average number of yards gained per carry. Round to the nearest hundredth.

98. **Consumerism** A case of diet cola costs $6.79. If there are 24 cans in a case, find the cost per can. Round to the nearest cent.

99. **Carpentry** Anne is building a bookcase that is 3.4 feet long. How many complete shelves can be cut from a 12-foot board?

100. **Travel** When the Massachusetts Turnpike opened, the toll for a passenger car that traveled the entire 136 miles of it was $5.60. Calculate the cost per mile. Round to the nearest cent.

101. **Consumerism** Neil purchased a truck for $14,307.60 and made a down payment of $1500. If the remaining balance was paid over five years in 60 equal monthly payments, find the monthly truck payment.

102. **Consumerism** Leanne purchased a high-definition 3D 1080p plasma television for $1208.76. She made a down payment of $300 and paid the remaining balance in 12 equal monthly payments. What were her monthly payments?

103. **Fuel Efficiency** A car with an odometer reading of 17,814.2 is filled with 9.4 gallons of gas. At an odometer reading of 18,130.4, the tank is empty and the car is filled with 12.4 gallons of gas. How many miles does the car travel on 1 gallon of gasoline?

104. **Carbon Footprint** One ton of coal can produce about 3000 kilowatt-hours of electricity. Suppose a family uses 25 kilowatt-hours of electricity per month. How many tons of coal will the family use in one year?

105. **Carbon Footprint** One barrel of oil produces approximately 800 kilowatt-hours of electricity. Suppose you use 27 kilowatt-hours of electricity per month. How many barrels of oil will you use in one year?

In the NEWS!

Tourists Boost the Economy

This past summer, 17.28 million visitors came to Washington, D.C., spending $5680 million.
Source: washington.org

Boston
↑ (90)
Mass. Turnpike

Stephen Finn/Shutterstock.com

106. ● **Carbon Footprint**   Use the information in the article at the right. Find the reduction in greenhouse gas emissions per month if 9 million U.S. households substituted chicken, fish, or eggs for red meat and dairy products one day a week.

Critical Thinking

107. ● **Education**   According to the National Center for Education Statistics, 10.03 million women and 7.46 million men were enrolled at institutions of higher learning in a recent year. How many more women than men were attending institutions of higher learning that year?

● **The Military**   The table at the right shows the advertising budgets of four branches of the U.S. armed services in a recent year. Use this table for Exercises 108 to 110.

108. Find the difference between the Army's advertising budget and the Marines' advertising budget.

Service	Advertising Budget
Army	$85.3 million
Air Force	$41.1 million
Navy	$20.5 million
Marines	$15.9 million

Source: CMR/TNS Media Intelligence

109. How many times greater was the Army's advertising budget than the Navy's advertising budget? Round to the nearest tenth.

110. What was the total of the advertising budgets for the four branches of the service?

111. ● **Population Growth**   The U.S. population of people ages 85 and over is expected to grow from 4.2 million in 2000 to 8.9 million in 2030. How many times greater is this population expected to be in 2030 than in 2000? Round to the nearest tenth.

112. ◣ Explain how the decimal point is moved when a number is divided by 10, 100, 1000, 10,000, etc.

113. ◣ **Sports**   Explain how baseball batting averages are determined. Then find Detroit Tiger's right fielder Magglio Ordonez's batting average with 216 hits out of 595 at bats. Round to the nearest thousandth.

Projects or Group Activities

For Exercises 114 to 119, insert $+$, $-$, $\times$, or $\div$ into the square so that the statement is true.

114. 3.45 ☐ 0.5 = 6.9

115. 3.46 ☐ 0.24 = 0.8304

116. 6.009 ☐ 4.68 = 1.329

117. 0.064 ☐ 1.6 = 0.1024

118. 9.876 ☐ 23.12 = 32.996

119. 3.0381 ☐ 1.23 = 2.47

For Exercises 120 to 123, fill in the square to make a true statement.

120. 6.47 − ☐ = 1.253

121. 6.47 + ☐ = 9

122. 0.009 ÷ ☐ = 0.36

123. ☐ × 1.06 = 0.2862

In the NEWS!

Reducing Food's Carbon Footprint

The production of red meat and dairy products results in far more greenhouse gas emissions than the production of other types of protein. Thus a diet lower in red meat and dairy can reduce your "carbon footprint." Some research suggests that for every 1 million U.S. households that substitute chicken, fish, or eggs for red meat and dairy products one day a week, greenhouse gas emissions may decrease by 2.8 million tons per year.

Source: Environmental Science and Technology

3.6 Comparing and Converting Fractions and Decimals

OBJECTIVE A   *To convert fractions to decimals*

To convert a fraction to a decimal, divide the numerator by the denominator.

HOW TO 1   Convert $\frac{5}{8}$ to a decimal.

Divide the numerator by the denominator.

$$
\begin{array}{r}
0.625 \\
8{\overline{\smash{\big)}\,5.000}} \\
\underline{-4\ 8} \\
20 \\
\underline{-16} \\
40 \\
\underline{-40} \\
0
\end{array}
$$

In this case, the remainder is 0. This fraction can be written as a **terminating decimal,** which is a decimal whose remainder is eventually 0.

$$\frac{5}{8} = 0.625$$

HOW TO 2   Convert $\frac{7}{11}$ to a decimal.

Divide the numerator by the denominator.

$$
\begin{array}{r}
0.6363 \\
11{\overline{\smash{\big)}\,7.0000}} \\
\underline{-6.6} \\
40 \\
\underline{-33} \\
70 \\
\underline{-66} \\
40 \\
\underline{-33} \\
7
\end{array}
$$

In this case, the remainder is never 0. This fraction can be written as a **repeating decimal,** which is a decimal whose remainder is never 0. When a remainder begins to repeat (as 4 does in this example), the digits in the quotient will begin to repeat.

It is common practice to write a bar over the repeating digits of a decimal.

$$\frac{7}{11} = 0.6363... = 0.\overline{63}$$

📋 **Take Note**

The decimal representation of every fraction either terminates or repeats. However, the repeating cycle may be quite long. For instance, there are 22 digits in the repeating cycle of the decimal representation of $\frac{9}{23}$.

EXAMPLE 1

Convert $\frac{5}{12}$ to a decimal.

Solution

$$
\begin{array}{r}
0.4166 \\
12{\overline{\smash{\big)}\,5.0000}} \\
\underline{-4\ 8} \\
20 \\
\underline{-12} \\
80 \\
\underline{-72} \\
80
\end{array}
$$

• Divide the numerator by the denominator. Continue to divide until the remainder is 0 or the remainder repeats.

$$\frac{5}{12} = 0.41\overline{6}$$

YOU TRY IT 1

Convert $\frac{11}{18}$ to a decimal.

Your solution

Solution on p. S10

EXAMPLE 2

Convert $\frac{5}{16}$ to a decimal.

Solution

$$
\begin{array}{r}
0.3125 \\
16\overline{)\ 5.0000} \\
-4\ 8 \\
\hline
20 \\
-\ 16 \\
\hline
40 \\
-\ 32 \\
\hline
80 \\
-\ 80 \\
\hline
0
\end{array}
$$

• Divide the numerator by the denominator. Continue to divide until the remainder is 0 or the remainder repeats.

$$\frac{5}{16} = 0.3125$$

YOU TRY IT 2

Convert $\frac{7}{25}$ to a decimal.

Your solution

EXAMPLE 3

Convert $\frac{32}{15}$ to a decimal.

Solution

$$
\begin{array}{r}
2.133 \\
15\overline{)\ 32.000} \\
-\ 30 \\
\hline
2\ 0 \\
-\ 1\ 5 \\
\hline
50 \\
-\ 45 \\
\hline
50
\end{array}
$$

• Divide the numerator by the denominator. Continue to divide until the remainder is 0 or the remainder repeats.

$$\frac{32}{15} = 2.1\overline{3}$$

YOU TRY IT 3

Convert $\frac{13}{6}$ to a decimal.

Your solution

Solutions on p. S11

OBJECTIVE B *To convert decimals to fractions*

To convert a decimal to a fraction, remove the decimal point and place the decimal part over a denominator equal to the place value of the last digit in the decimal. Then write the fraction in simplest form.

HOW TO 3 Convert 0.275 to a fraction.

$$0.275 = \underset{\text{thousandths}}{\frac{275}{1000}} = \frac{\cancel{5} \cdot \cancel{5} \cdot 11}{2 \cdot 2 \cdot 2 \cdot \cancel{5} \cdot \cancel{5} \cdot 5} = \frac{11}{40}$$

HOW TO 4 Convert 0.33 to a fraction.

$$0.33 = \underset{\text{hundredths}}{\frac{33}{100}} = \frac{3 \cdot 11}{2 \cdot 2 \cdot 5 \cdot 5} = \frac{33}{100}$$

EXAMPLE 4

Convert 7.45 to a mixed number.

Solution $7.45 = 7\dfrac{45}{100} = 7\dfrac{9}{20}$

YOU TRY IT 4

Convert 0.0005 to a fraction.

Your solution

Solution on p. S11

OBJECTIVE C   *To compare a fraction and a decimal*

One way to determine the order relation between a decimal and a fraction is to write the decimal as a fraction and then compare the fractions.

HOW TO 5   Place the correct symbol, $<$ or $>$, between the two numbers.

$$0.8 \qquad \frac{8}{9}$$

	0.8	$\dfrac{8}{9}$
Write the decimal as a fraction.	$\dfrac{8}{10}$	$\dfrac{8}{9}$
Write the fractions with a common denominator.	$\dfrac{72}{90}$	$\dfrac{80}{90}$
Compare the fractions.	$\dfrac{72}{90} <$	$\dfrac{80}{90}$

$$0.8 \; < \; \frac{8}{9}$$

EXAMPLE 5

Place the correct symbol, $<$ or $>$, between the two numbers.

$$0.7 \qquad \frac{3}{4}$$

Solution

$0.7 \qquad \dfrac{3}{4}$

$\dfrac{7}{10} \qquad \dfrac{3}{4}$ • Write the decimal as a fraction.

$\dfrac{14}{20} \qquad \dfrac{15}{20}$ • Write the fractions with a common denominator.

$\dfrac{14}{20} < \dfrac{15}{20}$ • Compare the fractions.

$0.7 \; < \; \dfrac{3}{4}$

YOU TRY IT 5

Place the correct symbol, $<$ or $>$, between the two numbers.

$$\frac{5}{6} \qquad 0.83$$

Your solution

Solution on p. S11

3.6 EXERCISES

✔ Concept Check

For Exercises 1 to 5, give the place value of the digit 3.

1. 0.45367   **2.** 0.40032   **3.** 4.3976   **4.** 7308.4987   **5.** 6.03049

6. 🖎 Explain the meaning of a terminating decimal and a repeating decimal.

🖎 For Exercises 7 to 10, without actually doing any division, state whether the decimal equivalent of the given fraction is greater than 1 or less than 1.

7. $\dfrac{97}{96}$ **8.** $\dfrac{2012}{2010}$ **9.** $\dfrac{79}{80}$ **10.** $\dfrac{1999}{2000}$

OBJECTIVE A   *To convert fractions to decimals*

For Exercises 11 to 35, convert the fraction to a terminating or a repeating decimal. Place a bar over any repeating digits.

11. $\dfrac{2}{3}$ **12.** $\dfrac{5}{9}$ **13.** $\dfrac{7}{8}$ **14.** $\dfrac{15}{16}$ **15.** $\dfrac{13}{18}$

16. $\dfrac{8}{15}$ **17.** $\dfrac{20}{33}$ **18.** $\dfrac{8}{11}$ **19.** $\dfrac{17}{36}$ **20.** $\dfrac{5}{12}$

21. $\dfrac{27}{37}$ **22.** $\dfrac{71}{111}$ **23.** $\dfrac{25}{27}$ **24.** $\dfrac{17}{22}$ **25.** $\dfrac{35}{74}$

26. $\dfrac{3}{40}$ **27.** $\dfrac{17}{20}$ **28.** $\dfrac{37}{80}$ **29.** $\dfrac{6}{7}$ **30.** $\dfrac{5}{13}$

31. $\dfrac{11}{32}$ **32.** $\dfrac{29}{4}$ **33.** $\dfrac{77}{20}$ **34.** $\dfrac{53}{22}$ **35.** $\dfrac{233}{55}$

OBJECTIVE B   *To convert decimals to fractions*

For Exercises 36 to 55, convert the decimal to a fraction or a mixed number.

36. 0.8   **37.** 0.4   **38.** 0.32   **39.** 0.48

40. 0.125   **41.** 0.485   **42.** 1.25   **43.** 3.75

44. 2.7125   **45.** 3.175   **46.** 9.05   **47.** 11.004

48. 8.437   **49.** 9.279   **50.** 2.25   **51.** 0.224

52. 0.0025   **53.** 0.052   **54.** 0.084   **55.** 0.00015

The repeating cycle of the decimal representation of some fractions may be quite long. For instance, there are 22 digits in the repeating cycle of $\frac{17}{23}$. In such cases, it may be convenient to round the decimal representation to a given place value. For Exercises 56 to 63, round the decimal representation of the fraction to the given place value.

56. $\frac{9}{71}$ Hundredths   **57.** $\frac{21}{67}$ Hundredths

58. $\frac{19}{53}$ Thousandths   **59.** $\frac{7}{43}$ Thousandths

60. $\frac{15}{29}$ Thousandths   **61.** $\frac{5}{56}$ Thousandths

62. $\frac{17}{23}$ Ten-thousandths   **63.** $\frac{12}{17}$ Ten-thousandths

OBJECTIVE C   *To compare a decimal and a fraction*

For Exercises 64 to 75, place the correct symbol, $<$ or $>$, between the two numbers.

64. 0.7 $\frac{3}{4}$ **65.** $\frac{7}{8}$ 0.9   **66.** $\frac{7}{16}$ 0.45   **67.** 0.13 $\frac{5}{40}$

68. $\frac{23}{40}$ 0.57   **69.** $\frac{12}{55}$ 0.22   **70.** 0.07 $\frac{1}{15}$ **71.** 0.55 $\frac{5}{9}$

72. $\frac{5}{12}$ 0.42   **73.** $\frac{17}{18}$ 0.94   **74.** $\frac{16}{9}$ 1.8   **75.** $\frac{22}{7}$ 3.14

Critical Thinking

76. 📱 **Air Pollution** An emissions test for cars requires that of the total engine exhaust, less than 1 part per thousand $\left(\frac{1}{1000} = 0.001\right)$ be hydrocarbon emissions. Using this figure, determine which of the cars in the table below would fail the emissions test.

Car	Total Engine Exhaust	Hydrocarbon Emission
1	367,921	360
2	401,346	420
3	298,773	210
4	330,045	320
5	432,989	450

Projects or Group Activities

As we have stated, the decimal representation of a fraction always terminates or repeats. In this project, we will explore terminating decimal representations.

77. Using a calculator, find the terminating decimal representation of each fraction shown below.

$$\frac{1}{2}, \frac{3}{4}, \frac{5}{8}, \frac{9}{16}, \frac{3}{10}, \frac{7}{20}, \frac{19}{32}, \frac{23}{40}, \frac{7}{25}, \frac{19}{50}$$

78. Find the prime factorization of each denominator in Exercise 77.

79. What are the only prime number factors of the denominators in Exercise 77?

80. Make up some fractions in simplest form, with denominators that contain only the prime factors you listed in Exercise 79. Find the decimal representations of these fractions. Do they all have terminating decimal representations?

81. Make up some fractions in simplest form, with denominators that contain at least one prime factor other than those you listed in Exercise 79. Find the decimal representations of these fractions. Do any of these fractions have terminating decimal representations?

82. Based on your results in Exercises 77 to 81, make a conjecture about the denominator of a fraction with a terminating decimal representation.

CHAPTER

3 | Summary

Key Words

A number written in **decimal notation** has three parts: a **whole-number part**, a **decimal point**, and a **decimal part**. The decimal part of a number represents a number less than 1. A number written in decimal notation is often simply called a **decimal**. [3.1A, p. 130]

Examples

For the decimal 31.25, 31 is the whole-number part and 25 is the decimal part.

Essential Rules and Procedures

To write a decimal in words, write the decimal part as if it were a whole number. Then name the place value of the last digit. The decimal point is read as "and." [3.1A, p. 130]

To write a decimal in standard form when it is written in words, write the whole-number part, replace the word *and* with a decimal point, and write the decimal part so that the last digit is in the given place-value position. [3.1A, p. 130]

To round a decimal to a given place value, use the same rules used with whole numbers, except drop the digits to the right of the given place value instead of replacing them with zeros. [3.1B, p. 132]

To add decimals, write the decimals so that the decimal points are on a vertical line. Add as you would with whole numbers. Then write the decimal point in the sum directly below the decimal points in the addends. [3.2A, p. 137]

To subtract decimals, write the decimals so that the decimal points are on a vertical line. Subtract as you would with whole numbers. Then write the decimal point in the difference directly below the decimal point in the subtrahend. [3.3A, p. 141]

Examples

The decimal 12.875 is written in words as twelve and eight hundred seventy-five thousandths.

The decimal forty-nine and sixty-three thousandths is written in standard form as 49.063.

2.7134 rounded to the nearest tenth is 2.7. 0.4687 rounded to the nearest hundredth is 0.47.

$$
\begin{array}{r}
\overset{1}{}\overset{1}{}\\
1.35\\
20.8\\
+\ 0.76\\
\hline
22.91
\end{array}
$$

$$
\begin{array}{r}
\overset{2\ \ 15}{}\ \ \overset{6\ \ 10}{}\\
3\,\cancel{5}.8\,\cancel{7}\,\cancel{0}\\
-\ \ 9.6\,4\,1\\
\hline
2\,6.2\,2\,9
\end{array}
$$

To multiply decimals, multiply the numbers as you would whole numbers. Then write the decimal point in the product so that the number of decimal places in the product is the sum of the numbers of decimal places in the factors. [3.4A, p. 146]

$$
\begin{array}{r}
26.83 \quad \text{2 decimal places} \\
\times \quad 0.45 \quad \text{2 decimal places} \\
\hline
13415 \\
10732 \quad\quad \\
\hline
12.0735 \quad \text{4 decimal places}
\end{array}
$$

To multiply a decimal by a power of 10, move the decimal point to the right the same number of places as there are zeros in the power of 10. If the power of 10 is written in exponential notation, the exponent indicates how many places to move the decimal point. [3.4A, p. 147]

$$3.97 \cdot 10{,}000 = 39{,}700$$
$$0.641 \cdot 10^5 = 64{,}100$$

To divide decimals, move the decimal point in the divisor to the right so that the divisor is a whole number. Move the decimal point in the dividend the same number of places to the right. Place the decimal point in the quotient directly above the decimal point in the dividend. Then divide as you would with whole numbers. [3.5A, p. 155]

$$
\begin{array}{r}
6.2 \\
0.39.\overline{)\ 2.41.8} \\
-2\,34 \\
\hline
7\,8 \\
-7\,8 \\
\hline
0
\end{array}
$$

To divide a decimal by a power of 10, move the decimal point to the left the same number of places as there are zeros in the power of 10. If the power of 10 is written in exponential notation, the exponent indicates how many places to move the decimal point. [3.5A, p. 156]

$$972.8 \div 1000 = 0.9728$$
$$61.305 \div 10^4 = 0.0061305$$

To convert a fraction to a decimal, divide the numerator of the fraction by the denominator. Continue to divide until the remainder is 0 or the remainder repeats. [3.6A, p. 163]

$$\frac{7}{8} = 7 \div 8 = 0.875 \quad \bullet \text{ Terminating decimal}$$

$$\frac{5}{6} = 5 \div 6 = 0.8\overline{3} \quad \bullet \text{ Repeating decimal}$$

To convert a decimal to a fraction, remove the decimal point and place the decimal part over a denominator equal to the place value of the last digit in the decimal. [3.6B, p. 164]

0.85 is eighty-five <u>hundredths.</u>

$$0.85 = \frac{85}{100} = \frac{17}{20}$$

To find the order relation between a decimal and a fraction, first rewrite the decimal as a fraction. Then compare the two fractions. [3.6C, p. 165]

$$0.9 = \frac{9}{10} = \frac{36}{40}$$

$$\frac{7}{8} = \frac{35}{40}$$

$$\text{Because } \frac{36}{40} > \frac{35}{40}, 0.9 > \frac{7}{8}.$$

CHAPTER

3 | Review Exercises

1. Find the quotient of 3.6515 and 0.067.

2. Find the sum of 369.41, 88.3, 9.774, and 366.474.

3. Place the correct symbol, $<$ or $>$, between the two numbers.
0.055   0.1

4. Write 22.0092 in words.

5. Round 0.05678235 to the nearest hundred-thousandth.

6. Write $\frac{17}{80}$ as a terminating or repeating decimal. Place a bar over any repeating digits.

7. Convert 0.375 to a fraction.

8. Add: $3.42 + 0.794 + 32.5$

9. Write thirty-four and twenty-five thousandths in standard form.

10. Place the correct symbol, $<$ or $>$, between the two numbers.
$\frac{5}{8}$ 0.62

11. Convert $\frac{7}{22}$ to a terminating or repeating decimal. Place a bar over any repeating digits.

12. Convert 0.66 to a fraction.

13. Subtract: $27.31 - 4.4465$

14. Round 7.93704 to the nearest hundredth.

15. Find the product of 3.08 and 2.9.

16. Write 342.37 in words.

17. Write three and six thousand seven hundred fifty-three hundred-thousandths in standard form.

18. Multiply: 34.79
                   $\times$ 0.74

19. Divide: $0.053\overline{)0.349482}$

20. What is 7.796 decreased by 2.9175?

21. **Fuel Consumption**   Read the news clipping at the right. What is the total number of gallons of fuel saved this year by the airline? What is the airline's average cost per gallon of fuel for the year? Round to the nearest cent.

22. Banking   You had a balance of $895.68 in your checking account. You then wrote checks for $145.72 and $88.45. Find the new balance in your checking account.

23. **Travel**   In a recent year, 30.6 million Americans drove to their destinations over Thanksgiving, and 4.8 million Americans traveled by plane. (*Source:* AAA) How many times greater is the number who drove than the number who flew? Round to the nearest tenth.

24. **Nutrition**   According to the American School Food Service Association, 1.9 million gallons of milk are served in school cafeterias every day. How many gallons of milk are served in school cafeterias during a 5-day school week?

In the NEWS!

Airline Reduces Fuel Costs

One airline estimates that it will save $131 million in fuel costs this year by taking the following steps to reduce fuel consumption:

Remove outdated equipment and replace beverage carts with lighter-weight models: 2.9 million gallons saved

Wash airplane engines: 7.2 million gallons saved

Tow airplanes when they are on the ground: 3.6 million gallons saved

Install winglets to improve aerodynamics: 35.4 million gallons saved

Source: news.travel.aol.com

CHAPTER

3 | TEST

1. Place the correct symbol, $<$ or $>$, between the two numbers.

0.0068   0.000963

2. Subtract: $13.027 - 8.94$

3. Write 45.0302 in words.

4. Write two hundred nine and seven thousand eighty-six hundred-thousandths in standard form.

5. Convert 0.825 to a fraction.

6. Place the correct symbol, $<$ or $>$, between the two numbers.

$\dfrac{13}{8}$ 0.72

7. Find the quotient of 0.0569 and 0.037. Round to the nearest thousandth.

8. Find 9.23674 less than 37.003.

9. Subtract: $65.34 - 39.4592$

10. Convert $\dfrac{13}{40}$ to a terminating or repeating decimal. Place a bar over any repeating digits.

11. Round 7.0954625 to the nearest thousandth.

12. Divide: $1.392 \div 0.06$

13. Add: 270.93
              97.
               1.976
        $+$ 88.675

14. Convert $\dfrac{15}{22}$ to a terminating or repeating decimal. Place a bar over any repeating digits.

15. Find the product of 1.37 and 0.004.

16. Find the sum of 62.3, 4.007, and 189.65.

17. Find 17.1496 times 10^3.

18. What is 15.923 divided by 10^4?

19. Construction The cost of a $4\frac{1}{2}$-inch carriage bolt is $1.44. What is the cost of 15 of these carriage bolts?

20. Finances A car was bought for $16,734.40, with a down payment of $2500. The balance was paid in 36 monthly payments. Find the amount of each monthly payment.

21. Compensation You received a salary of $727.50, a commission of $1909.64, and a bonus of $450. Find your total income.

22. Consumerism A long-distance telephone call costs $.85 for the first 3 minutes and $.42 for each additional minute. Find the cost of a 12-minute long-distance telephone call.

Cumulative Review Exercises

1. Divide: $89)\overline{20,932}$

2. Simplify: $2^3 \cdot 4^2$

3. Simplify: $2^2 - (7 - 3) \div 2 + 1$

4. Find the LCM of 9, 12, and 24.

5. Write $\frac{22}{5}$ as a mixed number.

6. Write $4\frac{5}{8}$ as an improper fraction.

7. Write an equivalent fraction with the given denominator.

$$\frac{5}{12} = \frac{}{60}$$

8. Add: $\dfrac{3}{8} + \dfrac{5}{12} + \dfrac{9}{16}$

9. What is $5\frac{7}{12}$ increased by $3\frac{7}{18}$?

10. Subtract: $9\dfrac{5}{9} - 3\dfrac{11}{12}$

11. Multiply: $\dfrac{9}{16} \times \dfrac{4}{27}$

12. Find the product of $2\frac{1}{8}$ and $4\frac{5}{17}$.

13. Divide: $\dfrac{11}{12} \div \dfrac{3}{4}$

14. What is $2\frac{3}{8}$ divided by $2\frac{1}{2}$?

15. Simplify: $\left(\dfrac{2}{3}\right)^2 \cdot \left(\dfrac{3}{4}\right)^3$

16. Simplify: $\left(\dfrac{2}{3}\right)^2 - \left(\dfrac{2}{3} - \dfrac{1}{2}\right) + 2$

17. Write 65.0309 in words.

18. Add: 379.006
              27.523
               9.8707
        +   88.2994

19. What is 29.005 decreased by 7.9286?

20. Multiply: $\begin{array}{r} 9.074 \\ \times\ \ 6.09 \end{array}$

21. Divide: $8.09\overline{)17.42963}$
Round to the nearest thousandth.

22. Convert $\frac{11}{15}$ to a terminating or a repeating decimal. Place a bar over any repeating digits.

23. Convert 0.425 to a fraction.

24. Place the correct symbol, $<$ or $>$, between the two numbers.
$$\frac{8}{9} \quad 0.98$$

25. ● **Vacation** The graph at the right shows the number of legally-mandated vacation days per year for several countries. How many more vacation days does Sweden mandate than Germany?

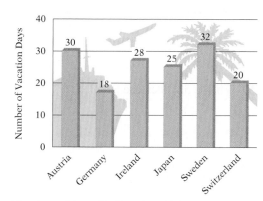

Number of Legally Mandated Vacation Days

Sources: Economic Policy Institute; *World Almanac*

26. **Health** A patient is put on a diet to lose 24 pounds in 3 months. The patient loses $9\frac{1}{2}$ pounds the first month and $6\frac{3}{4}$ pounds the second month. How much weight must the patient lose during the third month to achieve the goal?

27. **Banking** You have a checking account balance of $814.35. You then write checks for $42.98, $16.43, and $137.56. Find your checking account balance after you write the checks.

28. **Mechanics** A machine lathe takes 0.017 inch from a brass bushing that is 1.412 inches thick. Find the resulting thickness of the bushing.

29. **Taxes** The state income tax on your business is $820 plus 0.08 times your profit. You made a profit of $64,860 last year. Find the amount of income tax you paid last year.

30. **Finances** You bought a camera costing $410.96. The down payment was $40, and the balance is to be paid in 8 equal monthly payments. Find the monthly payment.

Ratio and Proportion

4

Focus on Success

Are you making attending class a priority? Remember that to be successful, you must attend class. You need to be in class to hear your instructor's explanations and instructions, as well as to ask questions when something is unclear. Most students who miss a class fall behind and then find it very difficult to catch up. (See Class Time, page AIM-5.)

Monkey Business Images/shutterstock.com

Prep Test

Are you ready to succeed in this chapter? Take the Prep Test below to find out if you are ready to learn the new material.

1. Simplify: $\dfrac{8}{10}$

2. Simplify: $\dfrac{450}{650 + 250}$

3. Write $\dfrac{372}{15}$ as a terminating or repeating decimal.

4. Which is greater, 4×33 or 62×2?

5. Complete: $? \times 5 = 20$

SECTION

4.1 | Ratio

OBJECTIVE A   *To write the ratio of two quantities in simplest form*

Quantities such as 3 feet, 12 cents, and 9 cars are number quantities written with units.

3 feet

12 cents   These are some examples of units. Shirts, dollars, trees, miles,

9 cars   and gallons are further examples.

↑
units

A **ratio** is a comparison of two quantities that have the *same* units. This comparison can be written in three different ways:

1. As a fraction

2. As two numbers separated by a colon (:)

3. As two numbers separated by the word *to*

The ratio of the lengths of two boards, one 8 feet long and the other 10 feet long, can be written as

1. $\dfrac{8 \text{ feet}}{10 \text{ feet}} = \dfrac{8}{10} = \dfrac{4}{5}$

2. 8 feet : 10 feet = 8 : 10 = 4 : 5

3. 8 feet to 10 feet = 8 to 10 = 4 to 5

Writing the **simplest form of a ratio** means writing it so that the two numbers have no common factor other than 1.

This ratio means that the smaller board is $\frac{4}{5}$ the length of the longer board.

EXAMPLE 1

Write the comparison $6 to $8 as a ratio in simplest form using a fraction, a colon, and the word *to*.

Solution $\dfrac{\$6}{\$8} = \dfrac{6}{8} = \dfrac{3}{4}$

$6 : $8 = 6 : 8 = 3 : 4

$6 to $8 = 6 to 8 = 3 to 4

YOU TRY IT 1

Write the comparison 20 pounds to 24 pounds as a ratio in simplest form using a fraction, a colon, and the word *to*.

Your solution

EXAMPLE 2

Write the comparison 18 quarts to 6 quarts as a ratio in simplest form using a fraction, a colon, and the word *to*.

Solution $\dfrac{18 \text{ quarts}}{6 \text{ quarts}} = \dfrac{18}{6} = \dfrac{3}{1}$

18 quarts : 6 quarts = 18 : 6 = 3 : 1

18 quarts to 6 quarts = 18 to 6
$$= 3 \text{ to } 1$$

YOU TRY IT 2

Write the comparison 64 miles to 8 miles as a ratio in simplest form using a fraction, a colon, and the word *to*.

Your solution

Solutions on p. S11

OBJECTIVE B   *To solve application problems*

Christian Delbert/Shutterstock.com

The table below shows the number of board feet in stock at a lumber store for each of four types of wood. Use the table for Example 3 and You Try It 3.

Board Feet of Wood at a Lumber Store			
Pine	Ash	Oak	Cedar
20,000	18,000	10,000	12,000

EXAMPLE 3

Find, as a fraction in simplest form, the ratio of the number of board feet of pine to the number of board feet of oak.

Strategy

To find the ratio, write the ratio of board feet of pine (20,000) to board feet of oak (10,000) in simplest form.

Solution

$$\frac{20,000}{10,000} = \frac{2}{1}$$

The ratio is $\frac{2}{1}$.

YOU TRY IT 3

Find, as a fraction in simplest form, the ratio of the number of board feet of cedar to the number of board feet of ash.

Your strategy

Your solution

EXAMPLE 4

The cost of building a patio cover was $500 for labor and $700 for materials. What, as a fraction in simplest form, is the ratio of the cost of materials to the total cost for labor and materials?

Strategy

To find the ratio, write the ratio of the cost of materials ($700) to the total cost ($500 + $700) in simplest form.

Solution

$$\frac{\$700}{\$500 + \$700} = \frac{700}{1200} = \frac{7}{12}$$

The ratio is $\frac{7}{12}$.

YOU TRY IT 4

A company spends $600,000 a month for television advertising and $450,000 a month for radio advertising. What, as a fraction in simplest form, is the ratio of the cost of radio advertising to the total cost of radio and television advertising?

Your strategy

Your solution

Solutions on p. S11

4.1 EXERCISES

✔ Concept Check

1. How do you read $\frac{3}{8}$ as a ratio?

2. How do you read 8 : 3 as a ratio?

OBJECTIVE A *To write the ratio of two quantities in simplest form*

For Exercises 3 to 20, write the comparison as a ratio in simplest form using a fraction, a colon (:), and the word *to*.

3. 3 pints to 15 pints

4. 6 pounds to 8 pounds

5. $40 to $20

6. 10 feet to 2 feet

7. 3 miles to 8 miles

8. 2 hours to 3 hours

9. 6 minutes to 6 minutes

10. 8 days to 12 days

11. 35 cents to 50 cents

12. 28 inches to 36 inches

13. 30 minutes to 60 minutes

14. 25 cents to 100 cents

15. 32 ounces to 16 ounces

16. 12 quarts to 4 quarts

17. 30 yards to 12 yards

18. 12 quarts to 18 quarts

19. 20 gallons to 28 gallons

20. 14 days to 7 days

21. 🖉 To write a ratio that compares 3 days to 3 weeks, change 3 weeks into an equivalent number of _____.

22. 🖉 Is the ratio 3 : 4 the same as the ratio 4 : 3?

OBJECTIVE B *To solve application problems*

Budgets For Exercises 23 to 26, use the information in the table. Write ratios in simplest form using a fraction.

Family Budget						
Housing	Food	Transportation	Taxes	Utilities	Miscellaneous	Total
$1600	$800	$600	$700	$300	$800	$4800

23. Find the ratio of utilities costs to food costs.

24. Find the ratio of food costs to total expenses.

25. Find the ratio of housing costs to total expenses.

26. 🖉 Write a verbal description of two ratios represented by 1 : 2.

27. **Facial Hair**   Using the data in the news clipping at the right and the figure 110 million for the number of adult males in the United States, write the ratio of the number of men who participated in Movember to the number of adult males in the U.S. Write the ratio as a fraction in simplest form.

In the NEWS!

Grow a Mustache, Save a Life

Movember, a month-long mustache-growing event during November, raises money for the Prostate Cancer Foundation. Last year, 65,000 U.S. men took part in Movember, raising $7.5 million.

Source: The Sacramento Bee

28. **Real Estate**   A house with an original value of $180,000 increased in value to $220,000 in 5 years. What is the ratio of the increase in value to the original value of the house?

29. **Energy Prices**   The price per gallon of gasoline rose from $2.70 to $3.24 in one year. What is the ratio of the increase in price to the original price?

30. **Sports**   National Collegiate Athletic Association (NCAA) statistics show that for every 75,000 high school seniors playing basketball, about 2250 play college basketball as first-year students. Write the ratio of the number of first-year students playing college basketball to the number of high school seniors playing basketball.

31. **Sports**   NCAA statistics show that of about 3750 college seniors playing college basketball, about 45 will play as rookies in the National Basketball Association. Write the ratio of the number of National Basketball Association rookies to the number of college seniors playing basketball.

32. **Consumerism**   In a recent year, women spent $2 million on swimwear and purchased 92,000 swimsuits. During the same year, men spent $500,000 on swimwear and purchased 37,000 swimsuits. (*Source:* NPD Group) **a.** Find the ratio of the amount men spent on swimwear to the amount women spent on swimwear. **b.** Find the ratio of the amount men spent on swimwear to the total amount men and women spent on swimwear. Write the ratios as fractions in simplest form.

Critical Thinking

33. Is the value of a ratio always less than 1? Explain.

Projects or Group Activities

34. Ratios can be extended to include more than two numbers. For instance, the ratio of the sides of the triangle at the right below can be written $3 : 4 : 5$. The study of the ratios of the sides of a triangle is part of a branch of mathematics called **trigonometry,** which has important applications to science and engineering. The Canadarm2 uses trigonometry in the design of its robotic system on the international space station.

a. Are the sides of a triangle whose sides measure 18 inches, 24 inches, and 30 inches in the ratio $3 : 4 : 5$?

b. Are the sides of a triangle whose sides measure 9 inches, 16 inches, and 25 inches in the ratio $3 : 4 : 5$?

c. For the triangle at the right, find the ratio of Side B to Side A.

d. For the triangle at the right, find the ratio of Side B to Side C.

e. For the triangle at the right, find the ratio of Side A to Side C.

Side C: 5 feet   Side B: 3 feet   Side A: 4 feet

35. Get a large bag of M&Ms and find the ratio of the number of red, blue, green, yellow, and orange candies.

SECTION

4.2 | Rates

OBJECTIVE A | *To write rates*

A **rate** is a comparison of two quantities that have *different* units. A rate is written as a fraction.

A distance runner ran 26 miles in 4 hours. The distance-to-time rate is written

$$\frac{26 \text{ miles}}{4 \text{ hours}} = \frac{13 \text{ miles}}{2 \text{ hours}}$$

Notice that the above rate is written in simplest form. Writing the **simplest form of a rate** means writing it so that the two numbers that form the rate have no common factor other than 1.

 Point of Interest

Listed below are rates at which various crimes are committed in our nation.

Crime	Every
Larceny	4 seconds
Burglary	14 seconds
Robbery	60 seconds
Rape	6 minutes
Murder	31 minutes

EXAMPLE 1

Write "6 roof supports for every 9 feet" as a rate in simplest form.

Solution

$$\frac{6 \text{ supports}}{9 \text{ feet}} = \frac{2 \text{ supports}}{3 \text{ feet}}$$

YOU TRY IT 1

Write "15 pounds of fertilizer for 12 trees" as a rate in simplest form.

Your solution

Solution on p. S11

OBJECTIVE B | *To write unit rates*

A **unit rate** is a rate in which the number in the denominator is 1.

$$\frac{\$3.25}{1 \text{ pound}}$$ or \$3.25/pound is read "\$3.25 per pound."

To find a unit rate, divide the number in the numerator of the rate by the number in the denominator of the rate.

 Point of Interest

According to a Gallup Poll, women see doctors more often than men do. On average, men visit the doctor 3.8 times per year, whereas women go to the doctor 5.8 times per year.

APPLY THE CONCEPT

A car was driven 344 miles on 16 gallons of gasoline. How many miles did the car travel on 1 gallon of gasoline?

The rate that compares miles to gallons is $\frac{344 \text{ miles}}{16 \text{ gallons}}$.

To find the miles per gallon (the unit rate), divide the numerator (344 miles) by the denominator (16 gallons).

344 miles ÷ 16 gallons = 21.5 miles/gallon

The car traveled 21.5 miles per gallon of gasoline.

EXAMPLE 2

Write "300 feet in 8 seconds" as a unit rate.

Solution

$$\frac{300\ \text{feet}}{8\ \text{seconds}} \qquad \begin{array}{r} 37.5 \\ 8\overline{)300.0} \end{array}$$

37.5 feet/second

YOU TRY IT 2

Write "260 miles in 8 hours" as a unit rate.

Your solution

Solution on p. S11

OBJECTIVE C   *To solve application problems*

Denver Airport

Integrating Technology

To calculate the costs per mile using a calculator, perform four divisions:

683 ÷ 2475 =

536 ÷ 1464 =

525 ÷ 1302 =

483 ÷ 1050 =

In each case, round the number in the display to the nearest hundredth.

HOW TO 1   The table at the right shows miles flown and air fares for some routes in the continental United States. Determine the most expensive route and the least expensive route per mile.

Long Routes	Miles	Fare
New York–Los Angeles	2475	$683
San Francisco–Dallas	1464	$536
Denver–Pittsburgh	1302	$525
Minneapolis–Hartford	1050	$483

Strategy

Find the cost per mile for each route by dividing the fare by the miles flown. Compare the costs per mile to determine the most and least expensive routes.

Solution   New York–Los Angeles $\dfrac{683}{2475} \approx 0.28$

San Francisco–Dallas $\dfrac{536}{1464} \approx 0.37$

Denver–Pittsburgh $\dfrac{525}{1302} \approx 0.40$

Minneapolis–Hartford $\dfrac{483}{1050} = 0.46$

$0.28 < 0.37 < 0.40 < 0.46$

The Minneapolis–Hartford route is the most expensive per mile, and the New York–Los Angeles route is the least expensive per mile.

EXAMPLE 3

A motorcycle racer completed a 6-mile lap in 0.05 hour (3 minutes). Find the racer's speed in miles per hour.

Strategy

To find the speed in miles per hour, divide the length of the lap (6 miles) by the time (0.05 hour).

Solution

$$\frac{6\ \text{miles}}{0.05\ \text{hour}} = 120\ \text{miles/hour}$$

The racer's speed was 120 miles/hour.

YOU TRY IT 3

A landscape technician purchased 40 feet of $\frac{3}{4}$-inch PVC pipe for $22.40. What is the per-foot cost of the pipe?

Your strategy

Your solution

Solution on p. S11

4.2 EXERCISES

✔ Concept Check

1. 🔲 What is the difference between a ratio and a rate?

2. 🔲 How is a unit rate calculated?

OBJECTIVE A   *To write rates*

For Exercises 3 to 10, write each phrase as a rate in simplest form.

3. 3 pounds of meat for 4 people   **4.** 30 ounces in 24 glasses

5. $80 for 12 boards   **6.** 84 cents for 3 candy bars

7. 300 miles on 15 gallons   **8.** 88 feet in 8 seconds

9. 16 gallons in 2 hours   **10.** 25 ounces in 5 minutes

11. 🔲 If the rate at which water flows through a nozzle is given in gallons per minute, how do you find the rate in gallons per second?

OBJECTIVE B   *To write unit rates*

🔲 For Exercises 12 to 14, complete the unit rate.

12. 5 miles in ___ hour   **13.** 15 feet in ___ second   **14.** 5 grams of fat in ___ serving

For Exercises 15 to 24, write each phrase as a unit rate.

15. 10 feet in 4 seconds   **16.** 816 miles in 6 days

17. $3900 earned in 4 weeks   **18.** $51,000 earned in 12 months

19. 1100 trees planted on 10 acres

20. 3750 words on 15 pages

21. $131.88 earned in 7 hours

22. 628.8 miles in 12 hours

23. 409.4 miles on 11.5 gallons of gasoline

24. $11.05 for 3.4 pounds

25. Fuel Efficiency   A hybrid electric vehicle used 15 gallons of gasoline to travel 639 miles. How many miles per gallon did the car get?

26. Audio Technology   An audio-visual technician spent 2 hours preparing a surround sound recommendation for a homeowner. If the technician charged $99 for this service, what is the technician's hourly wage?

OBJECTIVE C   *To solve application problems*

Miles per Dollar   One measure of how expensive it is to drive your car is calculated as miles per dollar, which is the number of miles you drive on 1 dollar's worth of gasoline. Use this information for Exercises 27 and 28.

27. Suppose you get 26 miles per gallon of gasoline and gasoline costs $3.49 per gallon. Calculate your miles per dollar. Round to the nearest tenth.

28. Suppose you get 23 miles per gallon of gasoline and gasoline costs $3.15 per gallon. It costs you $44.10 to fill the tank. Calculate your miles per dollar. Round to the nearest tenth.

29. Bike Sharing   Use the information in the news clipping at the right. Find the average number of rides per day during the Hubway program's first month. Round to the nearest whole number of rides per day.

In the NEWS!

Hubway's First Month a Success

In recent years, bike sharing programs have been rolled out in cities across the United States and around the world. In its first 30 days of operation, Boston's Hubway program saw its bicycles used for 36,612 rides.

Source: boston.com

30. Construction   An architect designed a house that contains 1850 square feet. A home builder estimates that it will cost $172,050 to build the house. What is the estimated cost per square foot to build the house?

31. ● **Advertising**   The advertising fee for a 30-second spot for the 2011 Super Bowl was approximately $3 million. If 106 million viewers watched the Super Bowl, what is the advertiser's cost per viewer for a 30-second ad? Round to the nearest cent. (*Source:* money.cnn.com)

32. Air Flow   A tire containing 732 cubic inches of air is punctured and begins a slow leak. After 4 hours, the tire is flat and there are 36 cubic inches of air remaining in the tire. What is the rate, in cubic feet per minute, at which air escaped from the tire?

33. Gas Pump   A quality control inspector needs to measure the flow rate of a gasoline pump. The inspector pumps 10 gallons of gas into a container in 50 seconds. What is the rate, in gallons per minute, at which the pump dispenses gas?

⬤ **Exchange Rates**   One application of rates is in the area of international trade. Suppose a company in Canada purchases a shipment of sneakers from an American company. The Canadian company must exchange Canadian dollars for U.S. dollars in order to pay for the order. The number of Canadian dollars that are equivalent to 1 U.S. dollar is called the **exchange rate.** The table at the right below shows the exchange rates per U.S. dollar for three foreign countries and for the euro at the time of this writing. Use this table for Exercises 34 to 36.

34. How many euros would be paid for an order of American computer hardware costing $120,000?

35. Calculate the cost, in Japanese yen, of an American car costing $34,000.

36. 📷 What does the quantity 1.9831 × 2500 represent?

Exchange Rates per U.S. Dollar	
Russian Ruble	30.4006
Brazilian Real	1.9831
Japanese Yen	79.8700
Euro	0.7788

37. ⬤ **Demography**   The table below shows the population and area of three countries. The population density of a country is the number of people per square mile.

Country	Population	Area (in square miles)
Australia	21,767,000	2,968,000
India	1,189,173,000	1,269,000
United States	311,051,000	3,619,000

    a. Which country has the least population density?
    b. How many more people per square mile are there in India than in the United States? Round to the nearest whole number.

Critical Thinking

38. Compensation   You have a choice of receiving a wage of $34,000 per year, $2840 per month, $650 per week, or $18 per hour. Which pay choice would you take? Assume a 40-hour work week with 52 weeks of work per year.

39. ◼ The price–earnings ratio of a company's stock is one measure used by stock market analysts to assess the financial well-being of the company. Explain the meaning of the price–earnings ratio.

Projects or Group Activities

Other Bases for Rates   Some unit rates are so small that they are difficult to read, so a base other than 1 is used. Some common bases are 1000, 100,000, 1,000,000, and 1,000,000,000. For instance, a smog test on a car may be reported as 650 parts per million, abbreviated 650 ppm. This means that there are 650 smog molecules (such as nitrogen dioxide or carbon monoxide) per million molecules of exhaust. This rate is easier to understand than a unit rate of $\frac{650}{1,000,000} = 0.00065$ smog molecule per 1 molecule of exhaust.

40. ◖ Infant mortality rates are reported in deaths per 1000 live births. Work through the following steps to find the infant mortality rate in the United States for a recent year, given that there were 4,316,000 live births and 29,000 deaths.
  a. Divide the number of deaths by the number of live births.
  b. Multiply the answer by 1000. Round to the nearest tenth. This is the infant mortality rate per thousand.

41. The Environmental Projection Agency (EPA) has started using a new statistic on EPA fuel economy stickers—gallons of gas used per 100 miles driven. To find the number of gallons used per 100 miles, divide 100 by the car's miles-per-gallon (mpg) rating. What is the number of gallons per 100 miles for a car that has a rating of 28 mpg? Round to the nearest tenth.

42. The maximum amount of arsenic that is allowed in safe drinking water is 0.010 ppm. What is this amount in parts per billion (ppb)?

43. A safe level of beryllium in drinking water is set at 4 ppb. What is this amount in parts per million (ppm)?

✓ CHECK YOUR PROGRESS: CHAPTER 4

For Exercises 1 to 3, write the ratio in simplest form using a fraction and a colon.

1. 12 minutes to 48 minutes   **2.** 24 pounds to 36 pounds   **3.** 25 miles to 60 miles

For Exercises 4 to 6, write the rate as a unit rate. Round to the nearest tenth.

4. $96 in 4 hours   **5.** 100 yards in 9.6 seconds   **6.** 525 miles on 18 gallons of gasoline

7. Lawn Care   A fertilizer manufacturer recommends using 10 gallons of liquid fertilizer for every 400 square feet of lawn. What is the recommended amount of fertilizer per square foot of lawn?

8. Nutrition   There are 150 calories in an 8-ounce glass of whole milk. What is the number of calories per ounce in whole milk?

9. Consumerism   One dozen long-stemmed roses cost $51. What is the cost per rose?

10. Consumerism   A certain cyan print cartridge will print 2000 pages before it needs to be replaced. If the cost of the cartridge is $85, what is the cost per page for this cartridge?

4.3 Proportions

OBJECTIVE A *To determine whether a proportion is true*

 Point of Interest
Proportions were studied by the earliest mathematicians. Clay tablets uncovered by archaeologists show evidence of proportions in Egyptian and Babylonian cultures dating from 1800 B.C.

A **proportion** is an expression of the equality of two ratios or rates.

$$\frac{50 \text{ miles}}{4 \text{ gallons}} = \frac{25 \text{ miles}}{2 \text{ gallons}}$$

Note that the units of the numerators are the same and the units of the denominators are the same.

$$\frac{3}{6} = \frac{1}{2}$$

This is the equality of two ratios.

A proportion is **true** if the fractions are equal when written in simplest form.

In any true proportion, the **cross products** are equal.

HOW TO 1 Is $\frac{2}{3} = \frac{8}{12}$ a true proportion?

$$\frac{2}{3} \diagdown\!\!\!\!\diagup \frac{8}{12} \quad \begin{array}{l} 3 \times 8 = 24 \\ 2 \times 12 = 24 \end{array} \quad \begin{array}{l} \text{The cross products } are \text{ equal.} \\ \frac{2}{3} = \frac{8}{12} \text{ is a true proportion.} \end{array}$$

A proportion is **not true** if the fractions are not equal when reduced to simplest form.

If the cross products are not equal, then the proportion is not true.

HOW TO 2 Is $\frac{4}{5} = \frac{8}{9}$ a true proportion?

$$\frac{4}{5} \diagdown\!\!\!\!\diagup \frac{8}{9} \quad \begin{array}{l} 5 \times 8 = 40 \\ 4 \times 9 = 36 \end{array} \quad \begin{array}{l} \text{The cross products } are \text{ not} \text{ equal.} \\ \frac{4}{5} = \frac{8}{9} \text{ is not a true proportion.} \end{array}$$

EXAMPLE 1

Is $\frac{5}{8} = \frac{10}{16}$ a true proportion?

Solution

$$\frac{5}{8} \diagdown\!\!\!\!\diagup \frac{10}{16} \quad \begin{array}{l} 8 \times 10 = 80 \\ 5 \times 16 = 80 \end{array}$$

The cross products are equal.
The proportion is true.

EXAMPLE 2

Is $\frac{62 \text{ miles}}{4 \text{ gallons}} = \frac{33 \text{ miles}}{2 \text{ gallons}}$ a true proportion?

Solution

$$\frac{62}{4} \diagdown\!\!\!\!\diagup \frac{33}{2} \quad \begin{array}{l} 4 \times 33 = 132 \\ 62 \times 2 = 124 \end{array}$$

The cross products are not equal.
The proportion is not true.

YOU TRY IT 1

Is $\frac{6}{10} = \frac{9}{15}$ a true proportion?

Your solution

YOU TRY IT 2

Is $\frac{\$32}{6 \text{ hours}} = \frac{\$90}{8 \text{ hours}}$ a true proportion?

Your solution

Solutions on p. S11

OBJECTIVE B   *To solve proportions*

Tips for Success
An important element
of success is practice.
We cannot do anything
well if we do not practice
it repeatedly. Practice
is crucial to success
in mathematics. In this
objective you are learning
a new skill: how to solve a
proportion. You will need to
practice this skill over and
over again in order to be
successful at it.

Sometimes one of the numbers in a proportion is unknown. In this case, it is necessary to *solve* the proportion.

To **solve a proportion,** find a number to replace the unknown so that the proportion is true.

HOW TO 3   Solve: $\dfrac{9}{6} = \dfrac{3}{n}$

$\dfrac{9}{6} = \dfrac{3}{n}$

$9 \times n = 6 \times 3$ • Find the cross products.

$9 \times n = 18$

$n = 18 \div 9$ • Think of $9 \times n = 18$ as $9\overline{)18}$.

$n = 2$

Check:

$\dfrac{9}{6} \diagup\!\!\!\!\diagdown \dfrac{3}{2}$ $6 \times 3 = 18$
    $9 \times 2 = 18$

EXAMPLE 3

Solve $\dfrac{n}{12} = \dfrac{25}{60}$ and check.

Solution

$n \times 60 = 12 \times 25$ • Find the cross
$n \times 60 = 300$ products. Then
$n = 300 \div 60$ solve for n.
$n = 5$

Check:

$\dfrac{5}{12} \diagup\!\!\!\!\diagdown \dfrac{25}{60}$ $12 \times 25 = 300$
        $5 \times 60 = 300$

YOU TRY IT 3

Solve $\dfrac{n}{14} = \dfrac{3}{7}$ and check.

Your solution

EXAMPLE 4

Solve $\dfrac{4}{9} = \dfrac{n}{16}$. Round to the nearest tenth.

Solution

$4 \times 16 = 9 \times n$ • Find the cross
$64 = 9 \times n$ products. Then
$64 \div 9 = n$ solve for n.
$7.1 \approx n$

Note: A rounded answer is an approximation.
Therefore, the answer to a check will not be exact.

YOU TRY IT 4

Solve $\dfrac{5}{7} = \dfrac{n}{20}$. Round to the nearest tenth.

Your solution

Solutions on pp. S11–S12

EXAMPLE 5

Solve $\frac{28}{52} = \frac{7}{n}$ and check.

Solution

$28 \times n = 52 \times 7$ • **Find the cross**
$28 \times n = 364$ **products. Then**
$\quad\quad n = 364 \div 28$ **solve for n.**
$\quad\quad n = 13$

Check:

$$\frac{28}{52} \diagdown \frac{7}{13} \rightarrow \begin{array}{l} 52 \times 7 = 364 \\ 28 \times 13 = 364 \end{array}$$

YOU TRY IT 5

Solve $\frac{15}{20} = \frac{12}{n}$ and check.

Your solution

EXAMPLE 6

Solve $\frac{15}{n} = \frac{8}{3}$. Round to the nearest hundredth.

Solution

$15 \times 3 = n \times 8$
$\quad\quad 45 = n \times 8$
$45 \div 8 = n$
$\quad 5.63 \approx n$

YOU TRY IT 6

Solve $\frac{12}{n} = \frac{7}{4}$. Round to the nearest hundredth.

Your solution

EXAMPLE 7

Solve $\frac{n}{9} = \frac{3}{1}$ and check.

Solution

$n \times 1 = 9 \times 3$
$n \times 1 = 27$
$\quad\quad n = 27 \div 1$
$\quad\quad n = 27$

Check:

$$\frac{27}{9} \diagdown \frac{3}{1} \rightarrow \begin{array}{l} 9 \times 3 = 27 \\ 27 \times 1 = 27 \end{array}$$

YOU TRY IT 7

Solve $\frac{n}{12} = \frac{4}{1}$ and check.

Your solution

Solutions on p. S12

OBJECTIVE C   *To solve application problems*

The application problems in this objective require you to write and solve a proportion. When setting up a proportion, remember to keep the same units in the numerators and the same units in the denominators.

EXAMPLE 8

The dosage of a certain medication is 2 ounces for every 50 pounds of body weight. How many ounces of this medication are required for a person who weighs 175 pounds?

Strategy

To find the number of ounces of medication for a person weighing 175 pounds, write and solve a proportion using n to represent the number of ounces of medication for a 175-pound person.

Solution

$$\frac{2 \text{ ounces}}{50 \text{ pounds}} = \frac{n \text{ ounces}}{175 \text{ pounds}}$$

• The unit "ounces" is in the numerator. The unit "pounds" is in the denominator.

$$2 \times 175 = 50 \times n$$
$$350 = 50 \times n$$
$$350 \div 50 = n$$
$$7 = n$$

A 175-pound person requires 7 ounces of medication.

YOU TRY IT 8

Three tablespoons of a liquid plant fertilizer are to be added to every 4 gallons of water. How many tablespoons of fertilizer are required for 10 gallons of water?

Your strategy

Your solution

EXAMPLE 9

A mason determines that 9 cement blocks are required for a retaining wall that is 2 feet long. At this rate, how many cement blocks are required for a retaining wall that is 24 feet long?

Strategy

To find the number of cement blocks required for a retaining wall that is 24 feet long, write and solve a proportion using n to represent the number of blocks required.

Solution

$$\frac{9 \text{ cement blocks}}{2 \text{ feet}} = \frac{n \text{ cement blocks}}{24 \text{ feet}}$$

$$9 \times 24 = 2 \times n$$
$$216 = 2 \times n$$
$$216 \div 2 = n$$
$$108 = n$$

A 24-foot retaining wall requires 108 cement blocks.

YOU TRY IT 9

Twenty-four jars can be packed in 6 identical boxes. At this rate, how many jars can be packed in 15 boxes?

Your strategy

Your solution

Solutions on p. S12

4.3 EXERCISES

✔ Concept Check

Solving a proportion requires rewriting a multiplication problem as a division problem. For instance, the multiplication problem $7 \times 9 = 63$ has the related division problems $63 \div 9 = 7$ and $63 \div 7 = 9$. For Exercises 1 to 4, rewrite the given multiplication problem as a division problem whose quotient is n.

1. $n \times 15 = 45$ **2.** $12 \times n = 60$ **3.** $72 = n \times 9$ **4.** $54 = 6 \times n$

OBJECTIVE A   *To determine whether a proportion is true*

For Exercises 5 to 22, determine whether the proportion is true or not true.

5. $\dfrac{4}{8} = \dfrac{10}{20}$ **6.** $\dfrac{39}{48} = \dfrac{13}{16}$ **7.** $\dfrac{7}{8} = \dfrac{11}{12}$ **8.** $\dfrac{15}{7} = \dfrac{17}{8}$

9. $\dfrac{27}{8} = \dfrac{9}{4}$ **10.** $\dfrac{3}{18} = \dfrac{4}{19}$ **11.** $\dfrac{45}{135} = \dfrac{3}{9}$ **12.** $\dfrac{3}{4} = \dfrac{54}{72}$

13. $\dfrac{50 \text{ miles}}{2 \text{ gallons}} = \dfrac{25 \text{ miles}}{1 \text{ gallon}}$ **14.** $\dfrac{16 \text{ feet}}{10 \text{ seconds}} = \dfrac{24 \text{ feet}}{15 \text{ seconds}}$

15. $\dfrac{6 \text{ minutes}}{5 \text{ cents}} = \dfrac{30 \text{ minutes}}{25 \text{ cents}}$ **16.** $\dfrac{16 \text{ pounds}}{12 \text{ days}} = \dfrac{20 \text{ pounds}}{14 \text{ days}}$

17. $\dfrac{\$15}{4 \text{ pounds}} = \dfrac{\$45}{12 \text{ pounds}}$ **18.** $\dfrac{270 \text{ trees}}{6 \text{ acres}} = \dfrac{90 \text{ trees}}{2 \text{ acres}}$

19. $\dfrac{300 \text{ feet}}{4 \text{ rolls}} = \dfrac{450 \text{ feet}}{7 \text{ rolls}}$ **20.** $\dfrac{1 \text{ gallon}}{4 \text{ quarts}} = \dfrac{7 \text{ gallons}}{28 \text{ quarts}}$

21. $\dfrac{\$65}{5 \text{ days}} = \dfrac{\$26}{2 \text{ days}}$ **22.** $\dfrac{80 \text{ miles}}{2 \text{ hours}} = \dfrac{110 \text{ miles}}{3 \text{ hours}}$

23. 🐿 Suppose in a true proportion you switch the numerator of the first fraction with the denominator of the second fraction. Must the result be another true proportion?

24. 🐿 Write a true proportion in which the cross products are equal to 36.

OBJECTIVE B   *To solve proportions*

25. ⬚ Consider the proportion $\frac{n}{7} = \frac{9}{21}$ in Exercise 27. The simplest form of the ratio $\frac{9}{21}$ is $\frac{3}{7}$. Will solving the proportion $\frac{n}{7} = \frac{3}{7}$ give the same result for n as found in Exercise 27?

For Exercises 26 to 45, solve. Round to the nearest hundredth, if necessary.

26. $\frac{n}{4} = \frac{6}{8}$

27. $\frac{n}{7} = \frac{9}{21}$

28. $\frac{12}{18} = \frac{n}{9}$

29. $\frac{7}{21} = \frac{35}{n}$

30. $\frac{6}{n} = \frac{24}{36}$

31. $\frac{3}{n} = \frac{15}{10}$

32. $\frac{n}{6} = \frac{2}{3}$

33. $\frac{5}{12} = \frac{n}{144}$

34. $\frac{n}{5} = \frac{7}{8}$

35. $\frac{4}{n} = \frac{9}{5}$

36. $\frac{5}{12} = \frac{n}{8}$

37. $\frac{36}{20} = \frac{12}{n}$

38. $\frac{n}{15} = \frac{21}{12}$

39. $\frac{40}{n} = \frac{15}{8}$

40. $\frac{28}{8} = \frac{12}{n}$

41. $\frac{n}{30} = \frac{65}{120}$

42. $\frac{0.3}{5.6} = \frac{n}{25}$

43. $\frac{1.3}{16} = \frac{n}{30}$

44. $\frac{0.7}{9.8} = \frac{3.6}{n}$

45. $\frac{1.9}{7} = \frac{13}{n}$

OBJECTIVE C   *To solve application problems*

46. ⬚ Jesse walked 3 miles in 40 minutes. Let n be the number of miles Jesse can walk in 60 minutes at the same rate. To determine how many miles Jesse can walk in 60 minutes, a student used the proportion $\frac{40}{3} = \frac{60}{n}$. Is this a valid proportion to use in solving this problem?

47. **Nutrition**   A 6-ounce package of Puffed Wheat contains 600 calories. How many calories are contained in a 0.5-ounce serving of the cereal?

48. ⬤ **Health**   Using the information in the news clipping at the right and a figure of 309 million for the number of Americans, determine the number of **a.** overweight Americans and **b.** obese Americans.

49. **Fuel Efficiency**   A car travels 70.5 miles on 3 gallons of gas. Find the distance the car can travel on 14 gallons of gas.

In the NEWS!

Small Gains in Obesity Battle

A recent study shows a small but encouraging increase in the number of Americans of normal weight. Still, obesity remains a major health problem in the United States, with approximately 1 in 3 Americans falling in the overweight category, and 1 in 4 in the obese category.

Source: msnbc.com

50. **Landscaping**   Ron Stokes uses 2 pounds of fertilizer for every 100 square feet of lawn for landscape maintenance. At this rate, how many pounds of fertilizer did he use on a lawn that measures 3500 square feet?

51. **Gardening**   A nursery prepares a liquid plant food by adding 1 gallon of water for each 2 ounces of plant food. At this rate, how many gallons of water are required for 25 ounces of plant food?

52. **Masonry**   A brick wall 20 feet in length contains 1040 bricks. At the same rate, how many bricks would it take to build a wall 48 feet in length?

53. **Cartography**   The scale on the map at the right is "1.25 inches equals 10 miles." Find the distance between Carlsbad and Del Mar, which are 2 inches apart on the map.

54. **Architecture**   The scale on the plans for a new house is "1 inch equals 3 feet." Find the width and the length of a room that measures 5 inches by 8 inches on the drawing.

55. **Medicine**   The dosage for a medication is $\frac{1}{3}$ ounce for every 40 pounds of body weight. At this rate, how many ounces of medication should a physician prescribe for a patient who weighs 150 pounds? Write the answer as a decimal.

56. **Banking**   A bank requires a monthly payment of $33.45 on a $2500 loan. At the same rate, find the monthly payment on a $10,000 loan.

57. **Elections**   A pre-election survey showed that 2 out of every 3 eligible voters would cast ballots in the county election. At this rate, how many people in a county of 240,000 eligible voters would vote in the election?

58. **Interior Design**   A paint manufacturer suggests using 1 gallon of paint for every 400 square feet of wall. At this rate, how many gallons of paint would be required for a room that has 1400 square feet of wall?

59. **Insurance**   A 60-year-old male can obtain $10,000 of life insurance for $35.35 per month. At this rate, what is the monthly cost for $50,000 of life insurance?

60. ● **Food Waste**   At the rate given in the news clipping, find the cost of food wasted yearly by **a.** the average family of three and **b.** the average family of five.

61. **Manufacturing**   Suppose a computer chip manufacturer knows that in an average production run of 2000 circuit boards, 60 will be defective. How many defective circuit boards are expected in a run of 25,000 circuit boards?

62. **Investments**   You own 240 shares of stock in a computer company. The company declares a stock split of 5 shares for every 3 owned. How many shares of stock will you own after the stock split?

In the NEWS!

How Much Food Do You Waste?

In the United States, the estimated cost of food wasted each year by the average family of four is $590.

Source: University of Arizona

63. **Physics** The ratio of weight on the moon to weight on Earth is 1:6. If a bowling ball weighs 16 pounds on Earth, what would it weigh on the moon? Round to the nearest hundredth of a pound.

64. **Automobiles** When engineers designed a new car, they first built a model of the car. The ratio of the size of a part on the model to the actual size of the part is 2:5. If a door is 1.3 feet long on the model, what is the length of the door on the car?

65. **Investments** Carlos Capasso owns 50 shares of Texas Utilities that pay dividends of $153. At this rate, what dividend would Carlos receive after buying 300 additional shares of Texas Utilities?

Critical Thinking

66. **Gaming** Use the information in the news clipping at the right. Explain how a proportion can be used to determine the number of Nintendo DS systems sold given the number of Nintendo 3DS systems sold.

67. **Social Security** According to the Social Security Administration, the numbers of workers per retiree in the future are expected to be as given in the table below.
Why is the shrinking number of workers per retiree of importance to the Social Security Administration?

Year	2020	2030	2040
Number of workers per retiree	2.5	2.1	2.0

68. **Elections** A survey of voters in a city claimed that 2 people of every 5 who voted cast a ballot in favor of city amendment A and that 3 people of every 4 who voted cast a ballot against amendment A. Is this possible? Explain your answer.

Projects or Group Activities

69. **Anatomy** The average circumference (the distance around an object) of a baby's head at birth is approximately 13.7 inches. The average length of a baby at birth is approximately 20 inches. Measure the circumference of your head and your height in inches. Is the ratio of a baby's head circumference at birth to your head circumference equal to the ratio of a baby's length at birth to your height? Based on your findings, does the circumference of a person's head grow more slowly or more quickly than the person's height?

70. **Biology** One way biologists measure a wildlife population is by capturing a certain species of animal, tagging it, and then releasing it back into the wild. Suppose a biologist captures 100 trout from a lake, tags them, and releases them back into the water. One month later, the biologist captures 50 trout from the same lake and finds that 3 trout have tags. Based on this information, approximate the number of trout in the lake.

Michael Dunning/Getty Images

In the NEWS!

Old DS Outsells New 3D System

Figures released for the month of June show that the Nintendo DS handheld game system outsold the newer Nintendo 3DS by 2.7 systems to 1.
Source: msnbc.com

CHAPTER

4 | Summary

Key Words

Examples

A **ratio** is the comparison of two quantities with the same units. A ratio can be written in three ways: as a fraction, as two numbers separated by a colon (:), or as two numbers separated by the word *to*. A ratio is in **simplest form** when the two numbers do not have a common factor other than 1. [4.1A, p. 178]

The comparison 16 to 24 ounces can be written as a ratio in simplest form as $\frac{2}{3}$, 2 : 3, or 2 to 3.

A **rate** is the comparison of two quantities with different units. A rate is written as a fraction. A rate is in **simplest form** when the numbers that form the rate do not have a common factor other than 1. [4.2A, p. 182]

You earned $63 for working 6 hours. The rate is written in simplest form as $\frac{\$21}{2 \text{ hours}}$.

A **unit rate** is a rate in which the number in the denominator is 1. [4.2B, p. 182]

You traveled 144 miles in 3 hours. The unit rate is 48 miles per hour.

A **proportion** is an expression of the equality of two ratios or rates. A proportion is true if the fractions are equal when written in simplest form; in any true proportion, the **cross products** are equal. A proportion is not true if the fractions are not equal when written in simplest form; if the cross products are not equal, the proportion is not true. [4.3A, p. 188]

The proportion $\frac{3}{5} = \frac{12}{20}$ is true because the cross products are equal:

$3 \times 20 = 5 \times 12$.

The proportion $\frac{3}{4} = \frac{12}{20}$ is not true because the cross products are not equal:

$3 \times 20 \neq 4 \times 12$.

Essential Rules and Procedures

Examples

To find a unit rate, divide the number in the numerator of the rate by the number in the denominator of the rate. [4.2B, p. 182]

You earned $41 for working 4 hours.

$$\frac{41}{4} = 41 \div 4 = 10.25$$

The unit rate is $10.25/hour.

To solve a proportion, find a number to replace the unknown so that the proportion is true. [4.3B, p. 189]

$$\frac{6}{24} = \frac{9}{n}$$

$6 \times n = 24 \times 9$ • Find the cross products.

$6 \times n = 216$

$n = 216 \div 6$

$n = 36$

To set up a proportion, keep the same units in the numerators and the same units in the denominators. [4.3C, p. 190]

Three machines fill 5 cereal boxes per minute. How many boxes can 8 machines fill per minute?

$$\frac{3 \text{ machines}}{5 \text{ cereal boxes}} = \frac{8 \text{ machines}}{n \text{ cereal boxes}}$$

4 Review Exercises

1. Is $\frac{2}{9} = \frac{10}{45}$ a true proportion?

2. Write the comparison 32 dollars to 80 dollars as a ratio in simplest form using a fraction, a colon (:), and the word *to*.

3. Write "250 miles in 4 hours" as a unit rate.

4. Is $\frac{8}{15} = \frac{32}{60}$ a true proportion?

5. Solve the proportion.
$$\frac{16}{n} = \frac{4}{17}$$

6. Write "$500 earned in 40 hours" as a unit rate.

7. Write "$8.75 for 5 pounds" as a unit rate.

8. Write the comparison 8 feet to 28 feet as a ratio in simplest form using a fraction, a colon (:), and the word *to*.

9. Solve the proportion.
$$\frac{n}{8} = \frac{9}{2}$$

10. Solve the proportion. Round to the nearest hundredth.
$$\frac{18}{35} = \frac{10}{n}$$

11. Write the comparison 6 inches to 15 inches as a ratio in simplest form using a fraction, a colon (:), and the word *to*.

12. Is $\frac{3}{8} = \frac{10}{24}$ a true proportion?

13. Write "$35 in 4 hours" as a rate in simplest form.

14. Write "326.4 miles on 12 gallons" as a unit rate.

15. Write the comparison 12 days to 12 days as a ratio in simplest form using a fraction, a colon (:), and the word *to*.

16. Is $\frac{5}{7} = \frac{25}{35}$ a true proportion?

17. Solve the proportion. Round to the nearest hundredth.

$$\frac{24}{11} = \frac{n}{30}$$

18. Write "100 miles in 3 hours" as a rate in simplest form.

19. Business In 5 years, the price of a calculator went from $80 to $48. What is the ratio, as a fraction in simplest form, of the decrease in price to the original price?

20. Taxes The property tax on a $245,000 home is $4900. At the same rate, what is the property tax on a home valued at $320,000?

21. Consumerism Rita Sterling bought a computer system for $2400. Five years later, she sold the computer for $900. Find the ratio of the amount she received for the computer to the cost of the computer.

22. Manufacturing The total cost of manufacturing 1000 camera phones was $36,600. Of the phones made, 24 did not pass inspection. What is the cost per phone of the phones that *did* pass inspection?

23. Masonry A brick wall 40 feet in length contains 448 concrete blocks. At the same rate, how many blocks would it take to build a wall that is 120 feet in length?

24. Advertising A retail computer store spends $30,000 a year on radio advertising and $12,000 on newspaper advertising. Find the ratio, as a fraction in simplest form, of radio advertising to newspaper advertising.

25. Consumerism A 15-pound turkey costs $13.95. What is the cost per pound?

26. Travel Mahesh drove 198.8 miles in 3.5 hours. Find the average number of miles he drove per hour.

27. Insurance An insurance policy costs $9.87 for every $1000 of insurance. At this rate, what is the cost of $50,000 of insurance?

28. Investments Pascal Hollis purchased 80 shares of stock for $3580. What was the cost per share?

29. Landscaping Monique uses 1.5 pounds of fertilizer for every 200 square feet of lawn. How many pounds of fertilizer will she have to use on a lawn that measures 3000 square feet?

30. Real Estate A house had an original value of $160,000, but its value increased to $240,000 in 2 years. Find the ratio, as a fraction in simplest form, of the increase to the original value.

4   TEST

1. Write "$46,036.80 earned in 12 months" as a unit rate.

2. Write the comparison 40 miles to 240 miles as a ratio in simplest form using a fraction, a colon (:), and the word *to*.

3. Write "18 supports for every 8 feet" as a rate in simplest form.

4. Is $\frac{40}{125} = \frac{5}{25}$ a true proportion?

5. Write the comparison 12 days to 4 days as a ratio in simplest form using a fraction, a colon (:), and the word *to*.

6. Solve the proportion.
   $$\frac{5}{12} = \frac{60}{n}$$

7. Write "256.2 miles on 8.4 gallons of gas" as a unit rate.

8. Write the comparison 27 dollars to 81 dollars as a ratio in simplest form using a fraction, a colon (:), and the word *to*.

9. Is $\frac{5}{14} = \frac{25}{70}$ a true proportion?

10. Solve the proportion.
    $$\frac{n}{18} = \frac{9}{4}$$

11. Write "9 feet for 6 boards" as a rate in simplest form.

12. Write the comparison 18 feet to 30 feet as a ratio in simplest form using a fraction, a colon (:), and the word *to*.

13. **Investments** Fifty shares of a utility stock pay a dividend of $62.50. At the same rate, what is the dividend paid on 500 shares of the utility stock?

14. **Electricity** A transformer has 40 turns in the primary coil and 480 turns in the secondary coil. State the ratio of the number of turns in the primary coil to the number of turns in the secondary coil.

Primary coil   Secondary coil

15. **Travel** A plane travels 2421 miles in 4.5 hours. Find the plane's speed in miles per hour.

16. **Physiology** A research scientist estimates that the human body contains 88 pounds of water for every 100 pounds of body weight. At this rate, estimate the number of pounds of water in a college student who weighs 150 pounds.

17. **Business** If 40 feet of lumber costs $69.20, what is the per-foot cost of the lumber?

18. **Medicine** The dosage of a certain medication is $\frac{1}{4}$ ounce for every 50 pounds of body weight. How many ounces of this medication are required for a person who weighs 175 pounds? Write the answer as a decimal.

19. **Sports** A basketball team won 20 games and lost 5 games during the season. Write, as a fraction in simplest form, the ratio of the number of games won to the total number of games played.

20. **Manufacturing** A computer manufacturer discovers through experience that an average of 3 defective hard drives are found in every 100 hard drives manufactured. How many defective hard drives are expected to be found in the production of 1200 hard drives?

Cumulative Review Exercises

1. Subtract: 20,095
$\phantom{\text{Subtract: }} - 10,937$

2. Write $2 \cdot 2 \cdot 2 \cdot 2 \cdot 3 \cdot 3 \cdot 3$ in exponential notation.

3. Simplify: $4 - (5 - 2)^2 \div 3 + 2$

4. Find the prime factorization of 160.

5. Find the LCM of 9, 12, and 18.

6. Find the GCF of 28 and 42.

7. Write $\frac{40}{64}$ in simplest form.

8. Find $4\frac{7}{15}$ more than $3\frac{5}{6}$.

9. What is $4\frac{5}{9}$ less than $10\frac{1}{6}$?

10. Multiply: $\dfrac{11}{12} \times 3\dfrac{1}{11}$

11. Find the quotient of $3\frac{1}{3}$ and $\frac{5}{7}$.

12. Simplify: $\left(\dfrac{2}{5} + \dfrac{3}{4} \right) \div \dfrac{3}{2}$

13. Write 4.0709 in words.

14. Round 2.09762 to the nearest hundredth.

15. Divide: $8.09\overline{)16.0976}$
Round to the nearest thousandth.

16. Convert 0.06 to a fraction.

17. Write the comparison 25 miles to 200 miles as a ratio in simplest form using a fraction.

18. Write "87 cents for 6 pencils" as a rate in simplest form.

19. Write "250.5 miles on 7.5 gallons of gas" as a unit rate.

20. Solve $\frac{40}{n} = \frac{160}{17}$.

21. Travel   A car traveled 457.6 miles in 8 hours. Find the car's speed in miles per hour.

22. Solve the proportion.
$$\frac{12}{5} = \frac{n}{15}$$

23. Banking   You had $1024 in your checking account. You then wrote checks for $192 and $88. What is your new checking account balance?

24. Finance   Malek Khatri buys a tractor for $32,360. A down payment of $5000 is required. The balance remaining is paid in 48 equal monthly installments. What is the monthly payment?

25. Homework Assignments   Yuko is assigned to read a book containing 175 pages. She reads $\frac{2}{5}$ of the book during Thanksgiving vacation. How many pages of the assignment remain to be read?

26. Real Estate   A building contractor bought $2\frac{1}{3}$ acres of land for $84,000. What was the cost of each acre?

27. Consumerism   Benjamin Eli bought a shirt for $45.58 and a tie for $19.18. He used a $100 bill to pay for the purchases. Find the amount of change.

28. Compensation   If you earn an annual salary of $41,619, what is your monthly salary?

29. Erosion   A soil conservationist estimates that a river bank is eroding at the rate of 3 inches every 6 months. At this rate, how many inches will be eroded in 50 months?

30. Medicine   The dosage of a certain medication is $\frac{1}{2}$ ounce for every 50 pounds of body weight. How many ounces of this medication are required for a person who weighs 160 pounds? Write the answer as a decimal.

Percents

OBJECTIVES

SECTION 5.1

A To write a percent as a decimal or a fraction

B To write a decimal or a fraction as a percent

SECTION 5.2

A To find the amount when the percent and the base are given

B To solve application problems

SECTION 5.3

A To find the percent when the base and the amount are given

B To solve application problems

SECTION 5.4

A To find the base when the percent and the amount are given

B To solve application problems

SECTION 5.5

A To solve percent problems using proportions

B To solve application problems

Focus on Success

Did you read Ask the Authors at the front of this text? If you did, then you know that the authors' advice is that you practice, practice, practice—and then practice some more. The more time you spend doing math outside of class, the more successful you will be in this course. (See Ask the Authors, page i, and Make the Commitment to Succeed, page AIM-3.)

© iStockphoto.com/Pete Saloutos

Prep Test

Are you ready to succeed in this chapter? Take the Prep Test below to find out if you are ready to learn the new material.

For Exercises 1 to 6, multiply or divide.

1. $19 \times \dfrac{1}{100}$

2. 23×0.01

3. 0.47×100

4. $0.06 \times 47{,}500$

5. $60 \div 0.015$

6. $8 \div \dfrac{1}{4}$

7. Multiply $\dfrac{5}{8} \times 100$. Write the answer as a decimal.

8. Write $\dfrac{200}{3}$ as a mixed number.

9. Divide $28 \div 16$. Write the answer as a decimal.

5.1 Introduction to Percents

OBJECTIVE A *To write a percent as a decimal or a fraction*

Percent means "parts of 100." In the figure at the right, there are 100 parts. Because 13 of the 100 parts are shaded, 13% of the figure is shaded. The symbol % is the **percent sign.**

In most applied problems involving percents, it is necessary either to rewrite a percent as a decimal or a fraction or to rewrite a fraction or a decimal as a percent.

To write a percent as a decimal, remove the percent sign and multiply by 0.01.

$$13\% \quad = \quad 13 \times 0.01 \quad = \quad 0.13$$

Move the decimal point two places to the left. Then remove the percent sign.

Take Note

Recall that division is defined as multiplication by the reciprocal. Therefore, multiplying by $\frac{1}{100}$ is equivalent to dividing by 100.

To write a percent as a fraction, remove the percent sign and multiply by $\frac{1}{100}$.

$$13\% = 13 \times \frac{1}{100} = \frac{13}{100}$$

EXAMPLE 1

Write each percent as a decimal and as a fraction.
a. 120% **b.** 4.3% **c.** 0.45%

Solution

a. $120\% = 120 \times 0.01 = 1.2$

$120\% = 120 \times \frac{1}{100} = \frac{120}{100} = 1\frac{1}{5}$

b. $4.3\% = 4.3 \times 0.01 = 0.043$

$4.3\% = 4.3 \times \frac{1}{100}$

$= 4\frac{3}{10} \times \frac{1}{100}$ • $4.3 = 4\frac{3}{10}$

$= \frac{43}{10} \times \frac{1}{100} = \frac{43}{1000}$ • Multiply the fractions.

c. $0.45\% = 0.45 \times 0.01 = 0.0045$

$0.45\% = 0.45 \times \frac{1}{100}$

$= \frac{9}{20} \times \frac{1}{100}$ • $0.45 = \frac{45}{100} = \frac{9}{20}$

$= \frac{9}{2000}$ • Multiply the fractions.

YOU TRY IT 1

Write each percent as a decimal and as a fraction.
a. 125% **b.** 8.5% **c.** 0.25%

Your solution

Solution on p. S12

EXAMPLE 2

Write $16\frac{2}{3}\%$ as a fraction.

Solution
$$16\frac{2}{3}\% = 16\frac{2}{3} \times \frac{1}{100}$$
$$= \frac{50}{3} \times \frac{1}{100} = \frac{50}{300} = \frac{1}{6}$$

YOU TRY IT 2

Write $33\frac{1}{3}\%$ as a fraction.

Your solution

Solution on p. S12

OBJECTIVE B *To write a decimal or a fraction as a percent*

A decimal or a fraction can be written as a percent by multiplying by 100%.

HOW TO 1 Write 0.37 as a percent.

$$0.37 \quad = \quad 0.37 \times 100\% \quad = \quad 37\%$$

Move the decimal point two places to the right. Then write the percent sign.

When changing a fraction to a percent, if the fraction can be written as a terminating decimal, the percent is written in decimal form. If the decimal representation of the fraction is a repeating decimal, the answer is written with a fraction.

 Take Note

The decimal form of $\frac{3}{8}$ terminates.

$$\begin{array}{r} 0.375 \\ 8\overline{)3.000} \\ \underline{-2\,4} \\ 60 \\ \underline{-56} \\ 40 \\ \underline{-40} \\ 0 \end{array}$$

HOW TO 2 Write $\frac{3}{8}$ as a percent.

$$\frac{3}{8} = \frac{3}{8} \times \frac{100\%}{1}$$

$$= \frac{300\%}{8}$$

$$= 37.5\%$$

• $\dfrac{3}{8} = 0.375$ **is a terminating decimal.**

• **The answer is written in decimal form.**

 Take Note

The decimal form of $\frac{1}{6}$ repeats.

$$\begin{array}{r} 0.166\overline{} \\ 6\overline{)1.000} \\ \underline{-6} \\ 40 \\ \underline{-36} \\ 40 \\ \underline{-36} \\ 4 \end{array}$$

HOW TO 3 Write $\frac{1}{6}$ as a percent.

$$\frac{1}{6} = \frac{1}{6} \times \frac{100\%}{1}$$

$$= \frac{100\%}{6}$$

$$= 16\frac{2}{3}\%$$

• $\dfrac{1}{6} = 0.1\overline{6}$ **is a repeating decimal.**

• **The answer is written with a fraction.**

EXAMPLE 3

Write 0.015 and 2.3 as percents.

Solution

$$0.015 = 0.015 \times 100\%$$
$$= 1.5\%$$

$$2.3 = 2.3 \times 100\%$$
$$= 230\%$$

YOU TRY IT 3

Write 0.048 and 3.6 as percents.

Your solution

EXAMPLE 4

Write $\frac{19}{80}$ as a percent.

Solution

$$\frac{19}{80} \times \frac{100\%}{1} = \frac{1900\%}{80}$$
$$= 23.75\% \quad \bullet \text{ Write the answer in decimal form.}$$

YOU TRY IT 4

Write $\frac{5}{16}$ as a percent.

Your solution

EXAMPLE 5

Write $\frac{2}{3}$ as a percent.

Solution

$$\frac{2}{3} = \frac{2}{3} \times \frac{100\%}{1}$$
$$= \frac{200\%}{3}$$
$$= 66\frac{2}{3}\% \quad \bullet \text{ Write the answer with a fraction.}$$

YOU TRY IT 5

Write $\frac{5}{6}$ as a percent.

Your solution

5.1 EXERCISES

✔ Concept Check

1. Percent means "parts of ____."

2. If you answered correctly 85% of the questions on a 100-question exam, how many questions did you answer correctly?

3. To change a percent to a decimal, remove the percent sign and move the decimal point two places to the _____.

4. To change a fraction to a percent, multiply the fraction by _____.

OBJECTIVE A   *To write a percent as a decimal or a fraction*

For Exercises 5 to 26, write the percent as a decimal and as a fraction.

5. 72%   **6.** 65%   **7.** 23%   **8.** 79%   **9.** 36%

10. 69%   **11.** 59%   **12.** 24%   **13.** 41%   **14.** 25%

15. 25.4%   **16.** 34%   **17.** 57.9%   **18.** 73.6%

19. 6.2%   **20.** 6.9%   **21.** 6.4%   **22.** 7.5%

23. 0.25%   **24.** 0.875%   **25.** 0.55%   **26.** 0.74%

For Exercises 27 to 38, write as a fraction.

27. $66\frac{2}{3}\%$ **28.** $12\frac{1}{2}\%$ **29.** $83\frac{1}{3}\%$ **30.** $3\frac{1}{8}\%$ **31.** $11\frac{1}{9}\%$ **32.** $\frac{3}{8}\%$

33. $45\frac{5}{11}\%$ **34.** $15\frac{3}{8}\%$ **35.** $4\frac{2}{7}\%$ **36.** $5\frac{3}{4}\%$ **37.** $6\frac{2}{3}\%$ **38.** $8\frac{2}{3}\%$

39. 📝 When a certain percent is written as a fraction, the result is an improper fraction. Is the percent less than, equal to, or greater than 100%?

OBJECTIVE B   *To write a decimal or a fraction as a percent*

For Exercises 40 to 51, write as a percent.

40. 0.16   **41.** 0.73   **42.** 0.05   **43.** 0.01   **44.** 1.07   **45.** 2.94

46. 0.004   **47.** 0.006   **48.** 1.012   **49.** 3.106   **50.** 0.8   **51.** 0.7

For Exercises 52 to 71, write as a percent.

52. $\dfrac{27}{50}$ **53.** $\dfrac{17}{20}$ **54.** $\dfrac{9}{16}$ **55.** $\dfrac{2}{5}$ **56.** $\dfrac{5}{8}$ **57.** $\dfrac{1}{8}$

58. $\dfrac{3}{40}$ **59.** $1\dfrac{1}{2}$ **60.** $\dfrac{7}{40}$ **61.** $\dfrac{9}{4}$ **62.** $\dfrac{16}{5}$ **63.** $\dfrac{7}{8}$

64. $\dfrac{15}{50}$ **65.** $\dfrac{12}{25}$ **66.** $\dfrac{7}{30}$ **67.** $\dfrac{4}{9}$

68. $\dfrac{7}{12}$ **69.** $1\dfrac{2}{3}$ **70.** $2\dfrac{1}{6}$ **71.** $\dfrac{7}{18}$

72. Does a mixed number represent a percent greater than 100% or less than 100%?

73. A decimal number less than 0 has zeros in the tenths and hundredths places. Does the decimal represent a percent greater than 1% or less than 1%?

74. Write the part of the square that is shaded as a fraction, as a decimal, and as a percent. Write the part of the square that is not shaded as a fraction, as a decimal, and as a percent.

Critical Thinking

75. **The Food Industry** In a survey conducted by Opinion Research Corp. for Lloyd's Barbeque Co., people were asked to name their favorite barbeque side dishes. 38% named corn on the cob, 35% named cole slaw, 11% named corn bread, and 10% named fries. What percent of those surveyed named something other than corn on the cob, cole slaw, corn bread, or fries?

76. **Elections** If $\frac{2}{5}$ of the population voted in an election, what percent of the population did not vote?

Projects or Group Activities

There is a quantity similar to percent ("per hundred") called *per mil*, which means *per thousand*. The symbol for per mil is ‰. Using this symbol, $7‰ = \dfrac{7}{1000} = 0.007$. For Exercises 77 to 80, write each per mil as a fraction in simplest form and as a decimal.

77. 53‰   **78.** 25‰   **79.** 150‰   **80.** 600‰

For Exercises 81 to 84, write each per mil as a percent.

81. 5‰   **82.** 45‰   **83.** 625‰   **84.** 1000‰

SECTION

5.2 Percent Equations: Part I

OBJECTIVE A   *To find the amount when the percent and the base are given*

Problems involving percents frequently are solved using the basic percent equation.

> **The Basic Percent Equation**
>
> Percent × base = amount

APPLY THE CONCEPT

A real estate broker receives a commission that is 4% of a $285,000 house sale. Find the amount the broker receives.

To find the amount the broker receives, we must answer the question, "4% of $285,000 is what?" This sentence can be written using mathematical symbols and then solved for the unknown number.

4%	of	$285,000	is	what?
↓	↓	↓	↓	↓

Percent 4%	×	base 285,000	=	amount n

of   is written as × (times)
is   is written as = (equals)
what is written as n (the unknown number)

$$0.04 \times 285{,}000 = n$$
$$11{,}400 = n$$

Note that the percent is written as a decimal.

The broker receives a commission of $11,400.

When solving the basic percent equation, the percent is usually written as a decimal, as in the problem above. However, some percents are more easily written as a fraction than as a decimal. For example,

$$33\frac{1}{3}\% = \frac{1}{3} \qquad 66\frac{2}{3}\% = \frac{2}{3} \qquad 16\frac{2}{3}\% = \frac{1}{6} \qquad 83\frac{1}{3}\% = \frac{5}{6}$$

EXAMPLE 1

Find 5.7% of 160.

Solution

Percent × base = amount
$$0.057 \times 160 = n$$
$$9.12 = n$$

• The word *Find* is used instead of the words *what is*.

YOU TRY IT 1

Find 6.3% of 150.

Your solution

EXAMPLE 2

What is $33\frac{1}{3}\%$ of 90?

Solution

Percent × base = amount
$$\frac{1}{3} \times 90 = n$$
$$30 = n$$

• $33\frac{1}{3}\% = \frac{1}{3}$

YOU TRY IT 2

What is $16\frac{2}{3}\%$ of 66?

Your solution

Solutions on pp. S12–S13

OBJECTIVE B   *To solve application problems*

Solving percent problems requires identifying the three elements of the basic percent equation. Recall that these three parts are the *percent,* the *base,* and the *amount.* Usually the base follows the phrase "percent of."

During a recent year, Americans gave $291 billion to charities. The circle graph at the right shows where that money came from. Use these data for Example 3 and You Try It 3.

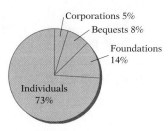

Charitable Giving
Sources: American Association of Fundraising Counsel; www.nps.gov

---

EXAMPLE 3

How much of the amount given to charities came from individuals?

Strategy

To determine the amount that came from individuals, write and solve the basic percent equation using *n* to represent the amount. The percent is 73%. The base is $291 billion.

Solution

Percent × base = amount
$$73\% \times 291 = n$$
$$0.73 \times 291 = n$$
$$212.43 = n$$

Individuals gave $212.43 billion to charities.

YOU TRY IT 3

How much of the amount given to charities was given by corporations?

Your strategy

Your solution

EXAMPLE 4

A quality control inspector found that 1.2% of 2500 camera phones inspected were defective. How many camera phones inspected were not defective?

Strategy

To find the number of nondefective phones:
• Find the number of defective phones. Write and solve the basic percent equation, using *n* to represent the number of defective phones (amount). The percent is 1.2% and the base is 2500.
• Subtract the number of defective phones from the number of phones inspected (2500).

Solution

$$1.2\% \times 2500 = n$$
$$0.012 \times 2500 = n$$
$$30 = n \text{ defective phones}$$

$$2500 - 30 = 2470$$

2470 camera phones were not defective.

YOU TRY IT 4

An electrician's hourly wage was $33.50 before an 8% raise. What is the new hourly wage?

Your strategy

Your solution

5.2 EXERCISES

✔ Concept Check

1. What is the basic percent equation?

For Exercises 2 to 4, without working the problem, determine whether the base is less than or greater than the amount.

2. What is 37% of 12?   **3.** 125.5% of 17 is what?   **4.** Find 0.5% of 33.

OBJECTIVE A   *To find the amount when the percent and the base are given*

For Exercises 5 to 22, solve.

5. 8% of 100 is what?

6. 16% of 50 is what?

7. 27% of 40 is what?

8. 52% of 95 is what?

9. 0.05% of 150 is what?

10. 0.075% of 625 is what?

11. 125% of 64 is what?

12. 210% of 12 is what?

13. Find 10.7% of 485.

14. Find 12.8% of 625.

15. What is 0.25% of 3000?

16. What is 0.06% of 250?

17. 80% of 16.25 is what?

18. 26% of 19.5 is what?

19. What is $1\frac{1}{2}$% of 250?

20. What is $5\frac{3}{4}$% of 65?

21. $16\frac{2}{3}$% of 120 is what?

22. What is $66\frac{2}{3}$% of 891?

23. Which is larger: 5% of 95, or 75% of 6?

24. Which is larger: 112% of 5, or 0.45% of 800?

25. Which is smaller: 79% of 16, or 20% of 65?

26. Which is smaller: 15% of 80, or 95% of 15?

27. Is 15% of a number greater than or less than the number?

28. Is 150% of a number greater than or less than the number?

> **OBJECTIVE B** *To solve application problems*

29. Read Exercise 30. Without doing any calculations, determine whether the number of people in the United States aged 18 to 24 who do not have health insurance is *less than, equal to,* or *greater than* 50 million.

30. **Health Insurance** Approximately 16.2% of the 50 million people in the United States who do not have health insurance are between the ages of 18 and 24. (*Source:* U.S. Census Bureau) About how many people in the United States aged 18 to 24 do not have health insurance?

31. **Aviation** Based on data from the Bureau of Transportation Statistics, there were 629.5 million domestic airline passengers in 2010. If it is forecasted that this number will increase by 22% by the year 2020, how many more domestic airline passengers will there be in 2020?

32. **Jewelry** An 18-carat, yellow-gold necklace contains 75% gold, 16% silver, and 9% copper. If the necklace weighs 25 grams, how many grams of copper are in the necklace?

33. **Jewelry** Fourteen-carat yellow gold contains 58.5% gold, 17.5% silver, and 24% copper. If a jeweler has a 50-gram piece of 14-carat yellow gold, how many grams each of gold, silver, and copper are in the piece?

In the NEWS!

E-Filing Still Rising

The Internal Revenue Service reports that of 141.5 million federal tax returns filed in 2010, about 69.8% were filed electronically.
Source: www.efile.com

34. **Car Lease Sales Tax** The base monthly payment for a car lease is $324.76 per month. If a sales tax of 7.25% is added to the base monthly payment, what is the total monthly lease payment? Round to the nearest cent.

35. **e-Filed Tax Returns** Use the information in the news clipping at the right. How many tax returns were filed electronically? Round to the nearest million.

36. **Email Spam** Based on data from Symantec Corporation, Rustock was one of the largest spam-sending botnets. During one year, Rustock was responsible for 47.5 percent of the approximately 93 million spam emails sent each day. How many spam emails did Rustock send each day that year?

37. **Car Payment** A state sales tax of 6.75% is added to the purchase of a car. If the purchase price of a car is $28,995, what is the total cost of the car, including sales tax? If that amount is repaid in 48 equal monthly payments, what is the monthly payment? Round to the nearest cent.

Critical Thinking

38. **Jewelry** Eighteen-carat white gold contains 75% gold, 15% silver, and 10% platinum. A jeweler wants to make a 2-ounce, 18-carat, white-gold ring. If gold costs $900 per ounce, silver costs $17.20 per ounce, and platinum costs $1900 per ounce, what is the cost of the metal used to make the ring?

Projects or Group Activities

The table at the right shows how to determine weekly federal withholding tax for a single person in 2011. Use this table for Exercises 39 to 43.

Income is between	Withholding amount
$0 and $40	$0
$40 and $204	$0 + 10% of amount over $40
$204 and $704	$16.40 + 15% of amount over $204
$704 and $1648	$91.40 + 25% of amount over $704
$1648 and $3394	$327.40 + 28% of amount over $1648
$3394 and $7332	$816.28 + 33% of amount over $3394
More than $7332	$2115.82 + 35% of amount over $7332

Source: Internal Revenue Service

39. What is the withholding tax for a person who earns $38 in one week?

40. What is the withholding tax for a person who earns $157 in one week?

41. What is the withholding tax for a person who earns $2542 in one week?

42. What is the withholding tax for a person who earns $8000 in one week?

43. Suppose a person earns $1648 in one week. Would the amount of withholding tax be different if the person used the $704 to $1648 bracket instead of the $1648 to $3394 bracket?

✔ CHECK YOUR PROGRESS: CHAPTER 5

For Exercises 1 to 4, write each percent as a decimal and as a fraction.

1. 85%   **2.** 4%   **3.** 0.25%   **4.** 180%

For Exercises 5 to 8, write the decimal as a percent.

5. 0.15   **6.** 0.027   **7.** 1.45   **8.** 0.00125

For Exercises 9 to 12, write the fraction as a percent.

9. $\dfrac{3}{5}$ **10.** $\dfrac{17}{40}$ **11.** $\dfrac{25}{60}$ **12.** $\dfrac{85}{50}$

13. 35% of 84 is what?   **14.** Find 5.5% of 250.

15. What is 33% of 120?   **16.** Find 0.2% of 78.

17. Salary Increase   A police officer earned $1445 per week before receiving a 5% increase in pay. What was the increase in the officer's weekly pay?

5.3 Percent Equations: Part II

OBJECTIVE A *To find the percent when the base and the amount are given*

The basic percent equation can be used to find an unknown percent.

APPLY THE CONCEPT

A student answered 68 questions correctly on an 80-question test. What percent of the questions did the student answer correctly?

To find the percent of questions that were answered correctly, we must answer the question, "What percent of 80 is 68?" This sentence can be written using mathematical symbols and then solved for the unknown percent.

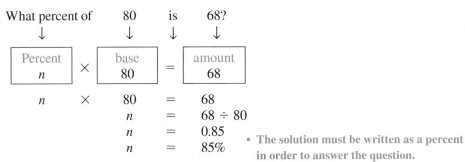

$$n \times 80 = 68$$
$$n = 68 \div 80$$
$$n = 0.85$$
$$n = 85\%$$

• The solution must be written as a percent in order to answer the question.

The student answered 85% of the questions correctly.

Integrating Technology

The percent key **%** on a scientific calculator moves the decimal point two places to the right when pressed after a multiplication or division computation. For the example at the right, enter

68 **÷** 80 **%** **=**

The display reads 85.

EXAMPLE 1

What percent of 40 is 27?

Solution   Percent × base = amount
$$n \times 40 = 27$$
$$n = 27 \div 40$$
$$n = 0.675$$
$$n = 67.5\%$$

YOU TRY IT 1

What percent of 32 is 16?

Your solution

EXAMPLE 2

What percent of 12 is 27?

Solution   Percent × base = amount
$$n \times 12 = 27$$
$$n = 27 \div 12$$
$$n = 2.25$$
$$n = 225\%$$

YOU TRY IT 2

What percent of 15 is 48?

Your solution

EXAMPLE 3

25 is what percent of 75?

Solution   Percent × base = amount
$$n \times 75 = 25$$
$$n = 25 \div 75$$
$$n = \frac{1}{3} = 33\frac{1}{3}\%$$

YOU TRY IT 3

30 is what percent of 45?

Your solution

Solutions on p. S13

OBJECTIVE B   *To solve application problems*

To solve percent problems, remember that it is necessary to identify the percent, base, and amount. Usually the base follows the phrase "percent of."

EXAMPLE 4

The monthly house payment for the Kaminski family is $787.50. What percent of the Kaminskis' monthly income of $3750 is the house payment?

Strategy

To find what percent of the income the house payment is, write and solve the basic percent equation using n to represent the percent. The base is $3750 and the amount is $787.50.

Solution

$n \times 3750 = 787.50$
$n = 787.50 \div 3750$
$n = 0.21 = 21\%$

The house payment is 21% of the monthly income.

YOU TRY IT 4

Tomo Nagata had an income of $33,500 and paid $5025 in income tax. What percent of the income is the income tax?

Your strategy

Your solution

EXAMPLE 5

Scientists recently released one of the most comprehensive estimates of the number of species on Earth. Earth supports an estimated 8.7 million species, of which 2.2 million live in the ocean. What percent of the species live on land? Round to the nearest tenth of a percent.

Strategy

To find the percent of the species living on land:
- Subtract the number of species living in the ocean from the total number of species (8.7 million − 2.2 million). This gives the number of species living on land.
- Write and solve the basic percent equation, using n to represent the percent of species living on land. The base is 8.7 million, and the amount is the number of species living on land.

Solution

8.7 million − 2.2 million = 5.5 million

There are 5.5 million species living on land.

$n \times 8.7 = 5.5$
$n = 5.5 \div 8.7$
$n \approx 0.632$

Approximately 63.2% of the species live on land.

YOU TRY IT 5

In a recent year, there were approximately 302.9 million wireless subscriber connections in the United States. Of these, approximately 112.1 million were subscribers using a smartphone. What percent of wireless subscribers were not using a smartphone? Round to the nearest tenth of a percent.

Your strategy

Your solution

Solutions on p. S13

5.3 EXERCISES

✔ Concept Check

For Exercises 1 to 4, without working the problem, determine whether the answer is *less than* or *greater than* 100%.

1. What percent of 6 is 12?

2. 8 is what percent of 40?

3. 16 is what percent of 8?

4. What percent of 15 is 3?

OBJECTIVE A *To find the percent when the base and amount are given*

For Exercises 5 to 25, solve.

5. What percent of 75 is 24?

6. What percent of 80 is 20?

7. 15 is what percent of 90?

8. 24 is what percent of 60?

9. What percent of 12 is 24?

10. What percent of 6 is 9?

11. What percent of 16 is 6?

12. What percent of 24 is 18?

13. 18 is what percent of 100?

14. 54 is what percent of 100?

15. 5 is what percent of 2000?

16. 8 is what percent of 2500?

17. What percent of 6 is 1.2?

18. What percent of 2.4 is 0.6?

19. 16.4 is what percent of 4.1?

20. 5.3 is what percent of 50?

21. 1 is what percent of 40?

22. 0.3 is what percent of 20?

23. What percent of 48 is 18?

24. What percent of 400 is 12?

25. What percent of 2800 is 7?

OBJECTIVE B *To solve application problems*

26. Read Exercise 28. Without doing any calculations, determine whether the percent of those surveyed who were irked by tailgaters is *less than* or *greater than* 25%.

27. ● **Sociology** Seven in ten couples disagree about financial issues. (*Source:* Yankelovich Partners for Lutheran Brotherhood) What percent of couples disagree about financial matters?

28. ● **Sociology** In a survey, 1236 adults nationwide were asked, "What irks you most about the actions of other motorists?" The response "tailgaters" was given by 293 people. (*Source:* Reuters/Zogby) What percent of those surveyed were most irked by tailgaters? Round to the nearest tenth of a percent.

29. ● **Agriculture** According to data from the U.S. Department of Agriculture, of the 63 billion pounds of vegetables produced in the United States in one year, 16 billion pounds were wasted. What percent of the vegetables produced were wasted? Round to the nearest tenth of a percent.

30. 🥧 **Wind Energy** In a recent year, wind machines in the United States generated 95 billion kilowatt-hours of electricity, enough to serve over 8.7 million households. The nation's total electricity production that year was 28,600 billion kilowatt-hours. (*Source:* Energy Information Administration) What percent of the total energy production was generated by wind machines? Round to the nearest tenth.

31. 🥧 **Diabetes** Approximately 8.3% of the American population has diabetes. Within this group, 18.8 million are diagnosed, while 7.0 million are undiagnosed. (*Source:* Centers for Disease Control) What percent of Americans with diabetes have not been diagnosed? Round to the nearest tenth of a percent.

32. 🥧 **Internal Revenue Service** See the news clipping at the right. What percent of Americans reporting an income of over $1 million were audited by the IRS? Round to the nearest hundredth of a percent.

33. **Construction** In a test of the breaking strength of concrete slabs for freeway construction, 3 of the 200 slabs tested did not meet safety requirements. What percent of the slabs did meet safety requirements?

In the NEWS!

$1 Million Audits

Of the 388,684 American taxpayers reporting an annual income of more than $1 million, 32,494 were audited by the Internal Revenue Service.

Source: Internal Revenue Service; Bloomberg Businessweek

Critical Thinking

🥧 **Pets** The graph at the right shows several categories of average lifetime costs of dog ownership. Use this graph for Exercises 34 to 36. Round answers to the nearest tenth of a percent.

34. What percent of the total amount is spent on food?

35. What percent of the total is spent on veterinary care?

36. What percent of the total is spent on all categories except training?

37. 🏔 **Sports** The Fun in the Sun organization claims to have taken a survey of 350 people, asking them to give their favorite outdoor temperature for hiking. The results are given in the table at the right. Explain why these results are not possible.

$1200 Training
$1400 Other
$1100 Flea and tick treatment
$4000 Food
$3000 Grooming, toys, house
$3900 Veterinary

Cost of Owning a Dog
Source: Based on data from the American Kennel Club, *USA Today* research

Favorite Temperature	Percent
Greater than 90	5%
80–89	28%
70–79	35%
60–69	32%
Below 60	13%

Projects or Group Activities

38. Suppose the annual rainfall for a city in 2012 was 10 inches. In 2013, the annual rainfall increases by 10% from 2012. In 2014, the annual rainfall decreases by 10% from 2013. Is the annual rainfall in 2014 *less than, equal to,* or *greater than* the annual rainfall in 2012?

39. A stock decreased in value from $25 per share to $20 per share.
   a. What was the amount of the decrease?
   b. What percent of the original value of a share is the decrease?
   c. By what percent would the stock need to increase to return to its original value?
   d. Are the answers to parts (b) and (c) the same?

5.4 Percent Equations: Part III

OBJECTIVE A *To find the base when the percent and the amount are given*

Point of Interest

One gigawatt-hour of energy can supply approximately 165 homes with power for a period of one year.

APPLY THE CONCEPT

In one year, a utility company produced approximately 14,500 gigawatt-hours of energy using renewable energy resources. This was 19% of the total amount of energy produced by the company that year. To find the total amount of energy produced that year by the company, we must answer the question, "19% of what number is 14,500?"

19%	of	what	is	14,500?
↓		↓	↓	↓

$$\boxed{\begin{array}{c}\text{Percent}\\19\%\end{array}} \times \boxed{\begin{array}{c}\text{base}\\n\end{array}} = \boxed{\begin{array}{c}\text{amount}\\14{,}500\end{array}}$$

$$0.19 \times n = 14{,}500$$
$$n = 14{,}500 \div 0.19$$
$$n \approx 76{,}316$$

The company produced approximately 76,316 gigawatt-hours of energy.

EXAMPLE 1

18% of what is 900?

Solution   Percent × base = amount
$$0.18 \times n = 900$$
$$n = 900 \div 0.18$$
$$n = 5000$$

YOU TRY IT 1

86% of what is 215?

Your solution

EXAMPLE 2

30 is 1.5% of what?

Solution   Percent × base = amount
$$0.015 \times n = 30$$
$$n = 30 \div 0.015$$
$$n = 2000$$

YOU TRY IT 2

15 is 2.5% of what?

Your solution

EXAMPLE 3

$33\frac{1}{3}\%$ of what is 7?

Solution   Percent × base = amount

$$\frac{1}{3} \times n = 7$$ • Note that the percent is written as a fraction.

$$n = 7 \div \frac{1}{3}$$

$$n = 21$$

YOU TRY IT 3

$16\frac{2}{3}\%$ of what is 5?

Your solution

Solutions on p. S13

OBJECTIVE B *To solve application problems*

To solve percent problems, it is necessary to identify the percent, the base, and the amount. Usually the base follows the phrase "percent of."

EXAMPLE 4

A business office bought a used copy machine for $900, which was 75% of the original cost. What was the original cost of the copier?

Strategy

To find the original cost of the copier, write and solve the basic percent equation, using n to represent the original cost (base). The percent is 75% and the amount is $900.

Solution

$$75\% \times n = 900$$
$$0.75 \times n = 900$$
$$n = 900 \div 0.75$$
$$n = 1200$$

The original cost of the copier was $1200.

YOU TRY IT 4

A used car has a value of $10,458, which is 42% of the car's original value. What was the car's original value?

Your strategy

Your solution

EXAMPLE 5

A carpenter's wage this year is $26.40 per hour, which is 110% of last year's wage. What was the increase in the hourly wage over last year?

Strategy

To find the increase in the hourly wage over last year:

• Find last year's wage. Write and solve the basic percent equation, using n to represent last year's wage (base). The percent is 110% and the amount is $26.40.
• Subtract last year's wage from this year's wage (26.40).

Solution

$$110\% \times n = 26.40$$
$$1.10 \times n = 26.40$$
$$n = 26.40 \div 1.10$$
$$n = 24.00 \qquad \text{• Last year's wage}$$

$$26.40 - 24.00 = 2.40$$

The increase in the hourly wage was $2.40.

YOU TRY IT 5

Chang's Sporting Goods has a tennis racket on sale for $89.60, which is 80% of the original price. What is the difference between the original price and the sale price?

Your strategy

Your solution

Solutions on pp. S13–S14

5.4 EXERCISES

Concept Check

For Exercises 1 to 4, without working the problem, determine whether the base is *less than* or *greater than* the amount.

1. 15% of what is 12?

2. 30 is 0.5% of what?

3. 20 is 125% of what?

4. 110% of what is 200?

OBJECTIVE A   *To find the base when the percent and amount are given*

For Exercises 5 to 25, solve.

5. 12% of what is 9?

6. 38% of what is 171?

7. 8 is 16% of what?

8. 54 is 90% of what?

9. 10 is 10% of what?

10. 37 is 37% of what?

11. 30% of what is 25.5?

12. 25% of what is 21.5?

13. 2.5% of what is 30?

14. 10.4% of what is 52?

15. 125% of what is 24?

16. 180% of what is 21.6?

17. 18 is 240% of what?

18. 24 is 320% of what?

19. 4.8 is 15% of what?

20. 87.5 is 50% of what?

21. 25.6 is 12.8% of what?

22. 45.014 is 63.4% of what?

23. 30% of what is 2.7?

24. 120 is $33\frac{1}{3}$% of what?

25. 84 is $16\frac{2}{3}$% of what?

OBJECTIVE B   *To solve application problems*

26. Read Exercise 27. Without doing any calculations, determine whether the number of travelers who allowed their children to miss school to go on a trip is *less than, equal to,* or *greater than* 1.738 million.

27. **Travel**   Of the travelers who, during a recent year, allowed their children to miss school to go on a trip, approximately 1.738 million allowed their children to miss school for more than a week. This represented 11% of the travelers who allowed their children to miss school. (*Source:* Travel Industry Association) About how many travelers allowed their children to miss school to go on a trip?

28. **Tablet Shipments**   Use the information in the news clipping at the right. Find the total number of media tablets shipped in 2010. Round to the nearest million.

In the NEWS!

Tablet Sales Surge

In their first year on the market, media tablets saw a surge in sales at the end of the year. The 10.1 million media tablets shipped worldwide in the fourth quarter represented 56.4% of all tablets shipped in 2010.
Source: International Data Corporation

29. ● **Marathons** In 2011, approximately 98.2% of the runners who started the Boston Marathon, or 23,913 people, crossed the finish line. (*Source:* Boston Athletic Association) How many runners started the Boston Marathon in 2011? Round to the nearest ten.

30. ● **Education** In the United States today, 29.6% of women and 30.3% of men have earned a bachelor's or graduate degree. (*Source:* Census Bureau) What additional information would you need in order to determine how many women in the United States have earned a bachelor's or graduate degree?

31. ● **Fuel Consumption** Use the information in the news clipping at the right. Sailing at full speed, how many tons of fuel per day does a large ship use?

32. ● **Taxes** A TurboTax online survey asked people how they planned to use their tax refunds. Seven hundred forty people, or 22% of the respondents, said they would save the money. How many people responded to the survey?

33. Manufacturing During a quality control test, Micronics found 24 defective computer boards. This amount was 0.8% of the computer boards tested.
a. How many computer boards were tested?
b. How many of the computer boards tested were not defective?

In the NEWS!

Reducing Cargo Ship Emissions

By using giant kites to power the ships and sailing at slower speeds, shipping companies are reducing the amount of fuel used by cargo ships, thus reducing the ships' CO_2 emissions. By reducing its speed by 20%, a large ship can lower its fuel use by 40%, saving 120 tons of fuel per day.

Source: www.guardian.uk.com

Critical Thinking

34. Nutrition The table at the right contains nutrition information about a breakfast cereal. The amount of thiamin in one serving of this cereal with skim milk is 0.45 milligram. Find the recommended daily allowance of thiamin for an adult.

NUTRITION INFORMATION

SERVING SIZE: 1.4 OZ WHEAT FLAKES WITH 0.4 OZ. RAISINS: 39.4 g. ABOUT 1/2 CUP
SERVINGS PER PACKAGE: 14

	CEREAL & RAISINS	WITH 1/2 CUP VITAMINS A & D SKIM MILK

PERCENTAGE OF U.S. RECOMMENDED DAILY ALLOWANCES (U.S. RDA)

	CEREAL & RAISINS	WITH 1/2 CUP SKIM MILK
PROTEIN	4	15
VITAMIN A	15	20
VITAMIN C	**	2
THIAMIN	25	30
RIBOFLAVIN	25	35
NIACIN	25	35
CALCIUM	**	15
IRON	100	100
VITAMIN D	10	25
VITAMIN B₆	25	25
FOLIC ACID..............	25	25
VITAMIN B₁₂	25	30
PHOSPHOROUS.........	10	15
MAGNESIUM.............	10	20
ZINC	25	30
COPPER..................	2	4

* 2% MILK SUPPLIES AN ADDITIONAL 20 CALORIES. 2 g FAT, AND 10 mg CHOLESTEROL.
** CONTAINS LESS THAN 2% OF THE U.S. RDA OF THIS NUTRIENT

Projects or Group Activities

35. a. Suppose you correctly answer 48 out of 60 questions on a test. What percent of the questions did you answer correctly?
b. Suppose you correctly answer 56 out of 80 questions on a second test. What percent of the questions did you answer correctly?
c. What is the average of the two percents in parts (a) and (b)?
d. Consider the total number of questions on the two tests and the total number you answered correctly. What percent of the questions did you answer correctly? Is this the same number you calculated in part (c)?
e. Your answers to parts (c) and (d) show that averaging the percent scores for two tests does not necessarily give the correct percent score for the combined tests. Under what conditions would the average of the percent scores give the true percent score for the combined tests? *Hint:* Consider the base of the basic percent equation.

5.5 Percent Problems: Proportion Method

OBJECTIVE A *To solve percent problems using proportions*

Problems that can be solved using the basic percent equation can also be solved using proportions.

The proportion method is based on writing two ratios. One ratio is the percent ratio, written as $\frac{\text{percent}}{100}$. The second ratio is the amount-to-base ratio, written as $\frac{\text{amount}}{\text{base}}$. These two ratios form the proportion

$$\frac{\text{percent}}{100} = \frac{\text{amount}}{\text{base}}$$

To use the proportion method, first identify the percent, the amount, and the base (the base usually follows the phrase "percent of").

Integrating Technology

To use a calculator to solve the proportions at the right for *n*, enter

23	×	45	÷	100	=
100	×	4	÷	25	=
100	×	12	÷	60	=

What is 23% of 45?

$$\frac{23}{100} = \frac{n}{45}$$

$23 \times 45 = 100 \times n$
$1035 = 100 \times n$
$1035 \div 100 = n$
$10.35 = n$

What percent of 25 is 4?

$$\frac{n}{100} = \frac{4}{25}$$

$n \times 25 = 100 \times 4$
$n \times 25 = 400$
$n = 400 \div 25$
$n = 16$

12 is 60% of what number?

$$\frac{60}{100} = \frac{12}{n}$$

$60 \times n = 100 \times 12$
$60 \times n = 1200$
$n = 1200 \div 60$
$n = 20$

EXAMPLE 1

15% of what is 7? Round to the nearest hundredth.

Solution

$$\frac{15}{100} = \frac{7}{n}$$

$15 \times n = 100 \times 7$
$15 \times n = 700$
$n = 700 \div 15$
$n \approx 46.67$

EXAMPLE 2

30% of 63 is what?

Solution

$$\frac{30}{100} = \frac{n}{63}$$

$30 \times 63 = 100 \times n$
$1890 = 100 \times n$
$1890 \div 100 = n$
$18.90 = n$

YOU TRY IT 1

26% of what is 22? Round to the nearest hundredth.

Your solution

YOU TRY IT 2

16% of 132 is what?

Your solution

Solutions on p. S14

> **OBJECTIVE B**   *To solve application problems*

EXAMPLE 3

An antiques dealer found that 86% of the 250 items that were sold during one month sold for under $1000. How many items sold for under $1000?

Strategy

To find the number of items that sold for under $1000, write and solve a proportion, using n to represent the number of items sold for less than $1000 (amount). The percent is 86%, and the base is 250.

Solution

$$\frac{86}{100} = \frac{n}{250}$$
$$86 \times 250 = 100 \times n$$
$$21{,}500 = 100 \times n$$
$$21{,}500 \div 100 = n$$
$$215 = n$$

215 items sold for under $1000.

YOU TRY IT 3

Last year it snowed 64% of the 150 days of the ski season at a resort. How many days did it snow?

Your strategy

Your solution

EXAMPLE 4

In a test of the strength of nylon rope, 5 of the 25 pieces tested did not meet the test standards. What percent of the nylon ropes tested did meet the test standards?

Strategy

To find the percent of ropes tested that met the test standards:

• Find the number of ropes that met the test standards $(25 - 5)$.
• Write and solve a proportion, using n to represent the percent of ropes that met the test standards. The base is 25, and the amount is the number of ropes that met the standards.

Solution

$25 - 5 = 20$ ropes met test standards.
$$\frac{n}{100} = \frac{20}{25}$$
$$n \times 25 = 100 \times 20$$
$$n \times 25 = 2000$$
$$n = 2000 \div 25$$
$$n = 80$$

80% of the ropes tested did meet the test standards.

YOU TRY IT 4

The Rincon Fire Department received 24 false alarms out of a total of 200 alarms received. What percent of the alarms received were not false alarms?

Your strategy

Your solution

Solutions on p. S14

5.5 EXERCISES

✔ Concept Check

1. Write a proportion that can be used to solve problems involving percent.

For Exercises 2 to 4, state whether the unknown n represents *percent, base,* or *amount.*

2. $\dfrac{45}{100} = \dfrac{28}{n}$

3. $\dfrac{n}{100} = \dfrac{30}{50}$

4. $\dfrac{n}{50} = \dfrac{30}{100}$

OBJECTIVE A   *To solve percent problems using proportions*

5. 26% of 250 is what?

6. What is 18% of 150?

7. 37 is what percent of 148?

8. What percent of 150 is 33?

9. 68% of what is 51?

10. 126 is 84% of what?

11. What percent of 344 is 43?

12. 750 is what percent of 50?

13. 82 is 20.5% of what?

14. 2.4% of what is 21?

15. What is 6.5% of 300?

16. 96% of 75 is what?

17. 7.4 is what percent of 50?

18. What percent of 1500 is 693?

19. 50.5% of 124 is what?

20. What is 87.4% of 255?

21. 33 is 220% of what?

22. 160% of what is 40?

23. Which equation(s) below can be used to answer the question, **a.** "What is 12% of 75?" and **b.** to answer the question, "75 is 12% of what?"

   (i) $\dfrac{12}{100} = \dfrac{75}{n}$ (ii) $0.12 \times 75 = n$ (iii) $\dfrac{12}{100} = \dfrac{n}{75}$ (iv) $0.12 \times n = 75$

OBJECTIVE B   *To solve application problems*

24. Read Exercise 25. Without doing any calculations, determine whether the length of time the drug will be effective is *less than* or *greater than* 6 hours.

25. **Medicine**   A manufacturer of an anti-inflammatory drug claims that the drug will be effective for 6 hours. An independent testing service determined that the drug was effective for only 80% of the length of time claimed by the manufacturer. Find the length of time the drug will be effective as determined by the testing service.

26. ● **Geography**   The land area of North America is approximately 9,400,000 square miles. This represents approximately 16% of the total land area of the world. What is the approximate total land area of the world?

27. ● **Girl Scout Cookies**   Using the information in the news clipping at the right, calculate the cash generated annually **a.** from sales of Thin Mints and **b.** from sales of Trefoil shortbread cookies.

In the NEWS!

Thin Mints Biggest Seller

Every year, sales from the Girl Scout cookies sold by about 2.7 million girls total $700 million. The most popular cookie, Thin Mints, earn 25% of total sales, while sales of Trefoil shortbread cookies represent only 9% of total sales.

Source: msnbc.com

Jeff Greenberg/age fotostock

28. ● **Charities**   In a recent year, the American Red Cross spent $132,105,934 on administrative expenses. This amount was 3.68% of its total revenue. Find the American Red Cross's total revenue for that year. Round to the nearest ten million.

29. ● **Education**   See the news clipping at the right. What percent of the baby boomers living in the United States have attended college? Round to the nearest tenth of a percent.

30. ● **Mining**   During one year, approximately 2,240,000 ounces of gold went into the manufacturing of electronic equipment in the United States. This was 16% of all the gold mined in the United States that year. How many ounces of gold were mined in the United States that year?

31. ● **Poultry**   In a recent year, North Carolina produced 963,000,000 pounds of turkey. This was 13.5% of the U.S. total in that year. Calculate the U.S. total turkey production for that year. Round to the nearest billion.

32. ● **Police Officers**   The graph at the right shows causes of death for police officers killed in the line of duty during a recent year. What percent of the deaths were due to traffic accidents? Round to the nearest tenth of a percent.

Critical Thinking

33. ● **The Federal Government**   In the 110th Senate, there were 49 Republicans, 49 Democrats, and 2 Independents. In the 110th House of Representatives, there were 202 Republicans, 233 Democrats, and 0 Independents. Which had the larger percentage of Republicans, the 110th Senate or the 110th House of Representatives?

Projects or Group Activities

Gold jewelry comes in various colors. Three typical colors are yellow gold, rose gold, and white gold. The table at the right shows the percent breakdown of the elements used to make three colors of 18-carat gold. Use this table for Exercises 34 to 36.

34. How many grams of each element are needed for a yellow-gold ring that weighs 8 grams?

35. How many grams of each element are needed for a rose-gold ring that weighs 6 grams?

36. How many grams of each element are needed for a white-gold ring that weighs 8 grams?

In the NEWS!

Over Half of Baby Boomers Have College Experience

Of the 78 million baby boomers living in the United States, 45 million have attended college. Twenty-three million baby boomers are high school graduates with no college experience.
Source: USA Today

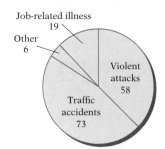

Numbers of Deaths for Police Officers Killed in the Line of Duty
Source: International Union of Police Associations

Color	Composition
Yellow	Gold, 75% Copper, 25%
Rose	Gold, 75% Copper, 20% Silver, 5%
White	Gold, 75% Palladium, 10% Nickel, 10% Zinc, 5%

CHAPTER

5 Summary

Key Words	Examples
Percent means "parts of 100." [5.1A, p. 204]	23% means 23 of 100 equal parts.

Essential Rules and Procedures	Examples
To write a percent as a decimal, drop the percent sign and multiply by 0.01. [5.1A, p. 204]	$87\% = 87(0.01) = 0.87$
To write a percent as a fraction, drop the percent sign and multiply by $\frac{1}{100}$. [5.1A, p. 204]	$56\% = 56\left(\frac{1}{100}\right) = \frac{56}{100} = \frac{14}{25}$
To write a decimal as a percent, multiply by 100%. [5.1B, p. 205]	$0.325 = 0.325(100\%) = 32.5\%$
To write a fraction as a percent, multiply by 100%. [5.1B, p. 205]	$\frac{7}{20} = \frac{7}{20} \times \frac{100\%}{1} = \frac{700\%}{20} = 35\%$

The Basic Percent Equation   [5.2A, p. 209]
The basic percent equation is

$$\text{Percent} \times \text{base} = \text{amount}$$

Solving percent problems requires identifying the three elements of this equation. Usually the base follows the phrase "percent of."

8% of 250 is what number?
Percent $\times$ base = amount
$$0.08 \times 250 = n$$
$$20 = n$$

Proportion Method of Solving a Percent Problem
[5.5A, p. 222]
The following proportion can be used to solve percent problems.

$$\frac{\text{percent}}{100} = \frac{\text{amount}}{\text{base}}$$

To use the proportion method, first identify the percent, the amount, and the base. The base usually follows the phrase "percent of."

8% of 250 is what number?
$$\frac{\text{percent}}{100} = \frac{\text{amount}}{\text{base}}$$
$$\frac{8}{100} = \frac{n}{250}$$
$$8 \times 250 = 100 \times n$$
$$2000 = 100 \times n$$
$$2000 \div 100 = n$$
$$20 = n$$

CHAPTER

5 | Review Exercises

1. What is 30% of 200?

2. 16 is what percent of 80?

3. Write $1\frac{3}{4}$ as a percent.

4. 20% of what is 15?

5. Write 12% as a fraction.

6. Find 22% of 88.

7. What percent of 20 is 30?

8. $16\frac{2}{3}\%$ of what is 84?

9. Write 42% as a decimal.

10. What is 7.5% of 72?

11. $66\frac{2}{3}\%$ of what is 105?

12. Write 7.6% as a decimal.

13. Find 125% of 62.

14. Write $16\frac{2}{3}\%$ as a fraction.

15. What percent of 25 is 40? Use the proportion method.

16. 20% of what number is 15? Use the proportion method.

17. Write 0.38 as a percent.

18. 78% of what is 8.5? Round to the nearest tenth.

19. What percent of 30 is 2.2? Round to the nearest tenth of a percent.

20. What percent of 15 is 92? Round to the nearest tenth of a percent.

21. Education   Trent missed 9 out of 60 questions on a history exam. What percent of the questions did he answer correctly? Use the proportion method.

22. Advertising   A company used 7.5% of its $60,000 advertising budget for newspaper advertising. How much of the advertising budget was spent on newspaper advertising?

23. **Energy**   The graph at the right shows the amounts spent by the average U.S. household for energy use. What percent of energy costs is spent on electricity? Round to the nearest tenth of a percent.

Where Your Energy Dollar Goes
The average U.S. household spent $4125 on energy use in a recent year. How it was spent:

Motor gasoline $2132

Fuel oil, kerosene $140

Natural gas $440

Electricity $1413

Source: Bureau of Labor Statistics

24. Consumerism   Joshua purchased a camcorder for $980 and paid a sales tax of 6.25% of the cost. What was the total cost of the camcorder?

25. Health   In a survey of 350 women and 420 men, 275 of the women and 300 of the men reported that they wore sunscreen often. To the nearest tenth of a percent, what percent of the women wore sunscreen often?

26. **Demography**   It is estimated that by the year 2050 the world's population will be 9,400,000,000. This is 155% of the population in 2000. (*Source:* U.S. Census Bureau) What was the world's population in 2000? Round to the nearest hundred million.

27. Computers   A computer system can be purchased for $1800. This is 60% of the cost 4 years ago. What was the cost of the computer system 4 years ago? Use the proportion method.

28. **Agriculture**   In a recent year, Wisconsin growers produced 281.72 million pounds of cranberries. This represented 49.25% of the total cranberry crop in the United States that year. Find the total cranberry crop in the United States that year. Round to the nearest million.

5 | TEST

1. Write 97.3% as a decimal.

2. Write $83\frac{1}{3}\%$ as a fraction.

3. Write 0.3 as a percent.

4. Write 1.63 as a percent.

5. Write $\frac{3}{2}$ as a percent.

6. Write $\frac{37}{40}$ as a percent.

7. What is 77% of 65?

8. 47.2% of 130 is what?

9. Write $\frac{11}{18}$ as a percent.

10. Write 0.75% as a fraction.

11. 12 is 15% of what?

12. 42.5 is 150% of what? Round to the nearest tenth.

13. 123 is 86% of what number? Use the proportion method. Round to the nearest tenth.

14. What percent of 12 is 120? Use the proportion method.

15. **Advertising**   A travel agency uses 6% of its $750,000 budget for advertising. What amount of the budget is spent on advertising?

16. **Agriculture**   During the packaging process for vegetables, spoiled vegetables are discarded by an inspector. In one day, an inspector found that 6.4% of the 1250 pounds of vegetables were spoiled. How many pounds of vegetables were not spoiled?

Nutrition   The table at the right contains nutrition information about a breakfast cereal. Solve Exercises 17 and 18 with information taken from this table.

17. The recommended amount of potassium per day for an adult is 3000 milligrams (mg). What percent, to the nearest tenth of a percent, of the daily recommended amount of potassium is provided by one serving of this cereal with skim milk?

18. The daily recommended number of calories for a 190-pound man is 2200 calories. What percent, to the nearest tenth of a percent, of the daily recommended number of calories is provided by one serving of this cereal with 2% milk?

19. **Employment**   The Urban Center Department Store has 125 permanent employees and must hire an additional 20 temporary employees for the holiday season. What percent of the number of permanent employees is the number hired as temporary employees for the holiday season?

20. **Education**   Conchita missed 7 out of 80 questions on a math exam. What percent of the questions did she answer correctly? Round to the nearest tenth of a percent.

21. **Manufacturing**   A manufacturer of digital cameras found 384 defective digital cameras during a quality control study. This amount was 1.2% of the digital cameras tested. Find the number of digital cameras tested.

22. **Real Estate**   A new house was bought for $285,000. Five years later, the house sold for $456,000. What percent of the original price was the increase?

23. **Wages**   An administrative assistant receives a wage of $16.24 per hour. This amount is 112% of last year's wage. What is the dollar increase in the hourly wage over last year? Use the proportion method.

24. **Demography**   A city has a population of 71,500. Ten years ago the population was 32,500. What percent of the population 10 years ago is the population now? Use the proportion method.

25. **Fees**   The annual license fee on a car is 1.4% of the value of the car. If the annual license fee is $350, what is the value of the car? Use the proportion method.

NUTRITION INFORMATION

SERVING SIZE: 1.4 OZ WHEAT FLAKES WITH 0.4 OZ. RAISINS: 39.4 g. ABOUT 1/2 CUP
SERVINGS PER PACKAGE: 14

	CEREAL & RAISINS	WITH 1/2 CUP VITAMINS A & D SKIM MILK
CALORIES	120	180
PROTEIN, g	3	7
CARBOHYDRATE, g	28	34
FAT, TOTAL, g	1	1*
UNSATURATED, g 1		
SATURATED, g 0		
CHOLESTEROL, mg	0	0*
SODIUM, mg	125	190
POTASSIUM, mg	240	440

* 2% MILK SUPPLIES AN ADDITIONAL 20 CALORIES. 2 g FAT, AND 10 mg CHOLESTEROL.
** CONTAINS LESS THAN 2% OF THE U.S. RDA OF THIS NUTRIENT

Cumulative Review Exercises

1. Simplify: $18 \div (7 - 4)^2 + 2$

2. Find the LCM of 16, 24, and 30.

3. Find the sum of $2\frac{1}{3}$, $3\frac{1}{2}$, and $4\frac{5}{8}$.

4. Subtract: $27\frac{5}{12} - 14\frac{9}{16}$

5. Multiply: $7\frac{1}{3} \times 1\frac{5}{7}$

6. What is $\frac{14}{27}$ divided by $1\frac{7}{9}$?

7. Simplify: $\left(\frac{3}{4}\right)^3 \cdot \left(\frac{8}{9}\right)^2 + \frac{1}{9}$

8. Simplify: $\left(\frac{2}{3}\right)^2 - \left(\frac{3}{8} - \frac{1}{3}\right) \div \frac{1}{2}$

9. Round 3.07973 to the nearest hundredth.

10. Subtract: 3.0902
    $- 1.9706$

11. Divide: $0.032\overline{)1.097}$
Round to the nearest ten-thousandth.

12. Convert $3\frac{5}{8}$ to a terminating or repeating decimal.

13. Convert 1.75 to a fraction.

14. Place the correct symbol, $<$ or $>$, between the two numbers.
$\frac{3}{8}$ 0.87

15. Solve the proportion $\frac{3}{8} = \frac{20}{n}$.
Round to the nearest tenth.

16. Write "$153.60 earned in 8 hours" as a unit rate.

17. Write $18\frac{1}{3}\%$ as a fraction.

18. Write $\frac{13}{18}$ as a percent.

19. 16.3% of 120 is what?

20. 24 is what percent of 18?

21. 12.4 is 125% of what?

22. What percent of 35 is 120? Round to the nearest tenth.

23. Taxes   Sergio has an income of $740 per week. One-fifth of his income is deducted for income tax payments. Find his take-home pay.

24. Finance   Eunice bought a used car for $12,530, with a down payment of $2000. The balance was paid in 36 equal monthly payments. Find the monthly payment.

25. Taxes   The gasoline tax is $.41 per gallon. Find the number of gallons of gasoline used during a month in which $172.20 was paid in gasoline taxes.

26. Taxes   The real estate tax on a $344,000 home is $6880. At the same rate, find the real estate tax on a home valued at $500,000.

27. ◖ **Lodging**   The graph at the right shows the breakdown of the locations of the 51,015 hotels throughout the United States. How many of these hotels are located along interstate highways? Round to the nearest whole number.

28. Elections   A survey of 300 people showed that 165 people favored a certain candidate for mayor. What percent of the people surveyed did not favor this candidate?

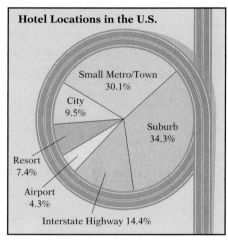

Hotel Locations in the U.S.

Small Metro/Town 30.1%
City 9.5%
Suburb 34.3%
Resort 7.4%
Airport 4.3%
Interstate Highway 14.4%

Source: American Hotel and Lodging Association

29. ◖ **Television**   According to the Cabletelevision Advertising Bureau, cable households watch television 36.5% of the time. On average, how many hours per week do cable households spend watching TV? Round to the nearest tenth.

30. ◖ **Health**   The Environmental Protection Agency found that 990 out of 5500 children tested had levels of lead in their blood that exceeded federal guidelines. What percent of the children tested had levels of lead that exceeded federal standards?

Applications for Business and Consumers

6

Focus on Success

Are you using the features of this text to learn the concepts being presented? The HOW TO feature includes a step-by-step solution to the type of exercise you will be working in your homework assignments and on exams. A numbered Example provides you with a fully-worked-out solution. After studying the Example, try completing the You Try It to the right of the Example. A complete solution to the You Try It is given in the back of the text. (See Use the Interactive Method, page AIM-8).

Helder Almeida/Shutterstock.com

Prep Test

Are you ready to succeed in this chapter? Take the Prep Test below to find out if you are ready to learn the new material.

1. Divide: $3.75 \div 5$

2. Multiply: 3.47×15

3. Subtract: $874.50 - 369.99$

4. Multiply: $0.065 \times 150,000$

5. Multiply: $1500 \times 0.06 \times 0.5$

6. Add: $1372.47 + 36.91 + 5.00 + 2.86$

7. Divide $10 \div 3$. Round to the nearest hundredth.

8. Divide $345 \div 570$. Round to the nearest thousandth.

9. Place the correct symbol, $<$ or $>$, between the two numbers.
0.379   0.397

6.1   Applications to Purchasing

OBJECTIVE A   *To find unit cost*

When items are packaged together, such as a six-pack of soda or a 10-pound bag of potatoes, we may want to find the cost of just one item—one can of soda or one pound of potatoes. The cost of one item, such as one can of soda or one pound of potatoes, is called the **unit cost.**

$$\text{Unit cost} = \frac{\text{cost of the package}}{\text{number of units in the package}}$$

APPLY THE CONCEPT ···

As a promotional sale, a store offers a case of 24 bottles of a sports drink for $25.95. What is the cost of one bottle of the sports drink?

$$\text{Unit cost} = \frac{\text{cost of the package}}{\text{number of units in the package}}$$

$$= \frac{\$25.95}{24 \text{ bottles}}$$

$$\approx \$1.08 \text{ per bottle}$$

The unit cost is approximately $1.08 per bottle.

APPLY THE CONCEPT ···

The cost of a 12-ounce package of salmon is $6.72. What is the cost of one ounce of salmon?

$$\text{Unit cost} = \frac{\text{cost of the package}}{\text{number of units in the package}}$$

$$= \frac{\$6.72}{12 \text{ ounces}}$$

$$= \$.56 \text{ per ounce}$$

The unit cost is $.56 per ounce.

EXAMPLE 1

Find the unit cost. Round to the nearest cent.
a. An 8-can value pack of canned chicken for $18.99.
b. 4 ounces of toothpaste for $2.59

Strategy

To find the unit cost, divide the cost of the package by the number of units in the package.

Solution

a. Unit cost $= \dfrac{\text{cost of the package}}{\text{number of units in the package}}$

$= \dfrac{\$18.99}{8 \text{ cans}} \approx \$2.37$ per can

b. Unit cost $= \dfrac{\text{cost of the package}}{\text{number of units in the package}}$

$= \dfrac{\$2.59}{4 \text{ ounces}} \approx \$.65$ per ounce

YOU TRY IT 1

Find the unit cost. Round to the nearest cent.
a. 12 Honey Crisp apples for $14.49
b. 15 pounds of potatoes for $10.00

Your strategy

Your solution

Solution on p. S14

OBJECTIVE B   *To find the most economical purchase*

Comparison shoppers often find the most economical buy by comparing unit costs.

APPLY THE CONCEPT ··

One store is selling 6 twelve-ounce cans of ginger ale for $2.99, and a second store is selling 24 twelve-ounce cans of ginger ale for $11.79. To find the better buy, compare the unit costs. Round each unit cost to the nearest tenth of a cent.

$2.99 \div 6 \approx 0.498$ $11.79 \div 24 \approx 0.491$

Unit cost: $.498 per can   Unit cost: $.491 per can

Because $.491 < $.498, the better buy is 24 cans for $11.79.

EXAMPLE 2

Find the more economical purchase: 5 pounds of nails for $4.80, or 4 pounds of nails for $3.78.

Strategy

To find the more economical purchase, compare the unit costs.

Solution

$4.80 \div 5 = 0.96$
$3.78 \div 4 = 0.945$
$\$.945 < \$.96$

The more economical purchase is 4 pounds for $3.78.

YOU TRY IT 2

Find the more economical purchase: 6 cans of fruit for $8.70, or 4 cans of fruit for $6.96.

Your strategy

Your solution

Solution on p. S14

OBJECTIVE C   *To find total cost*

© iStockphoto.com/epicture

An installer of floor tile found the unit costs of identical floor tiles at three stores.

Store 1	Store 2	Store 3
$1.22 per tile	$1.18 per tile	$1.28 per tile

By comparing the unit costs, the installer determined that store 2 would provide the most economical purchase.

The installer also uses the unit cost to find the total cost of purchasing 300 floor tiles at store 2. The **total cost** is found by multiplying the unit cost by the number of units purchased.

$$\boxed{\text{Unit cost}} \times \boxed{\text{number of units}} = \boxed{\text{total cost}}$$

$$1.18 \quad \times \quad 300 \quad = \quad 354$$

The total cost of 300 floor titles is $354.

EXAMPLE 3

One size of clear redwood lumber costs $5.43 per foot. How much would 25 feet of this clear redwood lumber cost?

Strategy

To find the total cost, multiply the unit cost (5.43) by the number of units (25).

Solution

$$\boxed{\text{Unit cost}} \times \boxed{\text{number of units}} = \boxed{\text{total cost}}$$

$$5.43 \quad \times \quad 25 \quad = \quad 135.75$$

The total cost of 25 feet of clear redwood lumber is $135.75.

YOU TRY IT 3

Pine saplings cost $9.96 each. How much would 7 pine saplings cost?

Your strategy

Your solution

Solution on p. S14

6.1 EXERCISES

✓ Concept Check

1. ▧ What is unit cost?

2. ▧ How is total cost calculated?

OBJECTIVE A *To find unit cost*

For Exercises 3 to 12, find the unit cost. Round to the nearest tenth of a cent.

3. Heinz B·B·Q sauce, 18 ounces for $.99

4. Birds-eye maple, 6 feet for $18.75

5. Diamond walnuts, $2.99 for 8 ounces

6. A&W root beer, 6 cans for $2.99

7. Ibuprofen, 50 tablets for $3.99

8. Visine eye drops, 0.5 ounce for $3.89

9. Adjustable wood clamps, 2 for $13.95

10. Corn, 6 ears for $2.85

11. Cheerios cereal, 15 ounces for $2.99

12. Doritos Cool Ranch chips, 14.5 ounces for $2.99

13. ▧ A store advertises a "buy one, get one free" sale on pint containers of ice cream. How would you find the unit cost of one pint of ice cream?

OBJECTIVE B *To find the most economical purchase*

For Exercises 14 to 23, suppose your local supermarket offers the following products at the given prices. Find the more economical purchase.

14. Sutter Home pasta sauce, 25.5 ounces for $3.29, or Muir Glen Organic pasta sauce, 26 ounces for $3.79

15. Kraft mayonnaise, 40 ounces for $3.98, or Springfield mayonnaise, 32 ounces for $3.39

16. Ortega salsa, 20 ounces for $3.29 or 12 ounces for $1.99

17. L'Oréal shampoo, 13 ounces for $4.69, or Cortexx shampoo, 12 ounces for $3.99

18. Golden Sun vitamin E, 200 tablets for $12.99 or 400 tablets for $18.69

19. Ultra Mr. Clean, 20 ounces for $2.67, or Ultra Spic and Span, 14 ounces for $2.19

20. 16 ounces of Kraft cheddar cheese for $4.37, or 9 ounces of Land O'Lakes cheddar cheese for $2.29

21. Bertolli olive oil, 34 ounces for $9.49, or Pompeian olive oil, 8 ounces for $2.39

22. Maxwell House coffee, 4 ounces for $3.99, or Sanka coffee, 2 ounces for $2.39

23. Wagner's vanilla extract, $3.95 for 1.5 ounces, or Durkee vanilla extract, 1 ounce for $2.84

24. If the number of units of a product in a package increases but the cost remains the same, does the unit cost increase or decrease?

25. If the total cost for the same number of units increases, does the unit cost increase or decrease?

OBJECTIVE C   *To find total cost*

26. Sliced bacon costs $4.59 per pound. Find the total cost of 3 pounds.

27. Used red brick costs $.98 per brick. Find the total cost of 75 bricks.

28. Kiwi fruit cost $.43 each. Find the total cost of 8 kiwi.

29. Boneless chicken filets cost $4.69 per pound. Find the cost of 3.6 pounds. Round to the nearest cent.

30. Herbal tea costs $.98 per ounce. Find the total cost of 6.5 ounces.

31. Swiss cheese costs $5.99 per pound. Find the total cost of 0.65 pound. Round to the nearest cent.

32. Gala apples cost $1.29 per pound. Find the total cost of 2.1 pounds. Round to the nearest cent.

33. Rib eye steak costs $9.49 per pound. Find the total cost of 2.8 pounds. Round to the nearest cent.

34. Suppose a store flyer advertises cantaloupes as "buy one, get one free." True or false? The total cost of 6 cantaloupes at the sale price is the same as the total cost of 3 cantaloupes at the regular price.

Critical Thinking

For Exercises 35 and 36, suppose a box of Tea A contains twice as many tea bags as a box of Tea B. Decide which box of tea is the more economical purchase.

35. The price of a box of Tea B is greater than half the price of a box of Tea A.

36. The price of a box of Tea A is less than twice the price of a box of Tea B.

37. What is the UPC (Universal Product Code) and how is it used?

ISBN 0-395-75524-7

65)

0 4 6 4 4 2 7 7 0 1 8 7

Projects or Group Activities

38. Some financial advisors recommend that long-term investors use dollar cost averaging. With this method, the same dollar amount is invested at regular intervals. The number of shares purchased for that amount varies depending on the cost per share. The table at the right shows the results for one investor. It is common when using this method to purchase a fraction of a share, rounded to the nearest thousandth. Complete the cost-per-share (unit cost) column. Round to the nearest cent. Then find the average unit cost of all shares purchased.

Investment Amount	Shares Purchased	Cost per Share
$250	29.296	
$250	26.743	
$250	27.981	
$250	25.522	
$250	23.377	
$250	22.187	

6.2 Percent Increase and Percent Decrease

OBJECTIVE A *To find percent increase*

 Point of Interest

Precious metals such as gold or silver are measured in troy ounces. The ounce used to measure the weight of everyday items, such as coffee, beans, or meat, is called an avoirdupois ounce. 1 troy ounce ≈ 1.097 (avoirdupois) ounces

Percent increase is used to show how much a quantity has increased over its original value. The statements "Food prices increased by 2.3% last year" and "City council members received a 4% pay increase" are examples of percent increase.

HOW TO 1 In a six-month period, the price of gold increased from $1424.80 per ounce to $1621.40 per ounce. What is the percent increase in the price of one ounce of gold for the six-month period? Round to the nearest tenth of a percent.

$$\boxed{\text{New value}} - \boxed{\text{original value}} = \boxed{\text{amount of increase}}$$

$$1621.40 - 1424.80 = 196.60$$

Now solve the basic percent equation for percent.

$$\text{Percent} \times \text{base} = \text{amount}$$

$$\boxed{\text{Percent increase}} \times \boxed{\text{original value}} = \boxed{\text{amount of increase}}$$

$$n \times 1424.80 = 196.60$$
$$n = 196.60 \div 1424.80$$
$$n \approx 0.138 = 13.8\%$$

The percent increase in the price of one ounce of gold is approximately 13.8%.

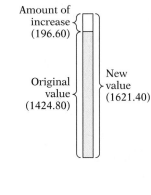

Amount of increase { (196.60)

Original value { (1424.80)

} New value (1621.40)

EXAMPLE 1

Based on data from Bloomberg New Energy Finance, it is estimated that there will be 1.6 million plug-in cars on the road by 2020, and 4 million by 2030. What percent increase in plug-in cars is predicted by this report?

Strategy

To find the percent increase:
• Find the amount of the increase.
• Solve the basic percent equation for *percent*.

Solution

$$\boxed{\text{New value}} - \boxed{\text{original value}} = \boxed{\text{amount of increase}}$$

$$4 \text{ million} - 1.6 \text{ million} = 2.4 \text{ million}$$

$$\text{Percent} \times \text{base} = \text{amount}$$
$$n \times 1.6 = 2.4$$
$$n = 2.4 \div 1.6$$
$$n = 1.5 = 150\%$$

The predicted percent increase is 150%.

YOU TRY IT 1

The average price of gasoline rose from $3.46 to $3.83 in 5 months. What was the percent increase in the price of gasoline? Round to the nearest percent.

Your strategy

Your solution

Solution on p. S15

EXAMPLE 2

Chris Carley was earning $17.86 an hour as a paramedic assistant before receiving a 15% increase in pay. What is Chris's new hourly pay?

Strategy

To find the new hourly wage:

- Solve the basic percent equation for *amount*.
- Add the amount of the increase to the original wage.

Solution

Percent × base = amount
0.15 × 17.86 = n
2.68 ≈ n

The amount of the increase was $2.68.

17.86 + 2.68 = 20.54

The new hourly wage is $20.54.

YOU TRY IT 2

Yolanda Liyama was making a wage of $12.50 an hour as a baker before receiving a 14% increase in hourly pay. What is Yolanda's new hourly wage?

Your strategy

Your solution

Solution on p. S15

OBJECTIVE B *To apply percent increase to business—markup*

Some of the expenses involved in operating a business are salaries, rent, equipment, and utilities. To pay these expenses and earn a profit, a business must sell a product at a higher price than it paid for the product.

Cost is the price a business pays for a product, and **selling price** is the price at which a business sells a product to a customer. The difference between selling price and cost is called **markup**.

$$\boxed{\text{Selling price}} - \boxed{\text{cost}} = \boxed{\text{markup}}$$

or

$$\boxed{\text{Cost}} + \boxed{\text{Markup rate}} = \boxed{\text{selling price}}$$

Markup is frequently expressed as a percent of a product's cost. This percent is called the **markup rate**.

$$\boxed{\text{Markup rate}} \times \boxed{\text{cost}} = \boxed{\text{markup}}$$

HOW TO 2 Suppose Bicycles Galore purchases a Felt Z4 bicycle for $2119.20 and sells it for $2649. What markup rate does Bicycles Galore use?

$$\boxed{\text{Selling price}} - \boxed{\text{cost}} = \boxed{\text{markup}}$$

2649.00 − 2119.20 = 529.80   • First find the markup.

Percent × base = amount   • Then solve the basic percent equation for *percent*.

$$\boxed{\text{Markup rate}} \times \boxed{\text{cost}} = \boxed{\text{markup}}$$

n × 2119.20 = 529.80

n = 529.80 ÷ 2119.20 = 0.25

The markup rate is 25%.

©Gorilla/Shutterstock.com

EXAMPLE 3

The manager of a sporting goods store determines that a markup rate of 56% is necessary to make a profit. What is the markup on a pair of skis that costs the store $225?

Strategy

To find the markup, solve the basic percent equation for *amount*.

Solution

Percent $\times$ base $=$ amount

Markup rate	$\times$	cost	$=$	markup

$$0.56 \quad \times \quad 225 \quad = \quad n$$
$$126 = n$$

The markup is $126.

YOU TRY IT 3

A bookstore manager determines that a markup rate of 20% is necessary to make a profit. What is the markup on a book that costs the bookstore $32?

Your strategy

Your solution

EXAMPLE 4

A plant nursery bought a yellow twig dogwood for $9.50 and used a markup rate of 65%. What is the selling price?

Strategy

To find the selling price:
- Find the markup by solving the basic percent equation for *amount*.
- Add the markup to the cost.

Solution

Percent $\times$ base $=$ amount

Markup rate	$\times$	cost	$=$	markup

$$0.65 \quad \times \quad 9.50 \quad = \quad n$$
$$6.18 \approx n$$

Cost	$+$	markup	$=$	selling price

$$9.50 \quad + \quad 6.18 \quad = \quad 15.68$$

The selling price is $15.68.

YOU TRY IT 4

A clothing store bought a leather jacket for $72 and used a markup rate of 55%. What is the selling price?

Your strategy

Your solution

Solutions on p. S15

OBJECTIVE C   *To find percent decrease*

Percent decrease is used to show how much a quantity has decreased from its original value. The statements "The number of family farms decreased by 2% last year" and "There has been a 50% decrease in the cost of a Pentium chip" are examples of percent decrease.

HOW TO 3   Data from the Internal Revenue Service show that between two recent years, the number of individuals with incomes over $500,000 per year fell from 862,227 to 729,451. Find the percent decrease in the number of individuals with incomes over $500,000. Round to the nearest tenth of a percent.

| Original value | − | new value | = | amount of decrease |

$$862,227 - 729,451 = 132,776$$

Now solve the basic percent equation for percent.

| Percent | × | base | = | amount |

| Percent decrease | × | original value | = | amount of decrease |

$$n \times 862,227 = 132,776$$
$$n = 132,776 \div 862,227$$
$$n \approx 0.154 = 15.4\%$$

The percent decrease in the number of individuals with incomes over $500,000 was approximately 15.4%.

Amount of decrease (132,776)

New value (729,451)

Original value (862,227)

Tips for Success

Note in the example below that solving a word problem involves stating a strategy and using the strategy to find a solution. If you have difficulty with a word problem, write down the known information. Be very specific. Write out a phrase or sentence that states what you are trying to find. See *AIM for Success* at the front of the book.

EXAMPLE 5

⬤ Between two recent years, annual attendance at New York Yankees baseball games decreased from approximately 3,766,000 people to approximately 3,654,000 people. (*Source:* espn.go.com) Find the percent decrease in attendance between these two years. Round to the nearest tenth of a percent.

Strategy

To find the percent decrease:

• Find the amount of the decrease.
• Solve the basic percent equation for *percent*.

Solution

| Original value | − | new value | = | amount of decrease |

$$3,766,000 - 3,654,000 = 112,000$$

Percent × base = amount
$$n \times 3,766,000 = 112,000$$
$$n = 112,000 \div 3,766,000$$
$$n \approx 0.030 = 3.0\%$$

The percent decrease in attendance was approximately 3.0%.

YOU TRY IT 5

⬤ The annual team payroll of the Colorado Rockies decreased from approximately $88,000,000 to approximately $84,227,000 between two years. (*Source:* Wikipedia; espn.go.com) Find the percent decrease in the annual payroll between these two years. Round to the nearest tenth of a percent.

Your strategy

Your solution

Solution on p. S15

EXAMPLE 6

The total sales for December at a stationery store were $96,000. In January, total sales showed an 8% decrease from December's sales. What were the total sales for January?

Strategy

To find the total sales for January:

- Find the amount of decrease by solving the basic percent equation for *amount.*
- Subtract the amount of decrease from the December sales.

Solution

Percent $\times$ base $=$ amount
0.08 $\times$ 96,000 $=$ n
7680 $=$ n

The decrease in sales was $7680.

$96,000 - 7680 = 88,320$

The total sales for January were $88,320.

YOU TRY IT 6

Fog decreased the normal 5-mile visibility at an airport by 40%. What was the visibility in the fog?

Your strategy

Your solution

Solution on p. S15

OBJECTIVE D   *To apply percent decrease to business—discount*

To promote sales, a store may reduce the regular price of some of its products temporarily. The reduced price is called the **sale price.** The difference between the regular price and the sale price is called the **discount.**

$$\boxed{\text{Regular price}} - \boxed{\text{sale price}} = \boxed{\text{discount}}$$

or

$$\boxed{\text{Regular price}} - \boxed{\text{discount}} = \boxed{\text{sale price}}$$

Discount is frequently stated as a percent of a product's regular price. This percent is called the **discount rate.**

$$\boxed{\text{Discount rate}} \times \boxed{\text{regular price}} = \boxed{\text{discount}}$$

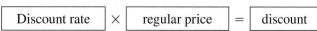

EXAMPLE 7

A Sanyo 42-inch LCD 1080p television that regularly sells for $498 is on sale for $449. Find the discount rate. Round to the nearest tenth of a percent.

Strategy

To find the discount rate:

- Find the discount.
- Solve the basic percent equation for *percent*.

Solution

Regular price	−	sale price	=	discount
498	−	449	=	49

Percent	×	base	=	amount
Discount rate	×	regular price	=	discount
n	×	498	=	49

$$n = 49 \div 498$$
$$n \approx 0.098$$

The discount rate is approximately 9.8%.

YOU TRY IT 7

A white azalea that regularly sells for $12.50 is on sale for $10.99. Find the discount rate. Round to the nearest tenth of a percent.

Your strategy

Your solution

EXAMPLE 8

A 20-horsepower lawn mower is on sale for 25% off the regular price of $1525. Find the sale price.

Strategy

To find the sale price:

- Find the discount by solving the basic percent equation for *amount*.
- Subtract to find the sale price.

Solution

Percent	×	base	=	amount
Discount rate	×	regular price	=	discount
0.25	×	1525	=	n

$$381.25 = n$$

Regular price	−	discount	=	sale price
1525	−	381.25	=	1143.75

The sale price is $1143.75.

YOU TRY IT 8

A hardware store is selling a Newport security door for 15% off the regular price of $225. Find the sale price.

Your strategy

Your solution

Solutions on p. S15

6.2 EXERCISES

✔ Concept Check

1. Which expression do you use when finding percent increase?
   (i) Original value − new value   **(ii)** New value − original value

2. Which expression do you use when finding percent decrease?
   (i) Original value − new value   **(ii)** New value − original value

3. ◣ What is the difference between markup and markup rate?

4. ◣ What is the difference between discount and discount rate?

OBJECTIVE A   *To find percent increase*

Solve. If necessary, round percents to the nearest tenth of a percent.

5. 🍂 **Halloween**   See the news clipping at the right. Find the percent increase in Halloween spending between the two years described.

6. **Fuel Efficiency**   An automobile manufacturer increased the average mileage on a car from 17.5 miles per gallon to 18.2 miles per gallon. Find the percent increase in mileage.

7. 🍂 **Bike Sharing**   Montreal's bike-sharing program had about 29,750 members during its second year, up from 7900 members during its first year. (*Source:* bixisystem.com) What was the percent increase in the number of members between these years?

8. 🍂 **Airfares**   In 2010, the average airfare from Boston to Los Angeles over the Thanksgiving holiday was $795. In 2011, the average airfare for the same trip was $880. (*Source:* The Boston Globe) Find the percent increase in the average Boston-to-Los Angeles airfare between Thanksgiving 2010 and Thanksgiving 2011.

9. 🍂 **Sports**   The first Winter Olympics, held in 1924, included 14 competitive events. Plans for the 2014 Winter Olympics include 98 competitive events. (*Source:* Wikipedia) Find the percent increase in the number of competitive events in the Winter Olympics from 1924 to 2014.

10. **Television**   Over a period of one year, the number of people subscribing to direct broadcasting satellite systems increased 87%. If the number of subscribers at the beginning of the year was 2.3 million, how many subscribers were there at the end of the year?

11. 🍂 **Pets**   In a recent year, Americans spent $50.84 billion on their pets. This was up from $28.5 billion a decade earlier. (*Source:* American Pet Products Association) Find the percent increase in the amount Americans spent on their pets during the 10-year period. Rounded to the nearest tenth.

12. 🍂 **Demography**   From 1970 to 2008, the average age of American mothers giving birth to their first child rose 17.3%. (*Source:* Centers for Disease Control and Prevention) If the average age in 1970 was 21.4 years, what was the average age in 2008? Round to the nearest tenth.

13. 🖋 **Compensation**   A welder earning $12 per hour is given a 10% raise. To find the new wage, we can multiply $12 by 0.10 and add the product to $12. Can the new wage be found by multiplying $12 by 1.10?

In the NEWS!

Spooky Increase in Spending

The holiday preferred by ghosts and goblins is more popular than ever this fall. Americans are predicted to spend a frightening $6.9 billion on Halloween this year, as compared to $5.8 billion last year.
Source: The Boston Globe

OBJECTIVE B   *To apply percent increase to business—markup*

The three important markup equations are:

(1) Selling price − cost = markup   (2) Cost + markup = selling price   (3) Markup rate × cost = markup

For Exercises 14 and 15, list, in the order in which they will be used, the markup equations needed to solve each problem. Do not solve.

14. A book that cost the seller $17 is sold for $23. Find the markup rate.

15. A DVD that cost the seller $12 has a markup rate of 55%. Find the selling price.

16. A window air conditioner cost AirRite Air Conditioning Systems $285. Find the markup on the air conditioner if the markup rate is 25% of the cost.

17. The manager of Brass Antiques has determined that a markup rate of 38% is necessary for a profit to be made. What is the markup on a brass doorknob that costs $45?

18. Computer Inc. uses a markup of $975 on a computer system that costs $3250. What is the markup rate on this system?

19. Saizon Pen & Office Supply uses a markup of $12 on a calculator that costs $20. What markup rate does this amount represent?

20. Giant Photo Service uses a markup rate of 48% on its Model ZA cameras, which cost the shop $162. What is the selling price?

21. The Circle R golf pro shop uses a markup rate of 45% on a set of Tour Pro golf clubs that costs the shop $210. What is the selling price?

22. Resner Builders' Hardware uses a markup rate of 42% for a table saw that costs $225. What is the selling price of the table saw?

23. Brad Burt's Magic Shop uses a markup rate of 48%. What is the selling price of a telescoping sword that costs $50?

OBJECTIVE C   *To find percent decrease*

Solve. If necessary, round to the nearest tenth of a percent.

24. 🌑 **Law School** Use the news clipping at the right to find the percent decrease in the number of people who took the LSATs between the two years described.

25. **Travel** A new bridge reduced the normal 45-minute travel time between two cities by 18 minutes. What percent decrease does this represent?

26. **Energy** By installing energy-saving equipment, the Pala Rey Youth Camp reduced its normal $800-per-month utility bill by $320. What percent decrease does this amount represent?

27. 🌑 **Criminology** Data from the Federal Bureau of Investigation show that the number of hate crimes in the United States decreased between two recent years, from 7783 incidents to 6604 incidents. What was the percent decrease in hate crimes between these two years?

> **In the NEWS!**
>
> **Fewer Students Take LSATs**
>
> This year, 155,050 people took the Law School Admission Test (LSATs). Last year, the LSATs were administered to 171,514 people.
>
> *Source:* Law School Admission Council

28. ● **Missing Persons**   See the news clipping at the right. Find the percent decrease over the last 10 years in the number of people entered into the National Crime Information Center's Missing Person File.

29. **Depreciation**   It is estimated that the value of a new car is reduced 30% after one year of ownership. Using this estimate, find how much value a $28,200 new car loses after one year.

30. **Employment**   A department store employs 1200 people during the holidays. At the end of the holiday season, the store reduces the number of employees by 45%. What is the decrease in the number of employees?

31. **Finance**   Juanita's average monthly expense for gasoline was $176. After joining a carpool, she was able to reduce the expense by 20%. What is her average monthly gasoline bill now?

32. **Investments**   An oil company paid a dividend of $1.60 per share. After a reorganization, the company reduced the dividend by 37.5%. What is the new dividend?

33. ● **Sports**   The graph at the right shows the total earnings of the top 30 members of the Ladies Professional Golf Association (LPGA) golf tour. What was the percent decrease in total earnings between the years 2008 and 2010?

34. ▨ In a math class, the average grade on the second test was 5% lower than the average grade on the first test. By what number should you multiply the first test average to find the difference between the average grades on the two tests?

In the NEWS!

Missing-Person Cases Decrease

This year, 692,944 missing-person cases were entered into the National Crime Information Center's Missing Person File. Ten years ago, the number was 876,213.
Source: www.fbi.gov

Total Earnings of Top 30 LPGA Members
Source: www.lpga.com

OBJECTIVE D   *To apply percent decrease to business—discount*

▨ The three important discount equations are:
(1) Regular price − sale price = discount
(2) Regular price − discount = sale price
(3) Discount rate × regular price = discount

For Exercises 35 and 36, list, in the order in which they will be used, the discount equations needed to solve each problem. Do not solve.

35. Shoes that regularly sell for $65 are on sale for 15% off the regular price. Find the sale price.

36. A radio with a regular price of $89 is on sale for $59. Find the discount rate.

37. The Austin College Bookstore is giving a discount of $8 on calculators that normally sell for $24. What is the discount rate?

38. A discount clothing store is selling a $72 sport jacket for $24 off the regular price. What is the discount rate?

39. A Blu-ray disc player that regularly sells for $400 is selling for 20% off the regular price. What is the discount?

40. Dacor Appliances is selling its $450 washing machine for 15% off the regular price. What is the discount?

41. An electric grill that regularly sells for $140 is selling for $42 off the regular price. What is the discount rate?

42. Quick Service Gas Station has its regularly-priced $125 tune-up on sale for 16% off the regular price. What is the sale price?

43. Tomatoes that regularly sell for $1.25 per pound are on sale for 20% off the regular price. What is the sale price?

44. An outdoor supply store has its regularly priced $160 sleeping bags on sale for $120. What is the discount rate?

45. Standard Brands ceiling paint that regularly sells for $20 per gallon is on sale for $16 per gallon. What is the discount rate?

Critical Thinking

46. ■ **Business**   A promotional sale at a department store offers 25% off the sale price. The sale price itself is 25% off the regular price. Is this the same as a sale that offers 50% off the regular price? If not, which sale gives the better price? Explain your answer.

Projects or Group Activities

47. ● **Demographics**   The graph at the right shows the numbers of people living in the United States for certain age groups, according to the 2000 and 2010 censuses. For the age groups shown, which age group had the greatest percent increase in population between the years 2000 and 2010?

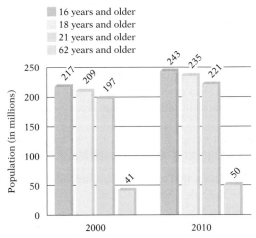

U.S. Population by Age Group

Source: U.S. Census Bureau

6.3 | Interest

OBJECTIVE A / *To calculate simple interest*

When you deposit money in a bank—for example, in a savings account—you are permitting the bank to use your money. The bank may lend the deposited money to customers to buy cars or make renovations on their homes. The bank pays you for the privilege of using your money. The amount paid to you is called **interest.** If you are the one borrowing money from the bank, the amount you pay for the privilege of using that money is also called interest.

The original amount deposited or borrowed is called the **principal.** The amount of interest paid is usually given as a percent of the principal. The percent used to determine the amount of interest is the **interest rate.**

> **Take Note**
> If you deposit $1000 in a savings account paying 5% interest, the $1000 is the principal and 5% is the interest rate.

Interest paid on the original principal is called **simple interest**. To calculate simple interest, multiply the principal by the interest rate per time period by the number of time periods. In this objective, we are working with annual interest rates, so the time period is years. The simple interest formula for an annual interest rate is given below.

Simple Interest Formula for Annual Interest Rates

Principal $\times$ annual interest rate $\times$ time (in years) $=$ interest

---

Interest rates generally are given as percents. Before performing calculations involving an interest rate, write the interest rate as a decimal.

HOW TO 1 Calculate the simple interest due on a 2-year loan of $1500 that has an annual interest rate of 7.5%.

Principal	$\times$	annual interest rate	$\times$	time (in years)	$=$	interest
1500	$\times$	0.075	$\times$	2	$=$	225

The simple interest due is $225.

When we borrow money, the total amount to be repaid to the lender is the sum of the principal and the interest. This amount is called the **maturity value of a loan.**

Maturity Value Formula for Simple Interest Loans

Principal $+$ interest $=$ maturity value

In HOW TO 1 above, the simple interest due on the loan of $1500 was $225. The maturity value of the loan is therefore $1500 + \$225 = \$1725$.

Take Note

The time of the loan must be in years. Eight months is $\frac{8}{12}$ of a year.

See Example 1. The time of the loan must be in years. 180 days is $\frac{180}{365}$ of a year.

HOW TO 2 Calculate the maturity value of a simple interest, 8-month loan of $8000 if the annual interest rate is 9.75%.

First find the interest due on the loan.

Principal	×	annual interest rate	×	time (in years)	=	interest
8000	×	0.0975	×	$\frac{8}{12}$	=	520

Find the maturity value.

Principal	+	interest	=	maturity value
8000	+	520	=	8520

The maturity value of the loan is $8520.

The monthly payment on a loan can be calculated by dividing the maturity value by the length of the loan in months.

Monthly Payment on a Simple Interest Loan

Maturity value ÷ length of the loan in months = monthly payment

---

In HOW TO 2 above, the maturity value of the loan is $8520. To find the monthly payment on the 8-month loan, divide 8520 by 8.

Maturity value	÷	length of the loan in months	=	monthly payment
8520	÷	8	=	1065

The monthly payment on the loan is $1065.

EXAMPLE 1

Kamal borrowed $500 from a savings and loan association for 180 days at an annual interest rate of 7%. What is the simple interest due on the loan?

Strategy

To find the simple interest due, multiply the principal (500) times the annual rate (7% = 0.07) times the time in years (180 days = $\frac{180}{365}$ year).

Solution

Principal	×	annual interest rate	×	time (in years)	=	interest
500	×	0.07	×	$\frac{180}{365}$	≈	17.26

The simple interest due is $17.26.

YOU TRY IT 1

A company borrowed $15,000 from a bank for 18 months at an annual interest rate of 8%. What is the simple interest due on the loan?

Your strategy

Your solution

Solution on p. S16

EXAMPLE 2

Calculate the maturity value of a simple interest, 9-month loan of $4000 if the annual interest rate is 8.75%.

Strategy

To find the maturity value:

- Use the simple interest formula to find the simple interest due.
- Find the maturity value by adding the principal and the interest.

Solution

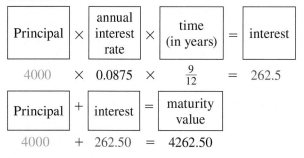

Principal	×	annual interest rate	×	time (in years)	=	interest
4000	×	0.0875	×	$\frac{9}{12}$	=	262.5

Principal	+	interest	=	maturity value
4000	+	262.50	=	4262.50

The maturity value is $4262.50.

YOU TRY IT 2

Calculate the maturity value of a simple interest, 90-day loan of $3800. The annual interest rate is 6%.

Your strategy

Your solution

EXAMPLE 3

The simple interest due on a 3-month loan of $1400 is $26.25. Find the monthly payment on the loan.

Strategy

To find the monthly payment:

- Find the maturity value by adding the principal and the interest.
- Divide the maturity value by the length of the loan in months (3).

Solution

Principal + interest = maturity value
  1400   + 26.25 =   1426.25

Maturity value ÷ length of the loan = payment
  1426.25   ÷   3   ≈   475.42

The monthly payment is $475.42.

YOU TRY IT 3

The simple interest due on a 1-year loan of $1900 is $152. Find the monthly payment on the loan.

Your strategy

Your solution

Solutions on p. S16

OBJECTIVE B   *To calculate finance charges on a credit card bill*

When a customer uses a credit card to make a purchase, the customer is actually receiving a loan. Therefore, there is frequently an added cost to the consumer who purchases on credit. This may be in the form of an annual fee and interest charges on purchases. The interest charges on purchases are called **finance charges.**

The finance charge on a credit card bill is calculated using the simple interest formula. In the last objective, the interest rates were annual interest rates. However, credit card companies generally issue *monthly* bills and express interest rates on credit card purchases as *monthly* interest rates. Therefore, when using the simple interest formula to calculate finance charges on credit card purchases, we use a monthly interest rate and express the time in months.

Note: In the simple interest formula, the time must be expressed in the same period as the rate. For an *annual* interest rate, the time must be expressed in years. For a *monthly* interest rate, the time must be expressed in months.

EXAMPLE 4

A credit card company charges a customer 1.5% per month on the unpaid balance of charges on the credit card. What is the finance charge for a month in which the customer has an unpaid balance of $254?

Strategy

To find the finance charge, multiply the principal, or unpaid balance (254), times the monthly interest rate (1.5%) times the number of months (1).

Solution

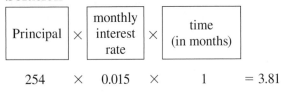

$$254 \quad \times \quad 0.015 \quad \times \quad 1 \quad = 3.81$$

The finance charge is $3.81.

YOU TRY IT 4

The credit card that Francesca uses charges her 1.6% per month on her unpaid balance. Find the finance charge when her unpaid balance for the month is $1250.

Your strategy

Your solution

Solution on p. S16

OBJECTIVE C   *To calculate compound interest*

Usually, the interest paid on money deposited or borrowed is compound interest. **Compound interest** is computed not only on the original principal but also on interest already earned. Here is an illustration.

Suppose $1000 is invested for 3 years at an annual interest rate of 9% compounded annually. Because this is an *annual* interest rate, we will calculate the interest earned each year.

During the first year, the interest earned is calculated as follows:

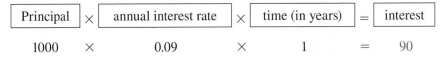

Principal	×	annual interest rate	×	time (in years)	=	interest
1000	×	0.09	×	1	=	90

At the end of the first year, the total amount in the account is

$$1000 + 90 = 1090$$

During the second year, the interest earned is calculated on the amount in the account at the end of the first year.

Principal	×	annual interest rate	×	time (in years)	=	interest
1090	×	0.09	×	1	=	98.10

Note that the interest earned during the second year ($98.10) is greater than the interest earned during the first year ($90). This is because the interest earned during the first year was added to the original principal, and the interest for the second year was calculated using this sum. If the account earned *simple* interest, the interest earned would be the same every year ($90).

At the end of the second year, the total amount in the account is the sum of the amount in the account at the end of the first year and the interest earned during the second year.

$$1090 + 98.10 = 1188.10$$

The interest earned during the third year is calculated using the amount in the account at the end of the second year ($1188.10).

Principal	×	annual interest rate	×	time (in years)	=	interest
1188.10	×	0.09	×	1	≈	106.93

The amount in the account at the end of the third year is

$$1188.10 + 106.93 = 1295.03$$

To find the interest earned for the three years, subtract the original principal from the new principal.

New principal	−	original principal	=	interest earned
1295.03	−	1000	=	295.03

Note that the compound interest earned is $295.03. The simple interest earned on the investment would have been only $1000 × 0.09 × 3 = $270.

In this example, the interest was compounded annually. However, interest can be compounded over other time periods.

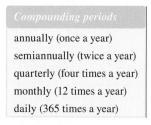

Compounding periods
annually (once a year)
semiannually (twice a year)
quarterly (four times a year)
monthly (12 times a year)
daily (365 times a year)

The more frequent the compounding periods, the more interest the account earns. For example, if, in the above example, the interest had been compounded quarterly rather than annually, the interest earned would have been greater.

Take Note

The interest earned each year keeps increasing. This is the effect of compound interest.

Calculating compound interest can be very tedious, so there are tables that can be used to simplify these calculations. A portion of a Compound Interest Table is given in the Appendix.

HOW TO 3   What is the value after 5 years of $1275 invested at 4.75% annual interest, compounded quarterly?

To find the interest earned, multiply the original principal (1275) by the factor found in the Compound Interest Table. To find the factor, first find the table headed "Compounded Quarterly" in the Compound Interest Table in the Appendix. Then look at the number where the 4.75% column and the 5-years row meet.

	Compounded Quarterly							
	4%	*4.25%*	*4.50%*	*4.75%*	*5.00%*	*5.25%*	*5.50%*	*5.75%*
1 year	1.04060	1.04320	1.04580	1.04840	1.05090	1.05350	1.05610	1.05880
5 years	1.22020	1.23540	1.25080	1.26630	1.28200	1.29800	1.31410	1.33040
10 years	1.48890	1.52620	1.56440	1.60350	1.64360	1.68470	1.72680	1.76990
15 years	1.81670	1.88540	1.95660	2.03050	2.10720	2.18670	2.26910	2.35460
20 years	2.21670	2.32920	2.44730	2.57130	2.70150	2.83820	2.98170	3.13240

The factor is 1.26630.

$$1275 \times 1.26630 = 1614.53$$

The value of the investment after 5 years is $1614.53.

EXAMPLE 5

An investment of $650 pays 6.75% annual interest, compounded semiannually. What is the interest earned in 5 years?

Strategy

To find the interest earned:

- Find the new principal by multiplying the original principal (650) by the factor found in the Compound Interest Table (1.39365).
- Subtract the original principal from the new principal.

Solution

$650 \times 1.39365 \approx 905.87$

The new principal is $905.87.

$905.87 - 650 = 255.87$

The interest earned is $255.87.

YOU TRY IT 5

An investment of $1000 pays 6% annual interest, compounded quarterly. What is the interest earned in 20 years?

Your strategy

Your solution

Solution on p. S16

6.3 EXERCISES

✔ Concept Check

1. What is the Simple Interest Formula for Annual Interest Rates?

2. A contractor obtained a 9-month loan for $80,000 at an annual simple interest rate of 9.75%. The simple interest due on the loan is $5850. Identify **a.** the principal, **b.** the interest, **c.** the interest rate, and **d.** the time period of the loan.

3. A 2-year student loan of $10,000 is made at an annual simple interest rate of 4.25%. The simple interest due on the loan is $850. Identify **a.** the principal, **b.** the interest, **c.** the interest rate, and **d.** the time period of the loan.

4. ◣ What is the difference between simple interest and compound interest?

OBJECTIVE A   *To calculate simple interest*

5. Find the simple interest that Jacob Zucker owes on a 2-year student loan of $8000 at an annual interest rate of 6%.

6. Find the simple interest that Kara Tanamachi owes on a $1\frac{1}{2}$-year loan of $1500 at an annual interest rate of 7.5%.

7. To finance the purchase of 15 new cars, the Tropical Car Rental Agency borrowed $100,000 for 9 months at an annual interest rate of 4.5%. What is the simple interest due on the loan?

Kenneth William Caleno/Shutterstock.com

8. A home builder obtained a preconstruction loan of $50,000 for 8 months at an annual interest rate of 9.5%. What is the simple interest due on the loan?

9. A bank lent Gloria Masters $20,000 at an annual interest rate of 8.8%. The period of the loan was 9 months. Find the simple interest due on the loan.

10. Eugene Madison obtained an 8-month loan of $4500 at an annual interest rate of 6.2%. Find the simple interest Eugene owes on the loan.

11. Jorge Elizondo took out a 75-day loan of $7500 at an annual interest rate of 5.5%. Find the simple interest due on the loan.

12. Kristi Yang borrowed $15,000. The term of the loan was 90 days, and the annual simple interest rate was 7.4%. Find the simple interest due on the loan.

13. The simple interest due on a 4-month loan of $4800 is $320. What is the maturity value of the loan?

14. The simple interest due on a 60-day loan of $6500 is $80.14. Find the maturity value of the loan.

15. William Carey borrowed $12,500 for 8 months at an annual simple interest rate of 4.5%. Find the total amount due on the loan.

16. You arrange for a 9-month bank loan of $9000 at an annual simple interest rate of 8.5%. Find the total amount you must repay to the bank.

17. Capital City Bank approves a home-improvement loan application for $14,000 at an annual simple interest rate of 5.25% for 270 days. What is the maturity value of the loan?

18. A credit union lends a member $5000 for college tuition. The loan is made for 18 months at an annual simple interest rate of 6.9%. What is the maturity value of the loan?

19. Action Machining Company purchased a robot-controlled lathe for $225,000 and financed the full amount at 8% annual simple interest for 4 years. The simple interest due on the loan is $72,000. Find the monthly payment.

20. For the purchase of a media center, a $1900 loan is obtained for 2 years at an annual simple interest rate of 9.4%. The simple interest due on the loan is $357.20. What is the monthly payment on the loan?

21. To attract new customers, Heller Ford is offering car loans at an annual simple interest rate of 4.5%.
   a. Find the interest charged to a customer who finances a car loan of $12,000 for 2 years.
   b. Find the monthly payment.

22. Cimarron Homes Inc. purchased a snow plow for $57,000 and financed the full amount for 5 years at an annual simple interest rate of 9%.
   a. Find the interest due on the loan.
   b. Find the monthly payment.

23. Dennis Pappas decided to build onto his present home instead of buying a new, larger house. He borrowed $142,000 for $5\frac{1}{2}$ years at an annual simple interest rate of 7.5%. Find the monthly payment.

Sue Smith/Shutterstock.com

24. Rosalinda Johnson took out a 6-month, $12,000 loan. The annual simple interest rate on the loan was 8.5%. Find the monthly payment.

25. Student A and Student B borrow the same amount of money at the same annual interest rate. Student A has a 2-year loan and Student B has a 1-year loan. In each case, state whether the first quantity is *less than, equal to,* or *greater than* the second quantity.
   a. Student A's principal; Student B's principal
   b. Student A's maturity value; Student B's maturity value
   c. Student A's monthly payment; Student B's monthly payment

OBJECTIVE B   *To calculate finance charges on a credit card bill*

26. A credit card company charges a customer 1.25% per month on the unpaid balance of charges on the credit card. What is the finance charge for a month in which the customer has an unpaid balance of $118.72?

27. The credit card that Dee Brown uses charges her 1.75% per month on her unpaid balance. Find the finance charge when the unpaid balance for the month is $391.64.

28. What is the finance charge on an unpaid balance of $12,368.92 on a credit card that charges 1.5% per month on any unpaid balance?

29. Suppose you have an unpaid balance of $995.04 on a credit card that charges 1.2% per month on any unpaid balance. What finance charge do you owe the company?

30. A credit card customer has an unpaid balance of $1438.20. What is the difference between monthly finance charges of 1.15% per month on the unpaid balance and monthly finance charges of 1.85% per month?

31. One credit card company charges 1.25% per month on any unpaid balance, and a second company charges 1.75%. What is the difference between the finance charges that these two companies assess on an unpaid balance of $687.45?

 Your credit card company requires a minimum monthly payment of $10. You plan to pay off the balance on your credit card by paying the minimum amount each month and making no further purchases using this credit card. For Exercises 32 and 33, state whether the finance charge for the second month will be *less than, equal to,* or *greater than* the finance charge for the first month, and state whether you will eventually be able to pay off the balance.

32. The finance charge for the first month was less than $10.

33. The finance charge for the first month was exactly $10.

OBJECTIVE C   *To calculate compound interest*

34. North Island Federal Credit Union pays 4% annual interest, compounded daily, on time savings deposits. Find the value after one year of $750 deposited in this account.

35. Tanya invested $2500 in a tax-sheltered annuity that pays 5.25% annual interest, compounded daily. Find the value of her investment after 20 years.

36. Sal Travato invested $3000 in a corporate retirement account that pays 7.5% annual interest, compounded semiannually. Find the value of his investment after 15 years.

37. To replace equipment, a farmer invested $20,000 in an account that pays 7% annual interest, compounded monthly. What is the value of the investment after 5 years?

38. Green River Lodge invests $75,000 in a trust account that pays 7.25% interest, compounded quarterly.
   a. What will the value of the investment be in 5 years?
   b. How much interest will be earned in the 5 years?

39. To save for retirement, a couple deposited $3000 in an account that pays 7% annual interest, compounded daily.
   a. What will be the value of the investment after 10 years?
   b. How much interest will be earned in the 10 years?

40. To save for a child's education, the Petersens deposited $2500 into an account that pays 8.25% annual interest, compounded daily. Find the amount of interest earned on this account over a 20-year period.

41. How much interest is earned in 2 years on $4000 deposited in an account that pays 6% interest, compounded quarterly?

42. The compound interest factor for a 5-year investment at an annual interest rate of 6%, compounded semiannually, is 1.34392. What does the expression $(3500 \times 1.34392) - 3500$ represent?

Critical Thinking

43. **Banking**   At 4 P.M. on July 31, you open a savings account that pays 5% annual interest, compounded daily, and you deposit $500 in the account. Your deposit is credited as of August 1. At the beginning of September, you receive a statement from the bank that shows that during the month of August, you received $2.12 in interest. The interest has been added to your account, bringing the total on deposit to $502.12. At the beginning of October, you receive a statement from the bank that shows that during the month of September, you received $2.06 in interest on the $502.12 on deposit. Explain why you received less interest during the second month when there was more money on deposit.

Projects or Group Activities

44. Banking   Suppose you have a savings account that earns interest at the rate of 6% per year, compounded monthly. On January 1, you open this account with a deposit of $100.
   a. On February 1, you deposit an additional $100 into the account. What is the value of the account after the deposit?
   b. On March 1, you deposit an additional $100 into the account. What is the value of the account after the deposit?
   c. You continue to deposit an additional $100 into the account on the first day of each month. What is the value of the account on December 31? *Note:* This type of savings plan, wherein equal amounts ($100) are saved at equal time intervals (every month), is called an annuity.

SECTION

6.4 | Real Estate Expenses

OBJECTIVE A | *To calculate the initial expenses of buying a home*

One of the largest investments that most people ever make is the purchase of a home. The major initial expense in the purchase is the **down payment,** which is normally a percent of the purchase price. This percent varies among banks, but it usually ranges from 5% to 25%.

The **mortgage** is the amount that is borrowed to buy real estate. The mortgage amount is the difference between the purchase price and the down payment.

HOW TO 1 A home is purchased for $140,000, and a down payment of $21,000 is made. Find the mortgage.

Purchase price	−	down payment	=	mortgage
140,000	−	21,000	=	119,000

The mortgage is $119,000.

 Take Note

Because *points* means "percent," a loan origination fee of $2\frac{1}{2}$ points is equal to

$2\frac{1}{2}\% = 2.5\% = 0.025$.

Another initial expense in buying a home is the **loan origination fee,** which is a fee that the bank charges for processing the mortgage papers. The loan origination fee is usually a percent of the mortgage and is expressed in **points,** which is the term banks use to mean "percent." For example, "5 points" means "5 percent."

Points	×	mortgage	=	loan origination fee

EXAMPLE 1

A house is purchased for $250,000, and a down payment that is 20% of the purchase price is made. Find the mortgage.

Strategy

To find the mortgage:

- Find the down payment by solving the basic percent equation for *amount.*
- Subtract the down payment from the purchase price.

Solution

Percent	×	base	=	amount
Percent	×	purchase price	=	down payment
0.20	×	250,000	=	*n*
		50,000	=	*n*

Purchase price	−	down payment	=	mortgage
250,000	−	50,000	=	200,000

The mortgage is $200,000.

YOU TRY IT 1

An office building is purchased for $1,500,000, and a down payment that is 25% of the purchase price is made. Find the mortgage.

Your strategy

Your solution

Solution on p. S16

EXAMPLE 2

A home is purchased with a mortgage of $165,000. The buyer pays a loan origination fee of $3\frac{1}{2}$ points. How much is the loan origination fee?

Strategy

To find the loan origination fee, solve the basic percent equation for *amount*.

Solution

Percent	×	base	= amount
Points	×	mortgage	= fee

$$0.035 \quad \times \quad 165{,}000 \quad = \quad n$$
$$5775 = n$$

The loan origination fee is $5775.

YOU TRY IT 2

The mortgage on a real estate investment is $180,000. The buyer paid a loan origination fee of $4\frac{1}{2}$ points. How much was the loan origination fee?

Your strategy

Your solution

Solution on p. S16

OBJECTIVE B   *To calculate the ongoing expenses of owning a home*

In addition to the initial expenses of buying a house, there are continuing monthly expenses involved in owning a home. The **monthly mortgage payment**, utilities, insurance, and **property tax** are some of these ongoing expenses. Of these expenses, the largest one is normally the monthly mortgage payment.

For a **fixed-rate mortgage**, the monthly mortgage payment remains the same throughout the life of the loan. The calculation of the monthly mortgage payment is based on the amount of the loan, the interest rate on the loan, and the number of years required to repay the loan. Calculation of the monthly mortgage payment is simplified by using a table such as the Monthly Payment Table in the Appendix, by using a calculator, or by using a spreadsheet program. We will use the table in the Appendix.

Integrating Technology

In general, when the answer to a problem involves money, the answer is rounded to the nearest cent. For HOW TO 2 at the right, enter

160000 ✕ 0.0080462 =

The display reads 1287.392. Round this number to the nearest hundredth: 1287.39. The answer is $1287.39.

HOW TO 2   Find the monthly mortgage payment on a 30-year, $160,000 mortgage at an annual interest rate of 9%. Use the Monthly Payment Table in the Appendix.

$$160{,}000 \times 0.0080462 \approx 1287.39$$

• Use the Monthly Payment Table to find the monthly payment factor, **0.0080462**.

The monthly mortgage payment is $1287.39.

The monthly mortgage payment includes the payment of both principal and interest on the mortgage. The interest charged during any one month is charged on the unpaid balance of the loan. By completing the Project on pages 264 to 265, you will see that as payments are made, the amount of the monthly payment that goes toward interest decreases, and the amount that goes toward the principal increases.

HOW TO 3 A chef obtained a 30-year mortgage of $245,000 at an annual interest rate of 5.75%. The chef's monthly mortgage payment is $1429.75. How much of the first month's mortgage payment is interest?

At the end of the first month, the chef owes simple interest on the amount borrowed ($245,000). The monthly simple interest rate is the annual interest rate, expressed as a decimal, divided by 12. Round this rate to six decimal places.

$$\text{Monthly simple interest rate} = \frac{\text{annual interest rate}}{12} = \frac{0.0575}{12} \approx 0.004792$$

To find the interest owed, solve the basic percent equation for amount. The base is the amount of the mortgage ($245,000).

Percent $\times$ base = amount
0.004792 $\times$ 245,000 = 1174.04

The interest owed for the first month of the loan is $1174.04.

If the interest owed the first month is subtracted from the monthly payment, the result is the amount of that month's payment that goes toward repaying the principal.

$$1429.75 - 1174.04 = 255.71$$

$255.71 of the payment went toward paying off the original loan. The remaining mortgage is $245,000.00 - $255.71 = $244,744.29.

Take Note

Reread the paragraph that precedes HOW TO 3. The reason for the change in the amount of interest owed each month is based on the calculation shown at the right. For the second month of the loan, the amount of interest owed is based on the remaining loan amount of $244,744.29.

EXAMPLE 3

A home was purchased for $239,000, with a down payment of 20% of the purchase price. The homeowner obtained a 30-year loan on the balance of the purchase price at an annual interest rate of 6.25%. What is the homeowner's monthly mortgage payment?

Strategy

To find the mortgage payment:
- Find the down payment.
- Subtract the down payment from the purchase price to find the mortgage.
- Multiply the mortgage by the factor in the Monthly Payment Table for a 30-year loan at 6.25%.

Solution

Percent $\times$ purchase price = down payment
  0.20 $\times$ 239,000   =   47,800

The down payment is $47,800.

Purchase price $-$ down payment = mortgage
  239,000 $-$ 47,800   = 191,200

The mortgage is $191,200.

The factor from the Monthly Payment Table is 0.0061572.

191,200 $\times$ 0.0061572 = 1177.26

The monthly mortgage payment is $1117.26.

YOU TRY IT 3

A hair salon was purchased for $185,000, with a down payment of 30% of the purchase price. The salon owner obtained a 20-year loan on the balance of the purchase price at an annual interest rate of 6%. What is the salon owner's monthly mortgage payment?

Your strategy

Your solution

Solution on p. S17

EXAMPLE 4

A plumbing contractor obtained a 20-year mortgage of $370,000 at an annual interest rate of 4.75%. The contractors's monthly mortgage payment is $2391.01. How much of the first month's mortgage payment is interest? How much of the first month's mortgage payment goes to paying off the principal?

Strategy

To find the amount of the first month's payment that is interest and the amount that goes to paying off the principal:

- Find the monthly simple interest rate.
- Use the basic percent equation to find the interest owed for the first month.
- Subtract the interest owed for the first month from the monthly payment to find the amount of the payment that goes to paying off the principal.

Solution

$$\text{Monthly simple interest rate} = \frac{\text{annual interest rate}}{12}$$

$$= \frac{0.0475}{12} \approx 0.003958$$

Percent × base = amount
0.003958 × 370,000 ≈ 1464.46

The interest owed for the first month is $1464.46.

Monthly payment	−	amount toward interest	=	amount toward principal
2391.01	−	1464.46	=	926.55

The amount paid toward the principal is $926.55.

YOU TRY IT 4

A facilities manager purchased a home and secured a 30-year mortgage of $296,000 at an annual interest rate of 4.5%. The manager's monthly mortgage payment is $1413.15. How much of the first month's mortgage payment is interest? How much of the first month's mortgage payment goes to paying off the principal?

Your strategy

Your solution

6.4 EXERCISES

✔ Concept Check

1. When purchasing real estate, what is the difference between the purchase price and the down payment called?

2. What does the term "3 points" mean when used by a banker?

OBJECTIVE A   *To calculate the initial expenses of buying a home*

3. A condominium at Mt. Baldy Ski Resort was purchased for $197,000, with a down payment of $24,550. Find the mortgage.

4. An insurance business was purchased for $173,000, with a down payment of $34,600. Find the mortgage.

5. Brian Stedman made a down payment of 25% of the $850,000 purchase price of an apartment building. How much was the down payment?

6. A clothing store was purchased for $625,000, and a down payment that was 30% of the purchase price was made. Find the down payment.

7. A loan of $150,000 is obtained to purchase a home. The loan origination fee is $2\frac{1}{2}$ points. Find the amount of the loan origination fee.

8. Security Savings & Loan requires a borrower to pay $3\frac{1}{2}$ points for a loan. Find the amount of the loan origination fee for a loan of $90,000.

9. Baja Construction Inc. is selling homes for $350,000. A down payment of 10% is required. Find the mortgage.

10. A cattle rancher purchased some land for $240,000. The bank requires a down payment of 15% of the purchase price. Find the mortgage.

11. Vivian Tom purchased a home for $210,000. Find the mortgage if the down payment Vivian made is 10% of the purchase price.

12. A mortgage lender requires a down payment of 5% of the $180,000 purchase price of a condominium. How much is the mortgage?

13. A home is purchased for $435,000. The mortgage lender requires a 10% down payment. Which expression below represents the mortgage?
   (i) $0.10 \times 435,000$
   (iii) $435,000 - 0.10 \times 435,000$
   (ii) $0.10 \times 435,000 - 435,000$
   (iv) $435,000 + 0.10 \times 435,000$

OBJECTIVE B   *To calculate the ongoing expenses of owning a home*

For Exercises 14 to 23, solve. Use the Monthly Payment Table in the Appendix. Round to the nearest cent.

14. An investor obtained a loan of $850,000 to buy a car wash business. The monthly mortgage payment was based on 25 years at 5.75%. Find the monthly mortgage payment.

15. A beautician obtained a 20-year mortgage of $90,000 to expand the business. The credit union charges an annual interest rate of 6%. Find the monthly mortgage payment.

16. A couple interested in buying a home determines that they can afford a monthly mortgage payment of $800. Can they afford to buy a home with a 30-year, $110,000 mortgage at 7.25% interest?

17. A lawyer is considering purchasing a new office building with a 15-year, $525,000 mortgage at 5% interest. The lawyer can afford a monthly mortgage payment of $4000. Can the lawyer afford the monthly mortgage payment on the new office building?

18. Maria Hernandez purchased a home for $210,000 and made a down payment of 15% of the purchase price. The balance was financed for 15 years at an annual interest rate of 6%.
a. Find the mortgage.
b. Find the monthly mortgage payment.

19. Richard Chin purchased a patio home for $312,500 and made a down payment of 20% of the purchase price. The balance was financed for 30 years at an annual interest rate of 4.75%.
a. Find the mortgage.
b. Find the monthly mortgage payment.

20. The retail sales manager of a computer company purchased a large house for $799,000 and made a down payment of 30% of the purchase price. The balance was financed for 20 years at an annual interest rate of 4.25%. Find the monthly mortgage payment.

21. A copper mine worker purchased a home for $299,000 and made a down payment of 25% of the purchase price. The balance was financed for 30 years at an annual interest rate of 5.5%. Find the monthly mortgage payment.

22. Abacus Imports Inc. purchased a warehouse and secured a 20-year mortgage of $500,000 at an annual interest rate of 6%. The monthly mortgage payment is $3582.15. Find the amount of the first month's payment that is interest and the amount that goes toward paying off the principal.

23. A dentist purchased an existing dental practice and obtained a 30-year loan of $720,000 at an annual interest rate of 5%. The monthly mortgage payment is $3865.10. Find the amount of the first month's payment that is interest and the amount that goes toward the principal.

24. The monthly payment on a $300,000 mortgage is $1610. The mortgage is a 30-year loan at an annual interest rate of 5%. Which expression represents the amount of the first month's payment that goes toward the principal?
(i) $300,000 - \dfrac{0.05}{12} \times 1610$ **(ii)** $\dfrac{0.05(300,000 - 1610)}{12}$
(iii) $1610 - \dfrac{0.05}{12} \times 300,000$

Critical Thinking

25. Mortgages A couple considering a mortgage of $100,000 have a choice of loans. One loan is an 8% loan for 20 years, and the other loan is at 8% for 30 years. Find the amount of interest that the couple can save by choosing the 20-year loan.

Projects or Group Activities

26. In HOW TO 3 on page 261, we calculated the amount of the first monthly payment of a loan that was interest and the amount that was principal. In this project, you will continue these calculations for the next three months of that 30-year loan by completing the table below. This table, if completed for all 360 months of the loan, is called an *amortization schedule*. Remember that the amount of interest paid each month is based on the new principal amount at the beginning of that month.

Month	Principal	Monthly payment	Amount to interest	Amount to principal	New principal
1	245,000.00	1429.75	1174.04	255.71	244,744.29
2	244,744.29	1429.75			
3		1429.75			
4		1429.75			

✔ CHECK YOUR PROGRESS: CHAPTER 6

1. **Sports**   Twelve golf balls cost $45.99. Find the unit cost. Round to the nearest cent.

2. **Commerce**   Find the more economical purchase: 20 ounces of dark chocolate for $18.49 or 16 ounces of dark chocolate for $12.99.

3. **Agriculture**   The cost of bluegrass sod is $2.97 per square yard. What is the cost of 15 square yards of bluegrass sod?

4. ● **Demographics**   Between 1998 and 2011, the world's population increased from 7 billion to 8 billion people. What was the percent increase in the world's population between the given years? Round to the nearest tenth of a percent.

5. **Commerce**   A tire store purchased a high performance automobile tire for $225 and used a markup rate of 40%. What is the selling price of the tire?

6. **Sports**   At the beginning of a training program, a sports agent weighed 185 pounds. Six months later, the agent weighed 168 pounds. What was the percent decrease in the agent's weight? Round to the nearest tenth of a percent.

7. **Commerce**   A graphing calculator is on sale for 20% off the regular price of $89.95. Find the sale price.

8. **Loans**   The owner of a flower shop borrowed $1500 for 18 months at an annual simple interest rate of 8%. Find the interest the borrower will pay on the loan.

9. **Credit Cards**   A credit card company charges a customer 1.8% per month on the unpaid balance of charges on the credit card. What is the finance charge for a month in which the customer had an unpaid balance of $365?

10. **Investing**   What is the value after 10 years of a $2500 investment at 5.25% annual interest, compounded daily?

11. **Real Estate**   A plumber purchases a home for $236,000 and makes a down payment of 20% of the purchase price. What is the plumber's mortgage?

12. **Real Estate**   A couple buys a cabin and obtains a 15-year mortgage of $175,000 at an annual interest rate of 5.5%. What is the monthly mortgage payment?

6.5 Car Expenses

OBJECTIVE A *To calculate the initial expenses of buying a car*

The initial expenses involved in the purchase of a car usually include the down payment, the **license fees** (fees charged for authorization to operate a vehicle), and the **sales tax** (a tax levied by a state or municipality on purchases). The down payment may be very small or as much as 25% or 30% of the purchase price of the car, depending on the lending institution. License fees and sales tax are regulated by each state, so these expenses vary from state to state.

EXAMPLE 1

A car is purchased for $38,500, and the lender requires a down payment of 15% of the purchase price. Find the amount financed.

Strategy

To find the amount financed:

- Find the down payment by solving the basic percent equation for *amount*.
- Subtract the down payment from the purchase price.

Solution

Percent	×	base	=	amount
Percent	×	purchase price	=	down payment
0.15	×	38,500	=	n
			5775	= n

$38,500 - 5775 = 32,725$

The amount financed is $32,725.

YOU TRY IT 1

A down payment of 20% of the $19,200 purchase price of a new car is made. Find the amount financed.

Your strategy

Your solution

EXAMPLE 2

A sales clerk purchases a used car for $16,500 and pays a sales tax that is 5% of the purchase price. How much is the sales tax?

Strategy

To find the sales tax, solve the basic percent equation for *amount*.

Solution

Percent	×	base	=	amount
Percent	×	purchase price	=	sales tax
0.05	×	16,500	=	n
			825	= n

The sales tax is $825.

YOU TRY IT 2

A car is purchased for $27,350. The car license fee is 1.5% of the purchase price. How much is the license fee?

Your strategy

Your solution

Solutions on p. S17

OBJECTIVE B   *To calculate the ongoing expenses of owning a car*

 Take Note
The same formula that is used to calculate a monthly mortgage payment is used to calculate a monthly car payment.

In addition to the initial expenses of buying a car, there are continuing expenses involved in owning a car. These ongoing expenses include car insurance, gas and oil, general maintenance, and the monthly car payment. The monthly car payment is calculated using the Monthly Payment Table in the Appendix.

EXAMPLE 3

At a cost of $.38 per mile, how much does it cost to operate a car during a year in which the car is driven 15,000 miles?

Strategy

To find the cost, multiply the cost per mile (0.38) by the number of miles driven (15,000).

Solution

$15,000 \times 0.38 = 5700$

The cost is $5700.

YOU TRY IT 3

At a cost of $.41 per mile, how much does it cost to operate a car during a year in which the car is driven 23,000 miles?

Your strategy

Your solution

EXAMPLE 4

During one month, your total gasoline bill was $252 and the car was driven 1200 miles. What was the cost per mile for gasoline?

Strategy

To find the cost per mile, divide the cost for gasoline (252) by the number of miles driven (1200).

Solution

$252 \div 1200 = 0.21$

The cost per mile was $.21.

YOU TRY IT 4

For a year in which your total car insurance bill was $360 and the car was driven 15,000 miles, what was the cost per mile for car insurance?

Your strategy

Your solution

EXAMPLE 5

A car is purchased for $18,500 with a down payment of $3700. The balance is financed for 3 years at an annual interest rate of 6%. Find the monthly car payment.

Strategy

To find the monthly payment:
• Subtract the down payment from the purchase price to find the amount financed.
• Multiply the amount financed by the factor found in the Monthly Payment Table in the Appendix.

Solution

$18,500 - 3700 = 14,800$

$14,800 \times 0.0304219 \approx 450.24$

The monthly payment is $450.24.

YOU TRY IT 5

A truck is purchased for $25,900 with a down payment of $6475. The balance is financed for 4 years at an annual interest rate of 8%. Find the monthly payment.

Your strategy

Your solution

Solutions on p. S17

6.5 EXERCISES

Concept Check

1. ◤ If a car dealer requires a down payment of 20% of the purchase price of a car, how would you determine the amount of the down payment?

2. Which table in the Appendix is used to calculate a monthly car payment?

OBJECTIVE A   *To calculate the initial expenses of buying a car*

3. Amanda has saved $780 to make a down payment on a used minivan that costs $7100. The car dealer requires a down payment of 12% of the purchase price. Has she saved enough money to make the down payment?

4. A sedan was purchased for $23,500. A down payment of 15% of the purchase price was required. How much was the down payment?

5. A drapery installer bought a van to carry drapery samples. The purchase price of the van was $26,500, and a 4.5% sales tax was paid. How much was the sales tax?

6. A & L Lumber Company purchased a delivery truck for $28,500. A sales tax of 4% of the purchase price was paid. Find the sales tax.

7. A license fee of 2% of the purchase price is paid on a pickup truck costing $32,500. Find the license fee for the truck.

8. Your state charges a license fee of 1.5% on the purchase price of a car. How much is the license fee for a car that costs $16,998?

9. An electrician bought a $32,000 flatbed truck. A state license fee of $275 and a sales tax of 3.5% of the purchase price are required.
   a. Find the sales tax.
   b. Find the total cost of the sales tax and the license fee.

10. A physical therapist bought a used car for $9375 and made a down payment of $1875. The sales tax is 5% of the purchase price.
   a. Find the sales tax.
   b. Find the total cost of the sales tax and the down payment.

11. Martin bought a motorcycle for $16,200 and made a down payment of 25% of the purchase price. Find the amount financed.

12. A carpenter bought a utility van for $24,900 and made a down payment of 15% of the purchase price. Find the amount financed.

13. An author bought a sports car for $45,000 and made a down payment of 20% of the purchase price. Find the amount financed.

14. Tania purchased a used car for $13,500 and made a down payment of 25% of the cost. Find the amount financed.

15. ◤ The purchase price of a car is $25,700. The car dealer requires a down payment of 15% of the purchase price. There is a license fee of 2.5% of the purchase price and sales tax of 6% of the purchase price. What does the following expression represent? $25,700 + 0.025 \times 25,700 + 0.06 \times 25,700$

OBJECTIVE B *To calculate the ongoing expenses of owning a car*

16. A driver had $1100 in car expenses and drove the car 8500 miles. Would you use *multiplication* or *division* to find the driver's cost per mile to operate the car?

17. A car costs $.62 per mile to operate. Would you use *multiplication* or *division* to find the cost of driving the car 23,000 miles?

For Exercises 18 to 25, solve. When necessary, use the Monthly Payment Table in the Appendix. Round to the nearest cent.

18. A rancher financed $24,000 for the purchase of a truck through a credit union at 5% interest for 4 years. Find the monthly truck payment.

19. A car loan of $18,000 is financed for 3 years at an annual interest rate of 6.75%. Find the monthly car payment.

20. Based on information from the American Automobile Association (AAA), the cost of owning a compact car is $.586 per mile driven. Using this estimate, find how much it costs to operate a car during a year in which the car is driven 16,000 miles.

Expense	5-year cost
Taxes	$2573
Financing	$3650
Fuel	$14,764
Insurance	$11,457
Maintenance	$5685

21. The table at the right shows some of the estimated expenses of owning a midsize car for 5 years. If the car is driven 75,000 miles over the 5-year period, what is the cost per mile for these expenses?

22. A farmer purchased a tractor for $28,850 and made a 20% down payment. The balance was financed for 5 years at an annual interest rate of 5.25%.
    a. What was the amount of the down payment?
    b. How much was financed?
    c. What is the monthly payment?

23. An escrow officer purchased a Buick crossover vehicle for $36,995 and made a down payment of 20% of the purchase price. The balance was financed for 4 years at an annual interest rate of 4.5%. What is the monthly payment?

24. A tennis coach purchased a new Chevrolet Corvette for $56,500 and made a down payment of 25% of the purchase price. The balance was financed for 5 years at an annual interest rate of 5.5%. Find the monthly payment.

25. Last year you spent $2685 on gasoline for your car. The car was driven 15,000 miles. What was your cost per mile for gasoline?

Critical Thinking

26. **Car Loans** How much interest is paid on a 5-year car loan of $19,000 if the interest rate is 6.25%? Round to the nearest dollar.

Projects or Group Activities

27. One of the greatest costs of owning a car is depreciation. A conservative estimate is that a car will depreciate in value by 17% of the purchase price by the end of the first year. During the second year, the car will depreciate by approximately 12% of the depreciated value. For the next 3 years, the car will depreciate by 10% of its current value each year. If a new car is purchased for $30,000, what will be its value after 5 years? If the car is driven 75,000 miles during the five years, what is the cost per mile for depreciation?

6.6 | Wages

OBJECTIVE A | *To calculate commissions, total hourly wages, and salaries*

Commission, hourly wage, and salary are three ways to receive payment for doing work.

Commissions are usually paid to salespersons and are calculated as a percent of sales.

APPLY THE CONCEPT ···

As a real estate broker, Emma Smith receives a commission of 4.5% of the selling price of a house. Find the commission she earned for selling a home for $275,000.

To find the commission Emma earned, solve the basic percent equation for *amount*.

Percent	×	base	=	amount
Commission rate	×	total sales	=	commission
0.045	×	275,000	=	12,375

The commission is $12,375.

An employee who receives an **hourly wage** is paid a certain amount for each hour worked.

APPLY THE CONCEPT ···

A plumber receives an hourly wage of $28.25. Find the plumber's total wages for working 37 hours.

To find the plumber's total wages, multiply the hourly wage by the number of hours worked.

Hourly wage	×	number of hours worked	=	total wages
28.25	×	37	=	1045.25

The plumber's total wages for working 37 hours are $1045.25.

An employee who is paid a **salary** receives payment based on a weekly, biweekly (every other week), monthly, or annual time schedule. Unlike an employee who receives an hourly wage, a salaried worker does not receive additional pay for working more than the regularly scheduled workday.

APPLY THE CONCEPT ···

Ravi Basar is a computer operator who receives a weekly salary of $895. Find his salary for one month (4 weeks).

To find Ravi's salary for one month, multiply the salary per pay period by the number of pay periods.

Salary per pay period	×	number of pay periods	=	total salary
895	×	4	=	3580

Ravi's total salary for one month is $3580.

EXAMPLE 1

A pharmacist's hourly wage is $54.46. On Saturday, the pharmacist earns time and a half (1.5 times the regular hourly wage). How much does the pharmacist earn for working 6 hours on Saturday?

Strategy

To find the pharmacist's earnings:

• Find the hourly wage for working on Saturday by multiplying the regular hourly wage by 1.5.
• Multiply the Saturday hourly wage by the number of hours worked.

Solution

$54.46 \times 1.5 = 81.69$ $81.69 \times 6 = 490.14$

The pharmacist earns $490.14.

YOU TRY IT 1

A construction worker, whose hourly wage is $28.50, earns double time (2 times the regular hourly wage) for working overtime. Find the worker's wages for working 8 hours of overtime.

Your strategy

Your solution

EXAMPLE 2

An efficiency expert received a contract for $3000. The expert spent 75 hours on the project. Find the expert's hourly wage.

Strategy

To find the hourly wage, divide the total earnings by the number of hours worked.

Solution

$3000 \div 75 = 40$

The hourly wage was $40.

YOU TRY IT 2

A contractor for a bridge project receives an annual salary of $70,980. What is the contractor's monthly salary?

Your strategy

Your solution

EXAMPLE 3

Dani Greene earns $38,500 per year plus a 5.5% commission on sales over $100,000. During one year, Dani sold $150,000 worth of computers. Find Dani's total earnings for the year.

Strategy

To find the total earnings:

• Find the sales over $100,000.
• Multiply the commission rate by the sales over $100,000.
• Add the commission to the annual pay.

Solution

$150,000 - 100,000 = 50,000$
$50,000 \times 0.055 = 2750$ • Commission
$38,500 + 2750 = 41,250$

Dani earned $41,250.

YOU TRY IT 3

An insurance agent earns $37,000 per year plus a 9.5% commission on sales over $50,000. During one year, the agent's sales totaled $175,000. Find the agent's total earnings for the year.

Your strategy

Your solution

Solutions on pp. S17–S18

6.6 EXERCISES

✔ **Concept Check**

1. 📝 How are a salesperson's commissions determined?

2. 📝 How do you determine the weekly wage of an employee who receives an hourly wage?

OBJECTIVE A *To calculate commissions, total hourly wages, and salaries*

3. Lewis works in a clothing store and earns $11.50 per hour. How much does he earn for a 40-hour work week?

4. Sasha pays a gardener an hourly wage of $11. How much does she pay the gardener for working 25 hours?

5. A real estate agent receives a 3% commission for selling a house. Find the commission the agent earned for selling a house for $131,000.

6. Ron Caruso works as an insurance agent and receives a commission of 40% of the first year's premium. Find Ron's commission for selling a life insurance policy with a first-year premium of $1050.

7. A stockbroker receives a commission of 1.5% of the price of stock that is bought or sold. Find the commission on 100 shares of stock that were bought for $5600.

8. The owner of the Carousel Art Gallery receives a commission of 20% on paintings that are sold on consignment. Find the commission on a painting that sold for $22,500.

9. Keisha Brown receives an annual salary of $38,928 as a teacher of Italian. How much does Keisha receive each month?

10. An apprentice plumber receives an annual salary of $27,900. How much does the plumber receive per month?

11. Carlos receives a commission of 12% of his weekly sales as a sales representative for a medical supply company. Find the commission he earned during a week in which sales were $4500.

12. A golf pro receives a commission of 25% for selling a golf set. Find the commission the pro earned for selling a golf set costing $450.

13. Steven receives $5.75 per square yard to install carpet. How much does he receive for installing 160 square yards of carpet?

14. An indexer charges $3.75 per page for indexing technical material. How much does the indexer earn for indexing a 225-page book?

15. A nuclear chemist received $15,000 in consulting fees while working on a nuclear power plant. The chemist worked 120 hours on the project. Find the chemist's hourly wage.

16. Maxine received $3400 for working on a project as a computer consultant for 40 hours. Find her hourly wage.

17. Gil Stratton's hourly wage is $10.78. For working overtime, he receives double time.
    a. What is Gil's hourly wage for working overtime?
    b. How much does he earn for working 16 hours of overtime?

18. A lathe operator receives an hourly wage of $21.84. When working on Saturday, he receives time and a half.
    a. What is the lathe operator's hourly wage on Saturday?
    b. How much does he earn for working 8 hours on Saturday?

19. A stock clerk at a supermarket earns $12.68 an hour. For working the night shift, the clerk's wage increases by 15%.
    a. What is the increase in hourly pay for working the night shift?
    b. What is the clerk's hourly wage for working the night shift?

20. A nurse earns $31.50 an hour. For working the night shift, the nurse receives a 10% increase in pay.
    a. What is the increase in hourly pay for working the night shift?
    b. What is the hourly pay for working the night shift?

21. A salesperson receives a salary of $250 per week plus a commission of 15% on all sales over $1500. Find the salesperson's earnings during a week in which sales totaled $4826.

22. A veterinarian's assistant works 35 hours a week at $20 an hour. The assistant is paid time and a half for overtime hours. Which expression represents the assistant's earnings for a week in which the assistant worked 41 hours?
  (i) 41×20 **(ii)** $(35 \times 20) + (41 \times 30)$
  (iii) $(35 \times 20) + (6 \times 30)$ **(iv)** 41×30

Critical Thinking

The table below shows the average hourly wage and the average number of hours worked per week for a nonfarm worker in the United States for two months. Use this table for Exercises 23 to 25.

Nonfarm Workers in the United States	June	August
Average hourly earnings	$23.01	$23.09
Average hours worked per week	34.3	34.2

Source: Bureau of Labor Statistics

23. What were a nonfarm worker's average weekly earnings in June? Round to the nearest cent.

24. What were a nonfarm worker's average weekly earnings in August? Round to the nearest cent.

25. What was the percent increase in average hourly earnings of a nonfarm worker from June to August? Round to the nearest tenth of a percent.

Projects or Group Activities

26. According to CNN Money, for a recent year, the average student loan debt at graduation was approximately $26,000. Repaying a student loan is similar to repaying a mortgage or a car loan. The same Monthly Payment Table is used to determine the monthly loan payment. Suppose you have the average student loan debt and you schedule a 15-year repayment plan based on an annual interest rate of 4%.
  a. What is your monthly student loan payment?
  b. Suppose you earn an average hourly wage of $23.09 and work 160 hours in one month. What is your monthly wage?
  c. What percent of your monthly wage is your student loan payment? Round to the nearest tenth of a percent.

6.7 | Bank Statements

OBJECTIVE A   *To calculate checkbook balances*

Take Note

A **checking account** is a bank account that enables you to withdraw money or make payments to other people using checks. A **check** is a printed form that, when filled out and signed, instructs a bank to pay a specified sum of money to the person named on it.

A **deposit slip** is a form for depositing money in a checking account.

A checking account can be opened at most banks and savings and loan associations by depositing an amount of money in the bank. A checkbook contains checks and deposit slips, as well as a checkbook register in which to record checks written and amounts deposited in the checking account. A sample check is shown below.

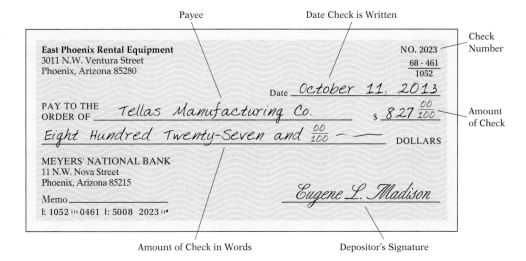

Each time a check is written, the amount of the check is subtracted from the amount in the account. When a deposit is made, the amount deposited is added to the amount in the account.

A portion of a checkbook register is shown below. The account holder had a balance of $587.93 before writing two checks, one for $286.87 and the other for $202.38, and making one deposit of $345.00.

		RECORD ALL CHARGES OR CREDITS THAT AFFECT YOUR ACCOUNT					BALANCE	
NUMBER	DATE	DESCRIPTION OF TRANSACTION	PAYMENT/DEBIT (−)	√ T	FEE (IF ANY) (−)	DEPOSIT/CREDIT (+)	$ 587	93
108	8/4	Plumber	$286 87		$	$	301	06
109	8/10	Car Payment	202 38				98	68
	8/14	Deposit				345 00	443	68

To find the current checking account balance, subtract the amount of each check from the previous balance. Then add the amount of the deposit.

The current checking account balance is $443.68.

EXAMPLE 1

A mail carrier had a checking account balance of $485.93 before writing two checks, one for $18.98 and another for $35.72, and making a deposit of $250. Find the current checking account balance.

Strategy

To find the current balance:

- Subtract the amount of each check from the old balance.
- Add the amount of the deposit.

Solution

$$
\begin{array}{rl}
485.93 & \\
-\ \ 18.98 & \text{first check} \\
\hline
466.95 & \\
-\ \ 35.72 & \text{second check} \\
\hline
431.23 & \\
+\ 250.00 & \text{deposit} \\
\hline
681.23 &
\end{array}
$$

The current checking account balance is $681.23.

YOU TRY IT 1

A cement mason had a checking account balance of $302.46 before writing a check for $20.59 and making two deposits, one in the amount of $176.86 and another in the amount of $94.73. Find the current checking account balance.

Your strategy

Your solution

Solution on p. S18

OBJECTIVE B   *To balance a checkbook*

Each month a bank statement is sent to the account holder. A **bank statement** is a document, either paper or electronic, showing all the transactions made to a bank account during the month. It shows the checks the bank has paid, the deposits received, and the current bank balance.

A bank statement and checkbook register are shown on the next page.

Balancing a checkbook, or determining whether the checking account balance is accurate, requires a number of steps.

1. In the checkbook register, put a check mark (✓) by each check paid by the bank and by each deposit recorded by the bank.

RECORD ALL CHARGES OR CREDITS THAT AFFECT YOUR ACCOUNT

NUMBER	DATE	DESCRIPTION OF TRANSACTION	PAYMENT/DEBIT (−)		√ T	FEE (IF ANY) (−)	DEPOSIT/CREDIT (+)		BALANCE $ 840	27
263	5/20	Dentist	$ 75	00	√	$	$		765	27
264	5/22	Post Office	33	61	√				731	66
265	5/22	Gas Company	67	14					664	52
	5/29	Deposit			√		192	00	856	52
266	5/29	Pharmacy	38	95	√				817	57
267	5/30	Telephone	63	85					753	72
268	6/2	Groceries	73	19	√				680	53
	6/3	Deposit			√		215	00	895	53
269	6/7	Insurance	103	00	√				792	53
	6/10	Deposit					225	00	1017	53
270	6/15	Photo Shop	16	63	√				1000	90
271	6/18	Newspaper	27	00					973	90

CHECKING ACCOUNT Monthly Statement   Account Number: 924-297-8

Date	Transaction	Amount	Balance
5/20	OPENING BALANCE		840.27
5/21	CHECK	75.00	765.27
5/23	CHECK	33.61	731.66
5/29	DEPOSIT	192.00	923.66
6/1	CHECK	38.95	884.71
6/1	INTEREST	4.47	889.18
6/3	CHECK	73.19	815.99
6/3	DEPOSIT	215.00	1030.99
6/9	CHECK	103.00	927.99
6/16	CHECK	16.63	911.36
6/20	SERVICE CHARGE	3.00	908.36
6/20	CLOSING BALANCE		908.36

2. Add to the current checkbook balance all checks that have been written but have not yet been paid by the bank and any interest paid on the account.

3. Subtract any service charges and any deposits not yet recorded by the bank. This is the checkbook balance.

4. Compare the balance with the bank balance listed on the bank statement. If the two numbers are equal, the bank statement and the checkbook balance.

Current checkbook balance:	973.90
Checks: 265	67.14
267	63.85
271	27.00
Interest:	+ 4.47
	1136.36
Service charge:	− 3.00
	1133.36
Deposit:	− 225.00
Checkbook balance:	908.36

Closing bank balance from bank statement $908.36	Checkbook balance = $908.36

The bank statement and the checkbook balance.

HOW TO 1

		RECORD ALL CHARGES OR CREDITS THAT AFFECT YOUR ACCOUNT									
NUMBER	DATE	DESCRIPTION OF TRANSACTION	PAYMENT/DEBIT (−)		√ T	FEE (IF ANY) (−)	DEPOSIT/CREDIT (+)		BALANCE $ 1620	42
413	3/2	Car Payment	$232	15	√	$	$		1388	27
414	3/2	Utilities	67	14	√				1321	13
415	3/5	Restaurant	78	14					1242	99
	3/8	Deposit			√		1842	66	3085	65
416	3/10	House Payment	672	14	√				2413	51
417	3/14	Insurance	177	10					2236	41

CHECKING ACCOUNT Monthly Statement			Account Number: 924-297-8
Date	Transaction	Amount	Balance
3/1	OPENING BALANCE		1620.42
3/4	CHECK	232.15	1388.27
3/5	CHECK	67.14	1321.13
3/8	DEPOSIT	1842.66	3163.79
3/10	INTEREST	6.77	3170.56
3/12	CHECK	672.14	2498.42
3/25	SERVICE CHARGE	2.00	2496.42
3/30	CLOSING BALANCE		2496.42

Balance the checkbook shown above.

1. In the checkbook register, put a check mark (✓) by each check paid by the bank and by each deposit recorded by the bank.

2. Add to the current checkbook balance all checks that have been written but have not yet been paid by the bank and any interest paid on the account.

Current checkbook balance:	2236.41
Checks: 415	78.14
417	177.10
Interest:	+ 6.77
	2498.42

3. Subtract any service charges and any deposits not yet recorded by the bank. This is the checkbook balance.

Service charge:	− 2.00
Checkbook balance:	2496.42

4. Compare the balance with the bank balance listed on the bank statement. If the two numbers are equal, the bank statement and the checkbook balance.

Closing bank balance from bank statement $2496.42	Checkbook balance = $2496.42

The bank statement and the checkbook balance.

EXAMPLE 2

Balance the checkbook shown below.

		RECORD ALL CHARGES OR CREDITS THAT AFFECT YOUR ACCOUNT							BALANCE	
NUMBER	DATE	DESCRIPTION OF TRANSACTION	PAYMENT/DEBIT (–)		√ T	FEE (IF ANY) (–)	DEPOSIT/CREDIT (+)		$ 412	64
345	1/14	Phone Bill	$ 54	75	√	$	$		357	89
346	1/19	News Shop	18	98	√				338	91
347	1/23	Theater Tickets	95	00					243	91
	1/31	Deposit			√		947	00	1190	91
348	2/5	Cash	250	00	√				940	91
349	2/12	Rent	840	00					100	91

CHECKING ACCOUNT Monthly Statement		Account Number: 924-297-8	
Date	Transaction	Amount	Balance
1/10	OPENING BALANCE		412.64
1/18	CHECK	54.75	357.89
1/23	CHECK	18.98	338.91
1/31	DEPOSIT	947.00	1285.91
2/1	INTEREST	4.52	1290.43
2/10	CHECK	250.00	1040.43
2/10	CLOSING BALANCE		1040.43

Solution

Current checkbook balance:		100.91
Checks: 347		95.00
349		840.00
Interest:	+	4.52
		1040.43
Service charge:	–	0.00
		1040.43
Deposit:	–	0.00
Checkbook balance:		1040.43

Closing bank balance from bank statement: $1040.43

Checkbook balance: $1040.43

The bank statement and the checkbook balance.

Balance the checkbook shown below.

RECORD ALL CHARGES OR CREDITS THAT AFFECT YOUR ACCOUNT

NUMBER	DATE	DESCRIPTION OF TRANSACTION	PAYMENT/DEBIT (−)		√ T	FEE (IF ANY) (−)	DEPOSIT/CREDIT (+)		BALANCE $ 903	17
	2/15	Deposit	$			$	$ 523	84	1427	01
234	2/20	Mortgage	773	21					653	80
235	2/27	Cash	200	00					453	80
	3/1	Deposit					523	84	977	64
236	3/12	Insurance	275	50					702	14
237	3/12	Telephone	78	73					623	41

CHECKING ACCOUNT Monthly Statement			Account Number: 314-271-4
Date	Transaction	Amount	Balance
2/14	OPENING BALANCE		903.17
2/15	DEPOSIT	523.84	1427.01
2/21	CHECK	773.21	653.80
2/28	CHECK	200.00	453.80
3/1	INTEREST	2.11	455.91
3/14	CHECK	275.50	180.41
3/14	CLOSING BALANCE		180.41

Your solution

Solution on p. S18

6.7 EXERCISES

✔ Concept Check

1. ◼ When a check is written, who is the payee?

2. If the money in a checking account earns interest, is the earned interest a deposit or a withdrawal?

OBJECTIVE A   *To calculate checkbook balances*

3. You had a checking account balance of $342.51 before making a deposit of $143.81. What is your new checking account balance?

4. The business checking account for R and R Tires showed a balance of $1536.97. What is the balance in this account after a deposit of $439.21 is made?

5. A nutritionist had a checking account balance of $1204.63 before writing one check for $119.27 and then another check for $260.09. Find the current checkbook balance.

6. Sam had a checking account balance of $3046.93 before writing a check for $1027.33 and then making a deposit of $150.00. Find the current checkbook balance.

7. The business checking account for a dry cleaner had a balance of $3476.85 before a deposit of $1048.53 was made. The store manager then wrote two checks, one for $848.37 and another for $676.19. Find the current checkbook balance.

8. Joel had a checking account balance of $427.38 before a deposit of $127.29 was made. Joel then wrote two checks, one for $43.52 and one for $249.78. Find the current checkbook balance.

9. A carpenter had a checkbook balance of $404.96 before making a deposit of $350 and writing a check for $71.29. Is there enough money in the account to purchase a refrigerator for $675?

10. A taxi driver had a checkbook balance of $149.85 before making a deposit of $245 and writing a check for $387.68. Is there enough money in the account for the bank to pay the check?

11. A sporting goods store has the opportunity to buy downhill skis and cross-country skis at a manufacturer's closeout sale. The downhill skis will cost $3500, and the cross-country skis will cost $2050. There is currently $5625.42 in the store's checking account. Is there enough money in the account to make both purchases?

12. A lathe operator's current checkbook balance is $1143.42. The operator wants to purchase a utility trailer for $525 and a used piano for $650. Is there enough money in the account to make the two purchases?

◼ For Exercises 13 and 14, suppose the given account transactions take place in one day. State whether the account's ending balance on that day *must be less than, might be less than,* or *cannot be less than* its starting balance on that day.

13. Two deposits made and one check written   14. Three checks written

OBJECTIVE B   *To balance a checkbook*

15. Balance the checkbook.

		RECORD ALL CHARGES OR CREDITS THAT AFFECT YOUR ACCOUNT							BALANCE	
NUMBER	DATE	DESCRIPTION OF TRANSACTION	PAYMENT/DEBIT (–)		√ T	FEE (IF ANY) (–)	DEPOSIT/CREDIT (+)		$ 2466	79
223	3/2	Groceries	$ 167	32		$	$		2299	47
	3/5	Deposit					960	70	3260	17
224	3/5	Rent	860	00					2400	17
225	3/7	Gas & Electric	142	35					2257	82
226	3/7	Cash	300	00					1957	82
227	3/7	Insurance	218	44					1739	38
228	3/7	Credit Card	419	32					1320	06
229	3/12	Dentist	92	00					1228	06
230	3/13	Drug Store	47	03					1181	03
	3/19	Deposit					960	70	2141	73
231	3/22	Car Payment	241	35					1900	38
232	3/25	Cash	300	00					1600	38
233	3/25	Oil Company	166	40					1433	98
234	3/28	Plumber	155	73					1278	25
235	3/29	Department Store	288	39					989	86

CHECKING ACCOUNT Monthly Statement		Account Number: 122-345-1	
Date	Transaction	Amount	Balance
3/1	OPENING BALANCE		2466.79
3/5	DEPOSIT	960.70	3427.49
3/7	CHECK	167.32	3260.17
3/8	CHECK	860.00	2400.17
3/8	CHECK	300.00	2100.17
3/9	CHECK	142.35	1957.82
3/12	CHECK	218.44	1739.38
3/14	CHECK	92.00	1647.38
3/18	CHECK	47.03	1600.35
3/19	DEPOSIT	960.70	2561.05
3/25	CHECK	241.35	2319.70
3/27	CHECK	300.00	2019.70
3/29	CHECK	155.73	1863.97
3/30	INTEREST	13.22	1877.19
4/1	CLOSING BALANCE		1877.19

16. Balance the checkbook.

RECORD ALL CHARGES OR CREDITS THAT AFFECT YOUR ACCOUNT

NUMBER	DATE	DESCRIPTION OF TRANSACTION	PAYMENT/DEBIT (−)		√T	FEE (IF ANY) (−)	DEPOSIT/CREDIT (+)		BALANCE $ 1219 43	
	5/1	Deposit	$			$	$ 619	14	1838	57
515	5/2	Electric Bill	42	35					1796	22
516	5/2	Groceries	95	14					1701	08
517	5/4	Insurance	122	17					1578	91
518	5/5	Theatre Tickets	84	50					1494	41
	5/8	Deposit					619	14	2113	55
519	5/10	Telephone	37	39					2076	16
520	5/12	Newspaper	22	50					2053	66
	5/15	Deposit					619	14	2672	80
521	5/20	Computer Store	172	90					2499	90
522	5/21	Credit Card	313	44					2186	46
523	5/22	Eye Exam	82	00					2104	46
524	5/24	Groceries	107	14					1997	32
525	5/24	Deposit					619	14	2616	46
526	5/25	Oil Company	144	16					2472	30
527	5/30	Car Payment	288	62					2183	68
528	5/30	Mortgage Payment	877	42					1306	26

CHECKING ACCOUNT Monthly Statement			Account Number: 122-345-1
Date	**Transaction**	**Amount**	**Balance**
5/1	OPENING BALANCE		1219.43
5/1	DEPOSIT	619.14	1838.57
5/3	CHECK	95.14	1743.43
5/4	CHECK	42.35	1701.08
5/6	CHECK	84.50	1616.58
5/8	CHECK	122.17	1494.41
5/8	DEPOSIT	619.14	2113.55
5/15	INTEREST	7.82	2121.37
5/15	CHECK	37.39	2083.98
5/15	DEPOSIT	619.14	2703.12
5/23	CHECK	82.00	2621.12
5/23	CHECK	172.90	2448.22
5/24	CHECK	107.14	2341.08
5/24	DEPOSIT	619.14	2960.22
5/30	CHECK	288.62	2671.60
6/1	CLOSING BALANCE		2671.60

17. Balance the checkbook.

		RECORD ALL CHARGES OR CREDITS THAT AFFECT YOUR ACCOUNT							BALANCE	
NUMBER	DATE	DESCRIPTION OF TRANSACTION	PAYMENT/DEBIT (−)		√ T	FEE (IF ANY) (−)	DEPOSIT/CREDIT (+)		$ 2035	18
218	7/2	Mortgage	$ 984	60	$		$		1050	58
219	7/4	Telephone	63	36					987	22
220	7/7	Cash	200	00					787	22
	7/12	Deposit					792	60	1579	82
221	7/15	Insurance	292	30					1287	52
222	7/18	Investment	500	00					787	52
223	7/20	Credit Card	414	83					372	69
	7/26	Deposit					792	60	1165	29
224	7/27	Department Store	113	37					1051	92

CHECKING ACCOUNT Monthly Statement			Account Number: 122-345-1	
Date	Transaction		Amount	Balance
7/1	OPENING BALANCE			2035.18
7/1	INTEREST		5.15	2040.33
7/4	CHECK		984.60	1055.73
7/6	CHECK		63.36	992.37
7/12	DEPOSIT		792.60	1784.97
7/20	CHECK		292.30	1492.67
7/24	CHECK		500.00	992.67
7/26	DEPOSIT		792.60	1785.27
7/28	CHECK		200.00	1585.27
7/30	CLOSING BALANCE			1585.27

18. When balancing your checkbook, you find that all the deposits in your checkbook register have been recorded by the bank, four checks in the register have not yet been paid by the bank, and the bank did not include a service charge. Is the ending balance on the monthly bank statement *less than* or *greater than* the ending balance on the check register?

Critical Thinking

19. Define the words *credit* and *debit* as they apply to checkbooks.

Projects or Group Activities

20. Look at the numbers along the bottom of a check. What are those numbers and how are they used?

CHAPTER

6 | Summary

Key Words	Examples
The **unit cost** is the cost of one item. [6.1A, p. 234]	Three paperback books cost $36. The unit cost is the cost of one paperback book, $12.
Percent increase is used to show how much a quantity has increased over its original value. [6.2A, p. 239]	The city's population increased 5%, from 10,000 people to 10,500 people.
Cost is the price a business pays for a product. **Selling price** is the price at which a business sells a product to a customer. **Markup** is the difference between selling price and cost. **Markup rate** is the markup expressed as a percent of the product's cost. [6.2B, p. 240]	A business pays $90 for a pair of cross trainers; the cost is $90. The business sells the cross trainers for $135; the selling price is $135. The markup is $135 − $90 = $45.
Percent decrease is used to show how much a quantity has decreased from its original value. [6.2C, p. 242]	Sales decreased 10%, from 10,000 units in the third quarter to 9000 units in the fourth quarter.
Sale price is the price after a reduction from the regular price. **Discount** is the difference between the regular price and the sale price. **Discount rate** is the discount expressed as a percent of the product's regular price. [6.2D, p. 243]	A skateboard deck that regularly sells for $50 is on sale for $40. The regular price is $50. The sale price is $40. The discount is $50 − $40 = $10.
Interest is the amount paid for the privilege of using someone else's money. **Principal** is the amount of money originally deposited or borrowed. The percent used to determine the amount of interest is the **interest rate.** Interest computed on the original amount is called **simple interest.** The principal plus the interest owed on a loan is called the **maturity value.** [6.3A, p. 249]	Consider a 1-year loan of $5000 at an annual simple interest rate of 8%. The principal is $5000. The interest rate is 8%. The interest paid on the loan is $5000 × 0.08 = $400. The maturity value is $5000 + $400 = $5400.
The interest charged on purchases made with a credit card is called a **finance charge.** [6.3B, p. 251]	A credit card company charges 1.5% per month on any unpaid balance. The finance charge on an unpaid balance of $1000 is $1000 × 0.015 × 1 = $15.
Compound interest is computed not only on the original principal but also on the interest already earned. [6.3C, p. 252]	$10,000 is invested at 5% annual interest, compounded monthly. The value of the investment after 5 years can be found by multiplying 10,000 by the factor found in the Compound Interest Table in the Appendix. $10,000 × 1.283359 = $12,833.59
A **mortgage** is an amount that is borrowed to buy real estate. The **loan origination fee** is usually a percent of the mortgage and is expressed as **points.** [6.4A, p. 259]	The loan origination fee of 3 points paid on a mortgage of $200,000 is 0.03 × $200,000 = $6000.
A **commission** is usually paid to a salesperson and is calculated as a percent of sales. [6.6A, p. 270]	A commission of 5% on sales of $50,000 is 0.05 × $50,000 = $2500.

An employee who receives an **hourly wage** is paid a certain amount for each hour worked.   [6.6A, p. 270]

An employee is paid an hourly wage of $15. The employee's wages for working 10 hours are $15 × 10 = $150.

An employee who is paid a **salary** receives payment based on a weekly, biweekly, monthly, or annual time schedule. [6.6A, p. 270]

An employee who earns an annual salary of $60,000 is paid $60,000 ÷ 12 = $5000 per month.

Balancing a checkbook is a method of determining whether a checkbook balance is accurate.   [6.7B, pp. 276–280]

To balance a checkbook:

(1) Put a check mark in the checkbook register by each check paid by the bank and by each deposit recorded by the bank.

(2) Add to the current checkbook balance all checks that have been written but have not yet been paid by the bank and any interest paid on the account.

(3) Subtract any service charges and any deposits not yet recorded by the bank. This is the checkbook balance.

(4) Compare the balance with the bank balance listed on the bank statement. If the two numbers are equal, the bank statement and the checkbook balance.

Essential Rules and Procedures

Examples

To find unit cost, divide the total cost by the number of units.   [6.1A, p. 234]

Three paperback books cost $36. The unit cost is $36 ÷ 3 = $12 per book.

To find total cost, multiply the unit cost by the number of units purchased.   [6.1C, p. 236]

One melon costs $3. The total cost for 5 melons is $3 × 5 = $15.

Basic Markup Equations   [6.2B, p. 240]
Selling price − cost = markup
Cost + markup = selling price
Markup rate × cost = markup

A pair of cross trainers that cost a business $90 has a 50% markup rate. The markup is 0.50 × $90 = $45. The selling price is $90 + $45 = $135.

Basic Discount Equations   [6.2D, p. 243]
Regular price − sale price = discount
Regular price − discount = sale price
Discount rate × regular price = discount

A DVD box set is on sale for 20% off the regular price of $50. The discount is 0.20 × $50 = $10. The sale price is $50 − $10 = $40.

Simple Interest Formula for Annual Interest Rates
[6.3A, p. 249]
Principal × annual interest rate × time (in years) = interest

The simple interest due on a 2-year loan of $5000 that has an annual interest rate of 5% is $5000 × 0.05 × 2 = $500.

Maturity Value Formula for a Simple Interest Loan
[6.3A, p. 249]
Principal + interest = maturity value

The interest to be paid on a 2-year loan of $5000 is $500. The maturity value of the loan is $5000 + $500 = $5500.

Monthly Payment on a Simple Interest Loan   [6.3A, p. 250]
Maturity value ÷ length of the loan in months = monthly payment

The maturity value of a simple interest 8-month loan is $8000. The monthly payment is $8000 ÷ 8 = $1000.

CHAPTER

6 | Review Exercises

1. **Consumerism**   A 20-ounce box of cereal costs $3.90. Find the unit cost.

2. **Car Expenses**   An account executive had car expenses of $1025.58 for insurance, $1805.82 for gas, $37.92 for oil, and $288.27 for maintenance during a year in which 11,320 miles were driven. Find the cost per mile for these four items taken as a group. Round to the nearest tenth of a cent.

3. **Investments**   An oil stock was bought for $42.375 per share. Six months later, the stock was selling for $55.25 per share. Find the percent increase in the price of the stock over the 6 months. Round to the nearest tenth of a percent.

4. **Markup**   A sporting goods store uses a markup rate of 40%. What is the markup on a ski suit that costs the store $180?

5. **Simple Interest**   A contractor borrowed $100,000 from a credit union for 9 months at an annual interest rate of 4%. What is the simple interest due on the loan?

6. **Compound Interest**   A computer programmer invested $25,000 in a retirement account that pays 6% interest, compounded daily. What is the value of the investment in 10 years? Use the Compound Interest Table in the Appendix. Round to the nearest cent.

7. **Investments**   Last year an oil company had earnings of $4.12 per share. This year the earnings are $4.73 per share. What is the percent increase in earnings per share? Round to the nearest percent.

8. **Real Estate**   The monthly payment on a $350,000 mortgage is $2120.93. The mortgage is a 20-year loan at an annual interest rate of 4%. Find the amount of the first month's payment that goes to interest and the amount that goes to the principal.

9. **Car Expenses**   A used pickup truck is purchased for $24,450. A down payment of 8% is made, and the remaining cost is financed for 4 years at an annual interest rate of 5%. Find the monthly payment. Use the Monthly Payment Table in the Appendix. Round to the nearest cent.

Spike Mafford/Getty Images

10. **Compound Interest**   A fast-food restaurant invests $50,000 in an account that pays 7% annual interest, compounded quarterly. What is the value of the investment after one year? Use the Compound Interest Table in the Appendix.

11. **Real Estate**   Paula Mason purchased a home for $195,000. The lender requires a down payment of 15%. Find the amount of the down payment.

12. **Car Expenses**   A plumber bought a truck for $28,500. A state license fee of $315 and a sales tax of 6.25% of the purchase price are required. Find the total cost of the sales tax and the license fee.

13. **Markup**   Techno-Center uses a markup rate of 35% on all computer systems. Find the selling price of a computer system that costs the store $1540.

14. **Car Expenses**   Mien pays a monthly car payment of $222.78. For a month in which $65.45 is principal, how much of the payment is interest?

15. **Compensation**   The manager of the retail store at a ski resort receives a commission of 3% on all sales at the alpine shop. Find the total commission received for a month in which the shop had $108,000 in sales.

16. **Discount**   A suit that regularly costs $235 is on sale for 40% off the regular price. Find the sale price.

17. **Banking**   Luke had a checking account balance of $1568.45 before writing checks for $123.76, $756.45, and $88.77. He then deposited a check for $344.21. Find Luke's current checkbook balance.

18. **Simple Interest**   Pros' Sporting Goods borrowed $30,000 for 6 months at an annual interest rate of 8%. Find the maturity value of the loan.

19. **Real Estate**   A credit union requires a borrower to pay $2\frac{1}{2}$ points for a loan. Find the origination fee for a $75,000 loan.

20. **Consumerism**   Sixteen ounces of mouthwash cost $3.49. A 33-ounce container of the same brand of mouthwash costs $6.99. Which is the better buy?

21. **Real Estate**   The Sweeneys bought a home for $356,000. The family made a 10% down payment and financed the remainder with a 30-year loan at an annual interest rate of 7%. Find the monthly mortgage payment. Use the Monthly Payment Table in the Appendix. Round to the nearest cent.

22. **Compensation**   Richard Valdez receives $12.60 per hour for working 40 hours a week, and time and a half for working over 40 hours. Find his total income for a week in which he worked 48 hours.

23. **Banking**   The business checking account of a donut shop showed a balance of $9567.44 before checks of $1023.55, $345.44, and $23.67 were written, and checks of $555.89 and $135.91 were deposited. Find the current checkbook balance.

24. **Simple Interest**   The simple interest due on a 4-month loan of $55,000 is $1375. Find the monthly payment on the loan.

25. **Simple Interest**   A credit card company charges a customer 1.25% per month on the unpaid balance of charges on the card. What is the finance charge for a month in which the customer has an unpaid balance of $576?

CHAPTER

6 TEST

1. **Consumerism** Twenty feet of lumber cost $138.40. What is the cost per foot?

2. **Consumerism** Which is the more economical purchase: 3 pounds of tomatoes for $7.49 or 5 pounds of tomatoes for $12.59?

3. **Consumerism** Red snapper costs $4.15 per pound. Find the cost of $3\frac{1}{2}$ pounds. Round to the nearest cent.

4. **Business** An exercise bicycle increased in price from $415 to $498. Find the percent increase in the cost of the exercise bicycle.

5. **Markup** A department store uses a 40% markup rate. Find the selling price of a Blu-ray disc player that the store purchased for $315.

6. **Investments** The price of gold rose from $1498 per ounce to $1684 per ounce. What percent increase does this amount represent? Round to the nearest tenth of a percent.

7. **Consumerism** The price of a video camera dropped from $1120 to $896. What percent decrease does this price drop represent?

8. **Discount** A corner hutch with a regular price of $299 is on sale for 30% off the regular price. Find the sale price.

9. **Discount** A box of stationery that regularly sells for $9.50 is on sale for $5.70. Find the discount rate.

10. **Simple Interest** A construction company borrowed $75,000 for 4 months at an annual interest rate of 8%. Find the simple interest due on the loan.

11. **Simple Interest** Craig Allen borrowed $25,000 for 9 months at an annual interest rate of 9.2%. Find the maturity value of the loan.

12. **Simple Interest** A credit card company charges a customer 1.2% per month on the unpaid balance of charges on the card. What is the finance charge for a month in which the customer has an unpaid balance of $374.95?

13. **Compound Interest** Jorge, who is self-employed, placed $30,000 in an account that pays 6% annual interest, compounded quarterly. How much interest was earned in 10 years? Use the Compound Interest Table in the Appendix.

14. **Real Estate** A savings and loan institution is offering mortgage loans that have a loan origination fee of $2\frac{1}{2}$ points. Find the loan origination fee when a home is purchased with a loan of $134,000.

15. **Real Estate** A new housing development offers homes with a mortgage of $222,000 for 25 years at an annual interest rate of 8%. Find the monthly mortgage payment. Use the Monthly Payment Table in the Appendix.

16. **Car Expenses** A Chevrolet was purchased for $23,750, and a 20% down payment was made. Find the amount financed.

17. **Car Expenses** A rancher purchased an SUV for $33,714 and made a down payment of 15% of the cost. The balance was financed for 4 years at an annual interest rate of 7%. Find the monthly payment. Use the Monthly Payment Table in the Appendix.

18. **Compensation** Shaney receives an hourly wage of $30.40 an hour as an emergency room nurse. When called in at night, she receives time and a half. How much does Shaney earn for a week in which she works 30 hours at normal rates and 15 hours during the night?

19. **Banking** The business checking account for a pottery store had a balance of $7349.44 before checks for $1349.67 and $344.12 were written. The store manager then made a deposit of $956.60. Find the current checkbook balance.

20. **Banking** Balance the checkbook shown.

		RECORD ALL CHARGES OR CREDITS THAT AFFECT YOUR ACCOUNT							BALANCE	
NUMBER	DATE	DESCRIPTION OF TRANSACTION	PAYMENT/DEBIT (−)		√ T	FEE (IF ANY) (−)	DEPOSIT/CREDIT (+)		$ 1422	13
843	8/1	House Payment	$ 713	72		$	$		708	41
	8/4	Deposit					852	60	1561	01
844	8/5	Loan Payment	162	40					1398	61
845	8/6	Groceries	166	44					1232	17
846	8/10	Car Payment	322	37					909	80
	8/15	Deposit					852	60	1762	40
847	8/16	Credit Card	413	45					1348	95
848	8/18	Pharmacy	92	14					1256	81
849	8/22	Utilities	72	30					1184	51
850	8/28	Telephone	78	20					1106	31

CHECKING ACCOUNT Monthly Statement   Account Number: 122-345-1

Date	Transaction	Amount	Balance
8/1	OPENING BALANCE		1422.13
8/3	CHECK	713.72	708.41
8/4	DEPOSIT	852.60	1561.01
8/8	CHECK	166.44	1394.57
8/8	CHECK	162.40	1232.17
8/15	DEPOSIT	852.60	2084.77
8/23	CHECK	72.30	2012.47
8/24	CHECK	92.14	1920.33
9/1	CLOSING BALANCE		1920.33

Cumulative Review Exercises

1. Simplify: $12 - (10 - 8)^2 \div 2 + 3$

2. Add: $3\frac{1}{3} + 4\frac{1}{8} + 1\frac{1}{12}$

3. Find the difference between $12\frac{3}{16}$ and $9\frac{5}{12}$.

4. Find the product of $5\frac{5}{8}$ and $1\frac{9}{15}$.

5. Divide: $3\frac{1}{2} \div 1\frac{3}{4}$

6. Simplify: $\left(\frac{3}{4}\right)^2 \div \left(\frac{3}{8} - \frac{1}{4}\right) + \frac{1}{2}$

7. Divide: $0.059\overline{)3.0792}$
Round to the nearest tenth.

8. Convert $\frac{17}{12}$ to a terminating or a repeating decimal. Place a bar over any repeating digits.

9. Write "$410 in 8 hours" as a unit rate.

10. Solve the proportion $\frac{5}{n} = \frac{16}{35}$.
Round to the nearest hundredth.

11. Write $\frac{5}{8}$ as a percent.

12. Find 6.5% of 420.

13. Write 18.2% as a decimal.

14. What percent of 20 is 8.4?

15. 30 is 12% of what?

16. 65 is 42% of what? Round to the nearest hundredth.

17. **Meteorology** A series of late-summer storms produced rainfall amounts of $3\frac{3}{4}$, $8\frac{1}{2}$, and $1\frac{2}{3}$ inches during a 3-week period. Find the total rainfall during the 3 weeks.

18. **Taxes** The Homer family pays $\frac{1}{5}$ of their total monthly income for taxes. The family has a total monthly income of $4850. Find the amount of the monthly income that is paid for taxes.

19. **Consumerism** In 5 years, the cost of a scientific calculator went from $75 to $30. What is the ratio of the decrease in price to the original price?

20. **Fuel Efficiency** A compact car was driven 417.5 miles on 12.5 gallons of gasoline. Find the number of miles driven per gallon of gasoline.

21. **Consumerism** A 14-pound turkey costs $15.40. Find the unit cost. Round to the nearest cent.

22. **Investments** Eighty shares of a stock paid a dividend of $112. At the same rate, find the dividend on 200 shares of the stock.

23. **Discount** A laptop computer that regularly sells for $900 is on sale for 20% off the regular price. What is the sale price?

24. **Markup** A pro skate shop bought a grinding rail for $85 and used a markup rate of 40%. Find the selling price of the grinding rail.

25. **Compensation** Sook Kim, an elementary school teacher, received an increase in salary from $2800 per month to $3024 per month. Find the percent increase in her salary.

26. **Simple Interest** A contractor borrowed $120,000 for 6 months at an annual interest rate of 4.5%. How much simple interest is due on the loan?

27. **Car Expenses** A red Ford Mustang was purchased for $26,900, and a down payment of $2000 was made. The balance was financed for 3 years at an annual interest rate of 9%. Find the monthly payment. Use the Monthly Payment Table in the Appendix. Round to the nearest cent.

28. **Banking** A family had a checking account balance of $1846.78. A check for $568.30 was deposited into the account, and checks for $123.98 and $47.33 were written. Find the new checking account balance.

29. **Car Expenses** During one year, Anna Gonzalez spent $1840 on gasoline and oil, $820 on insurance, $185 on tires, and $432 on repairs for her car. Find the cost per mile to drive the car 10,000 miles during the year. Round to the nearest cent.

30. **Real Estate** A house has a mortgage of $172,000 for 20 years at an annual interest rate of 6%. Find the monthly mortgage payment. Use the Monthly Payment Table in the Appendix. Round to the nearest cent.

Appendix

Table of Properties

Properties of Real Numbers

Commutative Property of Addition
If a and b are real numbers, then $a + b = b + a$.

Commutative Property of Multiplication
If a and b are real numbers, then $a \cdot b = b \cdot a$.

Associative Property of Addition
If a, b, and c are real numbers, then
$(a + b) + c = a + (b + c)$.

Associative Property of Multiplication
If a, b, and c are real numbers, then
$(a \cdot b) \cdot c = a \cdot (b \cdot c)$.

Addition Property of Zero
If a is a real number, then $a + 0 = 0 + a = a$.

Multiplication Property of Zero
If a is a real number, then $a \cdot 0 = 0 \cdot a = 0$.

Multiplication Property of One
If a is a real number, then $a \cdot 1 = 1 \cdot a = a$.

Inverse Property of Addition
If a is a real number, then $a + (-a) = (-a) + a = 0$.

Inverse Property of Multiplication
If a is a real number and $a \neq 0$, then
$a \cdot \dfrac{1}{a} = \dfrac{1}{a} \cdot a = 1.$

Distributive Property
If a, b, and c are real numbers, then

$a(b + c) = ab + ac.$

Properties of Zero and One in Division

Any number divided by 1 is the number.
Division by zero is not allowed.

Any number other than zero divided by itself is 1.
Zero divided by a number other than zero is zero.

Compound Interest Table

Compounded Annually

	4%	4.25%	4.50%	4.75%	5.00%	5.25%	5.50%	5.75%
1 year	1.04000	1.04250	1.04500	1.04750	1.05000	1.05250	1.05500	1.05750
5 years	1.21665	1.23135	1.24618	1.26116	1.27628	1.29155	1.30696	1.32252
10 years	1.48024	1.51621	1.55297	1.59052	1.62889	1.66810	1.70814	1.74906
15 years	1.80094	1.86699	1.93528	2.00591	2.07893	2.15443	2.23248	2.31316
20 years	2.19112	2.29891	2.41171	2.52977	2.65330	2.78254	2.91776	3.05920
	6%	**6.25%**	**6.50%**	**6.75%**	**7.00%**	**7.25%**	**7.50%**	**7.75%**
1 year	1.06000	1.06250	1.06500	1.06750	1.07000	1.07250	1.07500	1.07750
5 years	1.33823	1.35408	1.37009	1.38624	1.40255	1.41901	1.43563	1.45240
10 years	1.79085	1.83354	1.87714	1.92167	1.96715	2.01360	2.06103	2.10947
15 years	2.39656	2.48276	2.57184	2.66390	2.75903	2.85732	2.95888	3.06379
20 years	3.20714	3.36185	3.52365	3.69282	3.86968	4.05458	4.24785	4.44985
	8%	**8.25%**	**8.50%**	**8.75%**	**9.00%**	**9.25%**	**9.50%**	**9.75%**
1 year	1.08000	1.08250	1.08500	1.08750	1.09000	1.09250	1.09500	1.09750
5 years	1.46933	1.48641	1.50366	1.52106	1.53862	1.55635	1.57424	1.59229
10 years	2.15892	2.20942	2.26098	2.31362	2.36736	2.42222	2.47823	2.53539
15 years	3.17217	3.28412	3.39974	3.51916	3.64248	3.76983	3.90132	4.03709
20 years	4.66096	4.88155	5.11205	5.35285	5.60441	5.86717	6.14161	6.42822
	10%	**10.25%**	**10.50%**	**10.75%**	**11.00%**	**11.25%**	**11.50%**	**11.75%**
1 year	1.10000	1.10250	1.10500	1.10750	1.11000	1.11250	1.11500	1.11750
5 years	1.61051	1.62889	1.64745	1.66617	1.68506	1.70412	1.72335	1.74276
10 years	2.59374	2.65330	2.71408	2.77611	2.83942	2.90402	2.96995	3.03721
15 years	4.17725	4.32194	4.47130	4.62547	4.78459	4.94880	5.11827	5.29314
20 years	6.72750	7.03999	7.36623	7.70681	8.06231	8.43336	8.82058	9.22467

To use this table:
1. Locate the section that gives the desired compounding period.
2. Locate the interest rate in the top row of that section.
3. Locate the number of years in the left-hand column of that section.
4. Locate the number where the interest-rate column and the number-of-years row meet. This is the compound interest factor.

Example An investment yields an annual interest rate of 10% compounded annually for 5 years.
The compounding period is "compounded annually."
The interest rate is 10%.

Compound Interest Table (continued)

Compounded Semiannually

	4%	4.25%	4.50%	4.75%	5.00%	5.25%	5.50%	5.75%
1 year	1.04040	1.04295	1.04551	1.04806	1.05063	1.05319	1.05576	1.05833
5 years	1.21899	1.23402	1.24920	1.26456	1.28008	1.29578	1.31165	1.32770
10 years	1.48595	1.52279	1.56051	1.59911	1.63862	1.67905	1.72043	1.76278
15 years	1.81136	1.87915	1.94939	2.02217	2.09757	2.17568	2.25660	2.34043
20 years	2.20804	2.31890	2.43519	2.55715	2.68506	2.81921	2.95987	3.10738

	6%	6.25%	6.50%	6.75%	7.00%	7.25%	7.50%	7.75%
1 year	1.06090	1.06348	1.06606	1.06864	1.07123	1.07381	1.07641	1.07900
5 years	1.34392	1.36032	1.37689	1.39365	1.41060	1.42773	1.44504	1.46255
10 years	1.80611	1.85046	1.89584	1.94227	1.98979	2.03841	2.08815	2.13905
15 years	2.42726	2.51721	2.61037	2.70686	2.80679	2.91029	3.01747	3.12846
20 years	3.26204	3.42419	3.59420	3.77243	3.95926	4.15510	4.36038	4.57553

	8%	8.25%	8.50%	8.75%	9.00%	9.25%	9.50%	9.75%
1 year	1.08160	1.08420	1.08681	1.08941	1.09203	1.09464	1.09726	1.09988
5 years	1.48024	1.49813	1.51621	1.53449	1.55297	1.57165	1.59052	1.60961
10 years	2.19112	2.24440	2.29891	2.35467	2.41171	2.47007	2.52977	2.59083
15 years	3.24340	3.36241	3.48564	3.61322	3.74532	3.88208	4.02366	4.17022
20 years	4.80102	5.03733	5.28497	5.54446	5.81636	6.10125	6.39972	6.71242

	10%	10.25%	10.50%	10.75%	11.00%	11.25%	11.50%	11.75%
1 year	1.10250	1.10513	1.10776	1.11039	1.11303	1.11566	1.11831	1.12095
5 years	1.62889	1.64839	1.66810	1.68801	1.70814	1.72849	1.74906	1.76984
10 years	2.65330	2.71719	2.78254	2.84939	2.91776	2.98768	3.05920	3.13234
15 years	4.32194	4.47899	4.64155	4.80981	4.98395	5.16418	5.35071	5.54374
20 years	7.03999	7.38313	7.74255	8.11902	8.51331	8.92625	9.35869	9.81153

Compound Interest Table (continued)

Compounded Quarterly

	4%	4.25%	4.50%	4.75%	5.00%	5.25%	5.50%	5.75%
1 year	1.04060	1.04318	1.04577	1.04835	1.05095	1.05354	1.05614	1.05875
5 years	1.22019	1.23538	1.25075	1.26630	1.28204	1.29796	1.31407	1.33036
10 years	1.48886	1.52617	1.56438	1.60352	1.64362	1.68470	1.72677	1.76987
15 years	1.81670	1.88539	1.95665	2.03054	2.10718	2.18666	2.26909	2.35457
20 years	2.21672	2.32918	2.44727	2.57128	2.70148	2.83820	2.98174	3.13244

	6%	6.25%	6.50%	6.75%	7.00%	7.25%	7.50%	7.75%
1 year	1.06136	1.06398	1.06660	1.06923	1.07186	1.07450	1.07714	1.07978
5 years	1.34686	1.36354	1.38042	1.39750	1.41478	1.43226	1.44995	1.46784
10 years	1.81402	1.85924	1.90556	1.95300	2.00160	2.05137	2.10235	2.15456
15 years	2.44322	2.53515	2.63047	2.72932	2.83182	2.93810	3.04830	3.16256
20 years	3.29066	3.45677	3.63115	3.81422	4.00639	4.20812	4.41987	4.64214

	8%	8.25%	8.50%	8.75%	9.00%	9.25%	9.50%	9.75%
1 year	1.08243	1.08509	1.08775	1.09041	1.09308	1.09576	1.09844	1.10112
5 years	1.48595	1.50426	1.52279	1.54154	1.56051	1.57970	1.59911	1.61875
10 years	2.20804	2.26281	2.31890	2.37635	2.43519	2.49544	2.55715	2.62035
15 years	3.28103	3.40386	3.53122	3.66325	3.80013	3.94205	4.08917	4.24168
20 years	4.87544	5.12031	5.37732	5.64705	5.93015	6.22724	6.53903	6.86622

	10%	10.25%	10.50%	10.75%	11.00%	11.25%	11.50%	11.75%
1 year	1.10381	1.10651	1.10921	1.11191	1.11462	1.11734	1.12006	1.12278
5 years	1.63862	1.65872	1.67905	1.69962	1.72043	1.74148	1.76278	1.78432
10 years	2.68506	2.75134	2.81921	2.88871	2.95987	3.03275	3.10738	3.18379
15 years	4.39979	4.56369	4.73359	4.90970	5.09225	5.28147	5.47761	5.68090
20 years	7.20957	7.56986	7.94792	8.34462	8.76085	9.19758	9.65579	10.13650

Compound Interest Table (continued)

Compounded Monthly

	4%	4.25%	4.50%	4.75%	5.00%	5.25%	5.50%	5.75%
1 year	1.04074	1.04334	1.04594	1.04855	1.05116	1.05378	1.05641	1.05904
5 years	1.22100	1.23630	1.25180	1.26748	1.28336	1.29943	1.31570	1.33218
10 years	1.49083	1.52844	1.56699	1.60651	1.64701	1.68852	1.73108	1.77469
15 years	1.82030	1.88962	1.96156	2.03622	2.11370	2.19412	2.27758	2.36420
20 years	2.22258	2.33614	2.45547	2.58087	2.71264	2.85111	2.99663	3.14953

	6%	6.25%	6.50%	6.75%	7.00%	7.25%	7.50%	7.75%
1 year	1.06168	1.06432	1.06697	1.06963	1.07229	1.07496	1.07763	1.08031
5 years	1.34885	1.36573	1.38282	1.40011	1.41763	1.43535	1.45329	1.47146
10 years	1.81940	1.86522	1.91218	1.96032	2.00966	2.06023	2.11206	2.16519
15 years	2.45409	2.54738	2.64420	2.74468	2.84895	2.95716	3.06945	3.18599
20 years	3.31020	3.47904	3.65645	3.84286	4.03874	4.24456	4.46082	4.68805

	8%	8.25%	8.50%	8.75%	9.00%	9.25%	9.50%	9.75%
1 year	1.08300	1.08569	1.08839	1.09110	1.09381	1.09652	1.09925	1.10198
5 years	1.48985	1.50846	1.52730	1.54637	1.56568	1.58523	1.60501	1.62504
10 years	2.21964	2.27545	2.33265	2.39127	2.45136	2.51294	2.57606	2.64074
15 years	3.30692	3.43242	3.56265	3.69780	3.83804	3.98358	4.13459	4.29130
20 years	4.92680	5.17766	5.44124	5.71818	6.00915	6.31486	6.63606	6.97352

	10%	10.25%	10.50%	10.75%	11.00%	11.25%	11.50%	11.75%
1 year	1.10471	1.10746	1.11020	1.11296	1.11572	1.11849	1.12126	1.12404
5 years	1.64531	1.66583	1.68660	1.70763	1.72892	1.75046	1.77227	1.79435
10 years	2.70704	2.77499	2.84463	2.91600	2.98915	3.06412	3.14095	3.21969
15 years	4.45392	4.62266	4.79776	4.97945	5.16799	5.36362	5.56661	5.77725
20 years	7.32807	7.70057	8.09192	8.50307	8.93502	9.38881	9.86555	10.36640

Compound Interest Table (continued)

Compounded Daily

	4%	4.25%	4.50%	4.75%	5.00%	5.25%	5.50%	5.75%
1 year	1.04081	1.04341	1.04602	1.04864	1.05127	1.05390	1.05654	1.05918
5 years	1.22139	1.23675	1.25231	1.26806	1.28400	1.30015	1.31650	1.33306
10 years	1.49179	1.52955	1.56827	1.60796	1.64866	1.69040	1.73318	1.77705
15 years	1.82206	1.89168	1.96395	2.03899	2.11689	2.19777	2.28174	2.36892
20 years	2.22544	2.33953	2.45947	2.58555	2.71810	2.85744	3.00392	3.15791

	6%	6.25%	6.50%	6.75%	7.00%	7.25%	7.50%	7.75%
1 year	1.06183	1.06449	1.06715	1.06982	1.07250	1.07519	1.07788	1.08057
5 years	1.34983	1.36680	1.38399	1.40140	1.41902	1.43687	1.45494	1.47323
10 years	1.82203	1.86815	1.91543	1.96391	2.01362	2.06458	2.11684	2.17041
15 years	2.45942	2.55338	2.65094	2.75222	2.85736	2.96653	3.07986	3.19752
20 years	3.31979	3.48997	3.66887	3.85694	4.05466	4.26250	4.48100	4.71070

	8%	8.25%	8.50%	8.75%	9.00%	9.25%	9.50%	9.75%
1 year	1.08328	1.08599	1.08871	1.09143	1.09416	1.09690	1.09965	1.10240
5 years	1.49176	1.51052	1.52951	1.54875	1.56823	1.58795	1.60791	1.62813
10 years	2.22535	2.28167	2.33942	2.39862	2.45933	2.52157	2.58539	2.65082
15 years	3.31968	3.44650	3.57817	3.71487	3.85678	4.00412	4.15709	4.31589
20 years	4.95216	5.20601	5.47286	5.75340	6.04831	6.35833	6.68424	7.02686

	10%	10.25%	10.50%	10.75%	11.00%	11.25%	11.50%	11.75%
1 year	1.10516	1.10792	1.11069	1.11347	1.11626	1.11905	1.12185	1.12466
5 years	1.64861	1.66934	1.69033	1.71159	1.73311	1.75490	1.77697	1.79931
10 years	2.71791	2.78669	2.85722	2.92953	3.00367	3.07968	3.15762	3.23753
15 years	4.48077	4.65194	4.82965	5.01414	5.20569	5.40454	5.61100	5.82533
20 years	7.38703	7.76567	8.16370	8.58214	9.02202	9.48445	9.97057	10.48160

Monthly Payment Table

	4%	4.25%	4.50%	4.75%	5.00%	5.25%	5.50%	5.75%
1 year	0.0851499	0.0852642	0.0853785	0.0854930	0.0856075	0.0857221	0.0858368	0.0859516
2 years	0.0434249	0.0435363	0.0436478	0.0437595	0.0438714	0.0439834	0.0440957	0.0442080
3 years	0.0295240	0.0296353	0.0297469	0.0298588	0.0299709	0.0300833	0.0301959	0.0303088
4 years	0.0225791	0.0226911	0.0228035	0.0229162	0.0230293	0.0231427	0.0232565	0.0233706
5 years	0.0184165	0.0185296	0.0186430	0.0187569	0.0188712	0.0189860	0.0191012	0.0192168
15 years	0.0073969	0.0075228	0.0076499	0.0077783	0.0079079	0.0080388	0.0081708	0.0083041
20 years	0.0060598	0.0061923	0.0063265	0.0064622	0.0065996	0.0067384	0.0068789	0.0070208
25 years	0.0052784	0.0054174	0.0055583	0.0057012	0.0058459	0.0059925	0.0061409	0.0062911
30 years	0.0047742	0.0049194	0.0050669	0.0052165	0.0053682	0.0055220	0.0056779	0.0058357
	6%	**6.25%**	**6.50%**	**6.75%**	**7.00%**	**7.25%**	**7.50%**	**7.75%**
1 year	0.0860664	0.0861814	0.0862964	0.0864115	0.0865267	0.0866420	0.0867574	0.0868729
2 years	0.0443206	0.0444333	0.0445463	0.0446593	0.0447726	0.0448860	0.0449996	0.0451134
3 years	0.0304219	0.0305353	0.0306490	0.0307629	0.0308771	0.0309915	0.0311062	0.0312212
4 years	0.0234850	0.0235998	0.0237150	0.0238304	0.0239462	0.0240624	0.0241789	0.0242957
5 years	0.0193328	0.0194493	0.0195661	0.0196835	0.0198012	0.0199194	0.0200379	0.0201570
15 years	0.0084386	0.0085742	0.0087111	0.0088491	0.0089883	0.0091286	0.0092701	0.0094128
20 years	0.0071643	0.0073093	0.0074557	0.0076036	0.0077530	0.0079038	0.0080559	0.0082095
25 years	0.0064430	0.0065967	0.0067521	0.0069091	0.0070678	0.0072281	0.0073899	0.0075533
30 years	0.0059955	0.0061572	0.0063207	0.0064860	0.0066530	0.0068218	0.0069921	0.0071641
	8%	**8.25%**	**8.50%**	**8.75%**	**9.00%**	**9.25%**	**9.50%**	**9.75%**
1 year	0.0869884	0.0871041	0.0872198	0.0873356	0.0874515	0.0875675	0.0876835	0.0877997
2 years	0.0452273	0.0453414	0.0454557	0.0455701	0.0456847	0.0457995	0.0459145	0.0460296
3 years	0.0313364	0.0314518	0.0315675	0.0316835	0.0317997	0.0319162	0.0320329	0.0321499
4 years	0.0244129	0.0245304	0.0246483	0.0247665	0.0248850	0.0250039	0.0251231	0.0252427
5 years	0.0202764	0.0203963	0.0205165	0.0206372	0.0207584	0.0208799	0.0210019	0.0211242
15 years	0.0095565	0.0097014	0.0098474	0.0099945	0.0101427	0.0102919	0.0104422	0.0105936
20 years	0.0083644	0.0085207	0.0086782	0.0088371	0.0089973	0.0091587	0.0093213	0.0094852
25 years	0.0077182	0.0078845	0.0080523	0.0082214	0.0083920	0.0085638	0.0087370	0.0089114
30 years	0.0073376	0.0075127	0.0076891	0.0078670	0.0080462	0.0082268	0.0084085	0.0085915
	10%	**10.25%**	**10.50%**	**10.75%**	**11.00%**	**11.25%**	**11.50%**	**11.75%**
1 year	0.0879159	0.0880322	0.0881486	0.0882651	0.0883817	0.0884983	0.0886151	0.0887319
2 years	0.0461449	0.0462604	0.0463760	0.0464919	0.0466078	0.0467240	0.0468403	0.0469568
3 years	0.0322672	0.0323847	0.0325024	0.0326205	0.0327387	0.0328572	0.0329760	0.0330950
4 years	0.0253626	0.0254828	0.0256034	0.0257243	0.0258455	0.0259671	0.0260890	0.0262113
5 years	0.0212470	0.0213703	0.0214939	0.0216180	0.0217424	0.0218673	0.0219926	0.0221183
15 years	0.0107461	0.0108995	0.0110540	0.0112095	0.0113660	0.0115234	0.0116819	0.0118413
20 years	0.0096502	0.0098164	0.0099838	0.0101523	0.0103219	0.0104926	0.0106643	0.0108371
25 years	0.0090870	0.0092638	0.0094418	0.0096209	0.0098011	0.0099824	0.0101647	0.0103480
30 years	0.0087757	0.0089610	0.0091474	0.0093348	0.0095232	0.0097126	0.0099029	0.0100941

To use this table:
1. Locate the desired interest rate in the top row.
2. Locate the number of years in the left-hand column.
3. Locate the number where the interest-rate column and the number-of-years row meet. This is the monthly payment factor.

Example A home has a 30-year mortgage at an annual interest rate of 6%.
The interest rate is 6%.
The number of years is 30.
The number where the row and column meet is 0.0059955. This is the monthly payment factor.

Solutions to "You Try It"

Solutions to Chapter 1 "You Try It"

SECTION 1.1

You Try It 1

A number line from 0 to 14 with a point marked at 6.

You Try It 2 **a.** $45 > 29$ **b.** $27 > 0$

You Try It 3 Thirty-six million four hundred sixty-two thousand seventy-five

You Try It 4 452,007

You Try It 5 $60,000 + 8000 + 200 + 80 + 1$

You Try It 6 $100,000 + 9000 + 200 + 7$

You Try It 7

Given place value
368,492
$8 > 5$

368,492 rounded to the nearest ten-thousand is 370,000.

You Try It 8

Given place value
3962
$6 > 5$

3962 rounded to the nearest hundred is 4000.

SECTION 1.2

You Try It 1

$$\begin{array}{r} {}^{1\,1}347 \\ +12{,}453 \\ \hline 12{,}800 \end{array}$$

• $7 + 3 = 10$
Write the 0 in the ones column. Carry the 1 to the tens column.
$1 + 4 + 5 = 10$
Write the 0 in the tens column. Carry the 1 to the hundreds column.
$1 + 3 + 4 = 8$

347 increased by 12,453 is 12,800.

You Try It 2

$$\begin{array}{r} {}^{2}95 \\ 88 \\ +\ 67 \\ \hline 250 \end{array}$$

• $5 + 8 + 7 = 20$
Write the 0 in the ones column. Carry the 2 to the tens column.

You Try It 3

$$\begin{array}{r} {}^{1\,1}\ {}^{2\,1}392 \\ 4{,}079 \\ 89{,}035 \\ +\ 4{,}992 \\ \hline 98{,}498 \end{array}$$

You Try It 4

Strategy To find the total square footage of Walmart stores in the United States, read the table to find the square footage of discount stores, Supercenters, Sam's Clubs, and neighborhood markets. Then add the four numbers.

Solution

$$\begin{array}{r} 68 \\ 560 \\ 81 \\ +\ \ 7 \\ \hline 716 \end{array}$$

The total square footage of Walmart stores in the United States is 716 million square feet.

SECTION 1.3

You Try It 1

$$\begin{array}{r} 8925 \\ -6413 \\ \hline 2512 \end{array}\qquad Check:\ \begin{array}{r} 6413 \\ +2512 \\ \hline 8925 \end{array}$$

You Try It 2

$$\begin{array}{r} 17{,}504 \\ -\ 9{,}302 \\ \hline 8{,}202 \end{array}\qquad Check:\ \begin{array}{r} 9{,}302 \\ +\ 8{,}202 \\ \hline 17{,}504 \end{array}$$

You Try It 3

$$\begin{array}{r} {}^{2}\ {}^{14}\ {}^{7}\ {}^{11} \\ \cancel{3}\ \cancel{4}\ \cancel{8}\ \cancel{1} \\ -\ \ 8\ 6\ 5 \\ \hline 2\ 6\ 1\ 6 \end{array}\qquad Check:\ \begin{array}{r} 865 \\ +\ 2616 \\ \hline 3481 \end{array}$$

You Try It 4

$$\begin{array}{r} {}^{15} \\ {}^{4}\ {}^{5}\ {}^{12} \\ 5\ 4,\cancel{5}\ \cancel{6}\ 2 \\ -1\ 4,4\ 8\ 5 \\ \hline 4\ 0,0\ 7\ 7 \end{array}\qquad Check:\ \begin{array}{r} 14{,}485 \\ +\ 40{,}077 \\ \hline 54{,}562 \end{array}$$

You Try It 5

$$\begin{array}{r} \overset{3}{\cancel{6}} \overset{10}{\cancel{4}} , 0\ 0\ 3 \\ -\ 5\ 4 , 9\ 3\ 6 \\ \hline \end{array}$$

• There are two zeros in the minuend. Borrow 1 thousand from the thousands column and write 10 in the hundreds column.

$$\begin{array}{r} \overset{3}{\cancel{6}} \overset{\overset{9}{10}}{\cancel{4}} , \overset{10}{\cancel{0}}\ 0\ 3 \\ -\ 5\ 4 , 9\ 3\ 6 \\ \hline \end{array}$$

• Borrow 1 hundred from the hundreds column and write 10 in the tens column.

$$\begin{array}{r} \overset{5}{\cancel{6}} \overset{\overset{13}{3}}{\cancel{4}} , \overset{\overset{9}{10}}{\cancel{0}}\ \overset{\overset{9}{10}}{\cancel{0}}\ \overset{13}{\cancel{3}} \\ -\ 5\ 4 , 9\ 3\ 6 \\ \hline 9 , 0\ 6\ 7 \end{array}$$

• Borrow 1 ten from the tens column and add 10 to the 3 in the ones column.

Check:
$$\begin{array}{r} 54{,}936 \\ +\ 9{,}067 \\ \hline 64{,}003 \end{array}$$

You Try It 6

Strategy To find the difference, subtract the population of the Northeast (55,317,240) from the population of the Midwest (66,927,001).

Solution
$$\begin{array}{r} 66{,}927{,}001 \\ -55{,}317{,}240 \\ \hline 11{,}609{,}761 \end{array}$$
There are 11,609,761 more people living in the Midwest than in the Northeast.

You Try It 7

Strategy To find your take-home pay:
▶ Add to find the total of the deductions (127 + 18 + 35).
▶ Subtract the total of the deductions from your total salary (638).

Solution
$$\begin{array}{r} 127 \\ 18 \\ +\ 35 \\ \hline 180 \end{array} \qquad \begin{array}{r} 638 \\ -\ 180 \\ \hline 458 \end{array}$$
180 in deductions
Your take-home pay is $458.

SECTION 1.4

You Try It 1

$$\begin{array}{r} \overset{3\ 5}{648} \\ \times\ \ \ 7 \\ \hline 4536 \end{array}$$

• $7 \times 8 = 56$
Write the 6 in the ones column.
Carry the 5 to the tens column.
$7 \times 4 = 28,\ 28 + 5 = 33$
$7 \times 6 = 42,\ 42 + 3 = 45$

You Try It 2

$$\begin{array}{r} 756 \\ \times\ 305 \\ \hline 3780 \\ 22680 \\ \hline 230{,}580 \end{array}$$

• $5 \times 756 = 3780$
Write a zero in the tens column for 0×756.
$3 \times 756 = 2268$

You Try It 3

Strategy To find the amount of food eaten in one year, multiply the amount eaten each day (150) by the number of days in one year (365).

Solution
$$\begin{array}{r} 150 \\ \times\ 365 \\ \hline 750 \\ 900 \\ 450 \\ \hline 54{,}750 \end{array}$$
The elephant will eat 54,750 pounds of food in one year.

You Try It 4

Strategy To find the total cost of the order:
▶ Find the cost of the sports jackets by multiplying the number of jackets (25) by the cost for each jacket (62).
▶ Add the product to the cost for the 80 suits (7600).

Solution
$$\begin{array}{r} 62 \\ \times\ 25 \\ \hline 310 \\ 124 \\ \hline 1550 \end{array} \qquad \begin{array}{r} 7600 \\ +\ 1550 \\ \hline 9150 \end{array}$$
1550 • Cost for jackets
The total cost of the order is $9150.

SECTION 1.5

You Try It 1

$$\begin{array}{r} 7 \\ 9\overline{)63} \end{array}$$
Check: $7 \times 9 = 63$

You Try It 2

$$\begin{array}{r} 453 \\ 9\overline{)\ 4077} \\ -36 \\ \hline 47 \\ -45 \\ \hline 27 \\ -27 \\ \hline 0 \end{array}$$
Check: $453 \times 9 = 4077$

ou Try It 3

$$\begin{array}{r} 705 \\ 9\overline{)\,6345} \\ -63 \\ \hline 04 \\ -0 \\ \hline 45 \\ -45 \\ \hline 0 \end{array}$$

- Think $9\overline{)4}$. Place 0 in quotient.
- Multiply 0×9. Subtract.
- Bring down the 5.

Check: $705 \times 9 = 6345$

ou Try It 4

$$\begin{array}{r} 870 \text{ r}5 \\ 6\overline{)\,5225} \\ -48 \\ \hline 42 \\ -42 \\ \hline 05 \\ -0 \\ \hline 5 \end{array}$$

- Think $6\overline{)5}$. Place 0 in quotient.
- Multiply 0×6. Subtract.

Check: $(870 \times 6) + 5 =$
$ 5220 + 5 = 5225$

ou Try It 5

$$\begin{array}{r} 3{,}058 \text{ r}3 \\ 7\overline{)\,21{,}409} \\ -21 \\ \hline 04 \\ -0 \\ \hline 40 \\ -35 \\ \hline 59 \\ -56 \\ \hline 3 \end{array}$$

- Think $7\overline{)4}$. Place 0 in quotient.
- Multiply 0×7. Subtract.

Check: $(3058 \times 7) + 3 =$
$ 21{,}406 + 3 = 21{,}409$

ou Try It 6

$$\begin{array}{r} 109 \\ 42\overline{)\,4578} \\ -42 \\ \hline 37 \\ -0 \\ \hline 378 \\ -378 \\ \hline 0 \end{array}$$

- Think $42\overline{)37}$. Place 0 in quotient.
- Multiply 0×42. Subtract.

Check: $(109 \times 42) = 4578$

You Try It 7

$$\begin{array}{r} 470 \text{ r}29 \\ 39\overline{)\,18{,}359} \\ -15\,6 \\ \hline 2\,75 \\ -2\,73 \\ \hline 29 \\ -0 \\ \hline 29 \end{array}$$

- Think $3\overline{)18}$. 6×39 is too large. Try 5. 5×39 is too large. Try 4.

Check: $(470 \times 39) + 29 =$
$ 18{,}330 + 29 = 18{,}359$

You Try It 8

$$\begin{array}{r} 62 \text{ r}111 \\ 534\overline{)\,33{,}219} \\ -32\,04 \\ \hline 1\,179 \\ -1\,068 \\ \hline 111 \end{array}$$

Check: $(62 \times 534) + 111 =$
$ 33{,}108 + 111 = 33{,}219$

You Try It 9

$$\begin{array}{r} 421 \text{ r}33 \\ 515\overline{)\,216{,}848} \\ -206\,0 \\ \hline 10\,84 \\ -10\,30 \\ \hline 548 \\ -515 \\ \hline 33 \end{array}$$

Check: $(421 \times 515) + 33 =$
$ 216{,}815 + 33 = 216{,}848$

You Try It 10

Strategy To find the number of tires that can be stored on each shelf, divide the number of tires (270) by the number of shelves (15).

Solution

$$\begin{array}{r} 18 \\ 15\overline{)\,270} \\ -15 \\ \hline 120 \\ -120 \\ \hline 0 \end{array}$$

Each shelf can store 18 tires.

You Try It 11

Strategy To find the number of cases produced in 8 hours:

▶ Find the number of cases produced in 1 hour by dividing the number of cans produced (12,600) by the number of cans to a case (24).

▶ Multiply the number of cases produced in 1 hour by 8.

Solution

$$
\begin{array}{r}
525 \\
24\overline{)\,12{,}600} \\
-12\ 0 \\
\hline
60 \\
-48 \\
\hline
120 \\
-120 \\
\hline
0
\end{array}
$$

$$
\begin{array}{r}
525 \\
\times\quad 8 \\
\hline
4200
\end{array}
$$

In 8 hours, 4200 cases are produced.

SECTION 1.6

You Try It 1 $2 \cdot 2 \cdot 2 \cdot 2 \cdot 3 \cdot 3 \cdot 3 = 2^4 \cdot 3^3$

You Try It 2 $10 \cdot 10 \cdot 10 \cdot 10 \cdot 10 \cdot 10 \cdot 10 = 10^7$

You Try It 3 $2^3 \cdot 5^2 = (2 \cdot 2 \cdot 2) \cdot (5 \cdot 5) = 8 \cdot 25$
$\qquad\qquad = 200$

You Try It 4 $5 \cdot (8 - 4)^2 \div 4 - 2$
$\quad = 5 \cdot 4^2 \div 4 - 2$ • Parentheses
$\quad = 5 \cdot 16 \div 4 - 2$ • Exponents
$\quad = 80 \div 4 - 2$ • Multiplication and
$\qquad\qquad\qquad\qquad$ division
$\quad = 20 - 2$ • Subtraction
$\quad = 18$

SECTION 1.7

You Try It 1 $40 \div 1 = 40$
$40 \div 2 = 20$
$40 \div 3 \qquad$ • Will not divide evenly
$40 \div 4 = 10$
$40 \div 5 = 8$
$40 \div 6 \qquad$ • Will not divide evenly
$40 \div 7 \qquad$ • Will not divide evenly
$40 \div 8 = 5 \qquad$ • Factors are repeating

1, 2, 4, 5, 8, 10, 20, and 40 are the factors of 40.

You Try It 2

$$
\begin{array}{r}
44 \\
\hline
2\,|\,22 \\
2\,|\,11 \\
11\,|\,1
\end{array}
$$

• $44 \div 2 = 22$
• $22 \div 2 = 11$
• $11 \div 11 = 1$

$44 = 2 \cdot 2 \cdot 11$

You Try It 3

$$
\begin{array}{r}
177 \\
\hline
3\,|\,59 \\
59\,|\,1
\end{array}
$$

• Try only 2, 3, 4, 7, and 11, because $11^2 > 59$.

$177 = 3 \cdot 59$

Solutions to Chapter 2 "You Try It"

SECTION 2.1

You Try It 1

	2	3	5
12 =	(2 · 2)	3	
27 =		(3 · 3 · 3)	
50 =	2		(5 · 5)

The LCM = $2 \cdot 2 \cdot 3 \cdot 3 \cdot 3 \cdot 5 \cdot 5 = 2700$.

You Try It 2

	2	3	5
36 =	(2 · 2)	3 · 3	
60 =	2 · 2	(3)	5
72 =	2 · 2 · 2	3 · 3	

The GCF = $2 \cdot 2 \cdot 3 = 12$.

You Try It 3

	2	3	5	11
11 =				11
24 =	2 · 2 · 2	3		
30 =	2	3	5	

Because no numbers are circled, the GCF = 1.

SECTION 2.2

You Try It 1 $4\dfrac{1}{4}$

You Try It 2 $\dfrac{17}{4}$

You Try It 3

$$
\begin{array}{r}
4 \\
5\overline{)\,22} \\
-20 \\
\hline
2
\end{array}
$$

$\dfrac{22}{5} = 4\dfrac{2}{5}$

You Try It 4

$$
\begin{array}{r}
4 \\
7\overline{)\,28} \\
-28 \\
\hline
0
\end{array}
$$

$\dfrac{28}{7} = 4$

u Try It 5 $\quad 14\overset{+\nearrow 5}{\underset{\times\nwarrow 8}{}} = \dfrac{112 + 5}{8} = \dfrac{117}{8}$

CTION 2.3

u Try It 1 $\quad 45 \div 5 = 9, \qquad \dfrac{3}{5} = \dfrac{3 \cdot 9}{5 \cdot 9} = \dfrac{27}{45}$

$\dfrac{27}{45}$ is equivalent to $\dfrac{3}{5}$.

u Try It 2 $\quad$ Write 6 as $\dfrac{6}{1}$.

$18 \div 1 = 18, \qquad 6 = \dfrac{6 \cdot 18}{1 \cdot 18} = \dfrac{108}{18}$

$\dfrac{108}{18}$ is equivalent to 6.

u Try It 3 $\quad \dfrac{16}{24} = \dfrac{\overset{1}{2} \cdot \overset{1}{2} \cdot \overset{1}{2} \cdot 2}{\underset{1}{2} \cdot \underset{1}{2} \cdot \underset{1}{2} \cdot 3} = \dfrac{2}{3}$

u Try It 4 $\quad \dfrac{8}{56} = \dfrac{\overset{1}{2} \cdot \overset{1}{2} \cdot \overset{1}{2}}{\underset{1}{2} \cdot \underset{1}{2} \cdot \underset{1}{2} \cdot 7} = \dfrac{1}{7}$

u Try It 5 $\quad \dfrac{15}{32} = \dfrac{3 \cdot 5}{2 \cdot 2 \cdot 2 \cdot 2 \cdot 2} = \dfrac{15}{32}$

u Try It 6 $\quad \dfrac{48}{36} = \dfrac{\overset{1}{2} \cdot \overset{1}{2} \cdot 2 \cdot 2 \cdot \overset{1}{3}}{\underset{1}{2} \cdot \underset{1}{2} \cdot \underset{1}{3} \cdot 3} = \dfrac{4}{3} = 1\dfrac{1}{3}$

CTION 2.4

u Try It 1
$$\begin{array}{r} \dfrac{3}{8} \\[2mm] + \dfrac{7}{8} \\[2mm] \hline \dfrac{10}{8} = \dfrac{5}{4} = 1\dfrac{1}{4} \end{array}$$
• The denominators are the same. Add the numerators. Place the sum over the common denominator.

u Try It 2
$$\begin{array}{r} \dfrac{7}{9} = \dfrac{35}{45} \\[2mm] + \dfrac{11}{15} = \dfrac{33}{45} \\[2mm] \hline \dfrac{68}{45} = 1\dfrac{23}{45} \end{array}$$
• The LCD is 45.

u Try It 3
$$\begin{array}{r} \dfrac{5}{12} = \dfrac{20}{48} \\[2mm] + \dfrac{9}{16} = \dfrac{27}{48} \\[2mm] \hline \dfrac{47}{48} \end{array}$$
• The LCD is 48.

You Try It 4
$$\begin{array}{r} \dfrac{3}{4} = \dfrac{30}{40} \\[2mm] \dfrac{4}{5} = \dfrac{32}{40} \\[2mm] + \dfrac{5}{8} = \dfrac{25}{40} \\[2mm] \hline \dfrac{87}{40} = 2\dfrac{7}{40} \end{array}$$
• The LCD is 40.

You Try It 5 $\quad 7 + \dfrac{6}{11} = 7\dfrac{6}{11}$

You Try It 6
$$\begin{array}{r} 29 \\[2mm] + 17\dfrac{5}{12} \\[2mm] \hline 46\dfrac{5}{12} \end{array}$$

You Try It 7
$$\begin{array}{r} 7\dfrac{4}{5} = 7\dfrac{24}{30} \\[2mm] 6\dfrac{7}{10} = 6\dfrac{21}{30} \\[2mm] + 13\dfrac{11}{15} = 13\dfrac{22}{30} \\[2mm] \hline 26\dfrac{67}{30} = 28\dfrac{7}{30} \end{array}$$
• The LCD is 30.

You Try It 8

Strategy $\quad$ To find the total time spent on the activities, add the three times $\left(4\dfrac{1}{2}, 3\dfrac{3}{4}, \text{ and } 1\dfrac{1}{3}\right)$.

Solution
$$\begin{array}{r} 4\dfrac{1}{2} = 4\dfrac{6}{12} \\[2mm] 3\dfrac{3}{4} = 3\dfrac{9}{12} \\[2mm] + 1\dfrac{1}{3} = 1\dfrac{4}{12} \\[2mm] \hline 8\dfrac{19}{12} = 9\dfrac{7}{12} \end{array}$$

The total time spent on the three activities was $9\dfrac{7}{12}$ hours.

You Try It 9

Strategy To find the overtime pay:
▶ Find the total number of overtime hours $\left(1\frac{2}{3} + 3\frac{1}{3} + 2\right)$.
▶ Multiply the total number of hours by the overtime hourly wage (36).

Solution

$$1\frac{2}{3}$$
$$3\frac{1}{3}$$
$$+\ 2$$
$$\overline{6\frac{3}{3} = 7 \text{ hours}}$$

$$\begin{array}{r} 36 \\ \times\ 7 \\ \hline 252 \end{array}$$

Jeff earned $252 in overtime pay.

SECTION 2.5

You Try It 1

$$\frac{16}{27}$$
$$-\ \frac{7}{27}$$
$$\overline{\frac{9}{27} = \frac{1}{3}}$$

• The denominators are the same. Subtract the numerators. Place the difference over the common denominator.

You Try It 2

$$\frac{13}{18} = \frac{52}{72}$$
$$-\ \frac{7}{24} = \frac{21}{72}$$
$$\overline{\frac{31}{72}}$$

• LCD = 72

You Try It 3

$$\frac{8}{9} = \frac{16}{18}$$
$$-\ \frac{5}{6} = \frac{15}{18}$$
$$\overline{\frac{1}{18}}$$

• LCD = 18

You Try It 4

$$21\frac{7}{9} = 21\frac{28}{36} = 20\frac{64}{36}$$
$$-\ 7\frac{11}{12} = 7\frac{33}{36} = 7\frac{33}{36}$$
$$\overline{\hspace{3cm} 13\frac{31}{36}}$$

• LCD = 36

You Try It 5

$$8\ \ = 7\frac{13}{13}$$
$$-\ 2\frac{4}{13} = 2\frac{4}{13}$$
$$\overline{\hspace{1.5cm} 5\frac{9}{13}}$$

• LCD = 13

You Try It 6

Strategy To find the time remaining before the plane lands, subtract the number of hours already in the air $\left(2\frac{3}{4}\right)$ from the total time of the trip $\left(5\frac{1}{2}\right)$.

Solution

$$5\frac{1}{2} = 5\frac{2}{4} = 4\frac{6}{4}$$
$$-\ 2\frac{3}{4} = 2\frac{3}{4} = 2\frac{3}{4}$$
$$\overline{\hspace{3cm} 2\frac{3}{4} \text{ hours}}$$

The plane will land in $2\frac{3}{4}$ hours.

You Try It 7

Strategy To find the amount of weight to be lost during the third month:
▶ Find the total weight loss during the first two months $\left(7\frac{1}{2} + 5\frac{3}{4}\right)$.
▶ Subtract the total weight loss from the goal (24 pounds).

Solution

$$7\frac{1}{2} = \ 7\frac{2}{4}$$
$$+\ 5\frac{3}{4} = \ 5\frac{3}{4}$$
$$\overline{\hspace{2cm} 12\frac{5}{4} = 13\frac{1}{4} \text{ pounds lost}}$$

$$24\ \ = 23\frac{4}{4}$$
$$-\ 13\frac{1}{4} = 13\frac{1}{4}$$
$$\overline{\hspace{2cm} 10\frac{3}{4} \text{ pounds}}$$

The patient must lose $10\frac{3}{4}$ pounds to achieve the goal.

SECTION 2.6

You Try It 1

$$\frac{4}{21} \times \frac{7}{44} = \frac{4 \cdot 7}{21 \cdot 44}$$
$$= \frac{\overset{1}{2} \cdot \overset{1}{2} \cdot \overset{1}{7}}{3 \cdot \underset{1}{7} \cdot \underset{1}{2} \cdot \underset{1}{2} \cdot 11} = \frac{1}{33}$$

ou Try It 2

$$\frac{7}{12} \times \frac{5}{6} = \frac{7 \cdot 5}{12 \cdot 6}$$

$$= \frac{7 \cdot 5}{2 \cdot 2 \cdot 3 \cdot 2 \cdot 3} = \frac{35}{72}$$

ou Try It 3

$$\frac{5}{16} \times \frac{12}{25} = \frac{5 \cdot 12}{16 \cdot 25}$$

$$= \frac{\cancel{5} \cdot \cancel{2} \cdot \cancel{2} \cdot 3}{2 \cdot 2 \cdot 2 \cdot \cancel{5} \cdot 5} = \frac{3}{20}$$

ou Try It 4

$$5\frac{2}{5} \times \frac{5}{9} = \frac{27}{5} \times \frac{5}{9} = \frac{27 \cdot 5}{5 \cdot 9}$$

$$= \frac{\cancel{3} \cdot \cancel{3} \cdot 3 \cdot \cancel{5}}{\cancel{5} \cdot \cancel{3} \cdot \cancel{3}} = \frac{3}{1} = 3$$

ou Try It 5

$$3\frac{2}{5} \times 6\frac{1}{4} = \frac{17}{5} \times \frac{25}{4} = \frac{17 \cdot 25}{5 \cdot 4}$$

$$= \frac{17 \cdot \cancel{5} \cdot 5}{\cancel{5} \cdot 2 \cdot 2} = \frac{85}{4} = 21\frac{1}{4}$$

ou Try It 6

trategy

To find the value of the house today, multiply the old value of the house (170,000) by $2\frac{1}{2}$.

olution

$$170,000 \times 2\frac{1}{2} = \frac{170,000}{1} \times \frac{5}{2}$$

$$= \frac{170,000 \cdot 5}{1 \cdot 2}$$

$$= 425,000$$

The value of the house today is $425,000.

ou Try It 7

trategy

To find the cost of the air compressor:

► Multiply to find the value of the drying chamber $\left(\frac{4}{5} \times 160,000\right)$.

► Subtract the value of the drying chamber from the total value of the two items (160,000).

olution

$$\frac{4}{5} \times \frac{160,000}{1} = \frac{640,000}{5}$$

$$= 128,000 \quad \bullet \text{ Value of the}$$
$$\text{drying chamber}$$

$$160,000 - 128,000 = 32,000$$

The cost of the air compressor was $32,000.

SECTION 2.7

You Try It 1

$$\frac{3}{7} \div \frac{2}{3} = \frac{3}{7} \times \frac{3}{2} = \frac{3 \cdot 3}{7 \cdot 2} = \frac{9}{14}$$

You Try It 2

$$\frac{3}{4} \div \frac{9}{10} = \frac{3}{4} \times \frac{10}{9}$$

$$= \frac{3 \cdot 10}{4 \cdot 9} = \frac{\cancel{3} \cdot 2 \cdot \cancel{5}}{2 \cdot 2 \cdot \cancel{3} \cdot 3} = \frac{5}{6}$$

You Try It 3

$$\frac{5}{7} \div 6 = \frac{5}{7} \div \frac{6}{1}$$

$$= \frac{5}{7} \times \frac{1}{6} = \frac{5 \cdot 1}{7 \cdot 6}$$

$$= \frac{5}{7 \cdot 2 \cdot 3} = \frac{5}{42}$$

You Try It 4

$$12\frac{3}{5} \div 7 = \frac{63}{5} \div \frac{7}{1} = \frac{63}{5} \times \frac{1}{7}$$

$$= \frac{63 \cdot 1}{5 \cdot 7} = \frac{3 \cdot 3 \cdot \cancel{7}}{5 \cdot \cancel{7}}$$

$$= \frac{9}{5} = 1\frac{4}{5}$$

You Try It 5

$$3\frac{2}{3} \div 2\frac{2}{5} = \frac{11}{3} \div \frac{12}{5}$$

$$= \frac{11}{3} \times \frac{5}{12} = \frac{11 \cdot 5}{3 \cdot 12}$$

$$= \frac{11 \cdot 5}{3 \cdot 2 \cdot 2 \cdot 3} = \frac{55}{36} = 1\frac{19}{36}$$

You Try it 6

$$2\frac{5}{6} \div 8\frac{1}{2} = \frac{17}{6} \div \frac{17}{2}$$

$$= \frac{17}{6} \times \frac{2}{17} = \frac{17 \cdot 2}{6 \cdot 17}$$

$$= \frac{\cancel{17} \cdot \cancel{2}}{2 \cdot 3 \cdot \cancel{17}} = \frac{1}{3}$$

You Try It 7

$$6\frac{2}{5} \div 4 = \frac{32}{5} \div \frac{4}{1}$$

$$= \frac{32}{5} \times \frac{1}{4} = \frac{32 \cdot 1}{5 \cdot 4}$$

$$= \frac{2 \cdot 2 \cdot 2 \cdot \cancel{2} \cdot \cancel{2}}{5 \cdot \cancel{2} \cdot \cancel{2}} = \frac{8}{5} = 1\frac{3}{5}$$

You Try It 8

Strategy   To find the number of products, divide the number of minutes in 1 hour (60) by the time to assemble one product $\left(7\frac{1}{2}\right)$.

Solution

$$60 \div 7\frac{1}{2} = \frac{60}{1} \div \frac{15}{2} = \frac{60}{1} \cdot \frac{2}{15}$$

$$= \frac{60 \cdot 2}{1 \cdot 15} = 8$$

The factory worker can assemble 8 products in 1 hour.

You Try It 9

Strategy   To find the length of the remaining piece:

▶ Divide the total length of the board (16) by the length of each shelf $\left(3\frac{1}{3}\right)$. This will give you the number of shelves cut, with a certain fraction of a shelf left over.

▶ Multiply the fractional part of the result in step 1 by the length of one shelf to determine the length of the remaining piece.

Solution

$$16 \div 3\frac{1}{3} = \frac{16}{1} \div \frac{10}{3}$$

$$= \frac{16}{1} \times \frac{3}{10} = \frac{16 \cdot 3}{1 \cdot 10}$$

$$= \frac{\overset{1}{2 \cdot 2 \cdot 2 \cdot 2 \cdot 3}}{\underset{1}{2 \cdot 5}} = \frac{24}{5}$$

$$= 4\frac{4}{5}$$

There are 4 pieces that are each $3\frac{1}{3}$ feet long. There is 1 piece that is $\frac{4}{5}$ of $3\frac{1}{3}$ feet long.

$$\frac{4}{5} \times 3\frac{1}{3} = \frac{4}{5} \times \frac{10}{3}$$

$$= \frac{4 \cdot 10}{5 \cdot 3} = \frac{2 \cdot 2 \cdot 2 \cdot \overset{1}{5}}{\underset{1}{5} \cdot 3}$$

$$= \frac{8}{3} = 2\frac{2}{3}$$

The length of the piece remaining is $2\frac{2}{3}$ feet.

SECTION 2.8

You Try It 1 $\dfrac{9}{14} = \dfrac{27}{42}$ $\dfrac{13}{21} = \dfrac{26}{42}$ $\dfrac{9}{14} > \dfrac{13}{21}$

You Try It 2

$$\left(\frac{1}{13}\right)^2 \cdot \left(\frac{1}{4} + \frac{1}{6}\right) \div \frac{5}{13}$$

$$= \left(\frac{1}{13}\right)^2 \cdot \left(\frac{5}{12}\right) \div \frac{5}{13}$$

$$= \left(\frac{1}{169}\right) \cdot \left(\frac{5}{12}\right) \div \frac{5}{13}$$

$$= \left(\frac{1 \cdot 5}{13 \cdot 13 \cdot 12}\right) \div \frac{5}{13}$$

$$= \left(\frac{1 \cdot 5}{13 \cdot 13 \cdot 12}\right) \times \frac{13}{5}$$

$$= \frac{1 \cdot \overset{1}{5} \cdot \overset{1}{13}}{13 \cdot 13 \cdot 12 \cdot \underset{1}{5}} = \frac{1}{156}$$

Solutions to Chapter 3 "You Try It"

SECTION 3.1

You Try It 1   The digit 4 is in the thousandths place.

You Try It 2   Fifty-five and six thousand eighty-three ten-thousandths

You Try It 3   806.00491   • 1 is in the hundred-thousandths place.

You Try It 4

Given place value

3.675849

4 < 5

3.675849 rounded to the nearest ten-thousandth is 3.6758.

You Try It 5

Given place value

48.907

0 < 5

48.907 rounded to the nearest tenth is 48.9.

You Try It 6

Given place value

31.8652

8 > 5

31.8652 rounded to the nearest whole number is 32.

You Try It 7   0.15   0.107

$$\frac{15}{100} \qquad \frac{107}{1000}$$

• Write the numbers as fractions.

$$\frac{150}{1000} \qquad \frac{107}{1000}$$

• Write the fractions with a common denominator.

$$\frac{150}{1000} > \frac{107}{1000}$$

• Compare the fractions

0.15 > 0.107

CTION 3.2

u Try It 1

$$\begin{array}{r} {}^{1\,2} \\ 4.62 \\ 27.9 \\ +\ 0.62054 \\ \hline 33.14054 \end{array}$$

• Place the decimal points on a vertical line.

u Try It 2

$$\begin{array}{r} {}^{1} \\ 6.05 \\ 12. \\ +\ 0.374 \\ \hline 18.424 \end{array}$$

u Try It 3

ategy Find the number of minutes for Facebook (19.2) and for Hulu (215.5) in the table. Then add the numbers.

lution 19.2 + 215.5 = 234.7

The total number of minutes watched per viewer for Internet users on Facebook and Hulu was 234.7 minutes.

u Try It 4

ategy To find the total income, add the four commissions (985.80, 791.46, 829.75, and 635.42) to the salary (875).

lution 875 + 985.80 + 791.46 + 829.75 + 635.42 = 4117.43

Anita's total income was $4117.43.

CTION 3.3

u Try It 1

$$\begin{array}{r} {}^{11\ \ 9} \\ 6\ \cancel{7}\ \cancel{10}\,13 \\ \cancel{7}\,2.\cancel{0}\,\cancel{3}\,9 \\ -\ \ 8.4\,7 \\ \hline 6\,3.5\,6\,9 \end{array}$$

Check: $\begin{array}{r} {}^{1\ 1\ 1} \\ 8.47 \\ +\ 63.569 \\ \hline 72.039 \end{array}$

u Try It 2

$$\begin{array}{r} {}^{14\ \ 9} \\ 2\ \cancel{4}\ \cancel{10}\,10 \\ \cancel{3}\,\cancel{5}.\cancel{0}\,\cancel{0} \\ -\ \ 9.6\,7 \\ \hline 2\,5.3\,3 \end{array}$$

Check: $\begin{array}{r} {}^{1\ 1\ 1} \\ 9.67 \\ +\ 25.33 \\ \hline 35.00 \end{array}$

u Try It 3

$$\begin{array}{r} {}^{16} \\ 2\ \cancel{6}\ 9\ 9\ 10 \\ \cancel{3}.\cancel{7}\,\cancel{0}\,\cancel{0} \\ -\ 1.9\,7\,1\,5 \\ \hline 1.7\,2\,8\,5 \end{array}$$

Check: $\begin{array}{r} {}^{1\ 1\ 1\ 1} \\ 1.9715 \\ +\ 1.7285 \\ \hline 3.7000 \end{array}$

u Try It 4

ategy To find the amount of change, subtract the cost of your breakfast (6.85) from 10.

lution

$$\begin{array}{r} 10.00 \\ -\ 6.85 \\ \hline 3.15 \end{array}$$

Your change was $3.15.

You Try It 5

Strategy To find the new balance:

► Add to find the total of the three checks (1025.60 + 79.85 + 162.47).
► Subtract the total from the previous balance (2472.69).

Solution

$$\begin{array}{r} 1025.60 \\ 79.85 \\ +\ 162.47 \\ \hline 1267.92 \end{array} \qquad \begin{array}{r} 2472.69 \\ -\ 1267.92 \\ \hline 1204.77 \end{array}$$

The new balance is $1204.77.

SECTION 3.4

You Try It 1

$$\begin{array}{r} 870 \\ \times\ \ 4.6 \\ \hline 522\,0 \\ 3480 \\ \hline 4002.0 \end{array}$$

• 1 decimal place

• 1 decimal place

You Try It 2

$$\begin{array}{r} 0.000086 \\ \times\ \ \ \ 0.057 \\ \hline 602 \\ 430 \\ \hline 0.000004902 \end{array}$$

• 6 decimal places
• 3 decimal places

• 9 decimal places

You Try It 3

$$\begin{array}{r} 4.68 \\ \times\ 6.03 \\ \hline 1404 \\ 28\,080 \\ \hline 28.2204 \end{array}$$

• 2 decimal places
• 2 decimal places

• 4 decimal places

You Try It 4 $6.9 \times 1000 = 6900$

You Try It 5 $4.0273 \times 10^2 = 402.73$

You Try It 6

Strategy To find the total bill:

► Find the number of gallons of water used by multiplying the number of gallons used per day (5000) by the number of days (62).
► Find the cost of water by multiplying the cost per 1000 gallons (1.39) by the number of 1000-gallon units used.
► Add the cost of the water to the meter fee (133.70).

Solution Number of gallons = 5000(62) = 310,000

$$\text{Cost of water} = \frac{310,000}{1000} \times 1.39 = 430.90$$

Total cost = 430.90 + 133.70 = 564.60

The total bill is $564.60.

You Try It 7

Strategy To find the cost of running the freezer for 210 hours, multiply the hourly cost (0.035) by the number of hours the freezer has run (210).

Solution

$$
\begin{array}{r}
0.035 \\
\times\ \ \ 210 \\
\hline
350 \\
7\ 0\ \ \ \\
\hline
7.350
\end{array}
$$

The cost of running the freezer for 210 hours is $7.35.

You Try It 8

Strategy To find the total cost of the electronic drum kit:
- ▶ Multiply the monthly payment (37.18) by the number of months (18).
- ▶ Add that product to the down payment (175.00).

Solution

$$
\begin{array}{r}
37.18 \\
\times\ \ \ 18 \\
\hline
29744 \\
3718\ \ \\
\hline
669.24
\end{array}
\qquad
\begin{array}{r}
175.00 \\
+\ 669.24 \\
\hline
844.24
\end{array}
$$

The total cost of the electronic drum kit is $844.24.

SECTION 3.5

You Try It 1

$$
\begin{array}{r}
2.7 \\
0.052.\overline{)\ 0.140.4} \\
-\ 104\ \ \\
\hline
36\ 4 \\
-\ 36\ 4 \\
\hline
0
\end{array}
$$

- Move the decimal point 3 places to the right in the divisor and the dividend. Write the decimal point in the quotient directly above the decimal point in the dividend.

You Try It 2

$$
\begin{array}{r}
0.4873 \approx 0.487 \\
76\overline{)\ 37.0420} \\
-\ 30\ 4\ \ \ \\
\hline
6\ 64\ \ \\
-\ 6\ 08\ \ \\
\hline
562\ \\
-\ 532\ \\
\hline
300 \\
-\ 228 \\
\hline
\end{array}
$$

- Write the decimal point in the quotient directly above the decimal point in the dividend.

You Try It 3

$$
\begin{array}{r}
72.73 \approx 72.7 \\
5.09.\overline{)\ 370.20.00} \\
-\ 356\ 3\ \ \ \\
\hline
13\ 90\ \ \\
-\ 10\ 18\ \ \\
\hline
3\ 720\ \\
-\ 3\ 563\ \\
\hline
1570 \\
-\ 1527 \\
\hline
\end{array}
$$

You Try It 4 $309.21 \div 10{,}000 = 0.030921$

You Try It 5 $42.93 \div 10^4 = 0.004293$

You Try It 6

Strategy To find how many times greater the average hourly earnings were, divide the 2010 average hourly earnings (19.07) by the 1980 average hourly earnings (6.85).

Solution $19.07 \div 6.85 \approx 2.8$
The average hourly earnings in 2010 were about 2.8 times greater than in 1980.

You Try It 7

Strategy To find the average number of people watching TV per day:
- ▶ Add the numbers of people watching each day of the week.
- ▶ Divide the total number of people watching by 7.

Solution $91.9 + 89.8 + 90.6 + 93.9 + 78.0$
$+\ 77.1 + 87.7 = $

$$\frac{609}{7} = 87$$

An average of 87 million people watch television per day.

SECTION 3.6

You Try It 1

$$
\begin{array}{r}
0.611 \\
18\overline{)\ 11.000} \\
-\ 10\ 8\ \ \\
\hline
20\ \ \\
-\ 18\ \ \\
\hline
20 \\
-\ 18 \\
\hline
2
\end{array}
$$

$$\frac{11}{18} = 0.6\overline{1}$$

- Divide the numerator by the denominator. Continue to divide until the remainder is 0 or the remainder repeats.

- Use a bar over the repeating digit.

You Try It 2

$$
\begin{array}{r}
0.28 \\
25{\overline{\smash{\big)}\,7.00}} \\
\underline{-\ 5\ 0} \\
2\ 00 \\
\underline{-\ 2\ 00} \\
0
\end{array}
$$
• The remainder is 0.

$$\frac{7}{25} = 0.28$$

You Try It 3

$$
\begin{array}{r}
2.166 \\
6{\overline{\smash{\big)}\,13.000}} \\
\underline{-\ 12} \\
1\ 0 \\
\underline{-\ 6} \\
40 \\
\underline{-\ 36} \\
40 \\
\underline{-\ 36} \\
4
\end{array}
$$
• The remainder repeats.

$$\frac{13}{6} = 2.1\overline{6}$$

You Try It 4 $0.0005 = \dfrac{5}{10,000} = \dfrac{1}{2000}$

You Try It 5

$$\frac{5}{6} \qquad 0.83$$

$$\frac{5}{6} \qquad \frac{83}{100}$$
• Write the decimal as a fraction.

$$\frac{250}{300} \qquad \frac{249}{300}$$
• Write the fractions with a common denominator.

$$\frac{250}{300} > \frac{249}{300}$$
• Compare the fractions.

$$\frac{5}{6} > 0.83$$

Solutions to Chapter 4 "You Try It"

SECTION 4.1

You Try It 1 $\dfrac{20 \text{ pounds}}{24 \text{ pounds}} = \dfrac{20}{24} = \dfrac{5}{6}$

20 pounds : 24 pounds = 20 : 24 = 5 : 6

20 pounds to 24 pounds = 20 to 24
                                        = 5 to 6

You Try It 2 $\dfrac{64 \text{ miles}}{8 \text{ miles}} = \dfrac{64}{8} = \dfrac{8}{1}$

64 miles : 8 miles = 64 : 8 = 8 : 1

64 miles to 8 miles = 64 to 8 = 8 to 1

You Try It 3

Strategy   To find the ratio, write the ratio of board feet of cedar (12,000) to board feet of ash (18,000) in simplest form.

Solution $\dfrac{12,000}{18,000} = \dfrac{2}{3}$

The ratio is $\frac{2}{3}$.

You Try It 4

Strategy   To find the ratio, write the ratio of the amount spent on radio advertising (450,000) to the amount spent on radio and television advertising (450,000 + 600,000) in simplest form.

Solution $\dfrac{\$450,000}{\$450,000 + \$600,000} = \dfrac{450,000}{1,050,000} = \dfrac{3}{7}$

The ratio is $\frac{3}{7}$.

SECTION 4.2

You Try It 1 $\dfrac{15 \text{ pounds}}{12 \text{ trees}} = \dfrac{5 \text{ pounds}}{4 \text{ trees}}$

You Try It 2 $\dfrac{260 \text{ miles}}{8 \text{ hours}}$

$$
\begin{array}{r}
32.5 \\
8{\overline{\smash{\big)}\,260.0}}
\end{array}
$$

32.5 miles/hour

You Try It 3

Strategy   To find the per-foot cost of the pipe, divide the total cost ($22.40) by the number of feet purchased (40 feet).

Solution $22.40 \div 40 = 0.56$

The cost of the pipe is $.56/foot.

SECTION 4.3

You Try It 1

$\dfrac{6}{10} \quad \dfrac{9}{15} \rightarrow 10 \times 9 = 90$
$\qquad\qquad\quad 6 \times 15 = 90$

The cross products are equal.
The proportion is true.

You Try It 2 $\dfrac{32}{6} \quad \dfrac{90}{8} \rightarrow 6 \times 90 = 540$
$\qquad\qquad\quad 32 \times 8 = 256$

The cross products are not equal.
The proportion is not true.

You Try It 3 $\dfrac{n}{14} = \dfrac{3}{7}$ • Find the cross products. Then solve for n.

$n \times 7 = 14 \times 3$
$n \times 7 = 42$
$\qquad n = 42 \div 7$
$\qquad n = 6$

Check: $\dfrac{6}{14} \quad \dfrac{3}{7} \rightarrow 14 \times 3 = 42$
$\qquad\qquad\qquad 6 \times 7 = 42$

You Try It 4
$$\frac{5}{7} = \frac{n}{20}$$

• Find the cross products. Then solve for n.

$$5 \times 20 = 7 \times n$$
$$100 = 7 \times n$$
$$100 \div 7 = n$$
$$14.3 \approx n$$

You Try It 5
$$\frac{15}{20} = \frac{12}{n}$$

• Find the cross products. Then solve for n.

$$15 \times n = 20 \times 12$$
$$15 \times n = 240$$
$$n = 240 \div 15$$
$$n = 16$$

Check: $\dfrac{15}{20} \times \dfrac{12}{16}$ → $20 \times 12 = 240$
→ $15 \times 16 = 240$

You Try It 6
$$\frac{12}{n} = \frac{7}{4}$$
$$12 \times 4 = n \times 7$$
$$48 = n \times 7$$
$$48 \div 7 = n$$
$$6.86 \approx n$$

You Try It 7
$$\frac{n}{12} = \frac{4}{1}$$
$$n \times 1 = 12 \times 4$$
$$n \times 1 = 48$$
$$n = 48 \div 1$$
$$n = 48$$

Check: $\dfrac{48}{12} \times \dfrac{4}{1}$ → $12 \times 4 = 48$
→ $48 \times 1 = 48$

You Try It 8

Strategy To find the number of tablespoons of fertilizer needed, write and solve a proportion using n to represent the number of tablespoons of fertilizer.

Solution

$$\frac{3 \text{ tablespoons}}{4 \text{ gallons}} = \frac{n \text{ tablespoons}}{10 \text{ gallons}}$$

• The unit "tablespoons" is in the numerator. The unit "gallons" is in the denominator.

$$3 \times 10 = 4 \times n$$
$$30 = 4 \times n$$
$$30 \div 4 = n$$
$$7.5 = n$$

For 10 gallons of water, 7.5 tablespoons of fertilizer are required.

You Try It 9

Strategy To find the number of jars that can be packed in 15 boxes, write and solve a proportion using n to represent the number of jars.

Solution

$$\frac{24 \text{ jars}}{6 \text{ boxes}} = \frac{n \text{ jars}}{15 \text{ boxes}}$$

$$24 \times 15 = 6 \times n$$
$$360 = 6 \times n$$
$$360 \div 6 = n$$
$$60 = n$$

60 jars can be packed in 15 boxes.

Solutions to Chapter 5 "You Try It"

SECTION 5.1

You Try It 1

a. $125\% = 125 \times 0.01 = 1.25$

$$125\% = 125 \times \frac{1}{100}$$
$$= \frac{125}{100} = \frac{5}{4} = 1\frac{1}{4}$$

b. $8.5\% = 8.5 \times 0.01 = 0.085$

$$8.5\% = 8.5 \times \frac{1}{100}$$
$$= 8\frac{1}{2} \times \frac{1}{100}$$
• $8.5 = 8\frac{5}{10} = 8\frac{1}{2}$
$$= \frac{17}{2} \times \frac{1}{100}$$
$$= \frac{17}{200}$$
• Multiply the fractio

c. $0.25\% = 0.25 \times 0.01 = 0.0025$

$$0.25\% = 0.25 \times \frac{1}{100}$$
$$= \frac{1}{4} \times \frac{1}{100}$$
• $0.25 = \frac{25}{100} = \frac{1}{4}$
$$= \frac{1}{400}$$
• Multiply the fractio

You Try It 2
$$33\frac{1}{3}\% = 33\frac{1}{3} \times \frac{1}{100}$$
$$= \frac{100}{3} \times \frac{1}{100}$$
$$= \frac{100}{300} = \frac{1}{3}$$

You Try It 3
$$0.048 = 0.048 \times 100\% = 4.8\%$$
$$3.6 = 3.6 \times 100\% = 360\%$$

You Try It 4
$$\frac{5}{16} \times \frac{100\%}{1}$$
$$= \frac{500\%}{16} = 31.25\%$$
• Write in decimal for

You Try It 5
$$\frac{5}{6} = \frac{5}{6} \times \frac{100\%}{1} = \frac{500\%}{6} = 83\frac{1}{3}\%$$

SECTION 5.2

You Try It 1
$$\text{Percent} \times \text{base} = \text{amount}$$
$$0.063 \times 150 = n$$
$$9.45 = n$$

u Try It 2

Percent × base = amount
$$\frac{1}{6} \times 66 = n \qquad \bullet \ 16\frac{2}{3}\% = \frac{1}{6}$$
$$11 = n$$

u Try It 3

·ategy

To determine the amount that came from corporations, write and solve the basic percent equation, using n to represent the amount. The percent is 5%. The base is $291 billion.

lution

Percent × base = amount
$$5\% \times 291 = n$$
$$0.05 \times 291 = n$$
$$14.55 = n$$

Corporations gave $14.55 billion to charities.

u Try It 4

·ategy

To find the new hourly wage:

▶ Find the amount of the raise. Write and solve the basic percent equation, using n to represent the amount of the raise (amount). The percent is 8%. The base is $33.50.
▶ Add the amount of the raise to the old wage (33.50).

lution

$$8\% \times 33.50 = n \qquad\qquad\qquad 33.50$$
$$0.08 \times 33.50 = n \qquad\qquad \underline{+\ \ 2.68}$$
$$2.68 = n \qquad\qquad\qquad 36.18$$

The new hourly wage is $36.18.

CTION 5.3

u Try It 1

Percent × base = amount
$$n \times 32 = 16$$
$$n = 16 \div 32$$
$$n = 0.50$$
$$n = 50\%$$

u Try It 2

Percent × base = amount
$$n \times 15 = 48$$
$$n = 48 \div 15$$
$$n = 3.2$$
$$n = 320\%$$

u Try It 3

Percent × base = amount
$$n \times 45 = 30$$
$$n = 30 \div 45$$
$$n = \frac{2}{3} = 66\frac{2}{3}\%$$

u Try It 4

·ategy

To find what percent of the income the income tax is, write and solve the basic percent equation, using n to represent the percent. The base is $33,500, and the amount is $5025.

Solution

$$n \times 33,500 = 5025$$
$$n = 5025 \div 33,500$$
$$n = 0.15 = 15\%$$

The income tax is 15% of the income.

You Try It 5

Strategy

To find the percent of wireless subscribers not using a smartphone:

▶ Subtract to find the number of subscribers not using a smartphone (302.9 million − 112.1 million).
▶ Write and solve the basic percent equation, using n to represent the percent. The base is 302.9 million, and the amount is the number of wireless subscribers not using a smartphone.

Solution

302.9 million − 112.1 million = 190.8 million

There were 190.8 million wireless subscribers not using a smartphone.
$$n \times 302.9 = 190.8$$
$$n = 190.8 \div 302.9$$
$$n \approx 0.6299$$

Approximately 63.0% of the wireless subscribers were not using a smartphone.

SECTION 5.4

You Try It 1

Percent × base = amount
$$0.86 \times n = 215$$
$$n = 215 \div 0.86$$
$$n = 250$$

You Try It 2

Percent × base = amount
$$0.025 \times n = 15$$
$$n = 15 \div 0.025$$
$$n = 600$$

You Try It 3

Percent × base = amount
$$\frac{1}{6} \times n = 5 \qquad \bullet \ 16\frac{2}{3}\% = \frac{1}{6}$$
$$n = 5 \div \frac{1}{6}$$
$$n = 30$$

You Try It 4

Strategy

To find the original value of the car, write and solve the basic percent equation, using n to represent the original value (base). The percent is 42%, and the amount is $10,458.

Solution

$$42\% \times n = 10,458$$
$$0.42 \times n = 10,458$$
$$n = 10,458 \div 0.42$$
$$n = 24,900$$

The original value of the car was $24,900.

You Try It 5

Strategy   To find the difference between the original price and the sale price:

- ▸ Find the original price. Write and solve the basic percent equation, using n to represent the original price (base). The percent is 80%, and the amount is $89.60.
- ▸ Subtract the sale price (89.60) from the original price.

Solution
$$80\% \times n = 89.60$$
$$0.80 \times n = 89.60$$
$$n = 89.60 \div 0.80$$
$$n = 112.00 \quad \text{(original price)}$$
$$112.00 - 89.60 = 22.40$$

The difference between the original price and the sale price is $22.40.

SECTION 5.5

You Try It 1
$$\frac{26}{100} = \frac{22}{n}$$
$$26 \times n = 100 \times 22$$
$$26 \times n = 2200$$
$$n = 2200 \div 26$$
$$n \approx 84.62$$

You Try It 2
$$\frac{16}{100} = \frac{n}{132}$$
$$16 \times 132 = 100 \times n$$
$$2112 = 100 \times n$$
$$2112 \div 100 = n$$
$$21.12 = n$$

You Try It 3

Strategy   To find the number of days it snowed, write and solve a proportion, using n to represent the number of days it snowed (amount). The percent is 64%, and the base is 150.

Solution
$$\frac{64}{100} = \frac{n}{150}$$
$$64 \times 150 = 100 \times n$$
$$9600 = 100 \times n$$
$$9600 \div 100 = n$$
$$96 = n$$

It snowed 96 days.

You Try It 4

Strategy   To find the percent of alarms that were not false alarms:

- ▸ Subtract to find the number of alarms that were not false alarms (200 − 24).

- ▸ Write and solve a proportion, using n to represent the percent of alarms that were not false. The base is 200, and the amou[nt] is the number of alarms that were not fal[se] alarms.

Solution
$$200 - 24 = 176$$
$$\frac{n}{100} = \frac{176}{200}$$
$$n \times 200 = 100 \times 176$$
$$n \times 200 = 17{,}600$$
$$n = 17{,}600 \div 200$$
$$n = 88$$

88% of the alarms were not false alarms.

Solutions to Chapter 6 "You Try It"

SECTION 6.1

You Try It 1

Strategy   To find the unit cost, divide the cost of the package by the number of units in the pack[age].

Solution   **a.** Unit cost $= \dfrac{\text{cost of the package}}{\text{number of units in the package}}$

$= \dfrac{\$14.99}{12 \text{ apples}} \approx \$1.208$ per apple

b. Unit cost $= \dfrac{\text{cost of the package}}{\text{number of units in the package}}$

$= \dfrac{\$10.00}{15 \text{ pounds}} \approx \$.667$ per pound

You Try It 2

Strategy   To find the more economical purchase, com[pare] the unit costs.

Solution
$$8.70 \div 6 = 1.45$$
$$6.96 \div 4 = 1.74$$
$$\$1.45 < \$1.74$$

The more economical purchase is 6 cans for $8.70.

You Try It 3

Strategy   To find the total cost, multiply the unit cos[t] (9.96) by the number of units (7).

Solution

Unit cost	×	number of units	=	total cost
9.96	×	7	=	69.72

The total cost is $69.72.

SECTION 6.2

You Try It 1
Strategy

To find the percent increase:

▶ Find the amount of the increase.
▶ Solve the basic percent equation for *percent*.

Solution

$$\boxed{\begin{array}{c}\text{New}\\\text{value}\end{array}} - \boxed{\begin{array}{c}\text{original}\\\text{value}\end{array}} = \boxed{\begin{array}{c}\text{amount of}\\\text{increase}\end{array}}$$

$$3.83 \quad - \quad 3.46 \quad = \quad 0.37$$

Percent × base = amount
$$n \quad \times 3.46 = \quad 0.37$$
$$n = 0.37 \div 3.46$$
$$n \approx 0.11 = 11\%$$

The percent increase was 11%.

You Try It 2
Strategy

To find the new hourly wage:

▶ Solve the basic percent equation for *amount*.
▶ Add the amount of the increase to the original wage.

Solution

Percent × base = amount
$$0.14 \quad \times 12.50 = \quad n$$
$$1.75 = n$$
$$12.50 + 1.75 = 14.25$$

The new hourly wage is $14.25.

You Try It 3
Strategy

To find the markup, solve the basic percent equation for *amount*.

Solution

Percent × base = amount

$$\boxed{\begin{array}{c}\text{Markup}\\\text{rate}\end{array}} \times \boxed{\text{cost}} = \boxed{\text{markup}}$$

$$0.20 \quad \times \quad 32 \quad = \quad n$$
$$6.4 = n$$

The markup is $6.40.

You Try It 4
Strategy

To find the selling price:

▶ Find the markup by solving the basic percent equation for *amount*.
▶ Add the markup to the cost.

Solution

Percent × base = amount

$$\boxed{\begin{array}{c}\text{Markup}\\\text{rate}\end{array}} \times \boxed{\text{cost}} = \boxed{\text{markup}}$$

$$0.55 \quad \times \quad 72 \quad = \quad n$$
$$39.60 = n$$

$$\boxed{\text{Cost}} + \boxed{\text{markup}} = \boxed{\begin{array}{c}\text{selling}\\\text{price}\end{array}}$$

$$72 \quad + \quad 39.60 \quad = \quad 111.60$$

The selling price is $111.60.

You Try It 5
Strategy

To find the percent decrease:

▶ Find the amount of the decrease.
▶ Solve the basic percent equation for *percent*.

Solution

$$\boxed{\begin{array}{c}\text{Original}\\\text{value}\end{array}} - \boxed{\begin{array}{c}\text{new}\\\text{value}\end{array}} = \boxed{\begin{array}{c}\text{amount of}\\\text{decrease}\end{array}}$$

$$88,000,000 - 84,227,000 = 3,773,000$$

Percent × base = amount
$$n \quad \times 88,000,000 = 3,773,000$$
$$n = 3,773,000 \div 88,000,000$$
$$n \approx 0.043$$

The percent decrease is 4.3%.

You Try It 6
Strategy

To find the visibility in the fog:

▶ Find the amount of decrease by solving the basic percent equation for *amount*.
▶ Subtract the amount of decrease from the original visibility.

Solution

Percent × base = amount
$$0.40 \quad \times \quad 5 \quad = \quad n$$
$$2 = n$$
$$5 - 2 = 3$$

The visibility in the fog was 3 miles.

You Try It 7
Strategy

To find the discount rate:

▶ Find the discount.
▶ Solve the basic percent equation for *percent*.

Solution

$$\boxed{\begin{array}{c}\text{Regular}\\\text{price}\end{array}} - \boxed{\begin{array}{c}\text{sale}\\\text{price}\end{array}} = \boxed{\text{discount}}$$

$$12.50 \quad - \quad 10.99 \quad = \quad 1.51$$

Percent × base = amount

$$\boxed{\begin{array}{c}\text{Discount}\\\text{rate}\end{array}} \times \boxed{\begin{array}{c}\text{regular}\\\text{price}\end{array}} = \boxed{\text{discount}}$$

$$n \quad \times \quad 12.50 \quad = \quad 1.51$$
$$n = 1.51 \div 12.50$$
$$n = 0.1208$$

The discount rate is 12.1%.

You Try It 8
Strategy

To find the sale price:

▶ Find the discount by solving the basic percent equation for *amount*.
▶ Subtract to find the sale price.

Solution

$$\text{Percent} \times \text{base} = \text{amount}$$

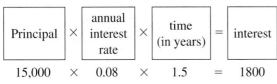

$$\boxed{\begin{array}{c}\text{Discount}\\\text{rate}\end{array}} \times \boxed{\begin{array}{c}\text{regular}\\\text{price}\end{array}} = \boxed{\text{discount}}$$

$$0.15 \quad\times\quad 225 \quad=\quad n$$
$$33.75 = n$$

$$\boxed{\begin{array}{c}\text{Regular}\\\text{price}\end{array}} - \boxed{\text{discount}} = \boxed{\begin{array}{c}\text{sale}\\\text{price}\end{array}}$$

$$225 \quad - \quad 33.75 \quad = 191.25$$

The sale price is $191.25.

SECTION 6.3

You Try It 1

Strategy To find the simple interest due, multiply the principal (15,000) times the annual interest rate (8% = 0.08) times the time in years (18 months = $\frac{18}{12}$ years = 1.5 years).

Solution

$$\boxed{\text{Principal}} \times \boxed{\begin{array}{c}\text{annual}\\\text{interest}\\\text{rate}\end{array}} \times \boxed{\begin{array}{c}\text{time}\\(\text{in years})\end{array}} = \boxed{\text{interest}}$$

$$15{,}000 \quad\times\quad 0.08 \quad\times\quad 1.5 \quad=\quad 1800$$

The interest due is $1800.

You Try It 2

Strategy To find the maturity value:

▶ Use the simple interest formula to find the simple interest due.
▶ Find the maturity value by adding the principal and the interest.

Solution

$$\boxed{\text{Principal}} \times \boxed{\begin{array}{c}\text{annual}\\\text{interest}\\\text{rate}\end{array}} \times \boxed{\begin{array}{c}\text{time}\\(\text{in years})\end{array}} = \boxed{\text{interest}}$$

$$3800 \quad\times\quad 0.06 \quad\times\quad \frac{90}{365} \quad\approx\quad 56.22$$

$$\boxed{\text{Principal}} + \boxed{\text{interest}} = \boxed{\begin{array}{c}\text{maturity}\\\text{value}\end{array}}$$

$$3800 \quad + \quad 56.22 \quad = \quad 3856.22$$

The maturity value is $3856.22.

You Try It 3

Strategy To find the monthly payment:

▶ Find the maturity value by adding the principal and the interest.
▶ Divide the maturity value by the length of the loan in months (12).

Solution

Principal + interest = maturity value

$$1900 \quad + \quad 152 \quad = \quad 2052$$

Maturity value ÷ length of the loan = payment

$$2052 \quad\div\quad 12 \quad=\quad 171$$

The monthly payment is $171.

You Try It 4

Strategy To find the finance charge, multiply the principal, or unpaid balance (1250), times the monthly interest rate (1.6%) times the number of months (1).

Solution

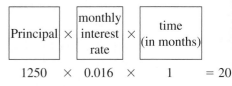

$$\boxed{\text{Principal}} \times \boxed{\begin{array}{c}\text{monthly}\\\text{interest}\\\text{rate}\end{array}} \times \boxed{\begin{array}{c}\text{time}\\(\text{in months})\end{array}}$$

$$1250 \quad\times\quad 0.016 \quad\times\quad 1 \quad= 20$$

The finance charge is $20.

You Try It 5

Strategy To find the interest earned:

▶ Find the new principal by multiplying the original principal (1000) by the factor found in the Compound Interest Table (3.29066).
▶ Subtract the original principal from the new principal.

Solution

$$1000 \times 3.29066 = 3290.66$$

The new principal is $3290.66.

$$3290.66 - 1000 = 2290.66$$

The interest earned is $2290.66.

SECTION 6.4

You Try It 1

Strategy To find the mortgage:

▶ Find the down payment by solving the basic percent equation for *amount*.
▶ Subtract the down payment from the purchase price.

Solution

$$\text{Percent} \times \text{base} = \text{amount}$$

$$\boxed{\text{Percent}} \times \boxed{\begin{array}{c}\text{purchase}\\\text{price}\end{array}} = \boxed{\begin{array}{c}\text{down}\\\text{payment}\end{array}}$$

$$0.25 \quad\times 1{,}500{,}000 = \quad n$$
$$375{,}000 = n$$

$$\boxed{\begin{array}{c}\text{Purchase}\\\text{price}\end{array}} - \boxed{\begin{array}{c}\text{down}\\\text{payment}\end{array}} = \boxed{\text{mortgage}}$$

$$1{,}500{,}000 - 375{,}000 = 1{,}125{,}000$$

The mortgage is $1,125,000.

You Try It 2

Strategy To find the loan origination fee, solve the basic percent equation for *amount*.

Solution

$$\text{Percent} \times \text{base} = \text{amount}$$

$$\boxed{\text{Points}} \times \boxed{\text{mortgage}} = \boxed{\text{fee}}$$

$$0.045 \quad\times\quad 180{,}000 \quad=\quad n$$
$$8100 = n$$

The loan origination fee was $8100.

Try It 3

Strategy

To find the mortgage payment:

▶ Find the down payment.
▶ Subtract the down payment from the purchase price to find the mortgage.
▶ Multiply the mortgage by the factor in the Monthly Payment Table for a 20-year loan at 6%.

Solution

Percent × purchase price = down payment
0.30 ×   185,000   =   55,000

The down payment is $55,500.

| Purchase price | − | down payment | = | mortgage |

185,000 −   55,500   =   129,500

The mortgage is $129,500.

The factor from the Monthly Payment Table is 0.0071643.

$129,500 \times 0.0071643 \approx 927.78$

The monthly mortgage payment is $927.78.

Try It 4

Strategy

To find the amount of the first month's payment that is interest and the amount that is principal:

▶ Find the monthly simple interest rate.
▶ Use the basic percent equation to find the interest owed for the first month.
▶ Subtract the interest owed for the first month from the monthly payment to find the amount of the payment that is principal.

Solution

Monthly simple interest rate
$$= \frac{\text{annual interest rate}}{12}$$
$$= \frac{0.045}{12} = 0.00375$$

Percent × base = amount
$0.00375 \times 296,000 = 1110$

The interest owed for the first month is $1110.

| Monthly payment | − | amount to interest | = | amount to principal |

1413.15 − 1110.00 = 303.15

The amount of the payment that goes to the principal is $303.15.

SECTION 6.5

Try It 1

Strategy

To find the amount financed:

▶ Find the down payment by solving the basic percent equation for *amount*.
▶ Subtract the down payment from the purchase price.

Solution

Percent × base = amount

| Percent | × | purchase price | = | down payment |

0.20 × 19,200 = n
3840 = n

The down payment is $3840.

$19,200 - 3840 = 15,360$

The amount financed is $15,360.

You Try It 2

Strategy

To find the license fee, solve the basic percent equation for *amount*.

Solution

Percent × base = amount

| Percent | × | purchase price | = | license fee |

0.015 × 27,350 = n
410.25 = n

The license fee is $410.25.

You Try It 3

Strategy

To find the cost, multiply the cost per mile (0.41) by the number of miles driven (23,000).

Solution

$23,000 \times 0.41 = 9430$

The cost is $9430.

You Try It 4

Strategy

To find the cost per mile for car insurance, divide the cost for insurance (360) by the number of miles driven (15,000).

Solution

$360 \div 15,000 = 0.024$

The cost per mile for insurance is $.024.

You Try It 5

Strategy

To find the monthly payment:

▶ Subtract the down payment from the purchase price to find the amount financed.
▶ Multiply the amount financed by the factor found in the Monthly Payment Table.

Solution

$25,900 - 6475 = 19,425$

$19,425 \times 0.0244129 \approx 474.22$

The monthly payment is $474.22.

SECTION 6.6

You Try It 1

Strategy

To find the worker's earnings:

▶ Find the worker's overtime wage by multiplying the hourly wage by 2.
▶ Multiply the number of overtime hours worked by the overtime wage.

Solution $28.50 \times 2 = 57$

The hourly wage for overtime is $57.

$57 \times 8 = 456$

The construction worker earns $456.

You Try It 2

Strategy   To find the monthly salary, divide the annual salary by the number of months in a year (12).

Solution $70,980 \div 12 = 5915$

The contractor's monthly salary is $5915.

You Try It 3

Strategy   To find the total earnings:
- ▶ Find the sales over $50,000.
- ▶ Multiply the commission rate by sales over $50,000.
- ▶ Add the commission to the annual salary.

Solution $175,000 - 50,000 = 125,000$

Sales over $50,000 totaled $125,000.

$125,000 \times 0.095 = 11,875$

Earnings from commissions totaled $11,875.

$37,000 + 11,875 = 48,875$

The insurance agent earned $48,875.

SECTION 6.7

You Try It 1

Strategy   To find the current balance:
- ▶ Subtract the amount of the check from the old balance.
- ▶ Add the amount of each deposit.

Solution

$$
\begin{array}{ll}
302.46 & \\
-\ 20.59 & \text{check} \\
\hline
281.87 & \\
176.86 & \text{first deposit} \\
+\ 94.73 & \text{second deposit} \\
\hline
553.46 &
\end{array}
$$

The current checking account balance is $553.46.

You Try It 2

$$
\begin{array}{ll}
\text{Current checkbook} & \\
\text{balance:} & 623.41 \\
\text{Check: 237} & +\ 78.73 \\
\hline
& 702.14 \\
\text{Interest:} & +\ \ 2.11 \\
\hline
& 704.25 \\
\text{Deposit:} & -523.84 \\
\hline
& 180.41
\end{array}
$$

Closing bank balance from bank statement: $180.41

Checkbook balance: $180.41

The bank statement and the checkbook balance

Answers to Selected Exercises

Answers to Chapter 1 Selected Exercises

1. 8   **2.** 1 2 3 4 5 6 7 8 9 10   **3.** a and D; b and E; c and A; d and B; e and F; f and C

SECTION 1.1

1. a. False   **b.** True   **c.** True   **d.** True   **3.**   **5.**

7. 37 < 49   **9.** 101 > 87   **11.** 2701 > 2071   **13.** 107 > 0   **15.** Yes   **17.** Three thousand seven hundred ninety
19. Fifty-eight thousand four hundred seventy-three   **21.** Four hundred ninety-eight thousand five hundred twelve
23. Six million eight hundred forty-two thousand seven hundred fifteen   **25.** 357   **27.** 63,780   **29.** 7,024,709   **31.** 5000 + 200 + 80 + 7
33. 50,000 + 8000 + 900 + 40 + 3   **35.** 200,000 + 500 + 80 + 3   **37.** 400,000 + 3000 + 700 + 5   **39.** No   **41.** 850
43. 4000   **45.** 53,000   **47.** 630,000   **49.** 250,000   **51.** 72,000,000   **53.** No. Round 3846 to the nearest hundred.

SECTION 1.2

1. Addition Property of Zero   **3.** Associative Property of Addition   **5.** Commutative Property of Addition   **7.** 28   **9.** 125   **11.** 102
13. 154   **15.** 1489   **17.** 828   **19.** 1584   **21.** 102,317   **23.** 79,326   **25.** 1804   **27.** 1579   **29.** 19,740   **31.** 7420
33. 120,570   **35.** 207,453   **37.** 24,218   **39.** 11,974   **41.** 9323   **43.** 77,139   **45.** 14,383   **47.** 9473   **49.** 33,247   **51.** 5058
53. 1992   **55.** 68,263   **57.** Cal.: 17,754   **59.** Cal.: 2872   **61.** Cal.: 101,712   **63.** Cal.: 158,763   **65.** Cal.: 261,595
                         Est.: 17,700   Est.: 2900   Est.: 101,000   Est.: 158,000   Est.: 260,000
67. Cal.: 946,718   **69.** Commutative Property of Addition   **71.** There were 144,928 multiple births during the year.
Est.: 940,000
73. The total gross income from the eight *Harry Potter* movies was $2,390,100,000.   **75.** The total gross income from the two highest-grossing
Harry Potter movies was $698,600,000.   **77. a.** During the three days, 1285 miles will be driven.   **b.** At the end of the trip, the odometer will
read 69,977 miles.   **79.** 14,636,300 barrels of crude oil are produced and imported per day.   **81.** No. For example, 0 + 2 = 2
85.

```
                    8
        ┌──────────────────────►
   2         6
 ┌───► ┌──────────────►
─┼──┼──┼──┼──┼──┼──┼──┼──┼──┼──┼─
 0  1  2  3  4  5  6  7  8  9  10
```

SECTION 1.3

1. 4; 5 + 4 = 9   **3.** 11; 0 + 11 = 11   **5.** 4   **7.** 9   **9.** 22   **11.** 60   **13.** 66   **15.** 31   **17.** 901   **19.** 791   **21.** 1125   **23.** 3131
25. 47   **27.** 925   **29.** 4561   **31.** 3205   **33.** 1222   **35.** 5 and 3   **37.** 53   **39.** 29   **41.** 8   **43.** 37   **45.** 58   **47.** 574
49. 337   **51.** 1423   **53.** 754   **55.** 2179   **57.** 6489   **59.** 889   **61.** 71,129   **63.** 698   **65.** 29,405   **67.** 49,624   **69.** 628
71. 6532   **73.** 4286   **75.** 4042   **77.** 5209   **79.** 10,378   **81.** ii and iii   **83.** 11,239   **85.** 8482   **87.** 625   **89.** 76,725
91. 23   **93.** 4648   **95.** Cal.: 29,837   **97.** Cal.: 36,668   **99.** Cal.: 101,998
                         Est.: 30,000   Est.: 40,000   Est.: 100,000
101. a. The honey bee has 91 more smell genes than the mosquito.   **b.** The mosquito has eight more taste genes than the fruit fly.
c. The honey bee has the best sense of smell.   **d.** The honey bee has the worst sense of taste.   **103.** The difference between the maximum
eruption heights is 15 feet.   **105.** 202,345 more women than men earned a bachelor's degree.   **107. a.** The smallest expected increase occurs
from 2010 to 2012.   **b.** The greatest expected increase occurs from 2018 to 2020.   **109.** Your new credit card balance is $360.

CHECK YOUR PROGRESS: CHAPTER 1*

1.

[1.1A]   **2.** $107 > 97$ [1.1A]   **3.** Eighty-two thousand seven hundred
forty-three   [1.1B]   **4.** Two million five hundred thirty thousand twenty-one   [1.1B]   **5.** 23,401   [1.1B]   **6.** 903,003   [1.1B]
7. $60,000 + 3000 + 200 + 90 + 1$ [1.1C]   **8.** 592,000   [1.1D]   **9.** 46,000   [1.1D]   **10.** 843,995   [1.2A]   **11.** 14,632   [1.2A]
12. 197,523   [1.2A]   **13.** 7058   [1.3B]   **14.** 8538   [1.3B]   **15.** The national debt is about \$14,800,000,000,000.   [1.1D]
16. Colonial Falls is 160 feet higher than Yosemite Falls.   [1.3C]   **17.** Janice contributed a total of \$130.   [1.2B]   **18.** Boys grow
60 centimeters from birth to age 5.   [1.3C]   **19.** Girls grow the most between birth and age 1.   [1.3C]   **20.** The golfer's total score
was 275.   [1.2B]

SECTION 1.4

1. 6×2 or $6 \cdot 2$ **3.** 4×7 or $4 \cdot 7$ **5.** Multiplication Property of One   **7.** Commutative Property of Multiplication   **9.** 12   **11.** 35
13. 25   **15.** 0   **17.** 72   **19.** 198   **21.** 335   **23.** 2492   **25.** 5463   **27.** 4200   **29.** 6327   **31.** 1896   **33.** 5056   **35.** 168
37. 46,963   **39.** 59,976   **41.** 19,120   **43.** 19,790   **45.** 140   **47.** 22,456   **49.** 18,630   **51.** 336   **53.** 910   **55.** 63,063
57. 33,520   **59.** 380,834   **61.** 541,164   **63.** 400,995   **65.** 105,315   **67.** 428,770   **69.** 260,000   **71.** 344,463   **73.** 41,808
75. 189,500   **77.** 401,880   **79.** 1,052,763   **81.** 4,198,388   **83.** Answers will vary. For example, 5 and 20   **85.** 198,423
87. 18,834   **89.** 260,178   **91.** Cal.: 440,076   **93.** Cal.: 6,491,166   **95.** Cal.: 18,728,744   **97.** Cal.: 57,691,192
　　　　　　　　　　　　　　　　Est.: 450,000　　　　　Est.: 6,300,000　　　　　Est.: 18,000,000　　　　　Est.: 54,000,000
99. The area is 2808 square feet.   **101.** The car could travel 516 miles on 12 gallons of gas.   **103. a.** eHarmony can take credit for
3794 marriages a week.   **b.** eHarmony can take credit for 197,830 marriages a year.   **105.** The estimated cost of the electricians'
labor is \$5100.   **107.** The total cost is \$2138.   **109.** There are 12 accidental deaths each hour, 288 deaths each day, and
105,120 deaths each year.   **111.** $21,978 \times 4 = 87,912$

SECTION 1.5

1. 2; $2 \times 4 = 8$ **3.** 6; $6 \times 5 = 30$ **5.** 6   **7.** 12   **9.** 7   **11.** 16   **13.** 210   **15.** 44   **17.** 703   **19.** 910
21. 5006   **23.** 6050   **25.** 1075   **27.** 1   **29.** 3 r1   **31.** 9 r7   **33.** 16 r1   **35.** 10 r4   **37.** 90 r3   **39.** 120 r5
41. 309 r3   **43.** 1160 r4   **45.** 708 r2   **47.** 3825 r1   **49.** 5710 r3   **51.** 11,430   **53.** 510   **55.** False
57. 1 r38   **59.** 1 r26   **61.** 21 r21   **63.** 30 r22   **65.** 5 r40   **67.** 9 r17   **69.** 200 r21   **71.** 303 r1   **73.** 67 r13
75. 708 r49   **77.** 1086 r7   **79.** 5007 r55   **81.** 12 r456   **83.** 4 r160   **85.** 160 r27   **87.** 1669 r14   **89.** 7950
91. Cal.: 5129   **93.** Cal.: 21,968   **95.** Cal.: 24,596   **97.** Cal.: 2836   **99.** Cal.: 3024   **101.** Cal.: 32,036
　　　Est.: 5000　　　　Est.: 20,000　　　　Est.: 22,500　　　　Est.: 3000　　　　Est.: 3000　　　　Est.: 30,000
103. Melissa's monthly salary is \$5754.   **105.** The cost of the gold alloy in each necklace is \$750.   **107.** The nursing student's average exam
score was 88.   **109.** The monthly payment is \$130.   **111.** The average monthly claim for theft was \$25,000.   **113.** The average number of
hours worked by employees in the United Kingdom is 33 hours.   **115.** Employees in the country with the most number of hours worked per year
(Greece) work an average of 15 hours more per week than do employees in the country with the least number of hours worked per year (Germany).
117. On average, the U.S. Postal Service processed 390 million pieces of mail per day.   **119.** The total of the deductions is \$350.
121. 49,500,000 more cases of eggs were sold by retail stores.   **123.** The average monthly expense for housing is \$976.
125. The total amount paid is \$11,860.   **127.** Subtraction   **129.** Division

SECTION 1.6

1. Five   **3.** i and iii   **5.** 2^3 **7.** $6^3 \cdot 7^4$ **9.** $2^3 \cdot 3^3$ **11.** $5 \cdot 7^5$ **13.** $3^3 \cdot 6^4$ **15.** $3^3 \cdot 5 \cdot 9^3$ **17.** 8   **19.** 400   **21.** 900
23. 972   **25.** 120   **27.** 360   **29.** 0   **31.** 90,000   **33.** 540   **35.** 4050   **37.** 11,025   **39.** 25,920   **41.** 4,320,000   **43.** 5
45. 23   **47.** 6   **49.** 5   **51.** 18   **53.** 10   **55.** 7   **57.** 8   **59.** 6   **61.** 52   **63.** 26   **65.** 52   **67.** 42   **69.** 16   **71.** 6
73. 8   **75.** 3   **77.** 4   **79.** 13   **81.** 0   **83.** $(2 \cdot 3 + 8) \cdot 4 - 2$ **85.** $2 \cdot (3 + 8 \cdot 4 - 2)$ **87.** No   **89.** No   **91. a.** 6561
b. 43,046,721   **c.** 43,046,721

SECTION 1.7

1. ii, iii, v, vi   **3.** 1, 2, 4   **5.** 1, 2, 5, 10   **7.** 1, 7   **9.** 1, 3, 9   **11.** 1, 13   **13.** 1, 2, 3, 6, 9, 18   **15.** 1, 2, 4, 7, 8, 14, 28, 56
17. 1, 3, 5, 9, 15, 45   **19.** 1, 29   **21.** 1, 2, 11, 22   **23.** 1, 2, 4, 13, 26, 52   **25.** 1, 2, 41, 82   **27.** 1, 3, 19, 57
29. 1, 2, 3, 4, 6, 8, 12, 16, 24, 48   **31.** 1, 5, 19, 95   **33.** 1, 2, 3, 6, 9, 18, 27, 54   **35.** 1, 2, 3, 6, 11, 22, 33, 66
37. 1, 2, 4, 5, 8, 10, 16, 20, 40, 80   **39.** 1, 2, 3, 4, 6, 8, 12, 16, 24, 32, 48, 96   **41.** 1, 2, 3, 5, 6, 9, 10, 15, 18, 30, 45, 90
43. True   **45.** $2 \cdot 3$ **47.** Prime   **49.** $2 \cdot 2 \cdot 2 \cdot 3$ **51.** $3 \cdot 3 \cdot 3$ **53.** $2 \cdot 2 \cdot 3 \cdot 3$ **55.** Prime   **57.** $2 \cdot 3 \cdot 3 \cdot 5$
59. $5 \cdot 23$ **61.** $2 \cdot 3 \cdot 3$ **63.** $2 \cdot 2 \cdot 7$ **65.** Prime   **67.** $2 \cdot 31$ **69.** $2 \cdot 11$ **71.** Prime   **73.** $2 \cdot 3 \cdot 11$
75. $2 \cdot 37$ **77.** Prime   **79.** $5 \cdot 11$ **81.** $2 \cdot 2 \cdot 2 \cdot 3 \cdot 5$ **83.** $2 \cdot 2 \cdot 2 \cdot 2 \cdot 2 \cdot 5$ **85.** $2 \cdot 2 \cdot 2 \cdot 3 \cdot 3 \cdot 3$
87. $5 \cdot 5 \cdot 5 \cdot 5$ **89.** False   **91.** Answers will vary. For example, 21, 33, 27, and 39

*Note: The numbers in brackets following the answers to the Check Your Progress exercises are a reference to the objective that corresponds to tha
problem. For example, the reference [1.2A] stands for Section 1.2, Objective A. This notation will be used for all Prep Tests, Check Your Progress
exercises, Chapter Reviews, Chapter Tests, and Cumulative Reviews throughout the text.

CHAPTER 1 REVIEW EXERCISES

. 600 [1.6A] **2.** 10,000 + 300 + 20 + 7 [1.1C] **3.** 1, 2, 3, 6, 9, 18 [1.7A] **4.** 12,493 [1.2A] **5.** 1749 [1.3B] **.** 2135 [1.5A] **7.** 101 > 87 [1.1A] **8.** $5^2 \cdot 7^5$ [1.6A] **9.** 619,833 [1.4B] **10.** 5409 [1.3B] **11.** 1081 [1.2A] **2.** 2 [1.6B] **13.** 45,700 [1.1D] **14.** Two hundred seventy-six thousand fifty-seven [1.1B] **15.** 1306 r59 [1.5C] **6.** 2,011,044 [1.1B] **17.** 488 r2 [1.5B] **18.** 17 [1.6B] **19.** 32 [1.6B] **20.** $2 \cdot 2 \cdot 2 \cdot 3 \cdot 3$ [1.7B] **1.** 2133 [1.3A] **22.** 22,761 [1.4B] **23.** The total pay for last week's work is $768. [1.4C] **24.** He drove 27 miles er gallon of gasoline. [1.5D] **25.** Each monthly car payment is $560. [1.5D] **26.** The total income from commissions $2567. [1.2B] **27.** The total amount deposited is $301. The new checking account balance is $817. [1.2B] **28.** The total f the car payments is $2952. [1.4C] **29.** More males were enrolled in U.S. colleges in 2009 than in 2005. [1.1A] **0.** The difference between the numbers of males and females enrolled in U.S. colleges in 2005 is 2,575,625. [1.3C] **31.** The number of ales enrolled in U.S. colleges increased by 1,313,579 students from 2005 to 2009. [1.3C] **32.** 2,940,236 more students were enrolled U.S. colleges in 2009 than in 2005. [1.3C]

CHAPTER 1 TEST

. 432 [1.6A; Example 3] **2.** Two hundred seven thousand sixty-eight [1.1B; Example 3] **3.** 15,069 [1.3B; Example 3] **.** 1, 2, 4, 5, 10, 20 [1.7A; Example 1] **5.** 6,854,144 [1.4B; HOW TO 3] **6.** 9 [1.6B; Example 4] **.** 900,000 + 6000 + 300 + 70 + 8 [1.1C; Example 6] **8.** 75,000 [1.1D; Example 8] **9.** 1121 r27 [1.5C; Example 8] **0.** $3^3 \cdot 7^2$ [1.6A; Example 1] **11.** 54,915 [1.2A; Example 1] **12.** $2 \cdot 2 \cdot 3 \cdot 7$ [1.7B; Example 2] **13.** 4 **.6B; Example 4] **14.** 726,104 [1.4A; Example 1] **15.** 1,204,006 [1.1B; Example 4] **16.** 8710 r2 [1.5B; Example 5] **7.** 21 > 19 [1.1A; Example 2] **18.** 703 [1.5A; Example 3] **19.** 96,798 [1.2A; Example 3] **20.** 19,922 **.3B; Example 4] **21.** The difference between projected total enrollment in 2016 and 2013 is 1,908,000 students. [1.3C; Example 6] **2.** The projected enrollment in pre-kindergarten through grade 12 in 2016 is 59,781,000 students. [1.2B; HOW TO 4] **3.** 3000 boxes were needed to pack the lemons. [1.5D; Example 10] **24.** A hummingbird will beat its wings 46,800 times in 900 seconds. **.4C; You Try It 3] **25.** The average speed was 66 miles per hour. [1.5D; HOW TO 3]

Answers to Chapter 2 Selected Exercises

PREP TEST

. 20 [1.4A] **2.** 120 [1.4A] **3.** 9 [1.4A] **4.** 10 [1.2A] **5.** 7 [1.3A] **6.** 2 r3 [1.5C] **7.** 1, 2, 3, 4, 6, 12 [1.7A] **.** 59 [1.6B] **9.** 7 [1.3A] **10.** 44 < 48 [1.1A]

SECTION 2.1

. 5, 10, 15, 20 **3.** 10, 20, 30, 40 **5.** Multiples of 6: 6, 12, 18, 24, 30, 36, 42, 48, 54, 60; multiples of 8: 8, 16, 24, 32, 40, 48, 56, 64, 72, 80; ommon multiples: 24, 48; least common multiple: 24 **7.** 1, 2, 4, 5, 10, 20 **9.** 1, 2, 4, 7, 14, 28 **11.** 40 **13.** 24 **15.** 12 **7.** 24 **19.** 60 **21.** 56 **23.** 32 **25.** 36 **27.** 660 **29.** 9384 **31.** 24 **33.** 30 **35.** 24 **37.** 576 **39.** 420 **1.** True **43.** 1 **45.** 3 **47.** 5 **49.** 25 **51.** 1 **53.** 4 **55.** 4 **57.** 4 **59.** 1 **61.** 7 **63.** 5 **65.** 8 **7.** 1 **69.** 25 **71.** 8 **73.** True **75.** They will have another day off together in 12 days. **79. a.** No **b.** Yes **c.** Yes **d.** Yes

SECTION 2.2

. Improper fraction; greater than 1 **3.** Proper fraction; less than 1 **5.** $\frac{3}{4}$ **7.** $\frac{7}{8}$ **9.** $1\frac{1}{2}$ **11.** $2\frac{5}{8}$ **13.** $3\frac{3}{5}$ **15.** $\frac{5}{4}$ **7.** $\frac{8}{3}$ **19.** $\frac{27}{8}$ **21.** **23.** **25.** False **27.** $5\frac{1}{3}$ **29.** 2 **31.** $3\frac{1}{4}$ **33.** $14\frac{1}{2}$ **35.** 17 **7.** $1\frac{7}{9}$ **39.** $1\frac{4}{5}$ **41.** 23 **43.** $1\frac{15}{16}$ **45.** $6\frac{1}{3}$ **47.** 5 **49.** 1 **51.** $\frac{14}{3}$ **53.** $\frac{26}{3}$ **55.** $\frac{59}{8}$ **57.** $\frac{25}{4}$ **59.** $\frac{121}{8}$ **1.** $\frac{41}{12}$ **63.** $\frac{34}{9}$ **65.** $\frac{38}{3}$ **67.** $\frac{38}{7}$ **69.** $\frac{63}{5}$ **71.** $\frac{41}{9}$ **73.** $\frac{117}{14}$ **77.** Answers will vary. For example, $\frac{17}{8}$

SECTION 2.3

. No. 5 does not divide evenly into 7. **3.** $\frac{5}{10}$ **5.** $\frac{9}{48}$ **7.** $\frac{12}{32}$ **9.** $\frac{9}{51}$ **11.** $\frac{12}{16}$ **13.** $\frac{27}{9}$ **15.** $\frac{20}{60}$ **17.** $\frac{44}{60}$ **9.** $\frac{12}{18}$ **21.** $\frac{35}{49}$ **23.** $\frac{10}{18}$ **25.** $\frac{21}{3}$ **27.** $\frac{35}{45}$ **29.** $\frac{60}{64}$ **31.** $\frac{21}{98}$ **33.** $\frac{30}{48}$ **35.** $\frac{15}{42}$ **37.** $\frac{102}{144}$ **39.** $\frac{1}{3}$ **1.** $\frac{1}{2}$ **43.** $\frac{1}{6}$ **45.** $1\frac{1}{9}$ **47.** 0 **49.** $\frac{9}{22}$ **51.** 3 **53.** $\frac{4}{21}$ **55.** $\frac{12}{35}$ **57.** $\frac{7}{11}$ **59.** $1\frac{1}{3}$ **61.** $\frac{3}{5}$ **63.** $\frac{1}{11}$ **5.** 4 **67.** $\frac{1}{3}$ **69.** $\frac{3}{5}$ **71.** $2\frac{1}{4}$ **73.** $\frac{1}{5}$ **75.** Answers will vary. For example, $\frac{4}{6}, \frac{6}{9}, \frac{8}{12}, \frac{10}{15}, \frac{12}{8}$. **77. a.** $\frac{4}{25}$ **b.** $\frac{4}{25}$

SECTION 2.4

1. 2, 5, 7   **3.** 8   **5.** 18   **7.** $\frac{3}{7}$ **9.** $\frac{2}{3}$ **11.** $\frac{4}{7}$ **13.** 1   **15.** $1\frac{4}{11}$ **17.** $3\frac{2}{5}$ **19.** $1\frac{3}{8}$ **21.** $1\frac{7}{15}$ **23.** $1\frac{5}{12}$

25. A whole number other than 1   **27.** The number 1   **29.** $1\frac{1}{6}$ **31.** $\frac{13}{14}$ **33.** $\frac{53}{60}$ **35.** $1\frac{1}{56}$ **37.** $\frac{23}{60}$ **39.** $1\frac{17}{18}$

41. $1\frac{11}{48}$ **43.** $1\frac{9}{20}$ **45.** $2\frac{17}{120}$ **47.** $2\frac{5}{72}$ **49.** $\frac{39}{40}$ **51.** $1\frac{19}{24}$ **53.** ii   **55.** $10\frac{1}{12}$ **57.** $9\frac{2}{7}$ **59.** $9\frac{47}{48}$ **61.** $8\frac{3}{13}$

63. $16\frac{29}{120}$ **65.** $24\frac{29}{40}$ **67.** $33\frac{7}{24}$ **69.** $10\frac{5}{36}$ **71.** $10\frac{5}{12}$ **73.** $14\frac{73}{90}$ **75.** $10\frac{13}{48}$ **77.** The length of the pole is $9\frac{7}{8}$ feet.

79. $9\frac{5}{24}$ **81.** $14\frac{1}{18}$ **83.** $11\frac{11}{12}$ **85.** No   **87.** The length of the shaft is $8\frac{9}{16}$ inches.   **89.** The sum represents the height of the table

91. The total length of the course is $10\frac{1}{2}$ miles.   **93.** The wall is $6\frac{5}{8}$ inches thick.

95. The minimum length of the bolt needed is $1\frac{3}{8}$ inches.   **97.** $\frac{1}{2}, \frac{1}{3}, \frac{1}{4}$ **99.** $\frac{1}{3} + \frac{1}{4}$ **101.** $\frac{1}{4} + \frac{1}{6}$

SECTION 2.5

1. 5, 3, 2   **3.** $\frac{11}{18}$ **5.** $\frac{2}{17}$ **7.** $\frac{1}{3}$ **9.** $\frac{1}{10}$ **11.** $\frac{5}{13}$ **13.** $\frac{1}{3}$ **15.** $\frac{4}{7}$ **17.** $\frac{1}{4}$ **19.** Yes   **21.** $\frac{1}{2}$ **23.** $\frac{19}{56}$

25. $\frac{1}{2}$ **27.** $\frac{11}{60}$ **29.** $\frac{1}{32}$ **31.** $\frac{19}{60}$ **33.** $\frac{5}{72}$ **35.** $\frac{11}{60}$ **37.** $\frac{29}{60}$ **39.** i   **41.** $5\frac{1}{5}$ **43.** $4\frac{7}{8}$ **45.** $\frac{16}{21}$ **47.** $5\frac{1}{2}$

49. $7\frac{5}{24}$ **51.** $1\frac{2}{5}$ **53.** $15\frac{11}{18}$ **55.** The distance is $21\frac{3}{4}$ inches.   **57.** $15\frac{11}{20}$ **59.** $4\frac{37}{45}$ **61.** No   **63.** The missing dimension

is $9\frac{1}{2}$ inches.   **65.** The desk is $\frac{3}{4}$ inch shorter than a standard size desk.   **67. a.** The hikers plan to travel $17\frac{17}{24}$ miles the first two days.

b. There will be $9\frac{19}{24}$ miles left to travel on the third day.   **69.** The difference represents how much farther the hikers plan to travel on the

second day than on the first day.   **71. a.** Yes   **b.** The wrestler needs to lose $3\frac{1}{4}$ pounds to reach the desired weight.

73. $\frac{11}{15}$ of the electrician's income is not spent on housing.   **75.** $6\frac{1}{8}$

CHECK YOUR PROGRESS: CHAPTER 2

1. 36 [2.1A]   **2.** 18 [2.1A]   **3.** 70 [2.1A]   **4.** 252 [2.1A]   **5.** 6 [2.1B]   **6.** 27 [2.1B]   **7.** 1 [2.1B]   **8.** 5 [2.1B]

9. $\frac{4}{5}$ [2.3B]   **10.** $\frac{1}{3}$ [2.3B]   **11.** Simplest form [2.3B]   **12.** 9 [2.3B]   **13.** $\frac{2}{3}$ [2.4A]   **14.** $\frac{1}{2}$ [2.5A]   **15.** $\frac{7}{18}$ [2.5B]

16. $\frac{3}{5}$ [2.4B]   **17.** $1\frac{25}{48}$ [2.4B]   **18.** $\frac{21}{52}$ [2.5B]   **19.** $\frac{23}{48}$ [2.5B]   **20.** $\frac{17}{20}$ [2.4B]   **21.** $9\frac{1}{6}$ [2.4C]   **22.** $18\frac{11}{18}$ [2.4C]

23. $6\frac{5}{14}$ [2.5C]   **24.** $2\frac{19}{56}$ [2.5C]   **25.** $13\frac{13}{18}$ [2.4C]   **26.** $17\frac{1}{20}$ [2.4C]   **27.** $3\frac{1}{4}$ [2.5C]   **28.** $2\frac{5}{12}$ [2.5C]

SECTION 2.6

1. 2, 9, $\frac{10}{27}$ **3.** Yes   **5.** $\frac{7}{12}$ **7.** $\frac{7}{48}$ **9.** $\frac{1}{48}$ **11.** $\frac{11}{14}$ **13.** 6   **15.** $\frac{5}{12}$ **17.** 6   **19.** $\frac{2}{3}$ **21.** $\frac{3}{16}$ **23.** $\frac{21}{80}$

25. 10   **27.** $\frac{1}{15}$ **29.** $\frac{2}{3}$ **31.** $\frac{7}{26}$ **33.** 4   **35.** $\frac{4}{9}$ **37.** Answers will vary. For example, $\frac{3}{4}$ and $\frac{4}{3}$.   **39.** $1\frac{1}{3}$ **41.** $2\frac{1}{2}$

43. $\frac{9}{34}$ **45.** 10   **47.** $16\frac{2}{3}$ **49.** 1   **51.** $\frac{1}{2}$ **53.** 30   **55.** 42   **57.** $12\frac{2}{3}$ **59.** $1\frac{4}{5}$ **61.** $1\frac{2}{3}$ **63.** $1\frac{2}{3}$ **65.** 0

67. $27\frac{2}{3}$ **69.** $8\frac{1}{16}$ **71.** 8   **73.** The distance is 54 feet.   **75.** 9   **77.** $\frac{5}{8}$ **79.** $3\frac{1}{40}$ **81.** Less than   **83.** The cost is $11.

85. The length is $3\frac{1}{12}$ feet.   **87.** The area is $27\frac{9}{16}$ square feet.   **89.** Each year, about 36 million acres of corn are turned into ethanol.

91. The weight is $54\frac{19}{36}$ pounds.   **93.** The total cost of the material is $363.   **95.** $\frac{1}{2}$ **97.** A

ECTION 2.7

$\frac{7}{3}$ **3.** $\frac{5}{4}$ **5.** $9, 4, \frac{27}{32}$ **7.** $\frac{5}{6}$ **9.** 1   **11.** 0   **13.** $\frac{1}{2}$ **15.** $\frac{1}{6}$ **17.** $\frac{7}{10}$ **19.** 2   **21.** 2   **23.** $\frac{1}{6}$ **25.** 6

. $\frac{1}{15}$ **29.** 2   **31.** $2\frac{1}{2}$ **33.** 3   **35.** $1\frac{1}{6}$ **37.** $3\frac{1}{3}$ **39.** True   **41.** 6   **43.** $\frac{1}{2}$ **45.** $\frac{1}{30}$ **47.** $1\frac{4}{5}$ **49.** 13   **51.** 3

. $\frac{1}{5}$ **55.** $\frac{11}{28}$ **57.** 120   **59.** $\frac{11}{40}$ **61.** $\frac{33}{40}$ **63.** $4\frac{4}{9}$ **65.** $\frac{13}{32}$ **67.** $10\frac{2}{3}$ **69.** $\frac{12}{53}$ **71.** $4\frac{62}{191}$ **73.** 68   **75.** $8\frac{2}{7}$

. $3\frac{13}{49}$ **79.** 4   **81.** $1\frac{3}{5}$ **83.** $\frac{9}{34}$ **85.** False   **87.** Less than   **89.** There are 12 servings in 16 ounces of cereal.

. Each acre costs \$24,000.   **93.** The nut will make 12 turns in moving $1\frac{7}{8}$ inches.   **95. a.** The total weight of the fat and bone is

$\frac{5}{12}$ pounds.   **b.** The chef can cut 28 servings from the roast.   **97.** The distance between each pair of posts is $2\frac{3}{4}$ inches.   **99.** $\frac{1}{2}$

)1. $\frac{1}{2}$ **103.** $\frac{2}{3}$ **105.** $\frac{2}{3}$ **107.** The recommended maximum monthly payment is \$1500.

)9. The board measures 14 inches by 7 inches by $1\frac{3}{4}$ inches when closed.   **111.** Each column is $2\frac{1}{4}$ inches wide.

13. Three times more people use Safari.   **115.** The unnamed browsers represent $\frac{1}{10}$ of the world browser market.

ECTION 2.8

Equal to   **3.** Less than   **5.** $\frac{11}{40} < \frac{19}{40}$ **7.** $\frac{2}{3} < \frac{5}{7}$ **9.** $\frac{5}{8} > \frac{7}{12}$ **11.** $\frac{7}{9} < \frac{11}{12}$ **13.** $\frac{13}{14} > \frac{19}{21}$ **15.** $\frac{7}{24} < \frac{11}{30}$ **17.** $\frac{4}{5}$

). $\frac{25}{144}$ **21.** $\frac{2}{9}$ **23.** $\frac{3}{125}$ **25.** $\frac{4}{45}$ **27.** $\frac{1}{30}$ **29.** $1\frac{1}{5}$ **31.** $\frac{17}{24}$ **33.** $\frac{7}{8}$ **35.** $1\frac{3}{8}$ **37.** $\frac{7}{8}$ **39.** $\frac{12}{125}$ **41.** $\frac{11}{32}$

3. $\frac{17}{24}$ **45.** $\frac{14}{15}$ **47.** $2\frac{7}{10}$ **49.** $\frac{21}{44}$ **51.** $\frac{25}{39}$ **53.** $1\frac{1}{9}$ **55.** $\frac{43}{48}$ **57. a.** More people choose a fast-food restaurant on the

asis of its location.   **b.** Location was the criterion cited by the most people.   **59.** $\left(\frac{7}{8} + \frac{2}{3}\right) \cdot \frac{1}{2} + \frac{5}{6}$

CHAPTER 2 REVIEW EXERCISES

. $\frac{2}{3}$ [2.3B]   **2.** $\frac{3}{16}$ [2.8B]   **3.** $\frac{13}{4}$ [2.2A]   **4.** $\frac{32}{44}$ [2.3A]   **5.** $\frac{11}{18} < \frac{17}{24}$ [2.8A]   **6.** $14\frac{19}{42}$ [2.5C]   **7.** $\frac{5}{36}$ [2.8B]

. $9\frac{1}{24}$ [2.6B]   **9.** 2 [2.7B]   **10.** $\frac{25}{48}$ [2.5B]   **11.** $3\frac{1}{3}$ [2.7B]   **12.** 4 [2.1B]   **13.** $\frac{24}{36}$ [2.3A]   **14.** $\frac{3}{4}$ [2.7A]

5. $1\frac{13}{18}$ [2.4B]   **16.** $16\frac{1}{2}$ [2.6B]   **17.** 36 [2.1A]   **18.** $\frac{4}{11}$ [2.3B]   **19.** $1\frac{1}{8}$ [2.4A]   **20.** $\frac{1}{8}$ [2.6A]   **21.** $18\frac{13}{54}$ [2.4C]

2. 5 [2.1B]   **23.** $3\frac{2}{5}$ [2.2B]   **24.** $\frac{1}{15}$ [2.8B]   **25.** $5\frac{7}{8}$ [2.4C]   **26.** 54 [2.1A]   **27.** $\frac{1}{3}$ [2.5A]   **28.** $\frac{19}{7}$ [2.2B]

9. 2 [2.7A]   **30.** $\frac{1}{15}$ [2.6A]   **31.** $10\frac{1}{8}$ [2.5C]   **32.** $1\frac{7}{8}$ [2.2A]   **33.** The total rainfall for the 3 months was $21\frac{7}{24}$ inches.

.4D]   34. The cost per acre was \$36,000. [2.7C]   **35.** The second checkpoint is $4\frac{3}{4}$ miles from the finish line. [2.5D]

6. The car can travel 243 miles. [2.6C]

CHAPTER 2 TEST

. $\frac{4}{9}$ [2.6A; Example 1]   **2.** 8 [2.1B; Example 2]   **3.** $1\frac{3}{7}$ [2.7A; Example 2]   **4.** $\frac{7}{24}$ [2.8B; You Try It 2]

. $\frac{49}{5}$ [2.2B; Example 5]   **6.** 8 [2.6B; Example 5]   **7.** $\frac{5}{8}$ [2.3B; Example 3]   **8.** $\frac{3}{8} < \frac{5}{12}$ [2.8A; Example 1]

. $\frac{5}{6}$ [2.8B; Example 2]   **10.** 120 [2.1A; Example 1]   **11.** $\frac{1}{4}$ [2.5A; Example 1]   **12.** $3\frac{3}{5}$ [2.2B; Example 3]

3. $2\frac{2}{19}$ [2.7B; Example 4]   **14.** $\frac{45}{72}$ [2.3A; Example 1]   **15.** $1\frac{61}{90}$ [2.4B; Example 4]   **16.** $13\frac{81}{88}$ [2.5C; Example 4]

7. $\frac{7}{48}$ [2.5B; Example 2]   **18.** $\frac{19}{96}$ [2.8B; You Try It 2]   **19.** $1\frac{11}{12}$ [2.4A; Example 1]   **20.** $22\frac{4}{15}$ [2.4C; Example 7]

1. $\frac{11}{4}$ [2.2A; Example 2]   **22.** The electrician earns \$840. [2.6C; Example 6]   **23.** 11 lots were available for sale. [2.7C; Example 8]

24. The actual length of wall A is $12\frac{1}{2}$ feet. The actual length of wall B is 18 feet. The actual length of wall C is $15\frac{3}{4}$ feet.   [2.7C, Example 8]

25. The total rainfall for the 3-month period was $21\frac{11}{24}$ inches.   [2.4D, Example 8]

CUMULATIVE REVIEW EXERCISES

1. 290,000   [1.1D]   **2.** 291,278   [1.3B]   **3.** 73,154   [1.4B]   **4.** 540 r12   [1.5C]   **5.** 1   [1.6B]   **6.** $2 \cdot 2 \cdot 11$ [1.7B]

7. 210   [2.1A]   **8.** 20   [2.1B]   **9.** $\frac{23}{3}$ [2.2B]   **10.** $6\frac{1}{4}$ [2.2B]   **11.** $\frac{15}{48}$ [2.3A]   **12.** $\frac{2}{5}$ [2.3B]   **13.** $1\frac{7}{48}$ [2.4B]

14. $14\frac{11}{48}$ [2.4C]   **15.** $\frac{13}{24}$ [2.5B]   **16.** $1\frac{7}{9}$ [2.5C]   **17.** $\frac{7}{20}$ [2.6A]   **18.** $7\frac{1}{2}$ [2.6B]   **19.** $1\frac{1}{20}$ [2.7A]   **20.** $2\frac{5}{8}$ [2.7B

21. $\frac{1}{9}$ [2.8B]   **22.** $5\frac{5}{24}$ [2.8B]   **23.** The amount in the checking account at the end of the week was $862.   [1.3C]   **24.** The total

income from the tickets was $1410.   [1.4C]   **25.** The total weight is $12\frac{1}{24}$ pounds.   [2.4D]   **26.** The length of the remaining piece is

$4\frac{17}{24}$ feet.   [2.5D]   **27.** The car travels 225 miles on $8\frac{1}{3}$ gallons of gas.   [2.6C]   **28.** 25 parcels can be sold from the remaining land.   [2.7C]

Answers to Chapter 3 Selected Exercises

PREP TEST

1. $\frac{3}{10}$ [2.2A]   **2.** 36,900   [1.1D]   **3.** Four thousand seven hundred ninety-one   [1.1B]   **4.** 6842   [1.1B]   **5.** 9394   [1.2A]
6. 1638   [1.3B]   **7.** 76,804   [1.4B]   **8.** 278 r18   [1.5C]

SECTION 3.1

1. Thousandths   **3.** Ten-thousandths   **5.** 0.3   **7.** 0.853   **9.** $\frac{59}{100}$ **11.** Thirty-seven hundredths   **13.** Nine and four tenths
15. Fifty-three ten-thousandths   **17.** Forty-five thousandths   **19.** Twenty-six and four hundredths   **21.** 3.0806   **23.** 407.03
25. 246.024   **27.** 73.02684   **29.** 6.2   **31.** 21.0   **33.** 18.41   **35.** 72.50   **37.** 936.291   **39.** 47   **41.** 7015   **43.** 2.97527
45. 700   **47.** 0.18 ounce   **49.** 26.2 miles   **51.** Answers will vary. For example, 0.572   **53.** $0.278 > 0.203$
55. $0.045 > 0.038$ **57.** $0.037 < 0.13$ **59.** $0.031 > 0.00987$ **61.** $0.02883 < 0.0305$ **63.** $0.0072 > 0.0008294$
65. Answers will vary. For example,   **a.** 0.15   **b.** 1.05   **c.** 0.001

SECTION 3.2

3. 150.1065   **5.** 95.8446   **7.** 69.644   **9.** 92.883   **11.** 113.205   **13.** 110.7666   **15.** 1.6466   **17.** 107.642
19. Cal.: 234.192   **21.** Cal.: 781.943   **23.** Yes   **25.** The length of the shaft is 4.35 feet.   **27.** The perimeter is 3.53 meters.
     Est.: 234   Est.: 782
29. The total average number of viewers per day for the three news programs was 21.1 million.   **31.** No, a 4-foot rope cannot be wrapped
around the box.   **33.** Three possible answers are bread, butter, and mayonnaise; raisin bran, butter, and bread; and lunch meat, milk, and popcorn.
35. $\frac{79}{1000} + \frac{13}{100}; \frac{209}{1000}$ **37.** $\frac{53}{1000} + \frac{9}{100} + \frac{1077}{10,000}; \frac{2507}{10,000}$

SECTION 3.3

1. 6.19   **3.** 0.0095   **5.** 5.627   **7.** 113.6427   **9.** 6.7098   **11.** 215.697   **13.** 53.8776   **15.** 72.7091   **17.** 0.3142   **19.** 1.023
21. 261.166   **23.** 655.32   **25.** 342.9268   **27.** 8.628   **29.** 184.728   **31.** 0.27598   **33.** $7.01 - 2.325$ **35.** $19.35 - 8.967$
37. Cal.: 2.74506   **39.** Cal.: 7.14925   **41.** The missing dimension is 2.59 feet.   **43.** The average price of a ticket increased by $.62.
     Est.: 3   Est.: 7
45. 33.5 million more people watched Super Bowl XLII than watched the Super Bowl post-game show.   **47. a.** 0.1   **b.** 0.01   **c.** 0.001
49. $\frac{87}{100} - \frac{531}{1000}; \frac{339}{1000}$ **51.** $\frac{97}{1000} - \frac{69,531}{1,000,000}; \frac{27,469}{1,000,000}$

CHECK YOUR PROGRESS: CHAPTER 3

1. $\dfrac{7}{10}$ [3.1C]   **2.** $\dfrac{17}{1000}$ [3.1C]   **3.** $\dfrac{93}{100}$ [3.1C]   **4.** $\dfrac{87}{100,000}$ [3.1C]   **5.** Twenty-three and forty-five thousandths [3.1A]

6. 305.0057 [3.1A]   **7.** 357.80 [3.1B]   **8.** $0.357 < 0.4$ [3.1C]   **9.** $0.056 > 0.0107$ [3.1C]   **10.** $0.00319 < 0.005$ [3.1C]

11. 16.18 [3.2A]   **12.** 17.97 [3.3A]   **13.** 116.217 [3.3A]   **14.** 90.3972 [3.2A]   **15.** 1000 [3.2A]   **16.** 18.1508 [3.3A]

SECTION 3.4

1. 10^2 **3.** 10^6 **5.** 10,000,000   **7.** 3   **9.** 5   **11.** 0.36   **13.** 0.25   **15.** 6.93   **17.** 1.84   **19.** 0.74   **21.** 39.5

23. 2.72   **25.** 0.603   **27.** 13.50   **29.** 4.316   **31.** 0.1323   **33.** 0.03568   **35.** 0.0784   **37.** 0.076   **39.** 34.48

41. 580.5   **43.** 20.148   **45.** 0.04255   **47.** 0.17686   **49.** 0.19803   **51.** 0.429   **53.** 2.116   **55.** 0.476   **57.** 1.022

59. 2.318   **61.** The height of the diving board is 9.8424 feet.   **63.** 3.2   **65.** 6.5   **67.** 6285.6   **69.** 35,700   **71.** 6.3

73. 3.9   **75.** 49,000   **77.** 6.7   **79.** 0.012075   **81.** 0.0117796   **83.** 0.31004   **85.** 0.082845   **87.** 5.175

89. Cal.: 91.2   **91.** Cal.: 1.0472   **93.** Cal.: 3.897   **95.** Cal.: 11.2406   **97.** Cal.: 0.371096   **99.** Cal.: 31.8528

Est.: 90   Est.: 0.8   Est.: 4.5   Est.: 12   Est.: 0.32   Est.: 30

101. The amount received is $14.06.   **103.** A U.S. homeowner's average annual cost of electricity is $1244.04.   **105.** The accountant's mileage deduction is $258.02.   **107.** The deduction for driving a car 2374 miles for business   **109.** You will pay $5.96 in taxes.

111. The area is 23.625 square feet.   **113. a.** The CRNA's overtime pay is $2240.25.   **b.** The CRNA's total income is $5680.25.

115. The federal government would have saved $125,120,000.   **117. a.** The total cost for grade 1 is $56.32.   **b.** The total cost for grade 2 is $74.04.   **c.** The total cost for grade 3 is $409.56.   **d.** The total cost is $539.92.

119. $1\dfrac{3}{10} \times 2\dfrac{31}{100} = \dfrac{13}{10} \times \dfrac{231}{100} = \dfrac{3003}{1000} = 3\dfrac{3}{1000} = 3.003$

SECTION 3.5

1. right; whole; right; divided   **3.** 0.82   **5.** 4.8   **7.** 89   **9.** 60   **11.** 84.3   **13.** 32.3   **15.** 5.06   **17.** 1.3   **19.** 0.11   **21.** 3.8

23. 6.3   **25.** 0.6   **27.** 2.5   **29.** 1.1   **31.** 0.81   **33.** 0.09   **35.** 40.70   **37.** 0.46   **39.** 0.019   **41.** 0.360   **43.** 0.103

45. 0.009   **47.** 1   **49.** 3   **51.** 1   **53.** 57   **55.** The length is 1.0375 meters.   **57.** 0.407   **59.** 4.267   **61.** 0.01037

63. 0.008295   **65.** 0.032   **67.** 0.23627   **69.** 0.000053   **71.** 0.0018932   **73.** 18.42   **75.** 16.07   **77.** 0.0135

79. 0.023678   **81.** 0.112   **83.** Cal.: 11.1632   **85.** Cal.: 884.0909   **87.** Cal.: 1.8269   **89.** Cal.: 58.8095   **91.** Cal.: 72.3053

            Est.: 10   Est.: 1000   Est.: 1.5   Est.: 50   Est.: 100

93. a. Use division to find the cost.   **b.** Use multiplication to find the cost.   **95.** The trucker must drive 35 miles.   **97.** 6.23 yards are gained per carry.   **99.** Three complete shelves can be cut from a 12-foot board.   **101.** The monthly payment was $213.46.   **103.** The car travels 35.5 miles on 1 gallon of gasoline.   **105.** You will use 0.405 barrel of oil.   **107.** 2.57 million more women than men were attending institutions of higher learning.   **109.** The Army's advertising budget was 4.2 times greater than the Navy's advertising budget.   **111.** The population of this segment is expected to be 2.1 times greater in 2030 than in 2000.   **115.** $\times$ **117.** $\times$ **119.** $\div$ **121.** 2.53   **123.** 0.27

SECTION 3.6

1. Thousandths   **3.** Tenths   **5.** Hundredths   **7.** Greater than 1   **9.** Less than 1   **11.** $0.\overline{6}$ **13.** 0.875   **15.** $0.7\overline{2}$ **17.** $0.\overline{60}$

19. $0.47\overline{2}$ **21.** $0.\overline{729}$ **23.** $0.\overline{925}$ **25.** $0.4\overline{729}$ **27.** 0.85   **29.** $0.\overline{857142}$ **31.** 0.34375   **33.** 3.85   **35.** $4.2\overline{36}$ **37.** $\dfrac{2}{5}$

39. $\dfrac{12}{25}$ **41.** $\dfrac{97}{200}$ **43.** $3\dfrac{3}{4}$ **45.** $3\dfrac{7}{40}$ **47.** $11\dfrac{1}{250}$ **49.** $9\dfrac{279}{1000}$ **51.** $\dfrac{28}{125}$ **53.** $\dfrac{13}{250}$ **55.** $\dfrac{3}{20,000}$ **57.** 0.31   **59.** 0.163

61. 0.089   **63.** 0.7059   **65.** $\dfrac{7}{8} < 0.9$ **67.** $0.13 > \dfrac{5}{40}$ **69.** $\dfrac{12}{55} < 0.22$ **71.** $0.55 < \dfrac{5}{9}$ **73.** $\dfrac{17}{18} > 0.94$ **75.** $\dfrac{22}{7} > 3.14$

77. 0.5, 0.75, 0.625, 0.5625, 0.3, 0.35, 0.59375, 0.575, 0.28, 0.38   **79.** 2 and 5   **81.** Answers will vary. For example, $\dfrac{5}{6} = 0.8\overline{3}$, $\dfrac{4}{11} = 0.\overline{36}$, $\dfrac{9}{13} = 0.\overline{692307}$. No.

CHAPTER 3 REVIEW EXERCISES

1. 54.5 [3.5A]   **2.** 833.958 [3.2A]   **3.** $0.055 < 0.1$ [3.1C]   **4.** Twenty-two and ninety-two ten-thousandths [3.1A]

5. 0.05678 [3.1B]   **6.** 0.2125 [3.6A]   **7.** $\dfrac{3}{8}$ [3.6B]   **8.** 36.714 [3.2A]   **9.** 34.025 [3.1A]   **10.** $\dfrac{5}{8} > 0.62$ [3.6C]

11. $0.3\overline{18}$ [3.6A]   **12.** $\dfrac{33}{50}$ [3.6B]   **13.** 22.8635 [3.3A]   **14.** 7.94 [3.1B]   **15.** 8.932 [3.4A]   **16.** Three hundred forty-two and thirty-seven hundredths [3.1A]   **17.** 3.06753 [3.1A]   **18.** 25.7446 [3.4A]   **19.** 6.594 [3.5A]   **20.** 4.8785 [3.3A]

21. The airline saved 49.1 million gallons of fuel. The average cost per gallon of fuel is $2.67. [3.2B; 3.5B]   **22.** The new balance in your account is $661.51. [3.3B]   **23.** The number who drove is 6.4 times greater than the number who flew. [3.5B]   **24.** During a 5-day school week, 9.5 million gallons of milk are served. [3.4B]

CHAPTER 3 TEST

1. $0.0068 > 0.000963$ [3.1C; Example 7]   **2.** 4.087   [3.3A; Example 1]   **3.** Forty-five and three hundred two ten-thousandths [3.1A; Example 2]   **4.** 209.07086   [3.1A; Example 3]   **5.** $\frac{33}{40}$ [3.6B; HOW TO 3]   **6.** $\frac{13}{8} > 0.72$ [3.6C; You Try It 5]
7. 1.538   [3.5A; Example 3]   **8.** 27.76626   [3.3A; Example 2]   **9.** 25.8808   [3.3A; Example 3]   **10.** 0.325   [3.6A; HOW TO 1]
11. 7.095   [3.1B; Example 4]   **12.** 23.2 [3.5A; Example 1]   **13.** 458.581   [3.2A; Example 2]   **14.** $0.68\overline{1}$ [3.6A; Example 1]
15. 0.00548   [3.4A; You Try It 3]   **16.** 255.957   [3.2A; You Try It 1]   **17.** 17,149.6   [3.4A; You Try It 5]   **18.** 0.0015923
[3.5A; Example 5]   **19.** The cost is $21.60.   [3.4B; Example 7]   **20.** The monthly payment is $395.40.   [3.5B; Example 7]
21. Your total income is $3087.14.   [3.2B; You Try It 4]   **22.** The cost of the call is $4.63.   [3.4B; Example 8]

CUMULATIVE REVIEW EXERCISES

1. 235 r17   [1.5C]   **2.** 128   [1.6A]   **3.** 3   [1.6B]   **4.** 72   [2.1A]   **5.** $4\frac{2}{5}$ [2.2B]   **6.** $\frac{37}{8}$ [2.2B]   **7.** $\frac{25}{60}$ [2.3A]
8. $1\frac{17}{48}$ [2.4B]   **9.** $8\frac{35}{36}$ [2.4C]   **10.** $5\frac{23}{36}$ [2.5C]   **11.** $\frac{1}{12}$ [2.6A]   **12.** $9\frac{1}{8}$ [2.6B]   **13.** $1\frac{2}{9}$ [2.7A]   **14.** $\frac{19}{20}$ [2.7B]
15. $\frac{3}{16}$ [2.8B]   **16.** $2\frac{5}{18}$ [2.8B]   **17.** Sixty-five and three hundred nine ten-thousandths   [3.1A]   **18.** 504.6991   [3.2A]
19. 21.0764   [3.3A]   **20.** 55.26066   [3.4A]   **21.** 2.154   [3.5A]   **22.** $0.7\overline{3}$ [3.6A]   **23.** $\frac{17}{40}$ [3.6B]   **24.** $\frac{8}{9} < 0.98$ [3.6C]
25. Sweden mandates 14 more vacation days than Germany.   [1.3C]   **26.** The patient must lose $7\frac{3}{4}$ pounds during the third month to achieve
the goal.   [2.5D]   **27.** Your checking account balance is $617.38.   [3.3B]   **28.** The resulting thickness is 1.395 inches.   [3.3B]
29. You paid $6008.80 in income tax last year.   [3.4B]   **30.** The amount of each payment is $46.37.   [3.5B]

Answers to Chapter 4 Selected Exercises

PREP TEST

1. $\frac{4}{5}$ [2.3B]   **2.** $\frac{1}{2}$ [2.3B]   **3.** 24.8   [3.6A]   **4.** 4×33 [1.4A]   **5.** 4   [1.5A]

SECTION 4.1

1. 3 to 8   **3.** $\frac{1}{5}$ 1:5 1 to 5   **5.** $\frac{2}{1}$ 2:1 2 to 1   **7.** $\frac{3}{8}$ 3:8 3 to 8   **9.** $\frac{1}{1}$ 1:1 1 to 1   **11.** $\frac{7}{10}$ 7:10 7 to 10   **13.** $\frac{1}{2}$ 1:2 1 to 2
15. $\frac{2}{1}$ 2:1 2 to 1   **17.** $\frac{5}{2}$ 5:2 5 to 2   **19.** $\frac{5}{7}$ 5:7 5 to 7   **21.** days   **23.** The ratio is $\frac{3}{8}$.   **25.** The ratio is $\frac{1}{3}$.
27. The ratio is $\frac{13}{22,000}$.   **29.** The ratio is $\frac{1}{5}$.   **31.** The ratio is $\frac{3}{250}$.   **35.** Answers will vary.

SECTION 4.2

3. $\frac{3 \text{ pounds}}{4 \text{ people}}$ **5.** $\frac{\$20}{3 \text{ boards}}$ **7.** $\frac{20 \text{ miles}}{1 \text{ gallon}}$ **9.** $\frac{8 \text{ gallons}}{1 \text{ hour}}$ **11.** Divide the number of gallons per minute by 60.   **13.** 1   **15.** 2.5 feet/second
17. $975/week   **19.** 110 trees/acre   **21.** $18.84/hour   **23.** 35.6 miles/gallon   **25.** The car got 42.6 miles/gallon.
27. The rate is 7.4 miles per dollar.   **29.** The average number of rides per day was 1220.   **31.** The cost per viewer is $.03.
33. The rate is 12 gallons/minute.   **35.** The cost is 2,715,580 yen.   **37. a.** Australia has the least population density.
b. There are 851 more people per square mile in India than in the United States.   **41.** The car gets about 3.6 gallons per 100 miles.
43. 0.004 ppm

CHECK YOUR PROGRESS: CHAPTER 4

1. $\frac{1}{4}$, 1:4   [4.1A]   **2.** $\frac{2}{3}$, 2:3   [4.1A]   **3.** $\frac{5}{12}$, 5:12   [4.1A]   **4.** $24/hour   [4.2B]   **5.** 10.4 yards/second   [4.2B]
6. 29.2 miles/gallon   [4.2B]   **7.** The recommended amount of fertilizer is 0.025 gallon/square foot.   [4.2C]
8. Whole milk has 18.75 calories/ounce.   [4.2C]   **9.** The cost per rose is $4.25.   [4.2C]   **10.** The cost per page is $.0425.   [4.2C]

SECTION 4.3

1. $n = 45 \div 15$ **3.** $72 \div 9 = n$ **5.** True   **7.** Not true   **9.** Not true   **11.** True   **13.** True   **15.** True   **17.** True
19. Not true   **21.** True   **23.** Yes   **25.** Yes   **27.** 3   **29.** 105   **31.** 2   **33.** 60   **35.** 2.22   **37.** 6.67   **39.** 21.33
41. 16.25   **43.** 2.44   **45.** 47.89   **47.** A 0.5-ounce serving contains 50 calories.   **49.** The car can travel 329 miles.   **51.** 12.5 gallons
of water are required.   **53.** The distance is 16 miles.   **55.** 1.25 ounces are required.   **57.** 160,000 people would vote.
59. The monthly payment is $176.75.   **61.** 750 defective circuit boards are expected in a run of 25,000.   **63.** A bowling ball
would weigh about 2.67 pounds on the moon.   **65.** The dividend would be $1071.

HAPTER 4 REVIEW EXERCISES

True [4.3A]   **2.** $\frac{2}{5}$ 2:5 2 to 5 [4.1A]   **3.** 62.5 miles/hour [4.2B]   **4.** True [4.3A]   **5.** 68 [4.3B]

$12.50/hour [4.2B]   **7.** $1.75/pound [4.2B]   **8.** $\frac{2}{7}$ 2:7 2 to 7 [4.1A]   **9.** 36 [4.3B]   **10.** 19.44 [4.3B]

. $\frac{2}{5}$ 2:5 2 to 5 [4.1A]   **12.** Not true [4.3A]   **13.** $\frac{\$35}{4\text{ hours}}$ [4.2A]   **14.** 27.2 miles/gallon [4.2B]

. $\frac{1}{1}$ 1:1 1 to 1 [4.1A]   **16.** True [4.3A]   **17.** 65.45 [4.3B]   **18.** $\frac{100\text{ miles}}{3\text{ hours}}$ [4.2A]   **19.** The ratio is $\frac{2}{5}$. [4.1B]

. The property tax is $6400. [4.3C]   **21.** The ratio is $\frac{3}{8}$. [4.1B]   **22.** The cost per phone is $37.50. [4.2C]

. 1344 blocks would be needed. [4.3C]   **24.** The ratio is $\frac{5}{2}$. [4.1B]   **25.** The turkey costs $.93/pound. [4.2C]

. The average was 56.8 miles/hour. [4.2C]   **27.** The cost is $493.50. [4.3C]   **28.** The cost is $44.75/share. [4.2C]

. 22.5 pounds of fertilizer will be used. [4.3C]   **30.** The ratio is $\frac{1}{2}$. [4.1B]

HAPTER 4 TEST

$3836.40/month [4.2B; Example 2]   **2.** $\frac{1}{6}$ 1:6 1 to 6 [4.1A; You Try It 1]   **3.** $\frac{9\text{ supports}}{4\text{ feet}}$ [4.2A; Example 1]

Not true [4.3A; Example 2]   **5.** $\frac{3}{1}$ 3:1 3 to 1 [4.1A; Example 2]   **6.** 144 [4.3B; HOW TO 3]

30.5 miles/gallon [4.2B; Apply the Concept]   **8.** $\frac{1}{3}$ 1:3 1 to 3 [4.1A; You Try It 1]   **9.** True [4.3A; Example 1]

. 40.5 [4.3B; Example 3]   **11.** $\frac{3\text{ feet}}{2\text{ boards}}$ [4.2A; Example 1]   **12.** $\frac{3}{5}$ 3:5 3 to 5 [4.1A; You Try It 1]

. The dividend is $625. [4.3C; Example 9]   **14.** The ratio is $\frac{1}{12}$. [4.1B; Example 3]   **15.** The plane's speed is

8 miles/hour. [4.2C; Example 3]   **16.** The college student's body contains 132 pounds of water. [4.3C; Example 8]

. The cost of the lumber is $1.73/foot. [4.2C; You Try It 3]   **18.** The amount of medication required is 0.875 ounce.

.3C; Example 8]   **19.** The ratio is $\frac{4}{5}$. [4.1B; Example 4]   **20.** 36 defective hard drives are expected to be found in the

oduction of 1200 hard drives. [4.3C; You Try It 9]

UMULATIVE REVIEW EXERCISES

9158 [1.3B]   **2.** $2^4 \cdot 3^3$ [1.6A]   **3.** 3 [1.6B]   **4.** $2 \cdot 2 \cdot 2 \cdot 2 \cdot 2 \cdot 5$ [1.7B]   **5.** 36 [2.1A]   **6.** 14 [2.1B]

$\frac{5}{8}$ [2.3B]   **8.** $8\frac{3}{10}$ [2.4C]   **9.** $5\frac{11}{18}$ [2.5C]   **10.** $2\frac{5}{6}$ [2.6B]   **11.** $4\frac{2}{3}$ [2.7B]   **12.** $\frac{23}{30}$ [2.8B]

. Four and seven hundred nine ten-thousandths [3.1A]   **14.** 2.10 [3.1B]   **15.** 1.990 [3.5A]   **16.** $\frac{3}{50}$ [3.6B]

. $\frac{1}{8}$ [4.1A]   **18.** $\frac{29¢}{2\text{ pencils}}$ [4.2A]   **19.** 33.4 miles/gallon [4.2B]   **20.** 4.25 [4.3B]   **21.** The car's speed is

.2 miles/hour. [4.2C]   **22.** 36 [4.3B]   **23.** Your new balance is $744. [1.3C]   **24.** The monthly payment is $570. [1.5D]

. 105 pages remain to be read. [2.6C]   **26.** The cost per acre was $36,000. [2.7C]   **27.** The change was $35.24. [3.3B]

. Your monthly salary is $3468.25. [3.5B]   **29.** 25 inches will erode in 50 months. [4.3C]   **30.** 1.6 ounces are required. [4.3C]

Answers to Chapter 5 Selected Exercises

REP TEST

$\frac{19}{100}$ [2.6B]   **2.** 0.23 [3.4A]   **3.** 47 [3.4A]   **4.** 2850 [3.4A]   **5.** 4000 [3.5A]   **6.** 32 [2.7B]   **7.** 62.5 [3.6A]

$66\frac{2}{3}$ [2.2B]   **9.** 1.75 [3.5A]

ECTION 5.1

100   **3.** left   **5.** 0.72, $\frac{18}{25}$ **7.** 0.23, $\frac{23}{100}$ **9.** 0.36, $\frac{9}{25}$ **11.** 0.59, $\frac{59}{100}$ **13.** 0.41, $\frac{41}{100}$ **15.** 0.254, $\frac{127}{500}$ **17.** 0.579, $\frac{579}{1000}$

. 0.062, $\frac{31}{500}$ **21.** 0.064, $\frac{8}{125}$ **23.** 0.0025, $\frac{1}{400}$ **25.** 0.0055, $\frac{11}{2000}$ **27.** $\frac{2}{3}$ **29.** $\frac{5}{6}$ **31.** $\frac{1}{9}$ **33.** $\frac{5}{11}$ **35.** $\frac{3}{70}$ **37.** $\frac{1}{15}$

. Greater than   **41.** 73%   **43.** 1%   **45.** 294%   **47.** 0.6%   **49.** 310.6%   **51.** 70%   **53.** 85%   **55.** 40%   **57.** 12.5%

. 150%   **61.** 225%   **63.** 87.5%   **65.** 48%   **67.** $44\frac{4}{9}$%   **69.** $166\frac{2}{3}$%   **71.** $38\frac{8}{9}$%   **73.** Less than   **75.** 6% of those surveyed named

omething other than corn on the cob, cole slaw, corn bread, or fries.   **77.** $\frac{53}{1000}$, 0.053   **79.** $\frac{3}{20}$, 0.15   **81.** 0.5%   **83.** 62.5%

ECTION 5.2

Percent × base = amount   **3.** Greater than   **5.** 8   **7.** 10.8   **9.** 0.075   **11.** 80   **13.** 51.895   **15.** 7.5   **17.** 13   **19.** 3.75

. 20   **23.** 5% of 95   **25.** 79% of 16   **27.** Less than   **29.** The number of people in the United States aged 18 to 24 without life insurance is

ss than 50 million.   **31.** There will be 138.49 million more passengers.   **33.** The piece contains 29.25 grams of gold, 8.75 grams of silver, and

2 grams of copper.   **35.** 99 million returns were filed electronically.   **37.** The total cost is $30,952.16. The monthly payment is $644.84.

. The withholding tax is $0.   **41.** The withholding tax is $577.72.   **43.** No

CHECK YOUR PROGRESS: CHAPTER 5

1. 0.85, $\frac{17}{20}$ [5.1A]   **2.** 0.04, $\frac{1}{25}$ [5.1A]   **3.** 0.0025, $\frac{1}{400}$ [5.1A]   **4.** 1.80, $1\frac{4}{5}$ [5.1A]   **5.** 15% [5.1B]   **6.** 2.7% [5.1B]
7. 145% [5.1B]   **8.** 0.125% [5.1B]   **9.** 60% [5.1B]   **10.** 42.5% [5.1B]   **11.** $41\frac{2}{3}$% [5.1B]   **12.** 170% [5.1B]
13. 29.4 [5.2A]   **14.** 13.75 [5.2A]   **15.** 39.6 [5.2A]   **16.** 0.156 [5.2A]   **17.** The weekly pay increase was $72.25. [5.2B]

SECTION 5.3

1. Greater than   **3.** Greater than   **5.** 32%   **7.** $16\frac{2}{3}$%   **9.** 200%   **11.** 37.5%   **13.** 18%   **15.** 0.25%   **17.** 20%   **19.** 400%
21. 2.5%   **23.** 37.5%   **25.** 0.25%   **27.** 70% of couples disagree about financial matters.   **29.** Approximately 25.4% of the vegetables
were wasted.   **31.** 27.1% of Americans with diabetes have not been diagnosed.   **33.** 98.5% of the slabs did meet safety requirements.
35. 26.7% of the total is spent on veterinary care.   **39. a.** $5 per share   **b.** 20%   **c.** 25%   **d.** No

SECTION 5.4

1. Greater than   **3.** Less than   **5.** 75   **7.** 50   **9.** 100   **11.** 85   **13.** 1200   **15.** 19.2   **17.** 7.5   **19.** 32   **21.** 200   **23.** 9
25. 504   **27.** 15.8 million travelers allowed their children to miss school to go on a trip.   **29.** 24,350 runners started the Boston Marathon in
2011.   **31.** A large cargo ship uses 300 tons of fuel per day.   **33. a.** 3000 boards were tested.   **b.** 2976 of the boards tested were not defective
35. a. 80%   **b.** 70%   **c.** 75%   **d.** 74%; no   **e.** When both tests have the same number of points

SECTION 5.5

1. $\frac{\text{percent}}{100} = \frac{\text{amount}}{\text{base}}$ **3.** percent   **5.** 65   **7.** 25%   **9.** 75   **11.** 12.5%   **13.** 400   **15.** 19.5   **17.** 14.8%   **19.** 62.62   **21.** 15
23. a. ii and iii   **b.** i and iv   **25.** The drug will be effective for 4.8 hours.   **27. a.** $175 million is generated annually from sales of Thin Mint
b. $63 million is generated annually from sales of Trefoil shortbread cookies.   **29.** 57.7% of baby boomers have attended college.
31. The U.S. total turkey production was 7 billion pounds.   **33.** The 110th Senate had the larger percentage of Republicans.   **35.** The rose-gold
ring contains 4.5 grams of gold, 1.2 grams of copper, and 0.3 gram of silver.

CHAPTER 5 REVIEW EXERCISES

1. 60 [5.2A]   **2.** 20% [5.3A]   **3.** 175% [5.1B]   **4.** 75 [5.4A]   **5.** $\frac{3}{25}$ [5.1A]   **6.** 19.36 [5.2A]   **7.** 150% [5.3A]
8. 504 [5.4A]   **9.** 0.42 [5.1A]   **10.** 5.4 [5.2A]   **11.** 157.5 [5.4A]   **12.** 0.076 [5.1A]   **13.** 77.5 [5.2A]   **14.** $\frac{1}{6}$ [5.1A]
15. 160% [5.5A]   **16.** 75 [5.5A]   **17.** 38% [5.1B]   **18.** 10.9 [5.4A]   **19.** 7.3% [5.3A]   **20.** 613.3% [5.3A]
21. The student answered 85% of the questions correctly. [5.5B]   **22.** The company spent $4500 on newspaper advertising. [5.2B]
23. 34.3% of energy costs is spent on electricity. [5.3B]   **24.** The total cost of the camcorder was $1041.25. [5.2B]
25. Approximately 78.6% of the women wore sunscreen often. [5.3B]   **26.** The world's population in 2000 was approximately 6,100,000,000
people. [5.4B]   **27.** The cost of the computer system 4 years ago was $3000. [5.5B]   **28.** The total cranberry crop that year was 572 million
pounds. [5.3B/5.5B]

CHAPTER 5 TEST

1. 0.973 [5.1A; Example 1]   **2.** $\frac{5}{6}$ [5.1A; Example 2]   **3.** 30% [5.1B; Example 3]   **4.** 163% [5.1B; Example 3]
5. 150% [5.1B; HOW TO 2]   **6.** 92.5% [5.1B; Example 4]   **7.** 50.05 [5.2A; Example 1]   **8.** 61.36 [5.2A; Example 1]
9. $61\frac{1}{9}$% [5.1B; HOW TO 3]   **10.** $\frac{3}{400}$ [5.1A; Example 1C]   **11.** 80 [5.4A; Example 2]   **12.** 28.3 [5.4A; Example 2]
13. 143.0 [5.5A; Example 1]   **14.** 1000% [5.5A; Example 1]   **15.** The amount spent for advertising is $45,000. [5.2B; Example 3]
16. 1170 pounds of vegetables were not spoiled. [5.2B; Example 4]   **17.** 14.7% of the daily recommended amount of potassium is
provided. [5.3B; Example 4]   **18.** 9.1% of the daily recommended number of calories is provided. [5.3B; Example 4]   **19.** The number of
temporary employees is 16% of the number of permanent employees. [5.3B; Example 4]   **20.** The student answered approximately 91.3% of
the questions correctly. [5.3B; Example 5]   **21.** 32,000 digital cameras were tested. [5.4B; Example 4]   **22.** The increase was 60% of the
original price. [5.3B; Example 5]   **23.** The dollar increase in the hourly wage is $1.74. [5.5B; Example 3]   **24.** The population now is 220%
of the population 10 years ago. [5.3B; Example 5/5.5B; Example 4]   **25.** The value of the car is $25,000. [5.5B; Example 3]

CUMULATIVE REVIEW EXERCISES

1. 4 [1.6B]   **2.** 240 [2.1A]   **3.** $10\frac{11}{24}$ [2.4C]   **4.** $12\frac{41}{48}$ [2.5C]   **5.** $12\frac{4}{7}$ [2.6B]   **6.** $\frac{7}{24}$ [2.7B]   **7.** $\frac{4}{9}$ [2.8B]   **8.** $\frac{13}{36}$ [2.8B]
9. 3.08 [3.1B]   **10.** 1.1196 [3.3A]   **11.** 34.2813 [3.5A]   **12.** 3.625 [3.6A]   **13.** $1\frac{3}{4}$ [3.6B]   **14.** $\frac{3}{8} < 0.87$ [3.6C]
15. 53.3 [4.3B]   **16.** $19.20/hour [4.2B]   **17.** $\frac{11}{60}$ [5.1A]   **18.** $72\frac{2}{9}$% [5.1B]   **19.** 19.56 [5.2A/5.5A]   **20.** $133\frac{1}{3}$% [5.3A/5.5A]
21. 9.92 [5.4A/5.5A]   **22.** 342.9% [5.3A/5.5A]   **23.** Sergio's take-home pay is $592. [2.6C]   **24.** The monthly payment is
$292.50. [3.5B]   **25.** 420 gallons were used during the month. [3.5B]   **26.** The real estate tax is $10,000. [4.3C]   **27.** 7346 hotels are
located along interstate highways. [5.2B/5.5B]   **28.** 45% of the people did not favor the candidate. [5.3B/5.5B]   **29.** The approximate
average number of hours spent watching TV in a week is 61.3 hours. [5.2B/5.5B]   **30.** 18% of the children tested had levels of lead that
exceeded federal standards. [5.3B/5.5B]

Answers to Chapter 6 Selected Exercises

PREP TEST

. 0.75   [3.5A]   **2.** 52.05   [3.4A]   **3.** 504.51   [3.3A]   **4.** 9750   [3.4A]   **5.** 45   [3.4A]   **6.** 1417.24   [3.2A]
. 3.33   [3.5A]   **8.** 0.605   [3.5A]   **9.** 0.379 < 0.397   [3.1C]

SECTION 6.1

. The unit cost is $.055 per ounce.   **5.** The unit cost is $.374 per ounce.   **7.** The unit cost is $.080 per tablet.
. The unit cost is $6.975 per clamp.   **11.** The unit cost is $.199 per ounce.   **13.** Divide the price of one pint by 2.
5. The Kraft mayonnaise is the more economical purchase.   **17.** The Cortexx shampoo is the more economical purchase.
9. The Ultra Mr. Clean is the more economical purchase.   **21.** The Bertolli olive oil is the more economical purchase.
3. The Wagner's vanilla extract is the more economical purchase.   **25.** Increase   **27.** The total cost is $73.50.
9. The total cost is $16.88.   **31.** The total cost is $3.89.   **33.** The total cost is $26.57.   **35.** Tea A is the more economical purchase.

SECTION 6.2

. ii   **5.** The percent increase is 19.0%.   **7.** The percent increase was 276.6%.   **9.** The percent increase is 600%.
1. The percent increase is 78.4%.   **13.** Yes   **15.** Use equation (3) and then equation (2).   **17.** The markup is $17.10.
9. The markup rate is 60%.   **21.** The selling price is $304.50.   **23.** The selling price is $74.   **25.** The percent decrease is 40%.
7. The percent decrease was 15.1%.   **29.** The car loses $8460 in value.   **31.** The new average monthly gasoline bill is $140.80.
3. The percent decrease was 19.6%.   **35.** Use equation (3) and then (2).   **37.** The discount rate is $33\frac{1}{3}$%.
9. The discount is $80.   **41.** The discount rate is 30%.   **43.** The sale price is $1.00 per pound.   **45.** The discount rate is 20%.
7. The age group with the greatest percent increase was 62 years and older.

SECTION 6.3

. Principal $\times$ annual interest rate $\times$ time (in years) = interest   **3. a.** $10,000   **b.** $850   **c.** 4.25%   **d.** 2 years
. The simple interest owed is $960.   **7.** The simple interest due is $3375.   **9.** The simple interest due is $1320.
1. The simple interest due is $84.76.   **13.** The maturity value is $5120.   **15.** The total amount due on the loan is $12,875.
7. The maturity value is $14,543.70.   **19.** The monthly payment is $6187.50.   **21. a.** The interest charged is $1080.
. The monthly payment is $545.   **23.** The monthly payment is $3039.02.   **25. a.** Student A's principal is equal to student B's principal.
. Student A's maturity value is greater than student B's maturity value.   **c.** Student A's monthly payment is less than student B's monthly
payment.   **27.** The finance charge is $6.85.   **29.** The finance charge is $11.94.   **31.** The difference between the finance charges is $3.44.
3. The finance charges for the first and second months are the same. No, you will not be able to pay off the balance.
5. The value of the investment after 20 years is $7143.60.   **37.** The value of the investment after 5 years is $28,352.60.
9. a. The value of the investment after 10 years will be $6040.86.   **b.** The amount of interest earned will be $3040.86.
1. The amount of interest earned is $505.94.

SECTION 6.4

. Mortgage   **3.** The mortgage is $172,450.   **5.** The down payment is $212,500.   **7.** The loan origination fee is $3750.
. The mortgage is $315,000.   **11.** The mortgage is $189,000.   **13.** iii   **15.** The monthly mortgage payment is $644.79.
7. No, the lawyer cannot afford the monthly mortgage payment.   **19. a.** The mortgage is $250,000.   **b.** The monthly mortgage payment
s $1304.13.   **21.** The monthly mortgage payment is $1273.27.   **23.** The amount that goes to interest is $3000. The amount that goes to the
principal is $865.10.   **25.** The couple can save $63,408 in interest.

CHECK YOUR PROGRESS: CHAPTER 6

. The unit cost is $3.83.   [6.1A]   **2.** The more economical purchase is 16 ounces for $12.99.   [6.1B]   **3.** The cost is $44.55.   [6.1C]
. The percent increase was 14.3%.   [6.2A]   **5.** The selling price of the tire is $315.   [6.2B]   **6.** The percent decrease was 9.2%.   [6.2C]
7. The sale price is $71.96.   [6.2D]   **8.** The borrower will pay $180 in interest.   [6.3A]   **9.** The finance charge is $6.57.   [6.3B]
0. The value after 10 years is $4225.99.   [6.3C]   **11.** The mortgage is $188,800.   [6.4A]   **12.** The monthly mortgage payment
s $1429.89.   [6.4B]

SECTION 6.5

. No, Amanda does not have enough money for the down payment.   **5.** The sales tax was $1192.50.   **7.** The license fee is $650.
. a. The sales tax is $1120.   **b.** The total cost of the sales tax and the license fee is $1395.   **11.** The amount financed is $12,150.
3. The amount financed is $36,000.   **15.** The expression represents the total cost of buying the car.   **17.** Use multiplication to find the cost.
9. The monthly car payment is $553.73.   **21.** The cost per mile is $.51.   **23.** The monthly payment is $674.89.
5. Your cost per mile for gasoline was $.18.   **27.** The car's value after 5 years will be $15,973.85. The cost per mile for depreciation is $.187.

SECTION 6.6

3. Lewis earns $460.   **5.** The real estate agent's commission is $3930.   **7.** The stockbroker's commission is $84.
9. Keisha's monthly salary is $3244.   **11.** Carlos earned a commission of $540.   **13.** Steven receives $920 for installing the carpet.
15. The chemist's hourly wage is $125.   **17. a.** Gil's hourly wage for working overtime is $21.56.   **b.** Gil earns $344.96 for working 16 hours
of overtime.   **19. a.** The increase in hourly pay is $1.90.   **b.** The clerk's hourly wage for working the night shift is $14.58.
21. The salesperson's earnings were $748.90.   **23.** The average weekly earnings in June were $789.24.   **25.** The percent increase was 0.3%.

SECTION 6.7

3. Your new checking account balance is $486.32.   **5.** The nutritionist's current balance is $825.27.   **7.** The current checking account
balance is $3000.82.   **9.** Yes, there is enough money in the carpenter's account to purchase the refrigerator.   **11.** Yes, there is enough money
in the account to make the two purchases.   **13.** The account's ending balance might be less than its starting balance on that day.
15. The bank statement and the checkbook balance.   **17.** The bank statement and the checkbook balance.

CHAPTER 6 REVIEW EXERCISES

1. The unit cost is $.195 per ounce or 19.5¢ per ounce.   [6.1A]   **2.** The cost is $.279 or 27.9¢ per mile.   [6.5B]
3. The percent increase is 30.4%.   [6.2A]   **4.** The markup is $72.   [6.2B]   **5.** The simple interest due is $3000.   [6.3A]
6. The value of the investment after 10 years is $45,550.75.   [6.3C]   **7.** The percent increase is 15%.   [6.2A]   **8.** The amount of the payment
that goes to interest is $1166.67. The amount that goes to the principal is $954.26.   [6.4B]   **9.** The monthly payment is $518.02.   [6.5B]
10. The value of the investment will be $53,593.   [6.3C]   **11.** The down payment is $29,250.   [6.4A]   **12.** The total cost of the sales tax
and license fee is $2096.25.   [6.5A]   **13.** The selling price is $2079.   [6.2B]   **14.** The interest paid is $157.33.   [6.5B]
15. The commission was $3240.   [6.6A]   **16.** The sale price is $141.   [6.2D]   **17.** The current checkbook balance is $943.68.   [6.7A]
18. The maturity value is $31,200.   [6.3A]   **19.** The origination fee is $1875.   [6.4A]   **20.** The more economical purchase is 33 ounces
for $6.99.   [6.1B]   **21.** The monthly mortgage payment is $2131.62.   [6.4B]   **22.** The total income was $655.20.   [6.6A]
23. The donut shop's checkbook balance is $8866.58.   [6.7A]   **24.** The monthly payment is $14,093.75.   [6.3A]
25. The finance charge is $7.20.   [6.3B]

CHAPTER 6 TEST

1. The cost per foot is $6.92.   [6.1A; Example 1]   **2.** The more economical purchase is 3 pounds for $7.49.   [6.1B; Example 2]
3. The total cost is $14.53.   [6.1C; Example 3]   **4.** The percent increase in the cost of the exercise bicycle is 20%.   [6.2A; Example 1]
5. The selling price of the Blu-ray disc player is $441.   [6.2B; Example 4]   **6.** The percent increase is 12.4%.   [6.2A; Example 1]
7. The percent decrease is 20%.   [6.2C; HOW TO 3]   **8.** The sale price of the corner hutch is $209.30.   [6.2D; Example 8]
9. The discount rate is 40%.   [6.2D; Example 7]   **10.** The simple interest due is $2000.   [6.3A; You Try It 1]   **11.** The maturity value
is $26,725.   [6.3A; Example 2]   **12.** The finance charge is $4.50.   [6.3B; Example 4]   **13.** The amount of interest earned in 10 years
was $24,420.60.   [6.3C; You Try It 5]   **14.** The loan origination fee is $3350.   [6.4A; Example 2]   **15.** The monthly mortgage payment
is $1713.44.   [6.4B; HOW TO 2]   **16.** The amount financed is $19,000.   [6.5A; Example 1]   **17.** The monthly payment is $686.22.
[6.5B; Example 5]   **18.** Shaney earnes $1596.   [6.6A; Example 1]   **19.** The current checkbook balance is $6612.25.   [6.7A; Example 1]
20. The bank statement and the checkbook balance.   [6.7B; Example 2]

CUMULATIVE REVIEW EXERCISES

1. 13   [1.6B]   **2.** $8\frac{13}{24}$ [2.4C]   **3.** $2\frac{37}{48}$ [2.5C]   **4.** 9   [2.6B]   **5.** 2   [2.7B]   **6.** 5   [2.8B]   **7.** 52.2   [3.5A]
8. $1.41\overline{6}$ [3.6A]   **9.** $51.25/hour   [4.2B]   **10.** 10.94   [4.3B]   **11.** 62.5%   [5.1B]   **12.** 27.3   [5.2A]   **13.** 0.182   [5.1A]
14. 42%   [5.3A]   **15.** 250   [5.4A]   **16.** 154.76   [5.4A/5.5A]   **17.** The total rainfall was $13\frac{11}{12}$ inches.   [2.4D]
18. The amount paid in taxes is $970.   [2.6C]   **19.** The ratio is $\frac{3}{5}$.   [4.1B]   **20.** 33.4 miles are driven per gallon.   [4.2C]
21. The unit cost is $1.10 per pound.   [4.2C]   **22.** The dividend is $280.   [4.3C]   **23.** The sale price is $720.   [6.2D]
24. The selling price of the grinding rail is $119.   [6.2B]   **25.** The percent increase in Sook Kim's salary is 8%.   [6.2A]
26. The simple interest due is $2700.   [6.3A]   **27.** The monthly car payment is $791.81.   [6.5B]   **28.** The family's new checking account
balance is $2243.77.   [6.7A]   **29.** The cost per mile is $.33.   [6.5B]   **30.** The monthly mortgage payment is $1232.26.   [6.4B]

Glossary

addend In addition, one of the numbers added. [1.2]

addition The process of finding the total of two numbers. [1.2]

Addition Property of Zero Zero added to a number does not change the number. [1.2]

approximation An estimated value obtained by rounding an exact value. [1.1]

Associative Property of Addition Numbers to be added can be grouped (with parentheses, for example) in any order; the sum will be the same. [1.2]

Associative Property of Multiplication Numbers to be multiplied can be grouped (with parentheses, for example) in any order; the product will be the same. [1.4]

average The sum of all the numbers divided by the number of those numbers. [1.5]

balancing a checkbook Determining whether the checking account balance is accurate. [6.7]

bank statement A document showing all the transactions in a bank account during the month. [6.7]

basic percent equation Percent times base equals amount. [5.2]

borrowing In subtraction, taking a unit from the next larger place value in the minuend and adding it to the number in the given place value in order to make that number larger than the number to be subtracted from it. [1.3]

carrying In addition, transferring a number to another column. [1.2]

check A printed form that, when filled out and signed, instructs a bank to pay a specified sum of money to the person named on it. [6.7]

checking account A bank account that enables you to withdraw money or make payments to other people, using checks. [6.7]

commission That part of the pay earned by a salesperson that is calculated as a percent of the salesperson's sales. [6.6]

common factor A number that is a factor of two or more numbers is a common factor of those numbers. [2.1]

common multiple A number that is a multiple of two or more numbers is a common multiple of those numbers. [2.1]

Commutative Property of Addition Two numbers can be added in either order; the sum will be the same. [1.2]

Commutative Property of Multiplication Two numbers can be multiplied in either order; the product will be the same. [1.4]

composite number A number that has whole-number factors besides 1 and itself. For instance, 18 is a composite number. [1.7]

compound interest Interest computed not only on the original principal but also on interest already earned. [6.3]

cost The price that a business pays for a product. [6.2]

cross product In a proportion, the product of the numerator on the left side of the proportion times the denominator on the right, and the product of the denominator on the left side of the proportion times the numerator on the right. [4.3]

decimal A number written in decimal notation. [3.1]

decimal notation Notation in which a number consists of a whole-number part, a decimal point, and a decimal part. [3.1]

decimal part In decimal notation, that part of the number that appears to the right of the decimal point. [3.1]

decimal point In decimal notation, the point that separates the whole-number part from the decimal part. [3.1]

denominator The part of a fraction that appears below the fraction bar. [2.2]

deposit slip A form for depositing money in a checking account. [6.7]

difference In subtraction, the result of subtracting two numbers. [1.3]

discount The difference between the regular price and the sale price. [6.2]

discount rate The percent of a product's regular price that is represented by the discount. [6.2]

dividend In division, the number into which the divisor is divided to yield the quotient. [1.5]

division The process of finding the quotient of two numbers. [1.5]

divisor In division, the number that is divided into the dividend to yield the quotient. [1.5]

down payment The percent of a home's purchase price that the bank, when issuing a mortgage, requires the borrower to provide. [6.4]

equivalent fractions Equal fractions with different denominators. [2.3]

expanded form The number 46,208 can be written in expanded form as $40,000 + 6000 + 200 + 0 + 8$. [1.1]

exponent In exponential notation, the raised number that indicates how many times the number to which it is attached is taken as a factor. [1.6]

exponential notation The expression of a number to some power, indicated by an exponent. [1.6]

factor In multiplication, one of the numbers in a product. [1.4]

factors of a number The whole-number factors of a number divide that number evenly. [1.7]

finance charges Interest charges on purchases made with a credit card. [6.3]

fixed-rate mortgage A mortgage in which the monthly payment remains the same for the life of the loan. [6.4]

fraction The notation used to represent the number of equal parts of a whole. [2.2]

fraction bar The bar that separates the numerator of a fraction from the denominator. [2.2]

graph of a whole number A heavy dot placed directly above that number on the number line. [1.1]

greater than A number that appears to the right of a given number on the number line is greater than the given number. [1.1]

greatest common factor (GCF) The largest common factor of two or more numbers. [2.1]

hourly wage Pay calculated on the basis of a certain amount for each hour worked. [6.6]

improper fraction A fraction greater than or equal to 1. [2.2]

interest Money paid for the privilege of using someone else's money. [6.3]

interest rate The percent used to determine the amount of interest. [6.3]

inverting a fraction Interchanging the numerator and denominator. [2.7]

least common denominator (LCD) The least common multiple of denominators. [2.4]

least common multiple (LCM) The smallest common multiple of two or more numbers. [2.1]

less than A number that appears to the left of a given number on the number line is less than the given number. [1.1]

license fees Fees charged for authorization to operate a vehicle. [6.5]

loan origination fee The fee a bank charges for processing mortgage papers. [6.4]

markup The difference between selling price and cost. [6.2]

markup rate The percent of a product's cost that is represented by the markup. [6.2]

maturity value of a loan The principal of a loan plus the interest owed on it. [6.3]

minuend In subtraction, the number from which another number (the subtrahend) is subtracted. [1.3]

mixed number A number greater than 1 that has a whole-number part and a fractional part. [2.2]

monthly mortgage payment One of 12 payments due each year to the lender of money to buy real estate. [6.4]

mortgage The amount borrowed to buy real estate. [6.4]

multiples of a number The products of that number and the numbers 1, 2, 3, ... [2.1]

multiplication The process of finding the product of two numbers. [1.4]

Multiplication Property of One The product of a number and 1 is the number. [1.4]

Multiplication Property of Zero The product of a number and zero is zero. [1.4]

number line A line on which a number can be graphed. [1.1]

numerator The part of a fraction that appears above the fraction bar. [2.2]

Order of Operations Agreement A set of rules that tells us in what order to perform the operations that occur in a numerical expression. [1.6]

percent Parts per hundred. [5.1]

percent decrease A decrease of a quantity, expressed as a percent of its original value. [6.2]

percent increase An increase of a quantity, expressed as a percent of its original value. [6.2]

period In a number written in standard form, each group of digits separated from other digits by a comma or commas. [1.1]

place value The position of each digit in a number written in standard form determines that digit's place value. [1.1]

place-value chart A chart that indicates the place value of every digit in a number. [1.1]

points A term banks use to mean percent of a mortgage; used to express the loan origination fee. [6.4]

prime factorization The expression of a number as the product of its prime factors. [1.7]

prime number A number whose only whole-number factors are 1 and itself. For instance, 13 is a prime number. [1.7]

principal The amount of money originally deposited or borrowed. [6.3]

product In multiplication, the result of multiplying two numbers. [1.4]

proper fraction A fraction less than 1. [2.2]

property tax A tax based on the value of real estate. [6.4]

proportion An expression of the equality of two ratios or rates. [4.3]

quotient In division, the result of dividing the divisor into the dividend. [1.5]

rate A comparison of two quantities that have different units. [4.2]

ratio A comparison of two quantities that have the same units. [4.1]

reciprocal of a fraction The fraction with the numerator and denominator interchanged. [2.7]

remainder In division, the quantity left over when it is not possible to separate objects or numbers into a whole number of equal groups. [1.5]

repeating decimal A decimal in which a block of one or more digits repeats forever. [3.6]

rounding Giving an approximate value of an exact number. [1.1]

salary Pay based on a weekly, biweekly, monthly, or annual time schedule. [6.6]

sale price The reduced price. [6.2]

sales tax A tax levied by a state or municipality on purchases. [6.5]

selling price The price for which a business sells a product to a customer. [6.2]

service charge An amount of money charged by a bank for handling a transaction. [6.7]

simple interest Interest computed on the original principal. [6.3]

simplest form of a fraction A fraction is in simplest form when there are no common factors in the numerator and denominator. [2.3]

simplest form of a rate A rate is in simplest form when the numbers that make up the rate have no common factor. [4.2]

simplest form of a ratio A ratio is in simplest form when the two numbers do not have a common factor. [4.1]

solve a proportion Find a solution of a proportion. [4.3]

standard form A whole number is in standard form when it is written using the digits 0, 1, 2, . . . , 9. An example is 46,208. [1.1]

subtraction The process of finding the difference between two numbers. [1.3]

subtrahend In subtraction, the number that is subtracted from another number (the minuend). [1.3]

sum In addition, the total of the numbers added. [1.2]

terminating decimal A decimal that has a finite number of digits after the decimal point, which means that it comes to an end and does not go on forever. [3.6]

total cost The unit cost multiplied by the number of units purchased. [6.1]

true proportion A proportion in which the fractions are equal. [4.3]

unit cost The cost of one item. [6.1]

unit rate A rate in which the number in the denominator is 1. [4.2]

whole numbers The whole numbers are 0, 1, 2, 3, ... [1.1]

whole-number part In decimal notation, that part of the number that appears to the left of the decimal point. [3.1]

Index

Contents

Name

Score

Graph the number on the number line.

1. 2

2. 6

3. 7

4. 1

1. _____

2. _____

3. _____

4. _____

Place the correct symbol, < or >, between the two numbers.

5. 54   47

6. 29   11

7. 96   97

5. _____

6. _____

7. _____

8. 9   13

9. 391   250

10. 1010   1110

8. _____

9. _____

10. _____

11. 1   64

12. 105   0

13. 666   777

11. _____

12. _____

13. _____

14. 32,000   3200

15. 5910   5901

16. 63,528   64,249

14. _____

15. _____

16. _____

1

Name   Score

Write the number in words.

1. 862   2. 308   3. 654   1. _____

                                                              2. _____

                                                              3. _____

4. 5125   5. 9040   6. 36,844   4. _____

                                                              _____

                                                              5. _____

                                                              _____

                                                              6. _____

                                                              _____

7. 380,751   8. 800,001   9. 7,640,723   7. _____

                                                              _____

                                                              8. _____

                                                              _____

                                                              9. _____

                                                              _____

Write the number in standard form.

10. Thirty-three   11. Two hundred sixty-four   10. _____

                                                                       11. _____

12. Nine thousand five hundred   13. Fifty-six thousand three hundred   12. _____
     twenty-seven   twenty
                                                                       13. _____

14. Four hundred sixty thousand 15. Four million twelve thousand   14. _____
     three hundred three   nine hundred eighty-six
                                                                       15. _____

16. One million five   17. Eight million one thousand fifty 16. _____

                                                                       17. _____

Name

Score

Write the number in expanded form.

1. 256

2. 4703

3. 9233

4. 23,040

5. 50,916

6. 75,049

7. 99,002

8. 234,782

9. 500,400

10. 787,000

11. 806,008

12. 920,010

13. 4,271,020

14. 6,000,213

1. _____

2. _____

3. _____

4. _____

5. _____

6. _____

7. _____

8. _____

9. _____

10. _____

11. _____

12. _____

13. _____

14. _____

Name

Score

Round the number to the given place value.

1. 747   Tens

2. 711   Tens

1. _____

2. _____

3. 361   Hundreds

4. 589   Hundreds

3. _____

4. _____

5. 1050   Hundreds

6. 7149   Hundreds

5. _____

6. _____

7. 4461   Thousands

8. 9620   Thousands

7. _____

8. _____

9. 74,510   Thousands

10. 69,372   Thousands

9. _____

10. _____

11. 250,650   Ten-thousands

12. 841,512   Ten-thousands

11. _____

12. _____

13. 3,467,000   Millions

14. 7,600,475   Millions

13. _____

14. _____

Name   Score

Add.

1.
$$\begin{array}{r} 391 \\ + 475 \end{array}$$

2.
$$\begin{array}{r} 568 \\ + 284 \end{array}$$

3.
$$\begin{array}{r} 821 \\ + 1774 \end{array}$$

4.
$$\begin{array}{r} 8515 \\ 5307 \\ + 4518 \end{array}$$

5.
$$\begin{array}{r} 7810 \\ 9537 \\ + 3284 \end{array}$$

6.
$$\begin{array}{r} 9478 \\ 3925 \\ + 6227 \end{array}$$

7.
$$\begin{array}{r} 1982 \\ 7650 \\ 4319 \\ + 3766 \end{array}$$

8.
$$\begin{array}{r} 6452 \\ 3339 \\ 2751 \\ + 8892 \end{array}$$

9.
$$\begin{array}{r} 9655 \\ 2356 \\ 8878 \\ + 1664 \end{array}$$

10.
$$\begin{array}{r} 19,600 \\ 45,328 \\ 69,871 \\ 24,443 \\ + 72,550 \end{array}$$

11.
$$\begin{array}{r} 36,450 \\ 88,718 \\ 30,957 \\ 56,329 \\ + 94,005 \end{array}$$

12.
$$\begin{array}{r} 77,653 \\ 82,280 \\ 11,999 \\ 70,554 \\ + 25,393 \end{array}$$

13. $567 + 23 + 849$

14. $723 + 96 + 452$

15. $4689 + 574 + 28{,}976$

16. $2762 + 749 + 69{,}858$

17. $465 + 8907 + 5293 + 51$

18. $118 + 6447 + 9549 + 26$

19. $35 + 8701 + 65{,}247 + 765$

20. $48 + 7449 + 26{,}835 + 98$

21.
$$\begin{array}{r} 39,153 \\ 877 \\ 5,442 \\ 2,986 \\ 43,298 \\ + 660 \end{array}$$

22.
$$\begin{array}{r} 6,471 \\ 8,889,988 \\ 19,927 \\ 34 \\ 45,638 \\ + \quad 345 \end{array}$$

1. _____

2. _____

3. _____

4. _____

5. _____

6. _____

7. _____

8. _____

9. _____

10. _____

11. _____

12. _____

13. _____

14. _____

15. _____

16. _____

17. _____

18. _____

19. _____

20. _____

21. _____

22. _____

Name _____   Score _____

Solve.

1. You paid $67 for a coat and $14 for a hat.   2. A homemaker has a monthly budget of   1. _____
    Find the total cost of the coat and hat. $225 for food, $65 for car expenses, and
                                                     $50 for entertainment. Find the total
                                                     amount budgeted for the three items each   2. _____
                                                     month.

3. The attendance at the Thursday afternoon   4. A hospital's emergency staff treated 83   3. _____
    lecture was 2592, and the attendance at the   people on Friday, 92 people on Saturday,
    Friday afternoon lecture was 643. Find the   and 64 people on Sunday. How many
    total attendance for the two lectures.   people did the emergency room staff treat
                                                     from Friday to Sunday?   4. _____

5. A real estate broker received commissions 6. During the first 4 months of the year, an 5. _____
    of $4650, $3920, $4425, and $2575 during   appliance store sold 675 toasters. The store
    a four month period. Find the total income   sold 127 toasters in May and 87 in June.
    from commissions for the four months.   How many toasters were sold during the
                                                     first six months of the year?   6. _____

7. You had a balance of $753 in your   8. You are leaving for a four-day vacation.   7. _____
    checking account before making deposits   The odometer on your car reads 61,795
    of $158, $269, and $374. What is your   miles. You plan to drive 185 miles the first
    new checking account balance?   day, 209 miles the second day, and 174
                                                     miles the third day. What will be your   8. _____
                                                     odometer reading at the end of the trip?

9. The new homeowner had the following   10. A software company made profits of   9. _____
    monthly expenses: mortgage–$900, $7,420,572, $1,764,025, and $6,871,429
    utilities–$194, insurance–$92, food–$526,   during its first three years. Find the
    and transportation–$78. Find the total costs   software company's total profit for the
    for the month.   three years.   10. _____

6

Name   Score

Subtract.

1. $\quad 9$ $\quad -4$	**2.** $\quad 6$ $\quad -3$	**3.** $\quad 7$ $\quad -6$	**1.** _____
			2. _____
			3. _____
4. $\quad 25$ $\quad -10$	**5.** $\quad 58$ $\quad -47$	**6.** $\quad 98$ $\quad -37$	**4.** _____
			5. _____
			6. _____
7. $\quad 179$ $\quad -84$	**8.** $\quad 453$ $\quad -53$	**9.** $\quad 164$ $\quad -93$	**7.** _____
			8. _____
			9. _____
10. $\quad 691$ $\quad -130$	**11.** $\quad 889$ $\quad -667$	**12.** $\quad 905$ $\quad -602$	**10.** _____
			11. _____
			12. _____
13. $\quad 8714$ $\quad -301$	**14.** $\quad 1539$ $\quad -722$	**15.** $\quad 2408$ $\quad -204$	**13.** _____
			14. _____
			15. _____
16. $\quad 3215$ $\quad -2100$	**17.** $\quad 4976$ $\quad -3724$	**18.** $\quad 5341$ $\quad -3210$	**16.** _____
			17. _____
			18. _____
19. $29-8$	**20.** $14-6$		**19.** _____
			20. _____
21. $863-42$	**22.** $827-16$		**21.** _____
			22. _____
23. $7538-532$	**24.** $1249-828$		**23.** _____
			24. _____
25. $9527-7416$	**26.** $7884-1733$		**25.** _____
			26. _____

Name _____   Score _____

Subtract.

1.   63
   − 19
	2. 84
	   − 26
		3. 98
		   − 39	

1. _____

2. _____

3. _____

4.   273   **5.**   432   **6.**   771
  − 185   − 378   − 592

4. _____

5. _____

6. _____

7.   3645   **8.**   5094   **9.**   1419
  − 376   − 695   − 453

7. _____

8. _____

9. _____

10.   6420   **11.**   8311   **12.**   4936
  − 3990   − 7499   − 1117

10. _____

11. _____

12. _____

13.   22,653   **14.**   53,417   **15.**   79,600
  − 18,734   − 26,718   − 35,752

13. _____

14. _____

15. _____

16.   83,602   **17.**   248,000   **18.**   900,721
  − 64,575   − 96,729   − 546,847

16. _____

17. _____

18. _____

19. 421 − 46   **20.** 725 − 88

19. _____

20. _____

21. 5303 − 627   **22.** 8263 − 782

21. _____

22. _____

23. 30,736 − 5947   **24.** 64,057 − 7316

23. _____

24. _____

25. 56,322 − 29,415   **26.** 94,032 − 78,450

25. _____

26. _____

Name _____ Score _____

Solve.

1. How much change will a customer receive after paying for a $27 purchase with a $50 bill?

2. The down payment on a boat costing $9655 is $1931. Find the amount that remains to be paid.

1. _____

2. _____

3. You drove a car 31,672 miles in a three-year period. You drove 9670 miles the first year and 11,426 miles the second year. How many miles did you drive the third year?

4. After a trip of 649 miles, the odometer of your car read 54,456 miles. What was the odometer reading at the beginning of your trip?

3. _____

4. _____

5. Your monthly food budget is $380. How much is left in the food budget after spending $169 on groceries?

6. You had a bank balance of $932. You then wrote checks for $183, $74, and $25. Find the new bank balance.

5. _____

6. _____

7. A lab technician receives a total salary of $4650 per month. Deductions from the check are $1068 for taxes, $278 for social security, and $84 for insurance. Find the lab technician's take-home pay.

8. A public relations executive has an expense account of $1100. The amount already spent includes $238 for transportation, $130 for food, and $366 for lodging. Find the balance remaining in the expense account.

7. _____

8. _____

9. Your monthly budget for household expenses is $800. After $238 is spent for food, $129 for clothes, and $48 for entertainment, how much is left in the budget?

10. How much larger is Texas than Wyoming? Texas is 266,873 square miles in area, and Wyoming is 97,809 square miles in area.

9. _____

10. _____

Name _____   Score _____

Multiply.

1.   9
   $\times\,7$
	2. 0
	   $\times\,6$
		3. 5
		   $\times\,4$

4.   6
   $\times\,8$
	5. 5
	   $\times\,3$
		6. 6
		   $\times\,6$

7.   69
   $\times\,\,\,3$
	8. 24
	   $\times\,\,\,7$
		9. 71
		   $\times\,\,\,6$

10.   49
   $\times\,\,\,5$
	11. 76
	   $\times\,\,\,9$
		12. 38
		   $\times\,\,\,4$

13.   158
   $\times\,\,\,\,\,2$
	14. 649
	   $\times\,\,\,\,\,8$
		15. 273
		   $\times\,\,\,\,\,6$

16.   845
   $\times\,\,\,\,\,5$
	17. 555
	   $\times\,\,\,\,\,7$
		18. 841
		   $\times\,\,\,\,\,3$

19.   1136
   $\times\,\,\,\,\,\,7$
	20. 4721
	   $\times\,\,\,\,\,\,6$
		21. 7894
		   $\times\,\,\,\,\,\,9$

22.   6543
   $\times\,\,\,\,\,\,4$
	23. 2199
	   $\times\,\,\,\,\,\,8$
		24. 3724
		   $\times\,\,\,\,\,\,5$

25.   17,234
   $\times\,\,\,\,\,\,\,\,3$
	26. 51,990
	   $\times\,\,\,\,\,\,\,\,7$
		27. 45,616
		   $\times\,\,\,\,\,\,\,\,9$

1. _____

2. _____

3. _____

4. _____

5. _____

6. _____

7. _____

8. _____

9. _____

10. _____

11. _____

12. _____

13. _____

14. _____

15. _____

16. _____

17. _____

18. _____

19. _____

20. _____

21. _____

22. _____

23. _____

24. _____

25. _____

26. _____

27. _____

Name _____   Score _____

Multiply.

1.   14
   × 28

2.   30
   × 62

3.   75
   × 42

4.   59
   × 11

5.   39
   × 45

6.   83
   × 96

7.   281
   × 64

8.   495
   × 37

9.   845
   × 56

10.   856
   × 71

11.   625
   × 18

12.   399
   × 57

13.   7815
   × 26

14.   5146
   × 83

15.   9488
   × 77

16.   3012
   × 61

17.   8400
   × 53

18.   3289
   × 32

19.   391
   × 465

20.   724
   × 831

21.   298
   × 665

22.   2911
   × 643

23.   5673
   × 394

24.   3485
   × 865

25.   3600
   × 240

26.   6412
   × 180

27.   8923
   × 336

1. _____
2. _____
3. _____
4. _____
5. _____
6. _____
7. _____
8. _____
9. _____
10. _____
11. _____
12. _____
13. _____
14. _____
15. _____
16. _____
17. _____
18. _____
19. _____
20. _____
21. _____
22. _____
23. _____
24. _____
25. _____
26. _____
27. _____

Name _____ Score _____

Solve.

1. The Environmental Protection Agency (EPA) estimates that a motorcycles gets 38 miles on one gallon of gas. How many miles could it get on 6 gallons of gas?

2. The truck driver drove at a constant speed of 53 miles per hour for 6 hours. Find the distance the truck driver traveled.

1. _____

2. _____

3. A librarian catalogued 27 shelves of books. Each shelf held 32 books. How many books did the librarian catalogue?

4. An investor receives a check for $394 each month. How much will the investor receive over a 24-month period?

3. _____

4. _____

5. A mechanic has a car payment of $254 each month. What is the total of car payments over a 12-month period?

6. A data-entry operator earns $494 for working a 40-hour week. Last week the operator worked an additional 5 hours at $18 per hour. Find the data-entry operator's total pay for last week's work.

5. _____

6. _____

7. It takes approximately 709 hours for the moon to make one revolution around Earth. How many hours would it take the moon to make 12 revolutions around Earth?

8. A baker can buy 1000 pounds of flour for $150 and one 100-pound bag of sugar for $32. The baker orders 1000 pounds of flour and fifteen 100-pound bags of sugar. What is the total cost of the order?

7. _____

8. _____

9. A gasoline storage tank contains 65,000 gallons of gasoline. A valve is opened which lets out 40 gallons each minute. How many gallons remain in the tank after 45 minutes?

10. The average annual salary of a publishing company's employees is $51,280. If there are 156 people employed at the company, what is the total amount spent annually on salaries?

9. _____

10. _____

Name _____   Score _____

Divide.

1. $3\overline{)6}$ 2. $2\overline{)4}$ 3. $9\overline{)9}$ 1. _____

                                                                                          2. _____

                                                                                          3. _____

4. $7\overline{)84}$ 5. $6\overline{)42}$ 6. $4\overline{)16}$ 4. _____

                                                                                          5. _____

                                                                                          6. _____

7. $5\overline{)95}$ 8. $9\overline{)72}$ 9. $3\overline{)33}$ 7. _____

                                                                                          8. _____

                                                                                          9. _____

10. $4\overline{)540}$ 11. $5\overline{)625}$ 12. $8\overline{)656}$ 10. _____

                                                                                          11. _____

                                                                                          12. _____

13. $7\overline{)343}$ 14. $3\overline{)1575}$ 15. $5\overline{)2280}$ 13. _____

                                                                                          14. _____

                                                                                          15. _____

16. $6\overline{)3162}$ 17. $4\overline{)1596}$ 18. $7\overline{)38,927}$ 16. _____

                                                                                          17. _____

                                                                                          18. _____

19. $5\overline{)57,395}$ 20. $6\overline{)31,404}$ 21. $8\overline{)61,112}$ 19. _____

                                                                                          20. _____

                                                                                          21. _____

Name _____　　　　　　　　　Score _____

Divide.

1. $3\overline{)7}$ 　　　　　　**2.** $2\overline{)9}$ 　　　　　　**3.** $5\overline{)6}$

4. $6\overline{)29}$ 　　　　　　**5.** $3\overline{)47}$ 　　　　　　**6.** $5\overline{)61}$

7. $4\overline{)73}$ 　　　　　　**8.** $7\overline{)48}$ 　　　　　　**9.** $9\overline{)40}$

10. $4\overline{)693}$ 　　　　　**11.** $7\overline{)355}$ 　　　　　**12.** $6\overline{)890}$

13. $5\overline{)269}$ 　　　　　**14.** $3\overline{)1178}$ 　　　　　**15.** $5\overline{)4957}$

16. $9\overline{)6234}$ 　　　　**17.** $4\overline{)5913}$ 　　　　**18.** $5\overline{)37,234}$

19. $3\overline{)24,652}$ 　　　**20.** $4\overline{)59,403}$ 　　　**21.** $8\overline{)72,641}$

1. _____

2. _____

3. _____

4. _____

5. _____

6. _____

7. _____

8. _____

9. _____

10. _____

11. _____

12. _____

13. _____

14. _____

15. _____

16. _____

17. _____

18. _____

19. _____

20. _____

21. _____

Name _____   Score _____

Divide.

1. $23\overline{)94}$

2. $36\overline{)76}$

3. $52\overline{)83}$

4. $73\overline{)374}$

5. $21\overline{)147}$

6. $48\overline{)598}$

7. $53\overline{)274}$

8. $37\overline{)4762}$

9. $77\overline{)7941}$

10. $41\overline{)5913}$

11. $63\overline{)7623}$

12. $55\overline{)4418}$

13. $18\overline{)1536}$

14. $86\overline{)6393}$

15. $45\overline{)8398}$

16. $98\overline{)6010}$

17. $62\overline{)4335}$

18. $92\overline{)54,392}$

19. $48\overline{)38,120}$

20. $799\overline{)66,427}$

21. $243\overline{)19,197}$

1. _____

2. _____

3. _____

4. _____

5. _____

6. _____

7. _____

8. _____

9. _____

10. _____

11. _____

12. _____

13. _____

14. _____

15. _____

16. _____

17. _____

18. _____

19. _____

20. _____

21. _____

Name _____   Score _____

Solve.

1. A farmer ships 120,000 bushels of corn in 8 railroad cars. Find the amount of corn shipped in each car, assuming each car holds the same amount.

2. A shipment of 8460 diodes requires testing. The diodes are divided equally among 15 employees. How many diodes must each employee test?

1. _____

2. _____

3. A lottery prize of $737,000 is divided equally among 4 winners. What amount does each winner receive?

4. The new movie premiered at 14 theatres last Friday. If 2240 people attended the premiere and they were distributed equally among the 14 theatres, how many people attended each theatre?

3. _____

4. _____

5. The total cost of a car, including finance charges, is $7632. This amount is to be repaid in 36 equal monthly payments. What is the amount of each payment?

6. A management consultant received a check for $1755 for 45 hours of work. What is the consultant's hourly wage?

5. _____

6. _____

7. A student obtains a no-interest loan of $4600 per year for three years. After that time the student must pay off the loan in equal monthly payments for a period of 120 months. What is the amount of the student's monthly payments?

8. A consumer makes a down payment of $4516 on a video entertainment center costing $6724. The balance is to be paid in 12 equal monthly payments. What is the payment for one month?

7. _____

8. _____

9. A fund-raising organization collected $1,128,193 in one year for 11 charities. If the charities share the money equally, how much will each one receive?

10. A tannery produces and packages 320 briefcases each hour. Ten briefcases are put in each package for shipment. How many packages of briefcases can be produced in 8 hours?

9. _____

10. _____

Name _____ Score _____

Write the number in exponential notation.

1. $4 \cdot 4 \cdot 4 \cdot 4$

2. $8 \cdot 8 \cdot 8 \cdot 8 \cdot 8 \cdot 8$

3. $3 \cdot 3 \cdot 3 \cdot 3 \cdot 4 \cdot 4$

4. $5 \cdot 5 \cdot 5 \cdot 5 \cdot 7 \cdot 7 \cdot 7$

5. $2 \cdot 6 \cdot 6 \cdot 6 \cdot 6 \cdot 6 \cdot 6 \cdot 6$

6. $6 \cdot 10 \cdot 10 \cdot 10 \cdot 10$

7. $2 \cdot 2 \cdot 2 \cdot 3 \cdot 3 \cdot 3 \cdot 3 \cdot 7 \cdot 7$

8. $5 \cdot 6 \cdot 7 \cdot 7 \cdot 8 \cdot 8 \cdot 8$

9. $4 \cdot 4 \cdot 5 \cdot 5 \cdot 5 \cdot 6 \cdot 6 \cdot 6 \cdot 7$

10. $7 \cdot 7 \cdot 7 \cdot 15 \cdot 15 \cdot 19 \cdot 19$

1. _____
2. _____
3. _____
4. _____
5. _____
6. _____
7. _____
8. _____
9. _____
10. _____

Simplify.

11. 2^4

12. 3^3

13. 4^3

14. $2^4 \cdot 3^5$

15. $4^2 \cdot 5^3$

16. $7^2 \cdot 8^3$

17. $0^5 \cdot 3^2 \cdot 6^4$

18. $2 \cdot 4^2 \cdot 10$

19. $5^2 \cdot 10^2 \cdot 15$

20. $3 \cdot 10^2 \cdot 7^3$

21. $2^3 \cdot 3^3 \cdot 4^3$

22. $7^2 \cdot 10 \cdot 3^4$

23. $9^2 \cdot 2^3 \cdot 6^2$

24. $5^3 \cdot 0^4 \cdot 8^3$

25. $5^2 \cdot 2^6 \cdot 9$

11. _____
12. _____
13. _____
14. _____
15. _____
16. _____
17. _____
18. _____
19. _____
20. _____
21. _____
22. _____
23. _____
24. _____
25. _____

Name _____   Score _____

Simplify by using the Order of Operations Agreement.

1. $8 - 2 + 6$

2. $9 - 3 + 5$

3. $7 + 4 \cdot 3$

4. $3 \cdot 3 - 9$

5. $10 - 4 \div 2$

6. $8 + 3 - 6$

7. $4^2 - 10$

8. $3(1 + 5) - 7$

9. $17 - 3^2$

10. $8 \cdot (7 + 3) \div 8$

11. $7 \cdot 3^2 + 16$

12. $2^2 - 2(12 \div 6)$

13. $13 + (9 - 7) \cdot 5$

14. $20 - 2 \cdot 3^2$

15. $4^2 + 6 \cdot (2 - 1)$

16. $2^4 + 7 \cdot (5 - 5)$

17. $3^2 \cdot 4 + 6 \cdot 2^3$

18. $8 \cdot 2 - 3^2$

19. $17 - 3 \cdot 5$

20. $14 + 4 \cdot 6$

21. $3 \cdot (8 - 7) + 10$

22. $11 - (11 - 2) \div 3$

23. $7 \cdot (8 - 5) + 12$

24. $14 \div (3 + 4) \cdot 2$

25. $8 - 5 + 9 \cdot 2 \div 3$

26. $6 \cdot 4 \div 3 \div 2 + 1$

27. $10(2 + 3) \div 5$

1. _____
2. _____
3. _____
4. _____
5. _____
6. _____
7. _____
8. _____
9. _____
10. _____
11. _____
12. _____
13. _____
14. _____
15. _____
16. _____
17. _____
18. _____
19. _____
20. _____
21. _____
22. _____
23. _____
24. _____
25. _____
26. _____
27. _____

Name _____   Score _____

Find all the factors of the number.

1. 2	**2.** 14	**3.** 21	**1.** _____
			2. _____
			3. _____
4. 15	**5.** 23	**6.** 40	**4.** _____
			5. _____
			6. _____
7. 38	**8.** 60	**9.** 58	**7.** _____
			8. _____
			9. _____
10. 62	**11.** 81	**12.** 51	**10.** _____
			11. _____
			12. _____
13. 99	**14.** 85	**15.** 70	**13.** _____
			14. _____
			15. _____
16. 88	**17.** 63	**18.** 35	**16.** _____
			17. _____
			18. _____
19. 45	**20.** 78	**21.** 55	**19.** _____
			20. _____
			21. _____
22. 114	**23.** 121	**24.** 117	**22.** _____
			23. _____
			24. _____
25. 150	**26.** 175	**27.** 181	**25.** _____
			26. _____
			27. _____

Name _____　　　　Score _____

Find the prime factorization.

1.　8

2.　30

3.　53

4.　10

5.　32

6.　64

7.　11

8.　20

9.　82

10.　35

11.　44

12.　69

13.　72

14.　88

15.　94

16.　60

17.　77

18.　100

19.　104

20.　112

21.　124

22.　130

23.　155

24.　200

25.　315

26.　500

27.　260

1. _____

2. _____

3. _____

4. _____

5. _____

6. _____

7. _____

8. _____

9. _____

10. _____

11. _____

12. _____

13. _____

14. _____

15. _____

16. _____

17. _____

18. _____

19. _____

20. _____

21. _____

22. _____

23. _____

24. _____

25. _____

26. _____

27. _____

Name _____   Score _____

Find the LCM.

1. 3, 4	**2.** 3, 7	**3.** 6, 9	1. _____
			2. _____
			3. _____
4. 8, 10	**5.** 4, 8	**6.** 9, 12	4. _____
			5. _____
			6. _____
7. 4, 9	**8.** 6, 15	**9.** 16, 24	7. _____
			8. _____
			9. _____
10. 15, 25	**11.** 28, 32	**12.** 4, 18	10. _____
			11. _____
			12. _____
13. 72, 108	**14.** 84, 126	**15.** 32, 128	13. _____
			14. _____
			15. _____
16. 3, 7, 9	**17.** 6, 12, 27	**18.** 3, 7, 11	16. _____
			17. _____
			18. _____
19. 9, 12, 24	**20.** 10, 25, 40	**21.** 4, 7, 21	19. _____
			20. _____
			21. _____
22. 2, 7, 11	**23.** 28, 32, 56	**24.** 16, 20, 40	22. _____
			23. _____
			24. _____
25. 8, 27, 36	**26.** 6, 12, 18	**27.** 2, 16, 32	25. _____
			26. _____
			27. _____

Name _____ Score _____

Find the GCF.

1. 3, 7	**2.** 3, 6	**3.** 9, 16
4. 8, 18	**5.** 10, 15	**6.** 30, 65
7. 15, 30	**8.** 36, 56	**9.** 18, 27
10. 21, 35	**11.** 15, 20	**12.** 30, 50
13. 48, 64	**14.** 39, 52	**15.** 37, 67
16. 4, 8, 10	**17.** 3, 5, 7	**18.** 3, 9, 12
19. 5, 11, 13	**20.** 10, 25, 30	**21.** 16, 40, 80
22. 16, 20, 32	**23.** 24, 32, 40	**24.** 18, 27, 81
25. 28, 44, 56	**26.** 17, 68, 85	**27.** 30, 75, 150

1. _____
2. _____
3. _____
4. _____
5. _____
6. _____
7. _____
8. _____
9. _____
10. _____
11. _____
12. _____
13. _____
14. _____
15. _____
16. _____
17. _____
18. _____
19. _____
20. _____
21. _____
22. _____
23. _____
24. _____
25. _____
26. _____
27. _____

Name

Score

Express the shaded portion of the circle as a fraction.

1.

2.

3.

4.

1. _____

2. _____

3. _____

4. _____

Express the shaded portion of the circles as a mixed number.

5.

6.

7.

8.

9.

10.

5. _____

6. _____

7. _____

8. _____

9. _____

10. _____

Express the shaded portion of the circles as an improper fraction.

11.

12.

13.

14.

11. _____

12. _____

13. _____

14. _____

Name   Score

Write the improper fraction as a mixed number or whole number.

1. $\dfrac{11}{3}$

2. $\dfrac{30}{5}$

3. $\dfrac{17}{9}$

4. $\dfrac{9}{2}$

5. $\dfrac{24}{9}$

6. $\dfrac{19}{4}$

7. $\dfrac{36}{12}$

8. $\dfrac{11}{6}$

9. $\dfrac{8}{8}$

10. $\dfrac{64}{8}$

11. $\dfrac{14}{1}$

12. $\dfrac{70}{14}$

1. _____
2. _____
3. _____
4. _____
5. _____
6. _____
7. _____
8. _____
9. _____
10. _____
11. _____
12. _____

Write the mixed number as an improper fraction.

13. $2\dfrac{1}{5}$

14. $7\dfrac{2}{3}$

15. $4\dfrac{7}{9}$

16. $2\dfrac{7}{8}$

17. $5\dfrac{2}{7}$

18. $6\dfrac{3}{5}$

19. $10\dfrac{3}{4}$

20. $9\dfrac{7}{10}$

21. $12\dfrac{5}{6}$

22. $7\dfrac{13}{15}$

23. $11\dfrac{1}{3}$

24. $16\dfrac{3}{8}$

13. _____
14. _____
15. _____
16. _____
17. _____
18. _____
19. _____
20. _____
21. _____
22. _____
23. _____
24. _____

Name

Score

Build an equivalent fraction with the given denominator.

1. $\dfrac{2}{3} = \dfrac{}{39}$

2. $\dfrac{5}{6} = \dfrac{}{18}$

3. $\dfrac{4}{7} = \dfrac{}{56}$

4. $\dfrac{1}{5} = \dfrac{}{25}$

5. $\dfrac{3}{4} = \dfrac{}{28}$

6. $\dfrac{6}{10} = \dfrac{}{30}$

7. $\dfrac{1}{2} = \dfrac{}{30}$

8. $\dfrac{4}{5} = \dfrac{}{45}$

9. $\dfrac{2}{9} = \dfrac{}{54}$

10. $\dfrac{8}{12} = \dfrac{}{48}$

11. $\dfrac{11}{13} = \dfrac{}{65}$

12. $\dfrac{5}{10} = \dfrac{}{70}$

13. $\dfrac{6}{7} = \dfrac{}{84}$

14. $6 = \dfrac{}{9}$

15. $8 = \dfrac{}{15}$

16. $\dfrac{2}{4} = \dfrac{}{36}$

17. $\dfrac{1}{3} = \dfrac{}{102}$

18. $\dfrac{5}{9} = \dfrac{}{180}$

19. $\dfrac{10}{15} = \dfrac{}{90}$

20. $\dfrac{17}{20} = \dfrac{}{96}$

21. $\dfrac{4}{11} = \dfrac{}{121}$

22. $\dfrac{8}{20} = \dfrac{}{240}$

23. $\dfrac{15}{16} = \dfrac{}{336}$

24. $\dfrac{7}{33} = \dfrac{}{165}$

25. $\dfrac{5}{8} = \dfrac{}{312}$

26. $\dfrac{14}{19} = \dfrac{}{437}$

27. $\dfrac{21}{25} = \dfrac{}{1075}$

1. _____
2. _____
3. _____
4. _____
5. _____
6. _____
7. _____
8. _____
9. _____
10. _____
11. _____
12. _____
13. _____
14. _____
15. _____
16. _____
17. _____
18. _____
19. _____
20. _____
21. _____
22. _____
23. _____
24. _____
25. _____
26. _____
27. _____

Name _____   Score _____

Reduce the fraction to simplest form.

1. $\dfrac{8}{12}$

2. $\dfrac{15}{25}$

3. $\dfrac{2}{16}$

4. $\dfrac{28}{49}$

5. $\dfrac{54}{81}$

6. $\dfrac{40}{64}$

7. $\dfrac{75}{90}$

8. $\dfrac{36}{27}$

9. $\dfrac{0}{15}$

10. $\dfrac{60}{96}$

11. $\dfrac{18}{36}$

12. $\dfrac{7}{18}$

13. $\dfrac{25}{100}$

14. $\dfrac{84}{144}$

15. $\dfrac{39}{13}$

16. $\dfrac{169}{234}$

17. $\dfrac{112}{126}$

18. $\dfrac{59}{177}$

19. $\dfrac{85}{65}$

20. $\dfrac{34}{238}$

21. $\dfrac{16}{34}$

22. $\dfrac{104}{240}$

23. $\dfrac{69}{150}$

24. $\dfrac{26}{75}$

25. $\dfrac{112}{160}$

26. $\dfrac{143}{182}$

27. $\dfrac{92}{23}$

1. _____
2. _____
3. _____
4. _____
5. _____
6. _____
7. _____
8. _____
9. _____
10. _____
11. _____
12. _____
13. _____
14. _____
15. _____
16. _____
17. _____
18. _____
19. _____
20. _____
21. _____
22. _____
23. _____
24. _____
25. _____
26. _____
27. _____

Name _____ Score _____

Add.

1. $\dfrac{3}{6}+\dfrac{2}{6}$

2. $\dfrac{5}{10}+\dfrac{6}{10}$

3. $\dfrac{7}{19}+\dfrac{3}{19}$

4. $\dfrac{2}{7}+\dfrac{4}{7}$

5. $\dfrac{4}{8}+\dfrac{3}{8}$

6. $\dfrac{11}{15}+\dfrac{4}{15}$

7. $\dfrac{5}{7}+\dfrac{9}{7}$

8. $\dfrac{3}{14}+\dfrac{1}{14}$

9. $\dfrac{3}{5}+\dfrac{6}{5}$

10. $\dfrac{13}{17}+\dfrac{2}{17}$

11. $\dfrac{2}{4}+\dfrac{1}{4}$

12. $\dfrac{7}{12}+\dfrac{5}{12}$

13. $\dfrac{1}{3}+\dfrac{2}{3}+\dfrac{4}{3}$

14. $\dfrac{5}{9}+\dfrac{4}{9}+\dfrac{7}{9}$

15. $\dfrac{4}{11}+\dfrac{9}{11}+\dfrac{1}{11}$

16. $\dfrac{7}{8}+\dfrac{10}{8}+\dfrac{3}{8}$

17. $\dfrac{6}{12}+\dfrac{2}{12}+\dfrac{3}{12}$

18. $\dfrac{5}{6}+\dfrac{8}{6}+\dfrac{1}{6}$

19. $\dfrac{3}{15}+\dfrac{9}{15}+\dfrac{1}{15}$

20. $\dfrac{6}{10}+\dfrac{1}{10}+\dfrac{8}{10}$

21. $\dfrac{3}{4}+\dfrac{6}{4}+\dfrac{8}{4}$

22. $\dfrac{6}{5}+\dfrac{2}{5}+\dfrac{3}{5}$

23. $\dfrac{7}{14}+\dfrac{3}{14}+\dfrac{8}{14}$

24. $\dfrac{8}{16}+\dfrac{2}{16}+\dfrac{9}{16}$

25. $\dfrac{4}{13}+\dfrac{11}{13}+\dfrac{14}{13}$

26. $\dfrac{15}{17}+\dfrac{12}{17}+\dfrac{5}{17}$

27. $\dfrac{2}{9}+\dfrac{6}{9}+\dfrac{9}{9}$

1. _____

2. _____

3. _____

4. _____

5. _____

6. _____

7. _____

8. _____

9. _____

10. _____

11. _____

12. _____

13. _____

14. _____

15. _____

16. _____

17. _____

18. _____

19. _____

20. _____

21. _____

22. _____

23. _____

24. _____

25. _____

26. _____

27. _____

Name _____ Score _____

Add.

1. $\dfrac{1}{4} + \dfrac{5}{6}$

2. $\dfrac{4}{15} + \dfrac{5}{9}$

3. $\dfrac{2}{3} + \dfrac{7}{8}$

4. $\dfrac{3}{4} + \dfrac{11}{16}$

5. $\dfrac{7}{9} + \dfrac{10}{12}$

6. $\dfrac{5}{6} + \dfrac{3}{8}$

7. $\dfrac{13}{14} + \dfrac{15}{18}$

8. $\dfrac{3}{14} + \dfrac{17}{21}$

9. $\dfrac{9}{10} + \dfrac{10}{16}$

10. $\dfrac{4}{16} + \dfrac{35}{40}$

11. $\dfrac{7}{12} + \dfrac{4}{8}$

12. $\dfrac{12}{15} + \dfrac{19}{20}$

13. $\dfrac{1}{2} + \dfrac{1}{4} + \dfrac{1}{6}$

14. $\dfrac{2}{5} + \dfrac{7}{10} + \dfrac{7}{15}$

15. $\dfrac{2}{3} + \dfrac{3}{7} + \dfrac{18}{21}$

16. $\dfrac{1}{4} + \dfrac{1}{3} + \dfrac{8}{9}$

17. $\dfrac{1}{2} + \dfrac{5}{8} + \dfrac{10}{12}$

18. $\dfrac{3}{5} + \dfrac{6}{7} + \dfrac{5}{9}$

19. $\dfrac{9}{12} + \dfrac{2}{4} + \dfrac{5}{16}$

20. $\dfrac{2}{3} + \dfrac{7}{9} + \dfrac{7}{10}$

21. $\dfrac{4}{5} + \dfrac{1}{6} + \dfrac{15}{18}$

22. $\dfrac{1}{2} + \dfrac{6}{7} + \dfrac{4}{8}$

23. $\dfrac{2}{3} + \dfrac{4}{6} + \dfrac{17}{18}$

24. $\dfrac{3}{4} + \dfrac{5}{7} + \dfrac{13}{14}$

25. $\dfrac{3}{6} + \dfrac{1}{8} + \dfrac{7}{10}$

26. $\dfrac{1}{5} + \dfrac{1}{11} + \dfrac{1}{15}$

27. $\dfrac{5}{6} + \dfrac{15}{24} + \dfrac{7}{8}$

1. _____
2. _____
3. _____
4. _____
5. _____
6. _____
7. _____
8. _____
9. _____
10. _____
11. _____
12. _____
13. _____
14. _____
15. _____
16. _____
17. _____
18. _____
19. _____
20. _____
21. _____
22. _____
23. _____
24. _____
25. _____
26. _____
27. _____

Name _____   Score _____

Add.

1. $3\frac{4}{9}$
   $+\ 2\frac{2}{3}$

2. $4\frac{2}{3}$
   $+\ 4\frac{5}{6}$

3. $5\frac{4}{7}$
   $+\ 7\frac{3}{4}$

4. 6
   $+\ 11\frac{7}{12}$

5. $8\frac{6}{14}$
   $+\ 3\ \frac{2}{8}$

6. $1\frac{4}{9}$
   $+\ 9\frac{11}{15}$

7. $6\frac{1}{2}+5\frac{2}{3}$

8. $7\frac{5}{6}+2\frac{13}{15}$

9. $4\frac{3}{5}+6\frac{4}{7}$

10. $1\frac{4}{9}+11\frac{15}{18}$

11. $3\frac{1}{4}+7\frac{1}{5}$

12. $18\frac{5}{8}+10\frac{9}{14}$

13. $5\frac{7}{10}+25\frac{4}{15}$

14. $9\frac{5}{6}+12\frac{1}{9}$

15. $3\frac{3}{7}+4\frac{7}{8}$

16. $8\frac{9}{10}+5\frac{11}{12}$

17. $15\frac{5}{11}+30\frac{2}{4}$

18. $21\frac{3}{5}+6\frac{5}{12}$

19. $3\frac{1}{3}+2\frac{1}{2}+9\frac{3}{4}$

20. $7\frac{4}{7}+1\frac{3}{14}+11\frac{2}{5}$

21. $6\frac{7}{9}+5\frac{11}{12}+10\frac{5}{10}$

22. $4\frac{5}{8}+8\frac{1}{2}+4\frac{7}{12}$

23. $2\frac{14}{15}+7\frac{17}{20}+1\frac{29}{30}$

24. $6\frac{15}{18}+9\frac{21}{30}+15\frac{11}{12}$

25. $1\frac{3}{4}+25\frac{3}{8}+6\frac{10}{12}$

26. $9\frac{3}{5}+5\frac{3}{5}+10\frac{3}{4}$

27. $2\frac{6}{7}+1\frac{1}{3}+14\frac{11}{21}$

1. _____
2. _____
3. _____
4. _____
5. _____
6. _____
7. _____
8. _____
9. _____
10. _____
11. _____
12. _____
13. _____
14. _____
15. _____
16. _____
17. _____
18. _____
19. _____
20. _____
21. _____
22. _____
23. _____
24. _____
25. _____
26. _____
27. _____

Name   Score

Solve.

1. Over a two-year period, a child grew $4\frac{5}{8}$ inches. If the child grew $1\frac{1}{2}$ inches the first year, how many inches did the child grow during the second year?

2. A wall that is $\frac{3}{4}$-inches thick is covered by a $\frac{5}{16}$-inch veneer. Find the total thickness after the never is installed.

1. _____

2. _____

3. A carpenter build a header by nailing a $1\frac{1}{4}$-inch board to a $2\frac{5}{8}$-inch beam. Find the total thickness of the header.

4. You bought stock in a publishing company for $18\frac{5}{8}$ ($18\frac{5}{8}$ per share). The price of the stock gained $4\frac{1}{2}$ ($4\frac{1}{2}$ per share) during a three-week period. Find the price of the stock at the end of the three weeks.

3. _____

4. _____

5. Find the length of the shaft in the following diagram.

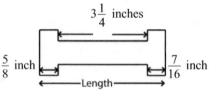

$3\frac{1}{4}$ inches

$\frac{5}{8}$ inch $\frac{7}{16}$ inch

Length

6. A electrician works $2\frac{1}{4}$ hours of overtime on Monday, $2\frac{3}{4}$ hours on Tuesday, and $2\frac{1}{2}$ hours on Wednesday. Find the total number of hours of overtime worked during the three days.

5. _____

6. _____

7. An artist places a $2\frac{7}{8}$-inch mat around a painting that is $16\frac{1}{2}$ inches long and $11\frac{3}{4}$ inches wide. Find the new dimensions of the picture.

8. A shopper bought $\frac{1}{2}$ pound of cheese, $\frac{3}{4}$ pound of ham, $\frac{3}{4}$ pound of bologna, and $1\frac{1}{4}$ pounds of salami. How many pounds of cold cuts did the shopper buy?

7. _____

8. _____

9. A recipe calls for $3\frac{1}{2}$ cups of rice, $2\frac{3}{4}$ cups of chopped celery, and $1\frac{1}{2}$ cups of sliced carrots. Find the total amount of rice, celery, and carrots needed for the recipe.

10. A plumber works $1\frac{1}{2}$ hours of overtime on Thursday and $2\frac{3}{4}$ hours on Friday. At a salary of $48 an hour, how much overtime pay does the plumber receive for the two days?

9. _____

10. _____

Name _____   Score _____

Subtract.

1.
$$\frac{7}{12}$$
$$-\frac{5}{12}$$

2.
$$\frac{17}{24}$$
$$-\frac{7}{24}$$

3.
$$\frac{13}{18}$$
$$-\frac{7}{18}$$

4.
$$\frac{23}{30}$$
$$-\frac{7}{30}$$

5.
$$\frac{14}{15}$$
$$-\frac{2}{15}$$

6.
$$\frac{9}{28}$$
$$-\frac{2}{28}$$

7.
$$\frac{16}{25}$$
$$-\frac{4}{25}$$

8.
$$\frac{31}{40}$$
$$-\frac{19}{40}$$

9.
$$\frac{21}{32}$$
$$-\frac{9}{32}$$

10.
$$\frac{13}{20}$$
$$-\frac{3}{20}$$

11.
$$\frac{8}{11}$$
$$-\frac{2}{11}$$

12.
$$\frac{12}{23}$$
$$-\frac{4}{23}$$

13.
$$\frac{43}{56}$$
$$-\frac{19}{56}$$

14.
$$\frac{24}{27}$$
$$-\frac{10}{27}$$

15.
$$\frac{5}{13}$$
$$-\frac{3}{13}$$

16.
$$\frac{15}{16}$$
$$-\frac{9}{16}$$

17.
$$\frac{11}{21}$$
$$-\frac{4}{21}$$

18.
$$\frac{23}{26}$$
$$-\frac{5}{26}$$

19.
$$\frac{7}{12}$$
$$-\frac{5}{12}$$

20.
$$\frac{44}{45}$$
$$-\frac{4}{45}$$

21.
$$\frac{14}{17}$$
$$-\frac{12}{17}$$

22.
$$\frac{49}{60}$$
$$-\frac{7}{60}$$

23.
$$\frac{13}{14}$$
$$-\frac{3}{14}$$

24.
$$\frac{8}{35}$$
$$-\frac{4}{35}$$

25.
$$\frac{14}{19}$$
$$-\frac{6}{19}$$

26.
$$\frac{26}{29}$$
$$-\frac{15}{29}$$

27.
$$\frac{15}{22}$$
$$-\frac{7}{22}$$

1. _____
2. _____
3. _____
4. _____
5. _____
6. _____
7. _____
8. _____
9. _____
10. _____
11. _____
12. _____
13. _____
14. _____
15. _____
16. _____
17. _____
18. _____
19. _____
20. _____
21. _____
22. _____
23. _____
24. _____
25. _____
26. _____
27. _____

Name   Score

Subtract.

1. $\dfrac{3}{5}$
   $-\dfrac{1}{4}$

2. $\dfrac{14}{15}$
   $-\dfrac{1}{6}$

3. $\dfrac{11}{14}$
   $-\dfrac{27}{42}$

4. $\dfrac{13}{21}$
   $-\dfrac{23}{49}$

5. $\dfrac{7}{8}$
   $-\dfrac{15}{32}$

6. $\dfrac{16}{19}$
   $-\dfrac{16}{57}$

7. $\dfrac{22}{27}$
   $-\dfrac{14}{45}$

8. $\dfrac{33}{40}$
   $-\dfrac{7}{16}$

9. $\dfrac{1}{6}$
   $-\dfrac{2}{13}$

10. $\dfrac{26}{35}$
    $-\dfrac{4}{15}$

11. $\dfrac{1}{4}$
    $-\dfrac{1}{10}$

12. $\dfrac{17}{36}$
    $-\dfrac{3}{20}$

13. $\dfrac{25}{27}$
    $-\dfrac{11}{18}$

14. $\dfrac{7}{8}$
    $-\dfrac{19}{24}$

15. $\dfrac{9}{10}$
    $-\dfrac{5}{12}$

16. $\dfrac{25}{33}$
    $-\dfrac{4}{9}$

17. $\dfrac{29}{35}$
    $-\dfrac{18}{25}$

18. $\dfrac{5}{8}$
    $-\dfrac{5}{18}$

19. $\dfrac{14}{15}$
    $-\dfrac{7}{12}$

20. $\dfrac{6}{7}$
    $-\dfrac{3}{5}$

21. $\dfrac{9}{14}$
    $-\dfrac{3}{10}$

22. $\dfrac{51}{60}$
    $-\dfrac{5}{12}$

23. $\dfrac{23}{25}$
    $-\dfrac{41}{50}$

24. $\dfrac{19}{21}$
    $-\dfrac{1}{6}$

25. $\dfrac{17}{24}$
    $-\dfrac{5}{9}$

26. $\dfrac{23}{26}$
    $-\dfrac{34}{39}$

27. $\dfrac{5}{8}$
    $-\dfrac{9}{20}$

1. _____
2. _____
3. _____
4. _____
5. _____
6. _____
7. _____
8. _____
9. _____
10. _____
11. _____
12. _____
13. _____
14. _____
15. _____
16. _____
17. _____
18. _____
19. _____
20. _____
21. _____
22. _____
23. _____
24. _____
25. _____
26. _____
27. _____

Name _____   Score _____

Subtract.

1.
$$8\frac{9}{11}$$
$$-4\frac{5}{11}$$

2.
$$26\frac{15}{16}$$
$$-11\frac{11}{16}$$

3.
$$59\frac{19}{24}$$
$$-18\frac{11}{24}$$

4.
$$15\frac{15}{26}$$
$$-6$$

5.
$$12$$
$$-7\frac{15}{16}$$

6.
$$17\frac{2}{5}$$
$$-9\frac{4}{5}$$

7.
$$44$$
$$-25\frac{4}{7}$$

8.
$$36\frac{5}{14}$$
$$-14\frac{9}{14}$$

9.
$$27\frac{2}{5}$$
$$-23\frac{4}{5}$$

10.
$$65\frac{7}{9}$$
$$-35\frac{5}{6}$$

11.
$$89\frac{11}{15}$$
$$-57\frac{17}{27}$$

12.
$$52\frac{17}{35}$$
$$-29$$

13.
$$41\frac{7}{12}$$
$$-17\frac{7}{16}$$

14.
$$84$$
$$-48\frac{7}{12}$$

15.
$$103\frac{3}{8}$$
$$-54\frac{4}{7}$$

16.
$$33\frac{8}{15}$$
$$-19\frac{8}{9}$$

17.
$$62\frac{17}{24}$$
$$-28\frac{11}{16}$$

18.
$$69\frac{19}{25}$$
$$-60\frac{23}{25}$$

19.
$$13$$
$$-7\frac{33}{40}$$

20.
$$77\frac{32}{35}$$
$$-38\frac{67}{70}$$

21.
$$24\frac{5}{12}$$
$$-15\frac{4}{9}$$

22.
$$43\frac{16}{21}$$
$$-34\frac{25}{42}$$

23.
$$12\frac{2}{5}$$
$$-9\frac{5}{6}$$

24.
$$289\frac{9}{14}$$
$$-163\frac{3}{8}$$

25.
$$154\frac{7}{10}$$
$$-78\frac{4}{5}$$

26.
$$91\frac{37}{40}$$
$$-38\frac{49}{60}$$

27.
$$74\frac{8}{15}$$
$$-57\frac{3}{20}$$

1. _____
2. _____
3. _____
4. _____
5. _____
6. _____
7. _____
8. _____
9. _____
10. _____
11. _____
12. _____
13. _____
14. _____
15. _____
16. _____
17. _____
18. _____
19. _____
20. _____
21. _____
22. _____
23. _____
24. _____
25. _____
26. _____
27. _____

Name _____ Score _____

Solve.

1. A planer removes $\frac{1}{4}$ inch from a $\frac{5}{6}$-inch board. Find the resulting thickness of the board.

2. A $2\frac{2}{9}$-foot piece is cut from a 4-foot board. How much of the board is left?

1. _____

2. _____

3. You painted $\frac{3}{5}$ of your house today. How much of the paint job remains to be done?

4. In an athletic competition, the two best long jump attempts measured $23\frac{3}{4}$ feet and $25\frac{1}{6}$ feet. Find the difference between the two best jumps.

3. _____

4. _____

5. Find the missing dimension.

$8\frac{5}{6}$ feet

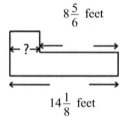

$14\frac{1}{8}$ feet

6. A plane trip from Boston to San Francisco takes $8\frac{1}{2}$ hours. After the plane is in the air to $5\frac{3}{4}$ hours, how much time remains before landing?

5. _____

6. _____

7. A three-day, $32\frac{1}{8}$-mile hike is planned. A hiker travels $10\frac{1}{5}$ miles the first day and $11\frac{3}{10}$ miles the second day. How many miles are left to travel on the third day?

8. For an upcoming role, an actor is put on a diet to lose 15 pounds. If $3\frac{1}{2}$ pounds are lost the first week and $2\frac{1}{4}$ pounds the second week, how many pounds must be lost to achieve the goal?

7. _____

8. _____

9. Two painters are staining a house. In one day, one painter stains $\frac{1}{5}$ of the house while the other stains $\frac{1}{4}$ of the house. How much of the job remains to be done?

10. A 10-mile race has 2 checkpoints. The first checkpoint is $4\frac{1}{2}$ miles from the starting point. The second checkpoint is $3\frac{5}{4}$ miles from the first checkpoint. How many miles is it from the second checkpoint to the finish line?

9. _____

10. _____

Name _____   Score _____

Multiply.

1. $\dfrac{4}{5} \times \dfrac{10}{13}$

2. $\dfrac{3}{4} \times \dfrac{8}{11}$

3. $\dfrac{4}{15} \times \dfrac{5}{9}$

4. $\dfrac{3}{10} \times \dfrac{5}{8}$

5. $\dfrac{5}{6} \times \dfrac{7}{11}$

6. $\dfrac{13}{18} \times \dfrac{1}{3}$

7. $\dfrac{4}{7} \times \dfrac{11}{16}$

8. $\dfrac{5}{9} \times \dfrac{5}{8}$

9. $\dfrac{5}{4} \times \dfrac{7}{10}$

10. $\dfrac{14}{15} \times \dfrac{7}{12}$

11. $\dfrac{5}{2} \times \dfrac{23}{20}$

12. $\dfrac{8}{15} \times \dfrac{6}{7}$

13. $\dfrac{9}{10} \times \dfrac{13}{18}$

14. $\dfrac{3}{7} \times \dfrac{5}{8}$

15. $\dfrac{12}{19} \times \dfrac{19}{6}$

16. $\dfrac{22}{14} \times \dfrac{16}{17}$

17. $\dfrac{21}{50} \times \dfrac{15}{24}$

18. $\dfrac{2}{5} \times \dfrac{15}{16}$

19. $\dfrac{7}{12} \times \dfrac{16}{9}$

20. $\dfrac{3}{8} \times \dfrac{10}{17}$

21. $\dfrac{6}{11} \times \dfrac{1}{4}$

22. $\dfrac{5}{6} \times \dfrac{9}{14}$

23. $\dfrac{1}{3} \times \dfrac{9}{10}$

24. $\dfrac{56}{85} \times \dfrac{51}{40}$

25. $\dfrac{9}{7} \times \dfrac{7}{9}$

26. $\dfrac{13}{66} \times \dfrac{11}{39}$

27. $\dfrac{6}{7} \times \dfrac{11}{13}$

1. _____
2. _____
3. _____
4. _____
5. _____
6. _____
7. _____
8. _____
9. _____
10. _____
11. _____
12. _____
13. _____
14. _____
15. _____
16. _____
17. _____
18. _____
19. _____
20. _____
21. _____
22. _____
23. _____
24. _____
25. _____
26. _____
27. _____

Name _____ Score _____

Multiply.

1. $4 \times \dfrac{7}{8}$

2. $7 \times \dfrac{2}{11}$

3. $7\dfrac{1}{2} \times \dfrac{4}{7}$

4. $\dfrac{2}{3} \times 3\dfrac{3}{4}$

5. $\dfrac{5}{6} \times 30$

6. $1\dfrac{4}{9} \times \dfrac{3}{10}$

7. $9 \times 3\dfrac{2}{3}$

8. $11\dfrac{1}{2} \times \dfrac{2}{13}$

9. $3\dfrac{4}{15} \times 3$

10. $\dfrac{4}{7} \times 2\dfrac{7}{12}$

11. $0 \times 3\dfrac{1}{6}$

12. $10 \times 5\dfrac{8}{15}$

13. $6\dfrac{3}{5} \times 8\dfrac{1}{6}$

14. $12\dfrac{3}{11} \times 7\dfrac{1}{3}$

15. $4\dfrac{5}{14} \times 15\dfrac{1}{2}$

16. $8\dfrac{3}{4} \times 6\dfrac{4}{5}$

17. $3\dfrac{5}{24} \times 12$

18. $2\dfrac{1}{7} \times 16\dfrac{4}{5}$

19. $8\dfrac{2}{15} \times 4\dfrac{7}{17}$

20. $1\dfrac{4}{9} \times 5\dfrac{1}{16}$

21. $9\dfrac{1}{3} \times 11\dfrac{5}{8}$

22. $7\dfrac{1}{2} \times 3\dfrac{9}{11}$

23. $19\dfrac{1}{4} \times 1\dfrac{5}{7}$

24. $4\dfrac{17}{18} \times 54$

25. $8\dfrac{4}{5} \times 14\dfrac{1}{6}$

26. $3\dfrac{3}{25} \times 2\dfrac{1}{2}$

27. $6\dfrac{1}{2} \times 9\dfrac{3}{13}$

1. _____
2. _____
3. _____
4. _____
5. _____
6. _____
7. _____
8. _____
9. _____
10. _____
11. _____
12. _____
13. _____
14. _____
15. _____
16. _____
17. _____
18. _____
19. _____
20. _____
21. _____
22. _____
23. _____
24. _____
25. _____
26. _____
27. _____

Name _____   Score _____

Solve.

1. An apprentice bricklayer earns $24 an hour. What are the bricklayer's total earnings after working $7\frac{1}{4}$ hours?

2. A sports car gets 21 miles on each gallon of gasoline. How many miles can the car travel on $5\frac{2}{3}$ gallons of gasoline?

1. _____

2. _____

3. A board is $8\frac{3}{4}$ feet long. One fourth of the board is cut off. What is the length of the piece cut off?

4. A plumber earns $320 for each day worked. What is the total of the plumber's earnings for working $4\frac{2}{5}$ days.

3. _____

4. _____

5. A family has an income of $3888 each month. The family spends $\frac{2}{9}$ of its income on rent. How much of the family's income (in dollars) is spent on rent each month?

6. A company budgets $\frac{1}{10}$ of its income each month for advertising. In June, the company had an income of $110,100. What is the amount budgeted for advertising in June?

5. _____

6. _____

7. A student read $\frac{2}{5}$ of a book containing 645 pages. How many pages did the student read?

8. A person can walk $3\frac{1}{4}$ miles in one hour. How many miles can the person walk in $1\frac{3}{4}$ hours?

7. _____

8. _____

9. An administrative assistant's gross weekly salary is $648. If $\frac{1}{4}$ of this amount is deducted for taxes, what is the administrative assistant's net weekly salary?

10. A sales representative has completed $\frac{3}{7}$ of a 1316-mile business trip. How many miles of the trip remain?

9. _____

10. _____

Name _____ Score _____

Divide.

1. $\dfrac{1}{9} \div \dfrac{2}{3}$

2. $\dfrac{5}{12} \div \dfrac{5}{16}$

3. $\dfrac{7}{10} \div \dfrac{14}{3}$

4. $\dfrac{3}{4} \div \dfrac{15}{6}$

5. $\dfrac{4}{11} \div \dfrac{12}{17}$

6. $3 \div \dfrac{9}{11}$

7. $\dfrac{4}{5} \div \dfrac{8}{5}$

8. $\dfrac{5}{24} \div \dfrac{5}{12}$

9. $\dfrac{10}{19} \div \dfrac{14}{19}$

10. $\dfrac{5}{9} \div \dfrac{2}{9}$

11. $\dfrac{16}{9} \div \dfrac{8}{3}$

12. $\dfrac{6}{11} \div \dfrac{3}{7}$

13. $0 \div \dfrac{1}{4}$

14. $\dfrac{9}{20} \div \dfrac{8}{55}$

15. $\dfrac{2}{15} \div \dfrac{7}{12}$

16. $\dfrac{9}{16} \div \dfrac{3}{28}$

17. $\dfrac{3}{4} \div \dfrac{15}{8}$

18. $\dfrac{7}{36} \div \dfrac{1}{8}$

19. $\dfrac{9}{20} \div \dfrac{11}{30}$

20. $\dfrac{14}{15} \div 7$

21. $\dfrac{5}{18} \div \dfrac{5}{9}$

22. $\dfrac{6}{18} \div \dfrac{12}{19}$

23. $\dfrac{4}{5} \div \dfrac{4}{5}$

24. $\dfrac{18}{35} \div \dfrac{3}{7}$

25. $\dfrac{1}{2} \div \dfrac{9}{8}$

26. $6 \div \dfrac{3}{8}$

27. $\dfrac{3}{7} \div \dfrac{9}{14}$

1. _____
2. _____
3. _____
4. _____
5. _____
6. _____
7. _____
8. _____
9. _____
10. _____
11. _____
12. _____
13. _____
14. _____
15. _____
16. _____
17. _____
18. _____
19. _____
20. _____
21. _____
22. _____
23. _____
24. _____
25. _____
26. _____
27. _____

Name _____

Score _____

Divide.

1. $\dfrac{3}{7} \div 3$

2. $8 \div \dfrac{16}{19}$

3. $24 \div \dfrac{4}{15}$

4. $4 \div 2\dfrac{2}{3}$

5. $\dfrac{4}{5} \div 2\dfrac{3}{4}$

6. $3\dfrac{3}{5} \div 9$

7. $1\dfrac{7}{12} \div \dfrac{7}{8}$

8. $21\dfrac{1}{4} \div 17$

9. $4\dfrac{3}{4} \div 3\dfrac{1}{3}$

10. $2\dfrac{3}{5} \div 2\dfrac{9}{10}$

11. $16\dfrac{3}{7} \div 1\dfrac{9}{14}$

12. $\dfrac{31}{35} \div 12\dfrac{2}{5}$

13. $15 \div 1\dfrac{1}{10}$

14. $18\dfrac{7}{16} \div 6\dfrac{3}{4}$

15. $30\dfrac{3}{8} \div 2\dfrac{1}{40}$

16. $5\dfrac{5}{12} \div 13\dfrac{13}{24}$

17. $\dfrac{3}{8} \div 8\dfrac{5}{8}$

18. $11\dfrac{1}{13} \div 48$

19. $9\dfrac{4}{8} \div 4\dfrac{9}{10}$

20. $18\dfrac{6}{22} \div 7\dfrac{1}{11}$

21. $20\dfrac{5}{9} \div 6\dfrac{2}{3}$

22. $\dfrac{25}{48} \div 15$

23. $3\dfrac{1}{2} \div 12\dfrac{11}{16}$

24. $4\dfrac{6}{7} \div 2\dfrac{1}{14}$

25. $9\dfrac{5}{11} \div 8\dfrac{2}{3}$

26. $17\dfrac{9}{14} \div \dfrac{13}{21}$

27. $10\dfrac{5}{18} \div 5\dfrac{5}{6}$

1. _____
2. _____
3. _____
4. _____
5. _____
6. _____
7. _____
8. _____
9. _____
10. _____
11. _____
12. _____
13. _____
14. _____
15. _____
16. _____
17. _____
18. _____
19. _____
20. _____
21. _____
22. _____
23. _____
24. _____
25. _____
26. _____
27. _____

Name _____   Score _____

Solve.

1. An investor purchased a $3\frac{1}{4}$-ounce gold coin for $2028. What was the price for one ounce?

2. A car traveled 143 miles in $3\frac{1}{4}$ hours. What was the car's average speed in miles per hour?

1. _____

2. _____

3. A station wagon used $15\frac{3}{10}$ gallons of gasoline on a 306-mile trip. How many miles did this car travel on one gallon of gasoline?

4. A volunteer for the psychology experiment answered "yes" to 18 of the questions on one questionnaire. This was $\frac{3}{8}$ of the total number of questions. Find the total number of questions on the questionnaire.

3. _____

4. _____

5. If 55,000 people voted for the new city ordinance, and this was $\frac{5}{6}$ of the total number of registered voters in the city, how many registered voters are there?

6. A $2\frac{1}{2}$-grain precious metal ingot sold for $30. Find the price per grain of the precious metal.

5. _____

6. _____

7. A doll maker uses $2\frac{2}{3}$ yards of fabric to make a doll. How many dolls can be made with 32 yards of fabric?

8. A building contractor bought $8\frac{1}{4}$ acres of land for $396,000. What was the cost for each acre?

7. _____

8. _____

9. A 14-foot piece of wood molding is cut into pieces $4\frac{1}{4}$ feet long. What is the length of the piece remaining after cutting as many pieces as possible?

10. Of the total number of students in the introductory mathematics class, $\frac{1}{3}$ were taking the course as a review and 82 students were taking the course for the first time. Find the total number of students in the mathematics class.

9. _____

10. _____

Name

Score

Place the correct symbol, < or >, between the two numbers.

1. $\dfrac{11}{17}$ $\dfrac{14}{17}$

2. $\dfrac{4}{5}$ $\dfrac{5}{9}$

3. $\dfrac{7}{10}$ $\dfrac{2}{3}$

4. $\dfrac{7}{12}$ $\dfrac{11}{15}$

5. $\dfrac{5}{7}$ $\dfrac{3}{4}$

6. $\dfrac{2}{3}$ $\dfrac{3}{5}$

7. $\dfrac{3}{10}$ $\dfrac{1}{6}$

8. $\dfrac{7}{9}$ $\dfrac{9}{14}$

9. $\dfrac{4}{11}$ $\dfrac{1}{2}$

10. $\dfrac{1}{4}$ $\dfrac{4}{15}$

11. $\dfrac{13}{20}$ $\dfrac{5}{7}$

12. $\dfrac{8}{13}$ $\dfrac{11}{18}$

13. $\dfrac{19}{24}$ $\dfrac{25}{36}$

14. $\dfrac{8}{15}$ $\dfrac{23}{35}$

15. $\dfrac{5}{9}$ $\dfrac{3}{5}$

16. $\dfrac{5}{22}$ $\dfrac{3}{8}$

17. $\dfrac{1}{4}$ $\dfrac{5}{26}$

18. $\dfrac{5}{12}$ $\dfrac{4}{9}$

19. $\dfrac{9}{16}$ $\dfrac{10}{17}$

20. $\dfrac{19}{22}$ $\dfrac{39}{46}$

21. $\dfrac{23}{30}$ $\dfrac{17}{20}$

22. $\dfrac{5}{6}$ $\dfrac{3}{4}$

23. $\dfrac{11}{14}$ $\dfrac{15}{19}$

24. $\dfrac{7}{24}$ $\dfrac{8}{15}$

25. $\dfrac{4}{5}$ $\dfrac{16}{21}$

26. $\dfrac{7}{15}$ $\dfrac{5}{8}$

27. $\dfrac{21}{25}$ $\dfrac{27}{35}$

1. _____
2. _____
3. _____
4. _____
5. _____
6. _____
7. _____
8. _____
9. _____
10. _____
11. _____
12. _____
13. _____
14. _____
15. _____
16. _____
17. _____
18. _____
19. _____
20. _____
21. _____
22. _____
23. _____
24. _____
25. _____
26. _____
27. _____

Name

Score

Simplify.

1. $\left(\dfrac{5}{11}\right)^2$

2. $\left(\dfrac{3}{7}\right)^2$

3. $\left(\dfrac{5}{8}\right)^2$

4. $\left(\dfrac{3}{5}\right)^2\left(\dfrac{5}{7}\right)$

5. $\left(\dfrac{3}{5}\right)\left(\dfrac{10}{21}\right)^2$

6. $\left(\dfrac{2}{15}\right)^2\left(\dfrac{3}{4}\right)^2$

7. $\left(\dfrac{1}{2}\right)^2\left(\dfrac{4}{7}\right)$

8. $\left(\dfrac{2}{21}\right)^2\left(\dfrac{3}{8}\right)$

9. $\left(\dfrac{2}{9}\right)^4\left(\dfrac{3}{16}\right)^2$

10. $\left(\dfrac{1}{3}\right)^6\left(\dfrac{9}{11}\right)^2$

11. $\left(\dfrac{5}{12}\right)^2\left(\dfrac{27}{50}\right)$

12. $\left(\dfrac{4}{5}\right)^2\left(\dfrac{10}{19}\right)^2$

13. $\left(\dfrac{5}{27}\right)^2\left(\dfrac{3}{10}\right)^3$

14. $\left(\dfrac{2}{9}\right)^3\left(\dfrac{3}{20}\right)^4$

15. $\left(\dfrac{5}{63}\right)\left(\dfrac{7}{15}\right)^2$

16. $\left(\dfrac{8}{15}\right)\left(\dfrac{5}{6}\right)\left(\dfrac{3}{8}\right)^2$

17. $\left(\dfrac{2}{5}\right)^2\left(\dfrac{5}{12}\right)^2\left(\dfrac{12}{17}\right)^2$

18. $\left(\dfrac{2}{3}\right)^2\left(\dfrac{3}{4}\right)^2\left(\dfrac{4}{7}\right)$

19. $\left(\dfrac{1}{2}\right)^3\left(\dfrac{3}{8}\right)\left(\dfrac{8}{9}\right)^2$

20. $4\cdot\left(\dfrac{5}{14}\right)\left(\dfrac{7}{10}\right)^2$

21. $\left(\dfrac{3}{5}\right)^2\left(\dfrac{2}{3}\right)^3\left(\dfrac{5}{8}\right)^3$

22. $\left(\dfrac{3}{7}\right)^2\left(\dfrac{14}{17}\right)\cdot17$

23. $\left(\dfrac{5}{11}\right)\left(\dfrac{2}{9}\right)^2\left(\dfrac{3}{4}\right)^2$

24. $\left(\dfrac{1}{6}\right)^2\left(\dfrac{1}{2}\right)^3\left(\dfrac{6}{7}\right)$

25. $\left(\dfrac{9}{16}\right)\left(\dfrac{2}{3}\right)^4\left(\dfrac{3}{13}\right)^3$

26. $\left(\dfrac{4}{5}\right)^2\left(\dfrac{7}{11}\right)\left(\dfrac{5}{14}\right)^2$

27. $13\cdot\left(\dfrac{1}{4}\right)^3\left(\dfrac{2}{13}\right)^2$

1. _____

2. _____

3. _____

4. _____

5. _____

6. _____

7. _____

8. _____

9. _____

10. _____

11. _____

12. _____

13. _____

14. _____

15. _____

16. _____

17. _____

18. _____

19. _____

20. _____

21. _____

22. _____

23. _____

24. _____

25. _____

26. _____

27. _____

Name _____

Score _____

Simplify using the Order of Operations Agreement.

1. $\dfrac{1}{4} + \dfrac{3}{7} - \dfrac{1}{6}$

2. $\dfrac{2}{3} - \dfrac{1}{5} + \dfrac{4}{9}$

3. $\dfrac{5}{8} + \dfrac{2}{9} \div \dfrac{8}{9}$

4. $\dfrac{4}{7} \div \dfrac{6}{11} + \dfrac{4}{5}$

5. $\dfrac{3}{4} \cdot \dfrac{5}{12} + \dfrac{9}{16}$

6. $\dfrac{1}{2} + \dfrac{4}{8} \cdot \dfrac{3}{10}$

7. $\left(\dfrac{5}{6}\right)^2 - \dfrac{2}{7}$

8. $\dfrac{7}{10} - \left(\dfrac{2}{3}\right)^3$

9. $\dfrac{5}{12} \cdot \left(\dfrac{4}{8} - \dfrac{8}{15}\right) + \dfrac{1}{3}$

10. $\dfrac{7}{8} \div \left(\dfrac{1}{4} + \dfrac{1}{10}\right) - \dfrac{7}{11}$

11. $\dfrac{3}{8} - \left(\dfrac{1}{2}\right)^3 + \dfrac{4}{9}$

12. $\dfrac{2}{5} + \left(\dfrac{2}{5}\right)^2 - \dfrac{4}{25}$

13. $\dfrac{1}{8} \div \left(\dfrac{1}{2}\right)^2 - \dfrac{1}{2}$

14. $\left(\dfrac{4}{7}\right)^2 \cdot \dfrac{3}{4} + \dfrac{11}{14}$

15. $\left(\dfrac{5}{8} + \dfrac{1}{4}\right) \cdot \dfrac{16}{21}$

16. $\dfrac{5}{6} \div \left(\dfrac{9}{10} - \dfrac{2}{15}\right)$

17. $\left(\dfrac{5}{9} + \dfrac{13}{18}\right) \div \left(\dfrac{2}{3}\right)^2$

18. $\left(\dfrac{1}{4}\right)^2 \cdot \left(\dfrac{7}{9} - \dfrac{1}{3}\right)$

19. $\dfrac{6}{7} \cdot \dfrac{14}{27} \div \dfrac{4}{9}$

20. $\left(\dfrac{1}{3}\right)^2 + \left(\dfrac{4}{5} - \dfrac{2}{3}\right) \div \dfrac{4}{5}$

21. $\left(\dfrac{4}{21}\right) \cdot \left(\dfrac{7}{8} + \dfrac{3}{4}\right) \div \dfrac{13}{14}$

22. $\dfrac{1}{6} + \left(\dfrac{1}{3} - \dfrac{3}{10}\right) \div \dfrac{7}{15}$

23. $\left(\dfrac{1}{2}\right)^3 - \left(\dfrac{2}{5}\right)\left(\dfrac{15}{22}\right) + \dfrac{1}{4}$

24. $\left(\dfrac{1}{3}\right)^2 + \left(\dfrac{5}{6} - \dfrac{3}{8}\right) \div \dfrac{5}{12}$

25. $\dfrac{8}{9} - \left(\dfrac{7}{10}\right)\left(\dfrac{2}{3}\right) \div \dfrac{4}{5}$

26. $\left(1\dfrac{1}{4} - \dfrac{2}{7} + \dfrac{1}{28}\right) \div \left(\dfrac{3}{13}\right)$

27. $\left(\dfrac{11}{12} - \dfrac{2}{3}\right) + \dfrac{15}{16} \div \left(\dfrac{1}{2}\right)^3$

1. _____

2. _____

3. _____

4. _____

5. _____

6. _____

7. _____

8. _____

9. _____

10. _____

11. _____

12. _____

13. _____

14. _____

15. _____

16. _____

17. _____

18. _____

19. _____

20. _____

21. _____

22. _____

23. _____

24. _____

25. _____

26. _____

27. _____

Name   Score

Write each decimal in words.

1. 0.39   **2.** 0.81   **3.** 2.007

1. _____

_____

2. _____

_____

3. _____

_____

4. 5.061   **5.** 15.4   **6.** 0.0086

4. _____

_____

5. _____

_____

6. _____

_____

7. 26.379   **8.** 514.3118   **9.** 1078.00002

7. _____

_____

8. _____

_____

9. _____

_____

Write each decimal in standard form.

10. Eight hundred thirty-four thousandths   **11.** Fifty-two millionths

10. _____

11. _____

12. Six and one hundred one ten-thousandths   **13.** Eighty-seven and nine hundred six thousandths

12. _____

13. _____

14. Four hundred sixty-two and thirty-five thousandths   **15.** Six thousand fourteen and one thousand eight ten-thousandths

14. _____

15. _____

16. Twenty-five and seven thousand two hundred ninety-three hundred-thousandths   **17.** Ninety-one and seventeen ten-thousandths

16. _____

17. _____

Name _____

Score _____

Round each decimal to the given place value.

1. 0.064 Tenths

2. 9.138 Tenths

3. 26.349 Tenths

4. 96.4501 Tenths

5. 65.34498 Hundredths

6. 13.01264 Hundredths

7. 517.677 Hundredths

8. 792.246 Hundredths

9. 2.09181 Thousandths

10. 6.27958 Thousandths

11. 79.4625 Thousandths

12. 51.00439 Thousandths

13. 0.04195 Ten-thousandths

14. 0.003642 Ten-thousandths

15. 4.37628 Ten-thousandths

16. 16.111919 Ten-thousandths

17. 0.249668 Hundred-thousandths

18. 0.009123 Hundred-thousandths

19. 7.880102 Hundred-thousandths

20. 11.732405 Hundred-thousandths

21. 1.49256 Nearest whole number

22. 3.60021 Nearest whole number

23. 70.50648 Nearest whole number

24. 0.0045895 Millionths

25. 0.10086438 Millionths

26. 2.11100649 Millionths

1. _____

2. _____

3. _____

4. _____

5. _____

6. _____

7. _____

8. _____

9. _____

10. _____

11. _____

12. _____

13. _____

14. _____

15. _____

16. _____

17. _____

18. _____

19. _____

20. _____

21. _____

22. _____

23. _____

24. _____

25. _____

26. _____

Name   Score

Add.

1. $4.825 + 31.7894 + 168.67$ 2. $25.25 + 7.4418 + 18.5$

3. $6.841 + 54 + 59.3254$ 4. $85.0013 + 1.407 + 3.1114$

5. $39.1 + 2.4713 + 28.008$ 6. $5.066 + 18.751 + 1.091$

7. $6.421 + 52.118 + 3 + 0.0098$ 8. $4.46 + 2.3845 + 2.5 + 0.0231$

9. $0.0014 + 83.9 + 46 + 148.0908$ 10. $75.514 + 0.199 + 29 + 8.356$

11.	0.2 + 1.09	12.	0.65 + 0.9	13.	4.215 + 6.8

14.	3.217 + 15.693	15.	12.093 + 3.146	16.	32.22 + 6.887

17.	2.7156 45.08 + 6.0406	18.	5.52 94.099 + 7.2148	19.	11 77.29 + 5.0531

20.	97.01 8.456 + 0.09	21.	42.056 15.6 + 0.336	22.	5.271 67.013 + 11.8

23.	75.603 2.74 29 + 53.008	24.	0.00051 6.8432 38.9121 + 4.786	25.	3.0018 2.9257 4.63 + 5.0578

1. _____
2. _____
3. _____
4. _____
5. _____
6. _____
7. _____
8. _____
9. _____
10. _____
11. _____
12. _____
13. _____
14. _____
15. _____
16. _____
17. _____
18. _____
19. _____
20. _____
21. _____
22. _____
23. _____
24. _____
25. _____

Name _____   Score _____

Solve.

1. You pay $819.12 for car insurance, $1258.75 for health insurance, and $617.20 for house insurance annually. Find the total amount spent annually on insurance.

2. Through a clothing catalogue, you purchased a bathrobe for $24.65, a pair of slippers for $7.98, and a shirt for $19.95. Find the total bill for the clothing.

1. _____

2. _____

3. Find the length of the shaft.

1.59 feet   2.66 feet

3.2 feet

◄——— Length ———►

4. It snowed for three consecutive days. It snowed 1.4 feet the first day, 0.3 feet the second day, and 2.25 feet the third day. Find the total snowfall for the three days.

3. _____

4. _____

5. An athlete bicycle 17.2 miles on Monday, 6.7 miles on Tuesday, and 12.4 miles on Wednesday. What was the total distance traveled for the three days?

6. The odometer of your car read 2456.2 miles. You drive 65.4 miles on Friday, 56.9 miles on Saturday, and 73.3 miles on Sunday. Find your odometer reading at the end of the three days.

5. _____

6. _____

7. You have $3641.59 in your checking account. You make deposits of $156.43, $341.97, $23.21, and $642.76. Find the amount in your checking account after making the deposits.

8. You have $821.65 in your checking account. You make deposits of $671.46, $88.90, $46.63, and $261.27. Find the amount in your checking account after making the deposits.

7. _____

8. _____

9. The deductions from a lab technician's weekly paycheck are as follows: $92.76 for taxes, $6.34 for insurance, and $21.25 for the company savings plan. Find the total weekly deduction.

10. A sales person's commission checks for six months are: $3259.04, $5462.36, $3423.96, $1350.98, $4812.74, and $3972.12. Find the total commission income for the six months.

9. _____

10. _____

Name _____
Score _____

Subtract and check.

1. $46.287 - 13.91$

2. $23.031 - 17.61$

3. $145.03 - 8.2174$

4. $650 - 56.413$

5. $14.1 - 11.7809$

6. $43.001 - 19.875$

7. $143.24 - 80.794$

8. $9.08 - 6.324$

9. $16.8263 - 9.93$

10. $\begin{array}{r} 0.452 \\ -0.39 \\ \hline \end{array}$

11. $\begin{array}{r} 0.847 \\ -0.25 \\ \hline \end{array}$

12. $\begin{array}{r} 9.406 \\ -6.315 \\ \hline \end{array}$

13. $\begin{array}{r} 28.72 \\ -6.318 \\ \hline \end{array}$

14. $\begin{array}{r} 0.17 \\ -0.0093 \\ \hline \end{array}$

15. $\begin{array}{r} 5.002 \\ -3.194 \\ \hline \end{array}$

16. $\begin{array}{r} 177.31 \\ -42.126 \\ \hline \end{array}$

17. $\begin{array}{r} 641 \\ -279.312 \\ \hline \end{array}$

18. $\begin{array}{r} 378.2 \\ -29.458 \\ \hline \end{array}$

19. $\begin{array}{r} 45.701 \\ -8.6225 \\ \hline \end{array}$

20. $\begin{array}{r} 31.006 \\ -12.7196 \\ \hline \end{array}$

21. $\begin{array}{r} 256.87 \\ -75.684 \\ \hline \end{array}$

22. $\begin{array}{r} 441.373 \\ -48.1356 \\ \hline \end{array}$

23. $\begin{array}{r} 729.338 \\ -95.8976 \\ \hline \end{array}$

24. $\begin{array}{r} 32 \\ -27.9841 \\ \hline \end{array}$

25. $\begin{array}{r} 94.05621 \\ -59.30712 \\ \hline \end{array}$

26. $\begin{array}{r} 7.65039 \\ -1.04882 \\ \hline \end{array}$

27. $\begin{array}{r} 83.66215 \\ -41.59876 \\ \hline \end{array}$

1. _____
2. _____
3. _____
4. _____
5. _____
6. _____
7. _____
8. _____
9. _____
10. _____
11. _____
12. _____
13. _____
14. _____
15. _____
16. _____
17. _____
18. _____
19. _____
20. _____
21. _____
22. _____
23. _____
24. _____
25. _____
26. _____
27. _____

Name _____   Score _____

Solve.

1. You buy a toaster for $16.83. How much change do you receive from a $20.00 bill?

2. A plane takes 0.021 inch off a board that is 1.6 inches thick. Find the resulting thickness of the board.

1. _____

2. _____

3. You bought a 5.3-pound roast. After you trimmed the fat, 3.5 pounds of meat remained. How much fat did you trim from the roast?

4. A competitive swimmer beat the team's record time of 56.27 seconds in the 100-meter freestyle competition by 0.89 seconds. What is the new record time?

3. _____

4. _____

5. During an experiment, a chemist noted that the temperature of a solution rose 5.75° the first minute and then rose another 7.5° the second minute. If the temperature of the solution was 38.25° after the first two minutes, what was the original temperature of the solution?

6. You had a balance of $895.60 in your checking account. You then wrote checks for $45.89, $5.79, and $19.50. Find the new balance in the checking account.

5. _____

6. _____

7. You had a balance of $1263.49 in your checking account. You then wrote checks for $54.91, $27.55, and $283.76. Find the new balance in the checking account.

8. You buy groceries for $32.78, shoes for $25.80, and a shirt for $16.95. How much change do you have left from a $100 bill?

7. _____

8. _____

9. A neighborhood deli had a monthly income of $7320.98 and expenses of $4600.29. Find the profit for the month.

10. A tax accountant has an income of $43,796.52 and pays $9,248.73 in taxes. Find the after tax income.

9. _____

10. _____

Name _____   Score _____

Multiply.

1.   0.5
     × 0.7

2.   6.4
     × 0.3

3.   5.6
     ×   9

4.   0.57
     ×   4

5.   0.28
     × 0.6

6.   5.1
     × 4.5

7.   0.96
     × 3.7

8.   2.63
     × 0.03

9.   5.83
     × 0.008

10.   0.67
     × 0.41

11.   52.9
     × 0.2

12.   1.07
     × 0.066

13.   24.8
     × 0.0019

14.   7.673
     × 0.45

15.   0.314
     × 0.061

16. 5.92×0.8

17. 0.76×0.6

18. 3.9×0.44

19. 8.21×10

20. 0.035×100

21. 6.8235×1000

22. 6.85×10^1

23. 0.035×10^2

24. 3.4×10^4

25.   3.278
     ×   4.6

26.   2.073
     ×   9.5

27.   0.063
     × 0.34

1. _____

2. _____

3. _____

4. _____

5. _____

6. _____

7. _____

8. _____

9. _____

10. _____

11. _____

12. _____

13. _____

14. _____

15. _____

16. _____

17. _____

18. _____

19. _____

20. _____

21. _____

22. _____

23. _____

24. _____

25. _____

26. _____

27. _____

Name _____   Score _____

Solve. Round to the nearest cent.

1. A sheet of plywood is 0.25 inch thick. Find the height of a stack of 150 sheets of plywood.

2. A shuttle bus transports students from a suburban college to work study jobs in the city and back again 5 times a day. If the distance between the college and the city is 11.3 miles, find the distance the shuttle bus travels in one day.

1. _____

2. _____

3. The cost of operating an electric saw for one hour is $0.062. How much does it cost to operate the motor for 55 hours?

4. Some states charge a meal tax on the food sold by restaurants. The tax in one state is found my multiplying the cost of the meal by 0.05. The mean you order at a restaurant costs $12.95. Find the total cost of the meal and tax.

3. _____

4. _____

5. A car is bought for $3600 down and payments of $141.50 each month for 24 months. Find the total cost of the car.

6. An inventory clerk earns a salary of $408 for a 40-hour work week. This week the clerk worked 7 hours of overtime at a rate of $15.30 for each hour of overtime. Find the inventory clerk's total income for this week.

5. _____

6. _____

7. You obtain a simple interest loan of $2450. The interest on the loan after one year is found my multiplying the loan amount by 0.12. Find the total amount due at the end of one year.

8. A nurse earns $811.20 for a 40-hour work week. This week the nurse worked 6 hours of overtime at a rate of $25.70 for each hour of overtime worked. Find the nurse's total income for the week.

7. _____

8. _____

9. You bought a house with payments of $1534.25 per month for 25 years. Find the total amount of the payments.

10. You bought a house with payments of $1024.50 per month for 20 years. Find the amount of the payments.

9. _____

10. _____

Name _____   Score _____

Divide.

1. $6\overline{)5.64}$ **2.** $0.7\overline{)2.24}$ **3.** $0.8\overline{)40}$ 1. _____

                                                                                      2. _____

                                                                                      3. _____

4. $0.3\overline{)25.95}$ **5.** $5\overline{)6.515}$ **6.** $2.9\overline{)0.899}$ 4. _____

                                                                                      5. _____

                                                                                      6. _____

7. $0.46\overline{)1.288}$ **8.** $0.09\overline{)42.3}$ **9.** $0.012\overline{)0.1116}$ 7. _____

                                                                                      8. _____

                                                                                      9. _____

Divide. Round to the nearest tenth.

10. $73.85 \div 9.6$ **11.** $0.473 \div 0.54$ **12.** $1.265 \div 0.043$ 10. _____

                                                                                      11. _____

                                                                                      12. _____

Divide. Round to the nearest hundredth.

13. $4.724 \div 17$ **14.** $8 \div 0.41$ **15.** $36.597 \div 53.2$ 13. _____

                                                                                      14. _____

                                                                                      15. _____

Divide. Round to the nearest thousandth.

16. $0.0717 \div 0.9$ **17.** $69.418 \div 83.5$ **18.** $0.4728 \div 57.5$ 16. _____

                                                                                      17. _____

                                                                                      18. _____

Divide. Round to the nearest whole number.

19. $34.19 \div 36$ **20.** $6.25 \div 0.4$ **21.** $5.125 \div 0.073$ 19. _____

                                                                                      20. _____

                                                                                      21. _____

Divide.

22. $7.23 \div 10$ **23.** $49.875 \div 10^2$ **24.** $3.7615 \div 10^3$ 22. _____

                                                                                      23. _____

                                                                                      24. _____

25. $53.072 \div 2.14$ **26.** $2.898 \div 0.92$ **27.** $0.01878 \div 0.03$ 25. _____

                                                                                      26. _____

                                                                                      27. _____

Name _____   Score _____

Solve.

1. A file clerk earns $79.20 for working an 8-hour day. How much does the file clerk earn in one hour?

2. An accountant earns $1390.40 for 35.2 hours' work. How much does the accountant earn in one hour?

1. _____

2. _____

3. You pay $1284.72 per year in life insurance premiums. You pay the premiums in 12 equal monthly payments. Find the amount of each monthly payment.

4. Gasoline tax is $0.19 per gallon. Find the number of gallons used during a month in which $518.84 was paid in taxes.

3. _____

4. _____

5. A tax of $1.39 is paid on each hair dryer sold by a store. This month the total tax paid on hair dryers was $31.97. How many hair dryers were sold?

6. A jogger ran 6.8 miles in 42.16 minutes. What was the jogger's average time per mile?

5. _____

6. _____

7. A $7,815.04 car can be bought for a down payment of $2677 and 36 equal monthly payments. Find the amount of each monthly payment.

8. Under the terms of your school loan, you must pay back a total of $15,655.20 over a ten-year period. What are your monthly payments?

7. _____

8. _____

9. A software company has 2,500,00 shares of stock. The company paid $8,125,000 in dividends. Find the dividend for each share of stock.

10. A 15.5-foot board is cut into pieces 3.3 feet long for a bookcase. What is the length of the piece remaining after cutting as many shelves as possible?

9. _____

10. _____

Name   Score

Convert the fraction to a decimal. Round to the nearest thousandth.

1. $\dfrac{5}{7}$ 2. $\dfrac{1}{15}$ 3. $\dfrac{5}{12}$

4. $\dfrac{8}{9}$ 5. $\dfrac{3}{14}$ 6. $\dfrac{6}{11}$

7. $2\dfrac{10}{17}$ 8. $\dfrac{7}{16}$ 9. $5\dfrac{2}{3}$

10. $\dfrac{9}{14}$ 11. $\dfrac{6}{7}$ 12. $\dfrac{5}{4}$

13. $8\dfrac{3}{22}$ 14. $15\dfrac{1}{2}$ 15. $\dfrac{53}{100}$

16. $\dfrac{35}{8}$ 17. $41\dfrac{3}{10}$ 18. $1\dfrac{2}{23}$

19. $6\dfrac{1}{3}$ 20. $\dfrac{5}{9}$ 21. $\dfrac{39}{11}$

22. $27\dfrac{1}{8}$ 23. $\dfrac{46}{7}$ 24. $\dfrac{13}{1000}$

25. $\dfrac{17}{18}$ 26. $6\dfrac{5}{9}$ 27. $10\dfrac{12}{21}$

1. _____
2. _____
3. _____
4. _____
5. _____
6. _____
7. _____
8. _____
9. _____
10. _____
11. _____
12. _____
13. _____
14. _____
15. _____
16. _____
17. _____
18. _____
19. _____
20. _____
21. _____
22. _____
23. _____
24. _____
25. _____
26. _____
27. _____

Name _____   Score _____

Convert the decimal to a fraction.

1. 0.7	**2.** 0.5	**3.** 0.46

1. _____

2. _____

3. _____

4. 0.74	**5.** 0.375	**6.** 0.205

4. _____

5. _____

6. _____

7. 2.55	**8.** 6.75	**9.** 18.4

7. _____

8. _____

9. _____

10. 12.3	**11.** 9.2	**12.** 14.5

10. _____

11. _____

12. _____

13. 4.138	**14.** 6.064	**15.** 3.35

13. _____

14. _____

15. _____

16. 9.93	**17.** $0.16\frac{4}{7}$	**18.** $0.93\frac{1}{3}$

16. _____

17. _____

18. _____

19. $0.11\frac{1}{9}$	**20.** 4.81	**21.** 0.055

19. _____

20. _____

21. _____

22. 0.015	**23.** 23.62	**24.** 0.44

22. _____

23. _____

24. _____

25. $0.83\frac{1}{3}$	**26.** $0.25\frac{1}{6}$	**27.** $0.77\frac{7}{9}$

25. _____

26. _____

27. _____

Name   Score

Place the correct symbol, < or >, between the numbers.

1. 0.23 0.3	**2.** 0.45 0.5	**3.** 4.54 4.45	**1.** _____
			2. _____
			3. _____
4. 7.10 7.01	**5.** 9.143 9.134	**6.** 0.091 0.101	**4.** _____
			5. _____
			6. _____
7. 0.399 $\frac{2}{5}$	**8.** 0.433 $\frac{7}{16}$	**9.** $\frac{5}{9}$ 0.54	**7.** _____
			8. _____
			9. _____
10. 0.58 $\frac{7}{12}$	**11.** $\frac{5}{7}$ 0.72	**12.** 0.26 $\frac{4}{15}$	**10.** _____
			11. _____
			12. _____
13. $\frac{1}{3}$ 0.32	**14.** $\frac{13}{16}$ 0.82	**15.** 0.626 $\frac{5}{8}$	**13.** _____
			14. _____
			15. _____
16. 0.4103 0.413	**17.** 0.25 0.256	**18.** 0.63 0.063	**16.** _____
			17. _____
			18. _____
19. 0.3 1.003	**20.** 0.7 0.079	**21.** 0.86 0.859	**19.** _____
			20. _____
			21. _____
22. $\frac{1}{8}$ 0.124	**23.** $\frac{11}{15}$ 0.734	**24.** 0.589 $\frac{3}{5}$	**22.** _____
			23. _____
			24. _____
25. 0.708 $\frac{17}{24}$	**26.** 0.167 $\frac{1}{6}$	**27.** $\frac{4}{7}$ 0.572	**25.** _____
			26. _____
			27. _____

Name _____   Score _____

Write the comparison as a ratio in simplest form using a fraction, a colon (:), and the word _to_.

1.	3 yards to 7 yards	2.	6 minutes to 16 minutes	1. _____
				2. _____
3.	12 months to 20 months	4.	33 tons to 44 tons	3. _____
				4. _____
5.	3 cents to 21 cents	6.	15 inches to 35 inches	5. _____
				6. _____
7.	20 days to 4 days	8.	23 quarts to 14 quarts	7. _____
				8. _____
9.	5 feet to 5 feet	10.	9 hours to 6 hours	9. _____
				10. _____
11.	$7 to $4	12.	12 pints to 36 pints	11. _____
				12. _____
13.	60 ounces to 55 ounces	14.	2 cups to 10 cups	13. _____
				14. _____
15.	28 pounds to 32 pounds	16.	70 years to 63 years	15. _____
				16. _____
17.	9 tons to 12 tons	18.	5 ounces to 11 ounces	17. _____
				18. _____
19.	14 days to 12 days	20.	3 minutes to 18 minutes	19. _____
				20. _____
21.	43 years to 86 years	22.	32 hours to 20 hours	21. _____
				22. _____
23.	27 feet to 12 feet	24.	$16 to $16	23. _____
				24. _____
25.	9 pounds to 10 pounds	26.	60 cents to 24 cents	25. _____
				26. _____

Name _____   Score _____

Solve.

1. You sleep 6 hours per day. Find the ratio of the number of hours you sleep to the number of hours in one day.

2. A bank cashed 176 checks on Thursday and 256 checks on Friday. Find the ratio of the number of checks cashed on Thursday to the number cashed on Friday.

1. _____

2. _____

3. In Rhode Island, the average summer and winter temperatures are 72°F and 28°F, respectively. Find the ratio of the summer temperature to the winter temperature.

4. For one month, a family spent $320 for food, and $720 for rent. Find the ratio of the amount spent for food to the amount spent for rent.

3. _____

4. _____

5. During one month, a furniture store sold 240 bedroom sets and 144 dining room sets. Find the ratio of dining room sets sold to the number of bedroom sets sold.

6. A home computer that sold for $2400 two years ago is now selling for $900. What is the ratio of the decrease in price to the original price?

5. _____

6. _____

7. Children in a town sold charity raffle tickets on Friday and Saturday. They sold 151 tickets on Friday and 453 tickets on Saturday. What is the ratio of the number of tickets sold on Saturday to the total number of tickets sold on both days?

8. A new homeowner bought a dining room table for $336 and 6 chairs for $92 each. What is the ratio for the total cost of the 6 chairs to the total cost of the dining room set?

7. _____

8. _____

9. The original value for a compact car was $7250. Two years later the car had a value of $5750. What is the ratio of the decrease in value to the original value?

10. A house had an original value of $72,000 but increased in value to $93,600 two years later. What is the ratio of the increase in value to the original value?

9. _____

10. _____

Name _____   Score _____

Write as a rate in simplest form.

1.   106 miles in 4 hours   2.   182 miles on 6 gallons of gasoline   1. _____

                                                                                          2. _____

3.   78 feet in 9 seconds   4. $310 for 15 toasters   3. _____

                                                                                          4. _____

5. $606 earned in 40 hours   6. $78 for 26 pounds   5. _____

                                                                                          6. _____

7. $2004 for 100 shares of stock   8.   4 tablets in 24 hours   7. _____

                                                                                          8. _____

9.   726 words in 12 minutes   10. $9150 earned in 6 months   9. _____

                                                                                          10. _____

11. 343 miles in 7 hours   12. 5512 words on 24 pages   11. _____

                                                                                          12. _____

13. $117 for 18 boards   14. 675 clams for 225 people   13. _____

                                                                                          14. _____

15. $10,816 earned in 26 weeks   16. 272 place settings on 34 tables   15. _____

                                                                                          16. _____

17. 615 pounds on 45 square inches 18. $203 for 29 feet   17. _____

                                                                                          18. _____

19. $5824 distributed among 4 departments   20. 868 seats in 8 lecture halls   19. _____

                                                                                          20. _____

21. 2144 miles on 64 gallons of gasoline   22. 570 calls in 12 hours   21. _____

                                                                                          22. _____

23. 135 cups of coffee in 9 urns   24. 156 houses on 612 acres   23. _____

                                                                                          24. _____

25. 1589 words on 14 pages   26. $247 for 19 pounds   25. _____

                                                                                          26. _____

Name _____   Score _____

Write as a unit rate.

1.	$30 for 12 feet	**2.**	323 miles on 7 gallons	**1.**	_____
				2.	_____
3.	402 pounds on 24 square inches	**4.**	$72,000 for 3 partners	**3.**	_____
				4.	_____
5.	126 gallons in 15 minutes	**6.**	498 miles in 10 hours	**5.**	_____
				6.	_____
7.	558 feet in 25 seconds	**8.**	$36 for 40 lbs	**7.**	_____
				8.	_____
9.	620 miles in 4 days	**10.**	204 heartbeats in 3 minutes	**9.**	_____
				10.	_____
11.	$18,000 earned in 12 months	**12.**	352 words in 5.5 minutes	**11.**	_____
				12.	_____
13.	$360.96 earned in 35.25 hours	**14.**	$15.52 for 16 plants	**13.**	_____
				14.	_____
15.	455.01 miles in 8.7 hours	**16.**	536.55 pounds on 73.5 square inches	**15.**	_____
				16.	_____
17.	$87.87 for 25.25 pounds	**18.**	216 words in 4.5 minutes	**17.**	_____
				18.	_____
19.	980.4 gallons in 17.2 minutes	**20.**	318.6 miles in 10.8 gallons	**19.**	_____
				20.	_____
21.	$500 for 4 partners	**22.**	$166.32 earned in 24.75 hours	**21.**	_____
				22.	_____
23.	252 heartbeats in 3.5 minutes	**24.**	888.3 miles in 7 days	**23.**	_____
				24.	_____
25.	$9000 earned in 8 months	**26.**	1107 feet in 90 seconds	**25.**	_____
				26.	_____

Name   Score

Solve. Round to the nearest hundredth.

1. An actuary makes $1620 in 40 hours. What is the actuary's wage per hour?

2. Twenty-four feet of lumber cost $62.16. What is the cost per foot?

1. _____

2. _____

3. During a city-wide power outage, the police station logged 651 calls in 5.25 hours. How many calls did the police station receive per hour?

4. A secretary typed a letter with 342 words in 6 minutes. Find the number of words typed in 1 minute.

3. _____

4. _____

5. A grocery store sells 3 pounds of grapes for $2.00. What is the cost of 1 pound?

6. During a sale, the house wares department of a store sold 48 coffee mugs for a total of $95.04. Find the cost per mug.

5. _____

6. _____

7. An investor purchased 350 shares of stock for $29,250. What is the cost per share?

8. A store bought 175 dish towels wholesale for $152.25 and sold them for $243.25. What was the store's profit per towel?

7. _____

8. _____

9. A company with 1,340,000 shares of stock distributed $2,412,000 in dividends. Find the dividend per share.

10. The total cost of making 5000 CDs was $6027. Of the CDs made, 100 did not meet company standards. What was the cost per CD for those CDs which met company standards?

9. _____

10. _____

Name　　　　　　　　　　　　　　　　　　　　　　　Score

Determine if the proportion is true or not true.

1.　$\dfrac{6}{7} = \dfrac{12}{14}$　　　　2.　$\dfrac{15}{9} = \dfrac{25}{15}$　　　　3.　$\dfrac{9}{18} = \dfrac{12}{24}$

4.　$\dfrac{16}{5} = \dfrac{80}{35}$　　　　5.　$\dfrac{3}{30} = \dfrac{11}{110}$　　　　6.　$\dfrac{25}{4} = \dfrac{80}{14}$

7.　$\dfrac{6}{8} = \dfrac{34}{46}$　　　　8.　$\dfrac{8}{2} = \dfrac{36}{9}$　　　　9.　$\dfrac{4}{5} = \dfrac{15}{16}$

10.　$\dfrac{7}{10} = \dfrac{35}{50}$　　　　11.　$\dfrac{24}{33} = \dfrac{34}{44}$　　　　12.　$\dfrac{18}{10} = \dfrac{63}{34}$

13.　$\dfrac{133 \text{ miles}}{3 \text{ hours}} = \dfrac{622 \text{ miles}}{14 \text{ hours}}$　　　　14.　$\dfrac{21 \text{ feet}}{5 \text{ seconds}} = \dfrac{63 \text{ feet}}{15 \text{ seconds}}$

15.　$\dfrac{606 \text{ words}}{10 \text{ minutes}} = \dfrac{302 \text{ words}}{5 \text{ minutes}}$　　　　16.　$\dfrac{48 \text{ cents}}{4 \text{ hours}} = \dfrac{60 \text{ cents}}{5 \text{ hours}}$

17.　$\dfrac{238 \text{ miles}}{7 \text{ gallons}} = \dfrac{476 \text{ miles}}{12 \text{ gallons}}$　　　　18.　$\dfrac{\$600}{36 \text{ hours}} = \dfrac{\$400}{24 \text{ hours}}$

19.　$\dfrac{155 \text{ minutes}}{25 \text{ miles}} = \dfrac{341 \text{ minutes}}{55 \text{ miles}}$　　　　20.　$\dfrac{126 \text{ calls}}{6 \text{ hours}} = \dfrac{86 \text{ calls}}{4 \text{ hours}}$

21.　$\dfrac{282 \text{ houses}}{47 \text{ acres}} = \dfrac{188 \text{ houses}}{33 \text{ acres}}$　　　　22.　$\dfrac{450 \text{ gallons}}{60 \text{ minutes}} = \dfrac{180 \text{ gallons}}{24 \text{ minutes}}$

23.　$\dfrac{6200 \text{ words}}{40 \text{ pages}} = \dfrac{7750 \text{ words}}{50 \text{ pages}}$　　　　24.　$\dfrac{375 \text{ cars}}{250 \text{ people}} = \dfrac{1218 \text{ cars}}{312 \text{ people}}$

25.　$\dfrac{\$17{,}520}{12 \text{ months}} = \dfrac{\$43{,}800}{30 \text{ months}}$　　　　26.　$\dfrac{\$4950}{200 \text{ shares}} = \dfrac{\$6180}{250 \text{ shares}}$

1.　_____

2.　_____

3.　_____

4.　_____

5.　_____

6.　_____

7.　_____

8.　_____

9.　_____

10.　_____

11.　_____

12.　_____

13.　_____

14.　_____

15.　_____

16.　_____

17.　_____

18.　_____

19.　_____

20.　_____

21.　_____

22.　_____

23.　_____

24.　_____

25.　_____

26.　_____

Name _____   Score _____

Solve. Round to the nearest hundredth.

1. $\dfrac{3}{5} = \dfrac{n}{10}$

2. $\dfrac{n}{8} = \dfrac{20}{32}$

3. $\dfrac{14}{24} = \dfrac{7}{n}$

4. $\dfrac{4}{28} = \dfrac{n}{196}$

5. $\dfrac{21}{n} = \dfrac{14}{16}$

6. $\dfrac{6}{20} = \dfrac{5}{n}$

7. $\dfrac{8}{n} = \dfrac{9}{27}$

8. $\dfrac{13}{36} = \dfrac{39}{n}$

9. $\dfrac{n}{18} = \dfrac{5}{9}$

10. $\dfrac{42}{15} = \dfrac{n}{12}$

11. $\dfrac{n}{8} = \dfrac{9}{12}$

12. $\dfrac{18}{n} = \dfrac{96}{132}$

13. $\dfrac{10}{20} = \dfrac{12}{n}$

14. $\dfrac{5}{11} = \dfrac{n}{9}$

15. $\dfrac{35}{14} = \dfrac{15}{n}$

16. $\dfrac{35}{n} = \dfrac{22}{11}$

17. $\dfrac{90}{n} = \dfrac{36}{3}$

18. $\dfrac{8}{18} = \dfrac{2}{n}$

19. $\dfrac{19}{n} = \dfrac{54}{135}$

20. $\dfrac{n}{28} = \dfrac{42}{18}$

21. $\dfrac{30}{n} = \dfrac{24}{14}$

22. $\dfrac{n}{15} = \dfrac{0.8}{5.6}$

23. $\dfrac{1.8}{18} = \dfrac{n}{12}$

24. $\dfrac{3.4}{20} = \dfrac{5.1}{n}$

25. $\dfrac{13.9}{n} = \dfrac{26.28}{51.7}$

26. $\dfrac{5149}{278} = \dfrac{156}{n}$

27. $\dfrac{n}{4.21} = \dfrac{6.793}{1.248}$

1. _____
2. _____
3. _____
4. _____
5. _____
6. _____
7. _____
8. _____
9. _____
10. _____
11. _____
12. _____
13. _____
14. _____
15. _____
16. _____
17. _____
18. _____
19. _____
20. _____
21. _____
22. _____
23. _____
24. _____
25. _____
26. _____
27. _____

Name _____ Score _____

Solve. Round to the nearest hundredth.

1. A life insurance policy costs $4.52 for every $1000 of insurance. At this rate, what is the cost for $20,000 worth of life insurance?

2. A liquid plant food is prepared by using one gallon of water for each 1.5 teaspoon of plant food. At this rate, how many teaspoons of plant food are required for 7 gallons of water?

1. _____

2. _____

3. A $19.75 sales tax is charged for a $395 purchase. At this rate, what is the sales tax for a $621 purchase?

4. The scale on the plans for a new office building is 1 inch equals 4 feet. How long is a room that measures $8\frac{1}{2}$ inches on the drawing?

3. _____

4. _____

5. A stock investment of 150 shares paid a dividend of $555. At this rate, what dividend would be paid on 280 shares of stock?

6. A bank demands a loan payment of $18.95 each month for every $1000 borrowed. At this rate, what is the monthly payment for a $6000 loan?

5. _____

6. _____

7. A transistor company expects that 3 out of 245 transistors will be defective. How many defective transistors will be found in a batch of 184,485 transistors?

8. A department store makes a profit of $15.20 on every 25 rolls of film sold. How much profit is made if 16 rolls of film are sold?

7. _____

8. _____

9. For every 10 people who work in a city, 7 of them commute by public transportation. If 34,600 people work in the city, how many of them do not take public transportation?

10. For every 15 gallons of water pumped into the holding tank, 8 gallons were pumped out. After 930 gallons had been pumped in, how much water remained in the tank?

9. _____

10. _____

64

Name _____   Score _____

Write as a fraction and as a decimal.

1.   39%

2.   64%

3.   125%

4.   26%

5.   85%

6.   20%

7.   450%

8.   19%

9.   55%

1. _____

2. _____

3. _____

4. _____

5. _____

6. _____

7. _____

8. _____

9. _____

Write as a fraction.

10. $7\frac{8}{9}\%$

11. $7\frac{2}{3}\%$

12. $25\frac{4}{5}\%$

13. $64\frac{1}{2}\%$

14. $43\frac{1}{3}\%$

15. $99\frac{3}{5}\%$

10. _____

11. _____

12. _____

13. _____

14. _____

15. _____

Write as a decimal.

16.   67.5%

17.   34.07%

18.   57.9%

19.   40%

20.   13.89%

21.   2.01%

16. _____

17. _____

18. _____

19. _____

20. _____

21. _____

Name   Score

Write as a percent.

1. 0.32	**2.** 0.96	**3.** 0.04	**1.** _____
			2. _____
			3. _____

4. 1.97	**5.** 2.14	**6.** 0.009	**4.** _____
			5. _____
			6. _____

7. 0.68	**8.** 0.12	**9.** 0.107	**7.** _____
			8. _____
			9. _____

Write as a percent. Round to the nearest tenth.

10. $\dfrac{25}{60}$ **11.** $1\dfrac{8}{9}$ **12.** $\dfrac{4}{7}$

10. _____
11. _____
12. _____

13. $64\dfrac{1}{2}\%$ **14.** $\dfrac{3}{5}$ **15.** $1\dfrac{5}{6}$

13. _____
14. _____
15. _____

Write as a percent. Write the remainder in fractional form.

16. $\dfrac{5}{11}$ **17.** $\dfrac{2}{9}$ **18.** $1\dfrac{1}{7}$

16. _____
17. _____
18. _____

19. $\dfrac{3}{8}$ **20.** $\dfrac{1}{15}$ **21.** $\dfrac{7}{12}$

19. _____
20. _____
21. _____

Name _____   Score _____

Solve.

1. 8% of 45 is what?

2. 15% of 100 is what?

3. 26% of 70 is what?

4. 53% of 90 is what?

5. What is 45% of 60?

6. What is 35% of 55?

7. What is 65% of 135.5?

8. What is 52% of 24.4?

9. What is 4% of 2800?

10. What is 0.02% of 250?

11. 5% of 900 is what?

12. 0.025% of 800 is what?

13. 150% of 98 is what?

14. 220% of 6 is what?

15. Find 12% of 540.

16. Find 30% of 17.5.

17. Find 7.9% of 120.

18. Find 2.5% of 440.

19. Find 0.08% of 375

20. Find 25% of 144.

21. What is 12.5% of 1540?

22. What is $6\frac{1}{4}$% of 620?

23. What is $33\frac{1}{3}$% of 591?

24. What is $83\frac{1}{3}$% of 72?

25. 43.18% of 800 is what?

26. 16.83% of 500 is what?

1. _____

2. _____

3. _____

4. _____

5. _____

6. _____

7. _____

8. _____

9. _____

10. _____

11. _____

12. _____

13. _____

14. _____

15. _____

16. _____

17. _____

18. _____

19. _____

20. _____

21. _____

22. _____

23. _____

24. _____

25. _____

26. _____

Name _____   Score _____

Solve.

1. A company uses 14% of its $55,000 budget for office supplies. What amount of the budget is spent for office supplies?

2. A company survey found that $16\frac{2}{3}\%$ of the employees were dissatisfied with the company's cafeteria. If 2400 employees were surveyed, how many employees were dissatisfied with the cafeteria?

3. A person purchases a television which costs $259 and pays a sales tax which is 5% of the cost. What is the sales tax on the television?

4. During a power outage, 9% of the city's 46,500 homes were without electricity. How many homes were affected by the power outage?

5. A nursery sold 450 geranium plants in June. In July, the nursery increased its sales by 8%. How many geranium plants were sold in July?

6. A restaurant serves 35% more ice cream in June than it does in May. How much ice cream does the restaurant serve in June if it serves 12 gallons of ice cream in May?

7. A quality control inspector found that 0.2% of the 2500 flathead screws inspected were defective. How many screws were not defective?

8. A plumber's hourly wage is $18.50 before an 8% raise. What is the new hourly wage?

9. A truck retail sales company makes a 5.3% profit on sales of $520,000. Find the profit.

10. An office building has an appraised value of $8,000,000. The real estate taxes are 2.35% of the appraised value of the building. Find the real estate taxes.

1. _____

2. _____

3. _____

4. _____

5. _____

6. _____

7. _____

8. _____

9. _____

10. _____

Name _____　　　　　Score _____

Solve.

1.　What percent of 112 is 35?　　　2.　What percent of 72 is 12?　　　1. _____

　　　　　　　　　　　　　　　　　　　　　　　　　　　　　　　　　2. _____

3.　What percent of 75 is 60?　　　4.　What percent of 45 is 27?　　　3. _____

　　　　　　　　　　　　　　　　　　　　　　　　　　　　　　　　　4. _____

5.　17 is what percent of 85?　　　6.　27 is what percent of 60?　　　5. _____

　　　　　　　　　　　　　　　　　　　　　　　　　　　　　　　　　6. _____

7.　What percent of 8 is 24?　　　　8.　What percent of 24 is 50?　　　7. _____

　　　　　　　　　　　　　　　　　　　　　　　　　　　　　　　　　8. _____

9.　15 is what percent of 100?　　　10.　54 is what percent of 150?　　9. _____

　　　　　　　　　　　　　　　　　　　　　　　　　　　　　　　　　10. _____

11.　135 is what percent of 3000?　12.　48 is what percent of 1200?　11. _____

　　　　　　　　　　　　　　　　　　　　　　　　　　　　　　　　　12. _____

13.　What percent of 620 is 465?　　14.　What percent of 130 is 13?　13. _____

　　　　　　　　　　　　　　　　　　　　　　　　　　　　　　　　　14. _____

15.　What percent of 5 is 1.5?　　　16.　What percent of 3.8 is 0.19?　15. _____

　　　　　　　　　　　　　　　　　　　　　　　　　　　　　　　　　16. _____

17.　18.5 is what percent of 3.7?　　18.　4.5 is what percent of 40?　17. _____

　　　　　　　　　　　　　　　　　　　　　　　　　　　　　　　　　18. _____

19.　0.05 is what percent of 10?　　20.　2.444 is what percent of 47?　19. _____

　　　　　　　　　　　　　　　　　　　　　　　　　　　　　　　　　20. _____

21.　What percent of 9000 is 2745?　22.　What percent of 7500 is 2500?　21. _____

　　　　　　　　　　　　　　　　　　　　　　　　　　　　　　　　　22. _____

23.　425 is what percent of 2550?　24.　163 is what percent of 815?　23. _____

　　　　　　　　　　　　　　　　　　　　　　　　　　　　　　　　　24. _____

25.　What percent of 83.2 is 7.904?　26.　What percent of 16.85 is 25.275?　25. _____

　　　　　　　　　　　　　　　　　　　　　　　　　　　　　　　　　26. _____

Name   Score

Solve.

1. A used car salesperson sold 6 of the 50 cars in the lot. What percent of the total number of cars in the lot were sold?

2. An investor received a dividend of $540 on an investment of $4500. What percent of the investment is the dividend?

1. _____

2. _____

3. A company's stock is trading at $55 and pays a dividend of $3.30. What percent of the stock price is the dividend?

4. A home sold for $35,900 in 1972. The same home in 1982 had a value of $82,570. What percent of the 1972 value is the 1982 value?

3. _____

4. _____

5. A survey of 1760 people showed that 352 people favored the incumbent mayor. What percent of the people surveyed favored the incumbent mayor?

6. Of the 3900 resistors tested, 117 were found defective. What percent of the total number of resistors were defective?

5. _____

6. _____

7. A total of $4200 was paid in taxes on an income of $16,800. Find the percent of the total income paid in taxes.

8. An advertising survey of 265 people found that 53 liked a new toothpaste. What percent of the people surveyed did not like the new toothpaste?

7. _____

8. _____

9. A 2.3-acre piece of oceanfront property is appraised at $250,000. The land is bought for $300,000. What percent of the appraised value is the purchase price?

10. A construction company spent $125,000 of its $1,000,000 equipment budget for a bulldozer. What percent of the equipment budget was spent for the bulldozer?

9. _____

10. _____

Name   Score

Solve.

1.   20% of what is 37?   2.   21% of what is 84?   1. _____

                                                                             2. _____

3.   12 is 24% of what?   4.   42 is 70% of what?   3. _____

                                                                             4. _____

5.   12 is 12% of what?   6.   35 is 50% of what?   5. _____

                                                                             6. _____

7.   25% of what is 30.75?   8.   60% of what is 110.4?   7. _____

                                                                             8. _____

9.   3.1% of what is 155?   10. 15.5% of what is 124?   9. _____

                                                                             10. _____

11. 130% of what is 741?   12. 250% of what is 40?   11. _____

                                                                             12. _____

13. 264 is 24% of what?   14. 63 is 18% of what?   13. _____

                                                                             14. _____

15. 1.26 is 2.8% of what?   16. 235.35 is 52.3% of what?   15. _____

                                                                             16. _____

17. 40% of what is 8.4?   18. 68% of what is 136?   17. _____

                                                                             18. _____

19. 0.6% of what is 5.34?   20. 0.75% of what is 12.75?   19. _____

                                                                             20. _____

21. 59 is $66\frac{2}{3}$ % of what? 22. 9.5 is $16\frac{2}{3}$ % of what? 21. _____

                                                                             22. _____

23. 20 is $83\frac{1}{3}$ % of what? 24. 86 is $33\frac{1}{3}$ % of what? 23. _____

                                                                             24. _____

25. 7.5% of what is 4.65?   26. 5.6% of what is 4.382?   25. _____

                                                                             26. _____

Name

Score

Solve.

1. A used car was purchased for $5750. This was 46% of the new car cost. Find the new car cost.

2. A growing city has 456 business establishments. This is 120% of the number of businesses in the city two years ago. How many business establishments were there in the city two years ago?

1. _____

2. _____

3. A student answered 14 of the questions on the two-hour exam incorrectly. This was 25% of the total number of exam questions. How many questions were on the exam?

4. A historian's personal library contains 108 fiction novels. This is 4% of the total number of books in the library. Find the number of books in the historian's library.

3. _____

4. _____

5. A police station received 8 calls concerning shoplifting in one day. This was $33\frac{1}{3}$% of the total number of calls received that day. How many calls in all did the police station receive?

6. A carpenter's wage this year is $17.25 an hour. This is 115% of last year's wage. What was the increase in the hourly wage over last year?

5. _____

6. _____

7. A company spent $184,000 on advertising in one year. This was 23% of the company's annual budget. What was the company's annual budget?

8. In a parking garage 147 spaces were occupied. This was 98% of the total number of parking spaces. Find the number of unoccupied spaces in the garage.

7. _____

8. _____

9. Defects were found in 1659 DVDs. This was 0.21% of the total number of DVDs produced in one month. Find the total number of DVDs produced in that month.

10. An apartment complex is bought for $6,000,000. This is 80% of its appraised value. Find the apartment complex's appraised value.

9. _____

10. _____

Name   Score

Solve.

1. 34% of 850 is what?   2. What is 15% of 400?

                 1. _____

                 2. _____

3. 54 is what percent of 180?   4. What percent of 120 is 42?

                 3. _____

                 4. _____

5. 90% of what is 54?   6. 146 is 73% of what?

                 5. _____

                 6. _____

7. What percent of 324 is 162?   8. What percent of 140 is 35?

                 7. _____

                 8. _____

9. 153 is 30% of what?   10. 7.5% of what is 60?

                 9. _____

                10. _____

11. 222 is what percent of 600?   12. 144 is what percent of 32?

                11. _____

                12. _____

13. What is 160% of 480?   14. 210% of 390 is what?

                13. _____

                14. _____

15. 27 is 45% of what?   16. 24% of what is 36?

                15. _____

                16. _____

17. What percent of 110 is 44?   18. 65 is what percent of 125?

                17. _____

                18. _____

19. What percent of 220 is 11?   20. What percent of 72 is 9?

                19. _____

                20. _____

21. 91 is what percent of 26?   22. What percent of 46 is 184?

                21. _____

                22. _____

23. 0.2% of what is 33?   24. 15 is 0.6% of what?

                23. _____

                24. _____

25. Find 1.75% of 8000.   26. 435 is what percent of 6000?

                25. _____

                26. _____

Name _____   Score _____

Solve.

1. A soccer team won 51 out of 68 games they played. What percent of the games played did they win?

2. During shipping, 600 of the 4800 light bulbs were damaged. What percent of the number of light bulbs were damaged in the shipping?

3. A supermarket reduced the price of roast beef to $2.24 per pound, which is 80% of the original price. What was the original price?

4. A growing company reinvested 63% of the $120,000 it earned into research and development. How much of the money earned was reinvested into research and development?

5. A monthly state income tax is 12% of the amount earned over $1800. What state income tax does a person pay on a salary of $3000?

6. During an inspection of 120 motorcycles, 3 of them did not pass the safety test. What percent of the motorcycles inspected did pass the safety test?

7. A down payment of $1305 was paid on a new car. The down payment is 15% of the cost of the car. Find the cost of the car.

8. An administrative assistant types 70 words per minute with 98% accuracy. During 5 minutes of typing, how many errors does the secretary make?

9. You bought a boat one year ago. Since then it has depreciated to $1018.50, which is 9.7% of the price you paid for it. How much did you pay for the boat?

10. A down payment of $15,600 was paid on a new house costing $78,000. What percent of the purchase price is the down payment?

1. _____

2. _____

3. _____

4. _____

5. _____

6. _____

7. _____

8. _____

9. _____

10. _____

Name _____   Score _____

Find the unit cost. Round to the nearest tenth of a cent.

1. Salad dressing, 8 ounces for $1.16	2. Non-dairy creamer, 11 ounces for $1.42	3. Soup, $10\frac{1}{2}$ ounces for $0.36	1. _____ 2. _____ 3. _____
4. Grape juice, 64 ounces for $1.78	5. Black pepper, 2 ounces for $0.63	6. Peanut butter, 28 ounces for $2.62	4. _____ 5. _____ 6. _____
7. Bouillon cubes, 15 for $0.59	8. Shampoo, 15 ounces for $2.87	9. Detergent, 49 ounces for $1.79	7. _____ 8. _____ 9. _____
10. Crackers, 7 ounces for $1.13	11. Anti-freeze, 64 ounces for $4.99	12. Fried chicken, 15 pieces for $8.99	10. _____ 11. _____ 12. _____
13. Pot pies, 3 for $0.89	14. Corn chips, 7 ounces for $1.39	15. Bagels, 8 for $0.79	13. _____ 14. _____ 15. _____
16. Shoe polish, $3\frac{1}{2}$ ounces for $1.48	17. Spaghetti, 16 ounces for $0.54	18. Potatoes, 5 pounds for $1.29	16. _____ 17. _____ 18. _____
19. Spray starch, 22 ounces for $1.29	20. Clothes pins, 24 for $1.29	21. Bread, 16 ounces for $0.88	19. _____ 20. _____ 21. _____
22. Photograph processing, 24 pictures for $10.08	23. Cat food, 18 ounces for $0.94	24. Shortening, 3 pounds for $2.69	22. _____ 23. _____ 24. _____

Name _____

Score _____

Find the more economical purchase.

1. Syrup,
   15 ounces for $0.94 or
   24 ounces for $1.51

2. Grape jelly,
   32 ounces for $1.29 or
   24 ounces for $0.94

3. Franks,
   16 ounces for $1.79 or
   12 ounces for $1.30

4. Facial tissue,
   175 for $0.79 or
   125 for $0.63

5. Aspirins,
   50 for $1.89 or
   75 for $3.00

6. Yogurt,
   6 ounces for $0.46 or
   10 ounces for $0.74

7. Cream cheese,
   8 ounces for $0.89 or
   12 ounces for $1.39

8. Peanut butter,
   18 ounces for $1.39 or
   22 ounces for $1.75

9. Orange juice,
   64 ounces for $1.35 or
   12 ounces for $0.33

10. Light bulbs,
    4 for $1.99 or
    6 for $3.11

11. Razor blades,
    9 for $1.27 or
    12 for $1.74

12. Ice cream,
    32 ounces for $2.79 or
    16 ounces for $1.44

13. Coffee,
    16 ounces for $2.49 or
    12 ounces for $2.16

14. Flour,
    5 pounds for $0.89 or
    2 pounds for $0.35

15. Mushrooms,
    8 ounces for $0.99 or
    2.5 ounces for $0.35

16. Charcoal,
    10 pounds for $2.67 or
    5 pounds for $1.35

17. Bread,
    24 ounces for $0.93 or
    18 ounces for $0.54

18. Frozen lemonade,
    6 ounces for $0.39 or
    12 ounces for $0.79

19. Sandwich bags,
    50 bags for $1.09 or
    60 bags for $1.44

20. Liquid detergent,
    9 ounces for $0.69 or
    6.5 ounces for $0.39

21. Biscuits,
    9 ounces for $0.59 or
    14 ounces for $0.92

22. Paper towels,
    119 sheets for $0.79 or
    144 sheets for $0.96

23. Cheese slices,
    12 ounces for $1.27 or
    8 ounces for $0.89

24. Bacon,
    12 ounces for $1.28 or
    20 ounces for $2.19

1. _____
2. _____
3. _____
4. _____
5. _____
6. _____
7. _____
8. _____
9. _____
10. _____
11. _____
12. _____
13. _____
14. _____
15. _____
16. _____
17. _____
18. _____
19. _____
20. _____
21. _____
22. _____
23. _____
24. _____

Name _____   Score _____

Solve.

1. Pork chops cost $1.79 per pound.
    Find the cost of 4 pounds.

2. Decorative stepping stones cost
    $1.15 per stone. Find the cost of
    24 stones.

3. Honeydew melons cost $1.99 each.
    Find the total cost of 4 melons.

4. Grapes cost $0.68 per pound. Find
    The cost of 2.8 pounds. Round
    to the nearest cent.

5. Potato chips cost 12.3¢ per ounce.
    Find the cost of 9.5 ounces. Round
    to the nearest cent.

6. Salami costs $3.49 per pound.
    Find the cost of 0.85 pounds.
    Round to the nearest cent.

7. Carrots cost $0.41 per pound. Find
    The total cost of 1.6 pounds. Round
    to the nearest cent.

8. Baked ham costs $3.59 per pound.
    Find the total cost of 3.2 pounds.
    Round to the nearest cent.

9. Peanuts cost $2.00 per pound. Find
    the total cost of $\frac{5}{8}$ pounds.

10. Motor oil costs $1.18 per quart.
    Find the cost of 6 quarts of oil.

11. A two-piece meal of fried chicken
    costs $2.65. Find the total cost of 4
    two-piece meals.

12. Raisins cost $1.79 per pound. Find
    the total cost of 0.75 pounds. Round
    to the nearest cent.

13. Heavy duty lawn bags cost $2.49 per
    package. How much change do you
    receive from $20.00 when purchasing
    4 packages of lawn bags?

14. Plywood costs $9.99 per sheet. How
    much change do you receive from
    $50.00 when purchasing 4 sheets of
    plywood?

15. Redwood stains costs $12.50 per gallon.
    How much change do you receive
    from $50.00 when purchasing 3 gallons?

16. Top soil costs $37.50 per truck load.
    How much change do you receive
    from $100.00 when purchasing
    2 truck loads of top soil?

1. _____

2. _____

3. _____

4. _____

5. _____

6. _____

7. _____

8. _____

9. _____

10. _____

11. _____

12. _____

13. _____

14. _____

15. _____

16. _____

Name _____   Score _____

Solve. Round to the nearest tenth of a percent or to the nearest tenth of a cent.

1. The value of a $7000 investment increased $1750. What percent increase does this represent?

2. A sweater which sold for $24 last month increased in price by $2. What percent increase does this represent?

1. _____

2. _____

3. The average price of fuel oil rose from $0.75 to $1.00 in six months. What was the percent increase in the price of fuel oil?

4. The number of students enrolled in a speed reading course increased from 60 to 66 during the first 10 days of school. What is the percent increase?

3. _____

4. _____

5. A manufacturer of ceiling fans increased its monthly out put of 1500 by 10%. What is the amount of increase?

6. An advertising agency increased its 200 billboards by 15% during the past year. How many billboards does the agency have now?

5. _____

6. _____

7. The employees of a manufacturing plant received a 6% increase in pay.
   a. What is the amount of the increase for an employee who makes $225 per week?
   b. What is the weekly wage for the employee after the wage increase?

8. A supervisor's salary this year is $32,000. This salary will increase by 8% next year.
   a. What is the amount of increase?
   b. What will the salary be next year?

7. a. _____

   b. _____

8. a. _____

   b. _____

9. A college increased its number of parking spaces from 1000 to 1050.
   a. How many new spaces were added?
   b. What percent increase does this represent?

10. A town plans to increase its 4000 water meters by 7.5%.
    a. How many more water meters is this?
    b. What will the total number of water meters be after this increase?

9. a. _____

   b. _____

10. a. _____

    b. _____

11. A cafeteria increased the number of items on the menu from 80 to 90. What percent of increase does this represent?

12. The amount of gasoline used by a fleet of cars increased from 200 to 230 gallons per day. What percent increase does this represent?

11. _____

12. _____

Name _____   Score _____

Solve.

1. A store manager used a markup rate of 30% on all desk lamps. What is the markup on a lamp which costs the store $26?

2. A manager of a natural food store determines that the markup rate of 17% is necessary to make a profit. What is the markup on an item which costs the dealer $2?

3. An automobile tire dealer uses a markup rate of 32%. What is the markup on tires which cost the dealer $34?

4. The markup on a necklace which costs a jeweler $60 is $36. What markup rate does this represent? (Solve the basic percent equation for percent.)

5. A beach-wear shop uses a markup rate of 40% on a bathing suit which costs the shop $34.
   a. What is the markup?
   b. What is the selling price?

6. A department store uses a markup rate of 44% on its Model XL food processor which costs the store $45.
   a. What is the markup?
   b. What is the selling price?

7. A produce market pays $1.09 for pineapples. The market uses a 55% markup rate.
   a. What is the markup?
   b. What is the selling price?

8. A garden shop uses a markup rate of 35% on a rose trellis which costs the store $26.
   a. What is the markup?
   b. What is the selling price?

9. A store uses a markup rate of 38%. What is the selling price for the DVD player which costs the store $47?

10. What is the selling price on a pair of jogging shoes which costs a store $31? The store uses a markup rate of 44%.

1. _____

2. _____

3. _____

4. _____

5. a. _____

   b. _____

6. a. _____

   b. _____

7. a. _____

   b. _____

8. a. _____

   b. _____

9. _____

10. _____

Name _____   Score _____

Solve.

1. A health spa sold 120 memberships in November. In May the spa sold 18 fewer memberships than in November. What was the percent decrease in the number of memberships sold?

2. A new bypass around a small town reduced the normal 40-minute driving time between two cities by 12 minutes. What percent decrease does this represent?

1. _____

2. _____

3. By washing all the clothes in cold water, a family was able to reduce its normal monthly utility bill of $125 by $15. What percent decrease does this represent?

4. By installing solar panels, a copying center reduced its normal $240 per month heating bill by $36. What percent decrease does this represent?

3. _____

4. _____

5. A golf resort employs 180 people during the golfing season. At the end of the season, the resort reduces the number of employees by 45%. What is the decrease in the number of employees?

6. It is estimated that the value of a motorcycle is reduced by 25% after one year of ownership. Using this estimate, how much value does a $1500 new motorcycle lose after one year?

5. _____

6. _____

7. A new process reduced the time needed to replate a piece of silverware from 16 minutes to 10 minutes.
   a. What is the amount of decrease?
   b. What percent decrease does this represent?

8. Because of a decrease in orders for telephones, a telephone center reduced the orders for phones from 140 per month to 91 per month.
   a. What is the amount of decrease?
   b. What percent decrease does this represent?

7. a. _____

   b. _____

8. a. _____

   b. _____

9. Last year a company earned a profit of $285,000. This year, the company's profits were 6% less than last year's.
   a. What was the amount of decrease?
   b. What was the profit this year?

10. Last year, a laptop computer cost $420 to produce. Mass production enabled this manufacturer to reduce this expense by 15%.
    a. What is the amount of decrease?
    b. What percent decrease does this represent?

9. a. _____

   b. _____

10. a. _____

    b. _____

11. The price of a new model digital camera dropped from $150 to $114 in ten months. What percent decrease does this represent?

12. As a result of computerized cash registers, the average customer check-out time has decreased from 10 minutes to 9.5 minutes. What percent decrease does this represent?

11. _____

12. _____

Name _____

Score _____

Solve.

1. To promote business, a store manager offers a small vacuum cleaner which regularly sells for $25 at $9 off the regular price. What is the discount rate?

2. A department store is giving a discount of $6 on an ice chest which normally sells for $40. What is the discount rate?

3. A sporting goods store is selling its $150 exercise bike for 20% off the regular price. What is the discount?

4. A jewelry store is selling $250 quartz watches at 30% off the regular price. What is the discount?

5. A stereo speaker set which regularly costs $450 is on sale for $90 off the regular price. What is the discount rate?

6. A hardware store is selling its $32 lock set for 15% off the regular price. What is the discount?

7. Colby cheese which regularly sells for $2.40 per pound is on sale for 25% off the regular price.
   a. What is the discount?
   b. What is the sale price?

8. The pro shop at the racketball club has its regularly priced $55 shoes on sale for 18% off the regular price.
   a. What is the discount?
   b. What is the sale price?

9. A gift shop has its picture frames which regularly cost $35 on sale for $30.80.
   a. What is the discount?
   b. What is the discount rate?

10. An automobile body shop has regularly priced $600 paint jobs on sale for $480.
    a. What is the discount?
    b. What is the discount rate?

11. During a going-out-of-business sale, all lawn and garden merchandise was reduced 40% off the regular price. What was the sale price of a lawn mower which normally sells for $230?

12. A store offering 35% off its stock of art supplies. What is the sale price of a set of paint brushes which regularly sells for $60?

1. _____

2. _____

3. _____

4. _____

5. _____

6. _____

7. a. _____

   b. _____

8. a. _____

   b. _____

9. a. _____

   b. _____

10. a. _____

    b. _____

11. _____

12. _____

Name _____   Score _____

Solve.

1. A rancher borrows $120,000 for 10 months at an annual interest rate of 18%. What is the simple interest due on the loan?

2. To finance the purchase of 8 new taxicabs, the owners of the fleet borrows $84,000 for 8 months at an annual interest rate of 16%. What is the simple interest due on the loan?

1. _____

2. _____

3. A mobile home dealer borrowed $160,000 at a 15.5% annual interest rate for four years. What is the simple interest due on the loan?

4. An executive was offered a $34,000 loan at a 14.5% annual interest rate for three years. Find the simple interest due on the loan.

3. _____

4. _____

5. You arrange for a 6-month bank loan of $6000 at an annual simple interest rate of 7.5%. Find the total amount you must repay to the bank.

6. A bank charges its customers an interest rate of 1.8% per month for transferring money into an account which is overdrawn. Find the interest owed to the bank for one month when $300 was transferred into an overdrawn account.

5. _____

6. _____

7. A copier is purchased and a $2100 loan is obtained for two years at a simple interest rate of 17%.
   a. Find the interest due on the loan.
   b. Find the monthly payment.
   $\left(\text{Monthly payment} = \dfrac{\text{loan amount} + \text{interest}}{\text{number of months}} \right)$

8. An oil well drilling company purchased two new helicopters for $65,000 and financed the full amount at 9% simple annual interest for four years.
   a. Find the interest due on the loan.
   b. Find the monthly payment.
   $\left(\text{Monthly payment} = \dfrac{\text{loan amount} + \text{interest}}{\text{number of months}} \right)$

7. a. _____

   b. _____

8. a. _____

   b. _____

9. A company purchased a computer system for $75,000 and financed the full amount for five years at a simple annual interest rate of 15%.
   a. Find the interest due on the loan.
   b. Find the monthly payment.

10. To reduce their inventory of new cars, a dealer is offering car loans at a simple annual interest rate of 11%.
    a. Find the interest charged to a customer who financed a car loan of $8200 for four years.
    b. Find the monthly payment.

9. a. _____

   b. _____

10. a. _____

    b. _____

Name _____   Score _____

Solve.

1. A credit card company charges a customer 1.5% per month on the customer's unpaid balance. Find the interest owed to the credit card company when the customer's unpaid balance for the month is $17,642.59.

2. Suppose you have an unpaid balance of $6753.27 on a credit card that charges 1.25% per month on any unpaid balance. What finance charges do you owe the company?

1. _____

2. _____

3. What is the finance charge on an unpaid balance of $21,453.38 on a credit card that charges 1.75% per month on any unpaid balance?

4. A credit card company charges a customer 1.25% per month on the customer's unpaid balance. Find the interest owed to the credit card company when the customer's unpaid balance for the month is $12,948.71.

3. _____

4. _____

5. Suppose you have an unpaid balance of $9487.43 on a credit card that charges 1.75% per month on any unpaid balance. What finance charges do you owe the company?

6. A credit card customer has an unpaid balance of $1348.56. What is the difference between monthly finance charges of 1.75% per month on the unpaid balance and monthly finance charges of 1.25% per month?

5. _____

6. _____

7. One credit card company charges 1.5% per month on any unpaid balance, and a second company charges 1.25%. What is the difference between the finance charges that these two companies assess on an unpaid balance of $3427.89?

8. You have an unpaid balance of $2675.43. What is the difference between monthly finance charges of 1.5% per month on the unpaid balance and monthly finance charges of 1.75% per month?

7. _____

8. _____

Name   Score

Solve. Use the Compound Interest Table. Round to the nearest cent.

1.   An investment of $1750 pays 8%
     annual interest compounded quarterly.
     What is the value of the investment
     after ten years?

2.   A time savings deposit pays 15%
     annual interest, compounded daily.
     Find the value of $800 deposited in
     this account after five years.

1. _____

2. _____

3.   A money market fund pays 14% annual
     interest, compounded daily. What is
     the value after 15 years of $3000
     invested in this money market fund?

4.   An investment group invests $40,000
     in a certificate of deposit which pays
     12% annual interest, compounded
     quarterly. Find the value of this
     investment after 20 years.

3. _____

4. _____

5.   To purchase additional park sites, a
     county treasurer invested $30,000 in
     an account which pays 8% annual
     interest, compounded quarterly. What
     is the value of the investment after
     5 years?

6.   An employee invests $4000 in a
     corporate retirement account which
     pays 10% annual interest, compounded
     semi-annually. Find the value of this
     investment after 15 years.

5. _____

6. _____

7.   An interior decorator deposited $4000
     in an account that pays 12% annual
     interest, compounded quarterly.
     a. What is the value of the investment
        in 15 years?
     b. How much interest was earned in
        the 15 years?

8.   A business invests $80,000 in an
     account which pays 9% annual
     interest compounded quarterly.
     a. What is the value of the
        investment in five years?
     b. How much interest was earned
        in five years?

7. a. _____

   b. _____

8. a. _____

   b. _____

9.   An investment of $6000 in an account
     which pays 12% annual interest
     compounded semi-annually, has a
     value of $34,460.90 after 15 years.
     a. What would have been the value
        if the 12% interest had been
        compounded daily over the
        15-year period?
     b. What is the difference in values of
        the investment after the 15 years?

10. A business has determined it will
     need $60,000 in five years for
     expansion. In an attempt to meet
     that goal, the business invests $40,000
     today in an account which pays 10%
     annual interest compounded quarterly.
     a. Find the value of the $40,000
        investment in five years.
     b. Will the business have enough
        money in the account for the
        planned expansion?

9. a. _____

   b. _____

10. a. _____

    b. _____

Name _____   Score _____

Solve.

1. A delicatessen is purchased for $260,000, and a down payment of $45,000 is made. Find the mortgage.

2. A beach house is purchased for $275,000, and a down payment of $95,000 is made. Find the mortgage.

1. _____

2. _____

3. A house is purchased for $72,300. The lender requires a down payment of 25%. Find the down payment.

4. A 2.5-acre parcel of land is purchased for $60,000. The lender requires a down payment of 20%. Find the down payment.

3. _____

4. _____

5. A marina is purchased for $175,000, and a down payment which is 18% of the purchase price is made. How much is the down payment?

6. An accountant makes a down payment of 20% of the $180,000 purchase price of an office building. How much is the down payment?

5. _____

6. _____

7. A credit union requires a borrower to pay $2\frac{1}{2}$ points for a loan. Find the loan origination fee for a loan of $80,000.

8. To purchase a small business, a person obtains a loan for $120,000. The loan origination fee is $4\frac{1}{2}$ points. Find the loan origination fee.

7. _____

8. _____

9. A farmer purchases some land for $150,000. The bank requires a down payment of 20%.
    a. Find the down payment.
    b. Find the mortgage.

10. A developer is selling a condominium for $88,000. A down payment of 10% is required.
    a. Find the down payment.
    b. Find the mortgage.

9. a. _____

   b. _____

10. a. _____

    b. _____

Name _____   Score _____

Solve. Use the Monthly Payment Table. Round to the nearest cent.

1. A self-storage business and a 20-year mortgage of $70,000 is obtained. The bank charges an annual interest rate of 16%. Find the monthly payment.

2. A group of investors obtained a loan of $200,000 to buy a small business. The monthly mortgage payment was based on 25 years at 17%. Find the monthly mortgage payment.

1. _____

2. _____

3. A company is considering purchasing a health club with a 25-year $350,000 mortgage at 18%. The treasurer has determined that the company can afford a monthly mortgage payment of $7000. can the company afford the monthly mortgage payment on the health club?

4. A couple interested in buying a home determines that they can afford a monthly mortgage payment of $685. Can they afford to buy a home with a 30-year $50,000 mortgage at 18% interest?

3. _____

4. _____

5. A county tax assessor has determined that the annual property tax on a $78,000 home is $765. Find the monthly property tax payment.

6. The annual property tax on a house is $680. Find the monthly property tax.

5. _____

6. _____

7. A home has a mortgage of $80,000 for 30 years at an annual interest rate of 17%.
   a. Find the monthly mortgage payment.
   b. During a month when $240.54 of the monthly mortgage payment is principal, how much of the payment is interest?

8. A factory which manufactures computer tables has a 20-year mortgage of $150,000 at an annual interest rate of 16%.
   a. Find the monthly mortgage payment.
   b. During a month when $268.88 of the monthly mortgage payment is principal, how much of the payment is interest?

7. a. _____

b. _____

8. a. _____

b. _____

9. A monthly mortgage on a home is $1320.40. The home owner must pay an annual property tax of $972. Find the total monthly payment for the mortgage and the property tax.

10. The monthly mortgage on a home is $1463.20. The owner must pay an annual property tax of $1171. Find the total monthly payment for the mortgage and the property tax.

9. _____

10. _____

Name _____ Score _____

Solve.

1. A car is purchased for $8500. A down payment of 12% is required. How much is the down payment?

2. A legal assistant has saved $970 to use as a down payment on a used car. The assistant's bank requires a down payment of 14% of the purchase price of a car. Does the assistant have enough saved to make a down payment on a car which costs $7850?

3. A carpenter purchases a used truck for $15,300 and must pay a sales tax of 4.5% of the purchase price. Find the sales tax.

4. A carpet salesperson buys a minivan to carry carpet samples. The purchase price of the minivan is $11,050 and a 4% sales tax is paid. How much is the sales tax?

5. A state charges a car license fee of 2% of the purchase price of a car. How much is the state car license fee for a car which costs $7595?

6. A license fee of 1.5% of the purchase price of a car is to be paid on a convertible costing $13,400. How much is the license fee for the car?

7. A pharmacist buys a car for $9550 with a down payment of $1750 and a sales tax of 3% of the purchase price.
   a. Find the sales tax.
   b. Find the total cost for the sales tax and the down payment.

8. An electrical contractor buys a $14,000 truck. A state license fee of $210 and a sales tax of 2.5% of the purchase price are required.
   a. Find the sales tax.
   b. Find the total cost for the sales tax and the license fee.

9. An airline employee buys a sports car for $24,000 and makes a down payment of 20% of the purchase price.
   a. Find the down payment.
   b. Find the amount financed.

10. A SUV is purchased for $10,500. A down payment of 15% is required. Find the amount financed.

1. _____

2. _____

3. _____

4. _____

5. _____

6. _____

7. a. _____

   b. _____

8. a. _____

   b. _____

9. a. _____

   b. _____

10. _____

Name   Score

Solve. Use the Monthly Payment Table. Round to the nearest cent.

1. A car loan of $5400 is financed through a credit union at an annual interest rate of 16% for 3 years. Find the monthly car payment.

2. A pickup truck is purchased by a furniture store owner and $9000 is financed through a bank at 15% interest for 48 months. Find the monthly payment.

1. _____

2. _____

3. It is estimated that when all costs of owning an economy car are considered, it costs $0.28 per mile to operate the car. Using this estimate, how much does it cost to operate a car during a year the car is driven 14,000 mi?

4. An estimate of the cost for care and maintenance of automobile tires is $0.016 per mile. Using this estimate, how much would it cost for care and maintenance during a year the car is driven 13,000 mi?

3. _____

4. _____

5. In a year when the total gasoline bill was $1680, the car was driven 12,000 miles. What was the cost per miles for gasoline?

6. A car owner spent $1600 on gas, oil, and car insurance during a period when the car was driven 15,000 miles. Find the cost per mile for gas, oil, and car insurance.

5. _____

6. _____

7. During the year, $2100 was paid in monthly car payments, $1100 was spent on gasoline, and car insurance cost $330. Find the total cost for car payments, gasoline, and insurance for the year.

8. A car owner pays a monthly car payment of $154.60. During a month when $79.80 of the monthly payment is principal, how much of the payment is interest?

7. _____

8. _____

9. A used car is purchased for $6275, and a down payment of $1275 is made. The balance is financed for 3 years at an interest rate of 15%.
    a. Find the amount financed.
    b. Find the monthly car payment.

10. A used car is purchased for $12,000, and a down payment of $3000 is made. The balance is financed for 4 years at an annual interest rate of 16%.
    a. Find the amount financed.
    b. Find the monthly car payment.

9. a. _____

    b. _____

10. a. _____

    b. _____

11. A four-wheel drive truck is purchased for $9600, and a down payment of $2100 is made. The balance is financed for 3 years at an annual interest rate of 17%. Find the monthly truck payment.

12. A $8995 car is purchased with a down payment of $1945. The balance is financed for 4 years at an annual interest rate of 16%. Find the monthly car payment.

11. _____

12. _____

Name _____   Score _____

Solve. Round to the nearest cent.

1. A part time sales clerk earns an hourly wage of $9.85. How much does the sales clerk earn during a 24-hour work week?

2. A checker in a food store earns $7.20 per hour. How much does the checker earn in a 40-hour work week?

1. _____

2. _____

3. A junior executive for a marketing research firm receives an annual salary of $43,800. How much does the executive receive per month?

4. A legal assistant receives $25,500 annually. How much does the assistant earn each month?

3. _____

4. _____

5. A brick layer's hourly wage is $24.25. For working overtime, the brick layer earns double time. What is the brick layer's hourly wage for working overtime?

6. A golf pro receives a commission of 20% for selling a set of golf clubs. Find the commission earned by the golf pro for selling a set of golf clubs which cost $390.

5. _____

6. _____

7. A sales representative for a computer store receives a commission of 11% on the weekly sales. Find the commission earned during a week when sales were $4100.

8. An agent for a leasing company receives a commission of 2.5% for leasing office space. Find the commission received by the agent for leasing an office space for $72,000.

7. _____

8. _____

9. A roofer receives $2.50 per square yard to install roofing. How much does the roofer receive for installing 180 square yards of roofing?

10. An acoustic consultant received a contract for $3600. The consultant spent 45 hours working on the project. Find the consultant's hourly wage.

9. _____

10. _____

11. A video technician's hourly wage is $14.60. For working overtime, the technician receives double time.
    a. What is the technician's hourly wage for working overtime?
    b. How much does the technician earn for working 12 hours of overtime?

12. A company which sells medical equipment pays its sales executives a commission of 12% of all sales over $120,000. During one year, a sales executive sold $440,000 worth of medical equipment.
    a. Find the amount of sales over $120,000.
    b. Find the commission earned by the sales executive.

11. a. _____

    b. _____

12. a. _____

    b. _____

Name _____   Score _____

Solve.

1. A nurse had a checking account balance of $504.37 before writing a check for $59.42. What is the current account balance?

2. A hotel manager had a checking account balance of $433.62 before making a deposit of $134.74. What is the current checking account balance?

1. _____

2. _____

3. The business checking account for a grocery store showed a balance of $2625.36. What is the balance in the account after making a deposit of $528.06?

4. An automobile rental firm had a balance of $3542.87 in its checking account. What is the balance in the account after writing a check for $1198.17?

3. _____

4. _____

5. A food broker had a checking account balance of $435.86 before writing a check for $38.44 and making a deposit of $170. Find the current checkbook balance.

6. A warranty clerk had a checking account balance of $279.54 before writing one check for $28.36 and another check for $19.15. Find the current checkbook balance.

5. _____

6. _____

7. An assistant manager had a checkbook balance of $218.74 before making a deposit of $145 and writing a check for $336.47. Is there enough money in the account for the bank to pay the check?

8. A receptionist had a checkbook balance of $135.87 before making a deposit of $260 and writing a check for $415. Is there enough money in the account for the bank to pay the check?

7. _____

8. _____

9. An inventory clerk's checkbook balance is $834.51. The clerk wants to purchase a TV for $495 and a used sofa for $275. Is there enough money in the account to make the two purchases?

10. A medical assistant has a current checkbook balance of $909.70. The assistant wants to purchase an organ for $725 and a stereo amplifier for $215.60. Is there enough money in the account to make the purchases?

9. _____

10. _____

Name _____   Score _____

Solve.

1. Your checkbook shows a balance of $417.25. The bank statement does not show a deposit of $172.54, and checks for $45.82 and $204.53 have not been cashed. What balance does the bank statement show?

2. Your checkbook shows a balance of $115.28. The bank statement does not show deposits of $96.82 and $112.58, and checks for $12.39 and $79.65 have not been cashed. What balance does the bank statement show?

1. _____

2. _____

3. Your checkbook shows a balance of $202.53. The bank statement does not show a deposit of $116.16, and checks for $49.85 and $189.12 have not been cashed. What balance does the bank statement show?

4. Your checkbook shows a balance of $523.69. The bank statement does not show a deposit of $117.13, and checks for $59.16 and $325 have not been cashed. What balance does the bank statement show?

3. _____

4. _____

5. Your checkbook shows a balance of $810.63. The bank statement does not show a deposit of $210.15, and checks for $112.95 and $315.42 have not been cashed. What balance does the bank statement show?

6. Your checkbook shows a balance of $608.07. The bank statement does not show a deposit of $98.58, and checks for $69.54 and $142.69 have not been cashed. What balance does the bank statement show?

5. _____

6. _____

7. Your checkbook shows a balance of $1025.67. The bank statement does not show a deposit of $405.14, and checks for $129.35 and $375 have not been cashed. What balance does the bank statement show?

8. Your checkbook shows a balance of $790.39. The bank statement does not show a deposit of $516.80, and checks for $217.56, $28.95 and $187.60 have not been cashed. What balance does the bank statement show?

7. _____

8. _____

9. Your checkbook shows a balance of $1468.72. The bank statement does not show a deposit of $851, and checks for $110.81, $350 and $94.26 have not been cashed. What balance does the bank statement show?

10. Your checkbook shows a balance of $1620.87. The bank statement does not show a deposit of $920.76, and checks for $268.71, $127.42 and $67.50 have not been cashed. What balance does the bank statement show?

9. _____

10. _____

CHAPTER 1

Objective 1.1A

1.
2.
3.
4.
5. > 6. > 7. < 8. < 9. > 10. < 11. < 12. > 13. < 14. > 15. > 16. <

Objective 1.1B

1. Eight hundred sixty-two 2. Three hundred eight 3. Six hundred fifty-four
4. Five thousand one hundred twenty-five 5. Nine thousand forty
6. Thirty-six thousand eight hundred forty-four 7. Three hundred eighty thousand seven hundred fifty-one
8. Eight hundred thousand one 9. Seven million six hundred forty thousand seven hundred twenty-three
10. 33 11. 274 12. 9527 13. 56,320 14. 460,303 15. 4,012,986 16. 1,000,0005 17. 8,001,050

Objective 1.1C

1. $200 + 50 + 6$ 2. $4000 + 700 + 3$ 3. $9000 + 200 + 30 + 3$ 4. $20,000 + 3000 + 40$
5. $50,000 + 900 + 10 + 6$ 6. $70,000 + 5000 + 40 + 9$ 7. $90,000 + 9000 + 2$
8. $200,000 + 30,000 + 4000 + 700 + 80 + 2$ 9. $500,000 + 400$ 10. $700,000 + 80,000 + 7000$
11. $800,000 + 6000 + 8$ 12. $900,000 + 20,000 + 10$ 13. $4,000,000 + 200,000 + 70,000 + 1000 + 20$
14. $6,000,000 + 200 + 10 + 3$

Objective 1.1D

1. 750 2. 710 3. 400 4. 600 5. 1100 6. 7100 7. 4000 8. 10,000
9. 75,000 10. 69,000 11. 250,000 12. 840,000 13. 3,000,000 14. 8,000,000

Objective 1.2A

1. 866 2. 852 3. 2595 4. 18,340 5. 20,631 6. 19,630 7. 17,717 8. 21,434
9. 22,553 10. 231,792 11. 306,459 12. 267,879 13. 1439 14. 1271
15. 34,239 16. 73,369 17. 14,716 18. 16,140 19. 74,748 20. 34,430
21. 92,416 22. 8,962,349

Objective 1.2B

1. $81 2. $340 3. 3235 people 4. 239 people 5. $15,570 6. 889 toasters 7. $1554
8. 62,363 miles 9. $1790 10. $8,643,446

Objective 1.3A

1. 5 2. 3 3. 1 4. 15 5. 11 6. 61 7. 95 8. 400 9. 71 10. 561 11. 222
12. 303 13. 8413 14. 817 15. 2204 16. 1115 17. 1252 18. 2131 19. 21
20. 8 21. 821 22. 811 23. 7006 24. 421 25. 2111 26. 6151

Objective 1.3B

1. 44 2. 58 3. 59 4. 88 5. 54 6. 179 7. 3269 8. 4399 9. 966 10. 2430
11. 812 12. 3819 13. 3919 14. 26,699 15. 43,848 16. 19,027 17. 151,271 18. 353,874
19. 375 20. 637 21. 4676 22. 7481 23. 24,789 24. 56,741 25. 26,907 26. 15,582

Objective 1.3C

1. $23 **2.** $7724 **3.** 10,576 miles **4.** 53,807 miles **5.** $211 **6.** $650 **7.** $3220
8. $366 **9.** $385 **10.** 169,064 square miles

Objective 1.4A

1. 63 **2.** 0 **3.** 20 **4.** 48 **5.** 15 **6.** 36 **7.** 207 **8.** 168 **9.** 426 **10.** 245 **11.** 684
12. 152 **13.** 316 **14.** 5192 **15.** 1638 **16.** 4225 **17.** 3885 **18.** 2523
19. 7952 **20.** 28,326 **21.** 71,046 **22.** 26,172 **23.** 17,592 **24.** 18,620 **25.** 51,702
26. 363,930 **27.** 410,544

Objective 1.4B

1. 392 **2.** 1860 **3.** 3150 **4.** 649 **5.** 1755 **6.** 7968 **7.** 17,984 **8.** 18,315
9. 47,320 **10.** 60,776 **11.** 11,250 **12.** 22,743 **13.** 203,190 **14.** 427,118 **15.** 730,576
16. 183,732 **17.** 445,200 **18.** 105,248 **19.** 181,815 **20.** 601,644 **21.** 198,170 **22.** 1,871,773
23. 2,235,162 **24.** 3,014,525 **25.** 864,000 **26.** 1,154,160 **27.** 2,998,128

Objective 1.4C

1. 228 miles **2.** 318 miles **3.** 864 books **4.** $9456 **5.** $3048 **6.** $584 **7.** 8508 hours
8. $630 **9.** 63,200 gallons **10.** $7,999,680

Objective 1.5A

1. 2 **2.** 2 **3.** 1 **4.** 12 **5.** 7 **6.** 4 **7.** 19 **8.** 8 **9.** 11 **10.** 135 **11.** 125 **12.** 82
13. 49 **14.** 525 **15.** 456 **16.** 527 **17.** 399 **18.** 5561 **19.** 11,479
20. 5234 **21.** 7639

Objective 1.5B

1. 2 r 1 **2.** 4 r 1 **3.** 1 r 1 **4.** 4 r 5 **5.** 15 r 2 **6.** 12 r 1 **7.** 18 r 1
8. 6 r 6 **9.** 4 r 4 **10.** 173 r 1 **11.** 50 r 5 **12.** 148 r 2 **13.** 53 r 4 **14.** 392 r 2
15. 991 r 2 **16.** 692 r 6 **17.** 1478 r 1 **18.** 7446 r 4 **19.** 8217 r 1 **20.** 14,850 r 3 **21.** 9080 r 1

Objective 1.5C

1. 4 r 2 **2.** 1 r 37 **3.** 1 r 31 **4.** 5 r 9 **5.** 7 **6.** 12 r 22 **7.** 5 r 9
8. 128 r 26 **9.** 103 r 10 **10.** 144 r 9 **11.** 121 **12.** 80 r 18 **13.** 85 r 6 **14.** 74 r 29
15. 186 r 28 **16.** 61 r 32 **17.** 69 r 57 **18.** 591 r 20 **19.** 794 r 8 **20.** 83 r 110 **21.** 79

Objective 1.5D

1. 15,000 bushels **2.** 564 **3.** $184,250 **4.** 160 people **5.** $212 **6.** $39
7. $115 **8.** $184 **9.** $102,563 **10.** 256 packages

Objective 1.6A

1. 4^4 **2.** 8^6 **3.** $3^4 \cdot 4^2$ **4.** $5^4 \cdot 7^3$ **5.** $2 \cdot 6^7$ **6.** $6 \cdot 10^4$ **7.** $2^3 \cdot 3^4 \cdot 7^2$ **8.** $5 \cdot 6 \cdot 7^2 \cdot 8^3$
9. $4^2 \cdot 5^3 \cdot 6^3 \cdot 7$ **10.** $7^3 \cdot 15^2 \cdot 19^2$ **11.** 16 **12.** 27 **13.** 64 **14.** 3888
15. 2000 **16.** 25,088 **17.** 0 **18.** 320 **19.** 37,500 **20.** 102,900 **21.** 13,824
22. 38,690 **23.** 139,968 **24.** 0 **25.** 14,400

Objective 1.6B

1. 10 **2.** 11 **3.** 19 **4.** 0 **5.** 8 **6.** 5 **7.** 6 **8.** 11 **9.** 8 **10.** 10 **11.** 79 **12.** 0 **13.** 23 **14.** 0
15. 22 **16.** 16 **17.** 84 **18.** 7 **19.** 2 **20.** 38 **21.** 13 **22.** 8 **23.** 33 **24.** 4 **25.** 9 **26.** 5 **27.** 10

Objective 1.7A

1. 1, 2 **2.** 1, 2, 7, 14 **3.** 1, 3, 7, 21 **4.** 1, 3, 5, 15 **5.** 1, 23 **6.** 1, 2, 4, 5, 8, 10, 20, 40
7. 1, 2, 19, 38 **8.** 1, 2, 3, 4, 5, 6, 10, 12, 15, 20, 30, 60 **9.** 1, 2, 29, 58 **10.** 1, 2, 31, 62 **11.** 1, 3, 9, 27, 81
12. 1, 3, 17, 51 **13.** 1, 3, 9, 11, 33, 99 **14.** 1, 5, 17, 85 **15.** 1, 2, 5, 7, 10, 14, 35, 70
16. 1, 2, 4, 8, 11, 22, 44, 88 **17.** 1, 3, 7, 9, 21, 63 **18.** 1, 5, 7, 35 **19.** 1, 3, 5, 9, 15, 45
20. 1, 2, 3, 6, 13, 26, 39, 78 **21.** 1, 5, 11, 55 **22.** 1, 2, 57, 114 **23.** 1, 11, 121 **24.** 1, 3, 9, 13, 39, 117
25. 1, 2, 3, 5, 6, 10, 15, 25, 30 50, 75, 150 **26.** 1, 5, 7, 25, 35, 175 **27.** 1, 181

Objective 1.7B

1. $2 \cdot 2 \cdot 2$ **2.** $2 \cdot 3 \cdot 5$ **3.** $1 \cdot 53$ **4.** $2 \cdot 5$ **5.** $2 \cdot 2 \cdot 2 \cdot 2 \cdot 2$ **6.** $2 \cdot 2 \cdot 2 \cdot 2 \cdot 2 \cdot 2$ **7.** $1 \cdot 11$
8. $2 \cdot 2 \cdot 5$ **9.** $2 \cdot 41$ **10.** $5 \cdot 7$ **11.** $2 \cdot 2 \cdot 11$ **12.** $3 \cdot 23$ **13.** $2 \cdot 2 \cdot 2 \cdot 3 \cdot 3$
14. $2 \cdot 2 \cdot 2 \cdot 11$ **15.** $2 \cdot 47$ **16.** $2 \cdot 2 \cdot 3 \cdot 5$ **17.** $7 \cdot 11$ **18.** $2 \cdot 2 \cdot 5 \cdot 5$ **19.** $2 \cdot 2 \cdot 2 \cdot 13$ **20.** $2 \cdot 2 \cdot 2 \cdot 2 \cdot 7$
21. $2 \cdot 2 \cdot 31$ **22.** $2 \cdot 5 \cdot 13$ **23.** $5 \cdot 31$ **24.** $2 \cdot 2 \cdot 2 \cdot 5 \cdot 5$ **25.** $3 \cdot 3 \cdot 5 \cdot 7$ **26.** $2 \cdot 2 \cdot 5 \cdot 5 \cdot 5$ **27.** $2 \cdot 2 \cdot 5 \cdot 13$

CHAPTER 2

Objective 2.1A

1. 12 **2.** 21 **3.** 18 **4.** 40 **5.** 8 **6.** 36 **7.** 36 **8.** 30 **9.** 48 **10.** 75 **11.** 224 **12.** 36
13. 216 **14.** 252 **15.** 128 **16.** 63 **17.** 108 **18.** 231 **19.** 72
20. 200 **21.** 84 **22.** 154 **23.** 224 **24.** 80 **25.** 216 **26.** 36 **27.** 32

Objective 2.1B

1. 1 **2.** 3 **3.** 1 **4.** 2 **5.** 5 **6.** 5 **7.** 15 **8.** 4 **9.** 9 **10.** 7 **11.** 5 **12.** 10 **13.** 16
14. 13 **15.** 1 **16.** 2 **17.** 1 **18.** 3 **19.** 1 **20.** 5 **21.** 8 **22.** 4 **23.** 8 **24.** 9 **25.** 14 **26.** 17 **27.** 15

Objective 2.2A

1. $\frac{5}{8}$ **2.** $\frac{5}{7}$ **3.** $\frac{3}{5}$ **4.** $\frac{1}{4}$ **5.** $1\frac{2}{3}$ **6.** $1\frac{3}{4}$ **7.** $2\frac{4}{5}$ **8.** $2\frac{1}{2}$

9. $3\frac{1}{2}$ **10.** $3\frac{7}{8}$ **11.** $2\frac{3}{8}$ **12.** $2\frac{5}{8}$ **13.** $2\frac{1}{5}$ **14.** $3\frac{1}{3}$

Objective 2.2B

1. $3\frac{2}{3}$ **2.** 6 **3.** $1\frac{8}{9}$ **4.** $4\frac{1}{2}$ **5.** $2\frac{2}{3}$ **6.** $4\frac{3}{4}$ **7.** 3 **8.** $1\frac{5}{6}$

9. 1 **10.** 8 **11.** 14 **12.** 5 **13.** $\frac{11}{5}$ **14.** $\frac{23}{3}$ **15.** $\frac{43}{9}$ **16.** $\frac{23}{8}$

17. $\frac{37}{7}$ **18.** $\frac{33}{5}$ **19.** $\frac{43}{4}$ **20.** $\frac{97}{10}$ **21.** $\frac{77}{6}$ **22.** $\frac{118}{15}$ **23.** $\frac{34}{3}$

24. $\frac{131}{8}$

Answers to Drill-and-Practice Pages

Objective 2.3A

1. 26 **2.** 15 **3.** 32 **4.** 5 **5.** 21 **6.** 18 **7.** 15 **8.** 36 **9.** 12 **10.** 32 **11.** 55 **12.** 35 **13.** 72
14. 54 **15.** 120 **16.** 18 **17.** 34 **18.** 100 **19.** 60 **20.** 68
21. 44 **22.** 96 **23.** 315 **24.** 35 **25.** 195 **26.** 322 **27.** 903

Objective 2.3B

1. $\frac{2}{3}$ **2.** $\frac{3}{5}$ **3.** $\frac{1}{8}$ **4.** $\frac{4}{7}$ **5.** $\frac{2}{3}$ **6.** $\frac{5}{8}$ **7.** $\frac{5}{6}$ **8.** $1\frac{1}{3}$ **9.** 0 **10.** $\frac{5}{8}$ **11.** $\frac{1}{2}$ **12.** $\frac{7}{18}$ **13.** $\frac{1}{4}$

14. $\frac{7}{12}$ **15.** 3 **16.** $\frac{13}{18}$ **17.** $\frac{8}{9}$ **18.** $\frac{1}{3}$ **19.** $1\frac{4}{13}$ **20.** $\frac{1}{7}$ **21.** $\frac{8}{17}$ **22.** $\frac{13}{30}$

23. $\frac{23}{50}$ **24.** $\frac{26}{75}$ **25.** $\frac{7}{10}$ **26.** $\frac{11}{14}$ **27.** 4

Objective 2.4A

1. $\frac{5}{6}$ **2.** $1\frac{1}{10}$ **3.** $\frac{10}{19}$ **4.** $\frac{6}{7}$ **5.** $\frac{7}{8}$ **6.** 1 **7.** 2 **8.** $\frac{2}{7}$ **9.** $1\frac{4}{5}$ **10.** $\frac{15}{17}$ **11.** $\frac{3}{4}$ **12.** 1

13. $2\frac{1}{3}$ **14.** $1\frac{7}{9}$ **15.** $1\frac{3}{11}$ **16.** $2\frac{1}{2}$ **17.** $\frac{11}{12}$ **18.** $2\frac{1}{3}$ **19.** $\frac{13}{15}$

20. $1\frac{1}{5}$ **21.** $4\frac{1}{4}$ **22.** $2\frac{1}{5}$ **23.** $1\frac{2}{7}$ **24.** $1\frac{3}{16}$ **25.** $2\frac{3}{13}$ **26.** $1\frac{15}{17}$

27. $1\frac{8}{9}$

Objective 2.4B

1. $\frac{11}{12}$ **2.** $\frac{37}{45}$ **3.** $1\frac{13}{24}$ **4.** $1\frac{7}{16}$ **5.** $1\frac{11}{18}$ **6.** $1\frac{5}{24}$ **7.** $1\frac{16}{21}$

8. $1\frac{1}{42}$ **9.** $1\frac{21}{40}$ **10.** $1\frac{1}{8}$ **11.** $1\frac{1}{12}$ **12.** $1\frac{3}{4}$ **13.** $\frac{11}{12}$ **14.** $1\frac{17}{30}$

15. $1\frac{20}{21}$ **16.** $1\frac{17}{36}$ **17.** $1\frac{23}{24}$ **18.** $2\frac{4}{315}$ **19.** $1\frac{9}{16}$ **20.** $2\frac{13}{90}$ **21.** $1\frac{4}{5}$

22. $1\frac{6}{7}$ **23.** $2\frac{5}{18}$ **24.** $2\frac{11}{28}$ **25.** $1\frac{13}{40}$ **26.** $\frac{59}{165}$ **27.** $2\frac{1}{3}$

Objective 2.4C

1. $6\frac{1}{9}$ **2.** $9\frac{1}{2}$ **3.** $13\frac{9}{28}$ **4.** $17\frac{7}{12}$ **5.** $11\frac{19}{28}$ **6.** $11\frac{8}{45}$ **7.** $12\frac{1}{6}$ **8.** $10\frac{7}{10}$

9. $11\frac{6}{35}$ **10.** $13\frac{5}{18}$ **11.** $10\frac{9}{20}$ **12.** $29\frac{15}{56}$ **13.** $30\frac{29}{30}$ **14.** $21\frac{17}{18}$ **15.** $8\frac{17}{56}$

16. $14\frac{49}{60}$ **17.** $45\frac{21}{22}$ **18.** $28\frac{1}{60}$ **19.** $15\frac{7}{12}$ **20.** $20\frac{13}{70}$ **21.** $23\frac{7}{36}$ **22.** $17\frac{17}{24}$

23. $12\frac{3}{4}$ **24.** $32\frac{9}{20}$ **25.** $33\frac{23}{24}$ **26.** $25\frac{19}{20}$ **27.** $18\frac{5}{7}$

Objective 2.4D

1. $3\frac{1}{8}$ inches **2.** $2\frac{1}{16}$ inches **3.** $3\frac{7}{8}$ inches **4.** $\$23\frac{1}{8}$ **5.** $4\frac{5}{16}$ inches **6.** $7\frac{1}{2}$ hours

7. $19\frac{3}{8}$ long and $14\frac{5}{8}$ inches wide **8.** $3\frac{1}{4}$ pounds **9.** $7\frac{3}{8}$ cups **10.** $\$204$

Objective 2.5A

1. $\frac{1}{6}$ 2. $\frac{5}{12}$ 3. $\frac{1}{3}$ 4. $\frac{8}{15}$ 5. $\frac{4}{5}$ 6. $\frac{1}{7}$ 7. $\frac{12}{25}$

8. $\frac{3}{10}$ 9. $\frac{3}{8}$ 10. $\frac{1}{2}$ 11. $\frac{6}{11}$ 12. $\frac{8}{23}$ 13. $\frac{3}{7}$ 14. $\frac{14}{27}$

15. $\frac{2}{13}$ 16. $\frac{3}{8}$ 17. $\frac{1}{3}$ 18. $\frac{9}{13}$ 19. $\frac{1}{6}$ 20. $\frac{8}{9}$ 21. $\frac{7}{10}$

22. $\frac{7}{10}$ 23. $\frac{5}{7}$ 24. $\frac{4}{35}$ 25. $\frac{8}{19}$ 26. $\frac{11}{29}$ 27. $\frac{4}{11}$

Objective 2.5B

1. $\frac{7}{20}$ 2. $\frac{1}{10}$ 3. $\frac{1}{7}$ 4. $\frac{22}{147}$ 5. $\frac{13}{32}$ 6. $\frac{32}{57}$ 7. $\frac{68}{135}$

8. $\frac{31}{80}$ 9. $\frac{1}{78}$ 10. $\frac{10}{21}$ 11. $\frac{3}{20}$ 12. $\frac{29}{90}$ 13. $\frac{17}{54}$ 14. $\frac{1}{12}$

15. $\frac{29}{60}$ 16. $\frac{31}{99}$ 17. $\frac{19}{175}$ 18. $\frac{25}{72}$ 19. $\frac{7}{20}$ 20. $\frac{9}{35}$ 21. $\frac{3}{10}$

22. $\frac{13}{30}$ 23. $\frac{1}{10}$ 24. $\frac{31}{42}$ 25. $\frac{11}{72}$ 26. $\frac{1}{78}$ 27. $\frac{7}{40}$

Objective 2.5C

1. $4\frac{4}{11}$ 2. $15\frac{1}{4}$ 3. $41\frac{1}{3}$ 4. $9\frac{15}{26}$ 5. $4\frac{1}{16}$ 6. $7\frac{3}{5}$ 7. $18\frac{3}{7}$

8. $21\frac{5}{7}$ 9. $3\frac{3}{5}$ 10. $29\frac{17}{18}$ 11. $32\frac{14}{135}$ 12. $23\frac{17}{35}$ 13. $24\frac{7}{48}$ 14. $35\frac{5}{12}$

15. $48\frac{45}{56}$ 16. $13\frac{29}{45}$ 17. $34\frac{1}{48}$ 18. $8\frac{21}{25}$ 19. $5\frac{7}{40}$ 20. $38\frac{67}{70}$ 21. $8\frac{35}{36}$

22. $9\frac{1}{6}$ 23. $2\frac{17}{30}$ 24. $126\frac{15}{56}$ 25. $75\frac{9}{10}$ 26. $53\frac{13}{120}$ 27. $17\frac{23}{60}$

Objective 2.5D

1. $\frac{7}{12}$ inch 2. $1\frac{7}{9}$ feet 3. $\frac{2}{5}$ 4. $\frac{7}{12}$ feet 5. $5\frac{7}{24}$ feet 6. $2\frac{3}{4}$ hours 7. $10\frac{5}{8}$ miles

8. $9\frac{1}{4}$ pounds 9. $\frac{11}{20}$ 10. $1\frac{7}{8}$ miles

Objective 2.6A

1. $\frac{8}{13}$ 2. $\frac{6}{11}$ 3. $\frac{4}{27}$ 4. $\frac{3}{16}$ 5. $\frac{35}{66}$ 6. $\frac{13}{54}$ 7. $\frac{11}{28}$

8. $\frac{25}{72}$ 9. $\frac{7}{8}$ 10. $\frac{49}{90}$ 11. $2\frac{7}{8}$ 12. $\frac{16}{35}$ 13. $\frac{13}{20}$ 14. $\frac{15}{56}$

15. 2 16. $10\frac{6}{17}$ 17. $1\frac{57}{119}$ 18. $\frac{3}{8}$ 19. $1\frac{1}{27}$ 20. $\frac{15}{68}$ 21. $\frac{3}{22}$

22. $\frac{15}{28}$ 23. $\frac{3}{10}$ 24. $\frac{21}{25}$ 25. 1 26. $\frac{1}{18}$ 27. $\frac{66}{91}$

Objective 2.6B

1. $3\frac{1}{2}$ 2. $1\frac{3}{11}$ 3. $4\frac{2}{7}$ 4. $2\frac{1}{2}$ 5. 25 6. $\frac{13}{30}$ 7. 33

8. $1\frac{10}{13}$ 9. $9\frac{4}{5}$ 10. $1\frac{10}{21}$ 11. 0 12. $55\frac{1}{3}$ 13. $53\frac{9}{10}$ 14. 90

15. $67\frac{15}{28}$ 16. $59\frac{1}{2}$ 17. $38\frac{1}{2}$ 18. 36 19. $35\frac{15}{17}$ 20. $7\frac{5}{16}$ 21. $108\frac{1}{2}$

22. $28\frac{7}{11}$ 23. 33 24. 267 25. $124\frac{2}{3}$ 26. $7\frac{4}{5}$ 27. 60

Objective 2.6C

1. $174 2. 119 miles 3. $2\frac{3}{16}$ feet 4. $1408 5. $864 6. $11,010 7. 258 pages

8. $5\frac{11}{16}$ miles 9. $486 10. 752 miles

Objective 2.7A

1. $\frac{1}{6}$ 2. $1\frac{1}{3}$ 3. $\frac{3}{20}$ 4. $\frac{3}{10}$ 5. $\frac{17}{33}$ 6. $3\frac{2}{3}$ 7. $\frac{1}{2}$

8. $\frac{1}{2}$ 9. $\frac{5}{7}$ 10. $3\frac{3}{4}$ 11. $\frac{2}{3}$ 12. $1\frac{3}{11}$ 13. 0 14. $1\frac{3}{8}$

15. $\frac{8}{35}$ 16. $5\frac{1}{4}$ 17. $\frac{2}{5}$ 18. $1\frac{5}{9}$ 19. $2\frac{5}{11}$ 20. $\frac{2}{15}$ 21. $\frac{1}{2}$

22. $\frac{19}{36}$ 23. 1 24. $1\frac{1}{5}$ 25. $\frac{4}{9}$ 26. 16 27. $\frac{2}{3}$

Objective 2.7B

1. $\frac{1}{7}$ 2. $9\frac{1}{2}$ 3. 90 4. $1\frac{1}{2}$ 5. $\frac{16}{55}$ 6. $\frac{2}{5}$ 7. $1\frac{17}{21}$

8. $1\frac{1}{4}$ 9. $1\frac{17}{40}$ 10. $\frac{26}{29}$ 11. 10 12. $\frac{1}{14}$ 13. $13\frac{7}{11}$ 14. $1\frac{1}{4}$

15. 15 16. $\frac{2}{5}$ 17. $\frac{1}{23}$ 18. $\frac{3}{13}$ 19. 2 20. $2\frac{15}{26}$ 21. $3\frac{1}{12}$

22. $\frac{5}{144}$ 23. $\frac{8}{29}$ 24. $2\frac{10}{29}$ 25. $1\frac{1}{11}$ 26. $28\frac{1}{2}$ 27. $1\frac{16}{21}$

Objective 2.7C

1. $624 2. 44 miles per hour 3. 20 miles 4. 48 questions 5. 66,000 registered voters

6. $12 7. 12 dolls 8. $48,000 9. $1\frac{1}{4}$ feet 10. 123 students

Objective 2.8A

1. < 2. > 3. > 4. < 5. < 6. > 7. > 8. > 9. < 10. < 11. < 12. > 13. > 14. <
15. < 16. < 17. > 18. < 19. < 20. > 21. < 22. > 23. < 24. < 25. > 26. < 27. >

Objective 2.8B

1. $\dfrac{25}{121}$ 2. $\dfrac{9}{49}$ 3. $\dfrac{25}{64}$ 4. $\dfrac{9}{35}$ 5. $\dfrac{20}{147}$ 6. $\dfrac{1}{100}$ 7. $\dfrac{1}{7}$

8. $\dfrac{1}{9}$ 9. $\dfrac{1}{128}$ 10. $\dfrac{1}{99}$ 11. $\dfrac{3}{32}$ 12. $\dfrac{32}{95}$ 13. $\dfrac{1}{15}$ 14. $\dfrac{9}{128}$

15. $\dfrac{1}{10}$ 16. $\dfrac{1}{16}$ 17. $\dfrac{1}{51}$ 18. $\dfrac{1}{7}$ 19. $\dfrac{1}{27}$ 20. $\dfrac{7}{10}$ 21. $\dfrac{1}{15}$

22. $2\dfrac{4}{7}$ 23. $\dfrac{2}{135}$ 24. $\dfrac{7}{54}$ 25. $\dfrac{3}{128}$ 26. $\dfrac{4}{77}$ 27. $\dfrac{1}{169}$

Objective 2.8B

1. $\dfrac{43}{84}$ 2. $\dfrac{41}{45}$ 3. $\dfrac{7}{8}$ 4. $1\dfrac{89}{105}$ 5. $\dfrac{7}{8}$ 6. $\dfrac{11}{16}$ 7. $\dfrac{103}{252}$

8. $\dfrac{109}{270}$ 9. $\dfrac{4}{9}$ 10. $1\dfrac{19}{22}$ 11. $\dfrac{25}{36}$ 12. $\dfrac{2}{5}$ 13. 0 14. $1\dfrac{3}{98}$

15. $\dfrac{2}{3}$ 16. $1\dfrac{2}{23}$ 17. $2\dfrac{7}{8}$ 18. $\dfrac{1}{36}$ 19. 1 20. $\dfrac{5}{18}$ 21. $\dfrac{1}{3}$

22. $\dfrac{5}{21}$ 23. $\dfrac{9}{88}$ 24. $1\dfrac{19}{90}$ 25. $\dfrac{11}{36}$ 26. $4\dfrac{1}{3}$ 27. $2\dfrac{1}{8}$

CHAPTER 3

Objective 3.1A

1. Thirty-nine hundredths   2. Eighty-one hundredths   3. Two and seven thousandths
4. Five and sixty-one thousandths   5. Fifteen and four tenths   6. Eighty-six ten-thousandths
7. Twenty-six and three hundred seventy-nine thousandths
8. Five hundred fourteen and three thousand one hundred eighteen ten-thousandths
9. One thousand seventy-eight and two hundred-thousandths   10. 0.834   11. 0.000052   12. 6.0101
13. 87.906   14. 462.035   15. 6014.1008   16. 25.07293   17. 91.0017

Objective 3.1B

1. 0.1   2. 9.1   3. 26.3   4. 96.5   5. 65.34   6. 13.01   7. 517.68
8. 792.25   9. 2.092   10. 6.280   11. 79.463   12. 51.004   13. 0.0420   14. 0.0036
15. 4.3763   16. 16.1119   17. 0.24967   18. 0.00912   19. 7.88010   20. 11.73241   21. 1
22. 4   23. 71   24. 0.004590   25. 0.100864   26. 2.111006

Objective 3.2A

1. 205.2844   2. 51.1918   3. 120.1664   4. 89.5197   5. 69.5793   6. 24.908   7. 61.5488
8. 9.3676   9. 277.9922   10. 113.069   11. 1.29   12. 1.55   13. 11.015   14. 18.91
15. 15.239   16. 39.107   17. 53.8362   18. 106.8338   19. 93.3431   20. 105.556   21. 57.992
22. 84.084   23. 160.351   24. 50.5418   25. 15.6153

Objective 3.2B

1. $2695.07   2. $52.58   3. 7.45 feet   4. 3.95 feet   5. 36.3 miles   6. 2651.8 miles   7. $4805.96
8. $1889.91   9. $120.35   10. $22,281.20

Answers to Drill-and-Practice Pages

Objective 3.3A

1. 32.377 **2.** 5.421 **3.** 136.8126 **4.** 593.587 **5.** 2.3191 **6.** 23.126 **7.** 62.446
8. 2.756 **9.** 6.8963 **10.** 0.062 **11.** 0.597 **12.** 3.091 **13.** 22.402 **14.** 0.1607
15. 1.808 **16.** 135.184 **17.** 361.688 **18.** 348.742 **19.** 37.0785 **20.** 18.2864 **21.** 181.186
22. 393.2374 **23.** 633.4404 **24.** 4.0159 **25.** 34.74909 **26.** 6.60157 **27.** 42.06339

Objective 3.3B

1. $3.17 **2.** 1.579 inches **3.** 0.7 pounds **4.** 55.38 seconds **5.** 25°C **6.** $824.42
7. $897.27 **8.** $24.47 **9.** $2720.69 **10.** $34,547.79

Objective 3.4A

1. 0.35 **2.** 1.92 **3.** 50.4 **4.** 2.28 **5.** 0.168 **6.** 22.95 **7.** 3.552
8. 0.0789 **9.** 0.04664 **10.** 0.2747 **11.** 10.58 **12.** 0.07062 **13.** 0.04712 **14.** 3.45285
15. 0.019154 **16.** 4.736 **17.** 0.456 **18.** 1.716 **19.** 82.1 **20.** 3.5 **21.** 6823.5
22. 68.5 **23.** 3.5 **24.** 34,000 **25.** 15.0788 **26.** 19.6935 **27.** 0.02142

Objective 3.4B

1. 37.5 inches **2.** 113 miles **3.** $3.41 **4.** $13.60 **5.** $6996 **6.** $515.10 **7.** $2744
8. $965.40 **9.** $460,275 **10.** $245,880

Objective 3.5A

1. 0.94 **2.** 3.2 **3.** 50 **4.** 86.5 **5.** 1.303 **6.** 0.31 **7.** 2.8
8. 470 **9.** 9.3 **10.** 7.7 **11.** 0.9 **12.** 29.4 **13.** 0.278 **14.** 19.51
15. 0.69 **16.** 0.080 **17.** 0.831 **18.** 0.008 **19.** 1 **20.** 16 **21.** 70
22. 0.723 **23.** 0.49875 **24.** 0.0037615 **25.** 24.8 **26.** 3.15 **27.** 0.626

Objective 3.5B

1. $9.90 **2.** $39.50 **3.** $107.06 **4.** 836 gallons **5.** 23 hairdryers **6.** 6.2 minutes **7.** $144.39
8. $130.46 **9.** $3.25 **10.** 2.3 feet

Objective 3.6A

1. 0.714 **2.** 0.067 **3.** 0.417 **4.** 0.889 **5.** 0.214 **6.** 0.545 **7.** 2.588
8. 0.438 **9.** 5.667 **10.** 0.643 **11.** 0.857 **12.** 1.25 **13.** 8.136 **14.** 15.5
15. 0.53 **16.** 4.375 **17.** 41.3 **18.** 1.087 **19.** 6.333 **20.** 0.556 **21.** 3.545
22. 27.111 **23.** 6.571 **24.** 0.013 **25.** 0.944 **26.** 6.556 **27.** 10.571

Objective 3.6B

1. $\frac{7}{10}$ **2.** $\frac{9}{10}$ **3.** $\frac{23}{50}$ **4.** $\frac{37}{50}$ **5.** $\frac{3}{8}$ **6.** $\frac{41}{200}$ **7.** $2\frac{11}{20}$

8. $6\frac{3}{4}$ **9.** $18\frac{2}{5}$ **10.** $12\frac{3}{10}$ **11.** $9\frac{1}{5}$ **12.** $14\frac{1}{2}$ **13.** $4\frac{69}{500}$ **14.** $6\frac{8}{125}$

15. $3\frac{7}{20}$ **16.** $9\frac{93}{100}$ **17.** $\frac{29}{175}$ **18.** $\frac{14}{15}$ **19.** $\frac{1}{9}$ **20.** $4\frac{81}{100}$ **21.** $\frac{11}{200}$

22. $\frac{3}{200}$ **23.** $23\frac{31}{50}$ **24.** $\frac{11}{25}$ **25.** $\frac{5}{6}$ **26.** $\frac{151}{600}$ **27.** $\frac{7}{9}$

Objective 3.6C

1. < **2.** < **3.** > **4.** > **5.** > **6.** < **7.** < **8.** < **9.** > **10.** < **11.** < **12.** < **13.** > **14.** <
15. > **16.** < **17.** < **18.** > **19.** < **20.** > **21.** > **22.** > **23.** < **24.** < **25.** < **26.** > **27.** <

CHAPTER 4

Objective 4.1A

1. $\frac{3}{7}$, 3:7, 3 to 7   **2.** $\frac{3}{8}$, 3:8, 3 to 8   **3.** $\frac{3}{5}$, 3:5, 3 to 5   **4.** $\frac{3}{4}$, 3:4, 3 to 4   **5.** $\frac{1}{7}$, 1:7, 1 to 7

6. $\frac{3}{7}$, 3:7, 3 to 7   **7.** $\frac{5}{1}$, 5:1, 5 to 1   **8.** $\frac{23}{14}$, 23:14, 23 to 14   **9.** $\frac{1}{1}$, 1:1, 1 to 1

10. $\frac{3}{2}$, 3:2, 3 to 2   **11.** $\frac{7}{4}$, 7:4, 7 to 4   **12.** $\frac{1}{3}$, 1:3, 1 to 3   **13.** $\frac{12}{11}$, 12:11, 12 to 11

14. $\frac{1}{5}$; 1:5, 1 to 5   **15.** $\frac{7}{8}$, 7:8, 7 to 8   **16.** $\frac{10}{9}$, 10:9, 10 to 9   **17.** $\frac{3}{4}$, 3:4, 3 to 4

18. $\frac{5}{11}$, 5:11, 5 to 11   **19.** $\frac{7}{6}$, 7:6, 7 to 6   **20.** $\frac{1}{6}$, 1:6, 1 to 6   **21.** $\frac{1}{2}$, 1:2, 1 to 2

22. $\frac{8}{5}$, 8:5, 8 to 5   **23.** $\frac{9}{4}$, 9:4, 9 to 4   **24.** $\frac{1}{1}$, 1:1, 1 to 1   **25.** $\frac{9}{10}$, 9:10, 9 to 10

26. $\frac{5}{2}$, 5:2, 5 to 2

Objective 4.1B

1. $\frac{1}{4}$ **2.** $\frac{11}{16}$ **3.** $\frac{18}{7}$ **4.** $\frac{4}{9}$ **5.** $\frac{3}{5}$ **6.** $\frac{5}{8}$ **7.** $\frac{3}{4}$

8. $\frac{23}{27}$ **9.** $\frac{6}{29}$ **10.** $\frac{3}{10}$

Objective 4.2A

1. $\dfrac{53 \text{ miles}}{2 \text{ hours}}$ **2.** $\dfrac{91 \text{ miles}}{3 \text{ gallons}}$ **3.** $\dfrac{26 \text{ feet}}{3 \text{ seconds}}$ **4.** $\dfrac{\$62}{3 \text{ toasters}}$ **5.** $\dfrac{\$303}{20 \text{ hours}}$ **6.** $\dfrac{\$3}{1 \text{ pound}}$ **7.** $\dfrac{\$501}{25 \text{ shares}}$

8. $\dfrac{1 \text{ tablet}}{6 \text{ hours}}$ **9.** $\dfrac{121 \text{ words}}{2 \text{ minutes}}$ **10.** $\dfrac{\$1525}{1 \text{ month}}$ **11.** $\dfrac{49 \text{ miles}}{1 \text{ hour}}$ **12.** $\dfrac{689 \text{ words}}{3 \text{ pages}}$ **13.** $\dfrac{\$13}{2 \text{ boards}}$ **14.** $\dfrac{3 \text{ clams}}{1 \text{ person}}$

15. $\dfrac{\$416}{1 \text{ week}}$ **16.** $\dfrac{8 \text{ place settings}}{1 \text{ table}}$ **17.** $\dfrac{41 \text{ pounds}}{3 \text{ square inches}}$ **18.** $\dfrac{\$7}{1 \text{ foot}}$ **19.** $\dfrac{\$1456}{1 \text{ department}}$

20. $\dfrac{217 \text{ seats}}{2 \text{ lecture halls}}$ **21.** $\dfrac{67 \text{ miles}}{2 \text{ gallons of gas}}$ **22.** $\dfrac{95 \text{ calls}}{2 \text{ hours}}$ **23.** $\dfrac{15 \text{ cups}}{1 \text{ urn}}$ **24.** $\dfrac{13 \text{ houses}}{51 \text{ acres}}$ **25.** $\dfrac{227 \text{ words}}{2 \text{ pages}}$

26. $\dfrac{\$13}{1 \text{ pound}}$

Objective 4.2B

1. \$2.50/foot   **2.** 19 miles/gallon   **3.** 16.75 pounds/square inch   **4.** \$24,000/partner   **5.** 8.4 gallons/minute
6. 49.8 miles/hour   **7.** 22.32 feet/second   **8.** \$0.90/pound   **9.** 155 miles/day   **10.** 68 heartbeats/minute
11. \$1500/month   **12.** 64 words/minute   **13.** \$10.24/hour   **14.** \$0.97/plant   **15.** 52.3 miles/hour
16. 7.3 pounds/square inch   **17.** \$3.48/pound   **18.** 48 words/minute   **19.** 57 gallons/minute
20. 29.5 miles/gallon   **21.** \$1250/partner   **22.** \$6.72/hour   **23.** 72 heartbeats/minute   **24.** 126.9 miles/day
25. \$1175/month   **26.** 12.3 feet/second

Objective 4.2C

1. $40.50 **2.** $2.59 **3.** 124 calls **4.** 57 words **5.** $0.67 **6.** $1.98 **7.** $83.57
8. $0.52 **9.** $1.80 **10.** $1.23

Objective 4.3A

1. True **2.** True **3.** True **4.** Not true **5.** True **6.** Not true **7.** Not true
8. True **9.** Not true **10.** True **11.** Not true **12.** Not true **13.** Not true **14.** True
15. Not true **16.** True **17.** Not true **18.** True **19.** True **20.** Not true **21.** Not true
22. True **23.** True **24.** Not true **25.** True **26.** Not true

Objective 4.3B

1. 6 **2.** 5 **3.** 12 **4.** 28 **5.** 24 **6.** 16.67 **7.** 24 **8.** 108 **9.** 10 **10.** 33.6 **11.** 6
12. 24.75 **13.** 24 **14.** 4.09 **15.** 6 **16.** 17.5 **17.** 7.5 **18.** 4.5 **19.** 47.5 **20.** 65.33
21. 17.5 **22.** 2.14 **23.** 1.2 **24.** 30 **25.** 27.35 **26.** 8.42 **27.** 22.92

Objective 4.3C

1. $90.40 **2.** 10.5 teaspoons **3.** $31.05 **4.** 34 feet **5.** $1036 **6.** $113.70
7. 2259 transistors **8.** $9.73 **9.** 10,380 people **10.** 434 gallons

CHAPTER 5

Objective 5.1A

1. $\frac{39}{100}$, 0.39 **2.** $\frac{16}{25}$, 0.64 **3.** $1\frac{1}{4}$, 1.25 **4.** $\frac{13}{50}$, 0.26 **5.** $\frac{17}{20}$, 0.80 **6.** $\frac{1}{5}$, 0.20 **7.** $4\frac{1}{4}$, 4.50

8. $\frac{19}{100}$, 0.19 **9.** $\frac{11}{20}$, 0.55 **10.** $\frac{71}{900}$ **11.** $\frac{23}{300}$ **12.** $\frac{129}{500}$ **13.** $\frac{129}{200}$ **14.** $\frac{13}{30}$

15. $\frac{399}{400}$ **16.** 0.675 **17.** 0.3407 **18.** 0.579 **19.** 0.40 **20.** 0.1389 **21.** 0.0201

Objective 5.1B

1. 32% **2.** 96% **3.** 4% **4.** 197% **5.** 214% **6.** 0.9% **7.** 68%
8. 12% **9.** 10.7% **10.** 41.7% **11.** 188.9% **12.** 57.1% **13.** 15.2% **14.** 60%
15. 183.3% **16.** $45\frac{5}{11}$% **17.** $22\frac{2}{9}$% **18.** $114\frac{2}{7}$% **19.** $37\frac{1}{2}$% **20.** $6\frac{2}{3}$% **21.** $58\frac{1}{3}$%

Objective 5.2A

1. 3.6 **2.** 15 **3.** 18.2 **4.** 47.7 **5.** 27 **6.** 19.25 **7.** 88.075
8. 12.688 **9.** 112 **10.** 0.05 **11.** 45 **12.** 0.2 **13.** 147 **14.** 13.2
15. 64.8 **16.** 5.25 **17.** 9.48 **18.** 11 **19.** 0.3 **20.** 36 **21.** 192.5
22. 38.75 **23.** 197 **24.** 60 **25.** 345.44 **26.** 84.15

Objective 5.2B

1. $7700 **2.** 400 employees **3.** $12.95 **4.** 2185 homes **5.** 486 plants **6.** 16.2 gallons
7. 2495 screws **8.** $19.98 **9.** $27,560 **10.** $188,000

Objective 5.3A

1. 31.25%   **2.** $16\frac{2}{3}\%$ **3.** 80%   **4.** 60%   **5.** 20%   **6.** 45%   **7.** 300%

8. 250%   **9.** 15%   **10.** 36%   **11.** 4.5%   **12.** 4%   **13.** 75%   **14.** 10%

15. 30%   **16.** 5%   **17.** 500%   **18.** 11.25%   **19.** 0.5%   **20.** 5.5%   **21.** 30.5%

22. $33\frac{1}{3}\%$ **23.** $66\frac{2}{3}\%$ **24.** 20%   **25.** 9.5%   **26.** 150%

Objective 5.3B

1. 12%   **2.** 12%   **3.** 6%   **4.** 230%   **5.** 20%   **6.** 3%   **7.** 25%   **8.** 80%   **9.** 120%   **10.** 12.5%

Objective 5.4A

1. 185   **2.** 400   **3.** 50   **4.** 60   **5.** 100   **6.** 70   **7.** 123

8. 184   **9.** 5000   **10.** 800   **11.** 570   **12.** 16   **13.** 1100   **14.** 350

15. 45   **16.** 450   **17.** 21   **18.** 200   **19.** 890   **20.** 1700   **21.** 88.5

22. 57   **23.** 24   **24.** 258   **25.** 62   **26.** 78.25

Objective 5.4B

1. $12,500   **2.** 380 business establishments   **3.** 56 questions   **4.** 2700 books   **5.** 24 calls   **6.** $2.25

7. $800,000   **8.** 3 spaces   **9.** 790,000 DVDs   **10.** $7,500,000

Objective 5.5A

1. 289   **2.** 60   **3.** 30%   **4.** 35%   **5.** 60   **6.** 200   **7.** 50%

8. 25%   **9.** 510   **10.** 800   **11.** 37%   **12.** 450%   **13.** 768   **14.** 819

15. 60   **16.** 150   **17.** 40%   **18.** 52%   **19.** 5%   **20.** 12.5%   **21.** 350%

22. 400%   **23.** 16,500   **24.** 2500   **25.** 140   **26.** 7.25%

Objective 5.5B

1. 75%   **2.** $12\frac{1}{2}\%$ **3.** $2.80   **4.** $75,600   **5.** $144   **6.** 97.5%   **7.** $8700

8. 7 errors   **9.** $10,500   **10.** 20%

CHAPTER 6

Objective 6.1A

1. $0.145 per ounce   **2.** $0.129 per ounce   **3.** $0.034 per ounce   **4.** $0.028 per ounce

5. $0.315 per ounce   **6.** $0.094 per ounce   **7.** $0.039 per ounce   **8.** $0.191 per ounce

9. $0.037 per ounce   **10.** $0.161 per ounce   **11.** $0.078 per ounce   **12.** $0.599 each   **13.** $0.297 each

14. $0.199 per ounce   **15.** 0.099 each   **16.** $0.423 per ounce   **17.** $0.034 per ounce

18. $0.258 per pound   **19.** $0.059 per ounce   **20.** $0.054 each   **21.** $0.055 per ounce   **22.** $0.042 each

23. $0.052 per ounce   **24.** $0.897 per pound

Objective 6.1B

1. 15 ounces for $0.94   **2.** 24 ounces for $0.94   **3.** 12 ounces for $1.30   **4.** 175 for $0.79   **5.** 50 for $1.89

6. 10 ounces for $0.74   **7.** 8 ounces for $0.89   **8.** 18 ounces for $1.39   **9.** 64 ounces for $1.35   **10.** 4 for $1.99

11. 9 for $1.27   **12.** $2.79 for 32 ounces   **13.** 16 ounces for $2.49   **14.** 2 pounds for $0.35   **15.** 8 ounces for $0.99

16. 10 pounds for $2.67   **17.** 18 ounces for $0.54   **18.** 6 ounces for $0.39   **19.** 50 for $1.09   **20.** $0.39 for 6.5 ounces

21. 9 ounces for $0.50   **22.** 119 sheets for $0.79   **23.** 12 ounces for $1.27   **24.** 12 ounces for $1.28

Answers to Drill-and-Practice Pages

Objective 6.1C

1. $7.16　**2.** $27.60　**3.** $7.96　**4.** $1.90　**5.** $1.17　**6.** $2.97　**7.** $0.66
8. $11.49　**9.** $1.25　**10.** $7.08　**11.** $10.60　**12.** $1.34　**13.** $10.04　**14.** $10.04
15. $12.50　**16.** $25.00

Objective 6.2A

1. 25%　**2.** $8\frac{1}{3}\%$　**3.** $33\frac{1}{3}\%$　**4.** 10%　**5.** 150 fans　**6.** 230 billboards

7a. $13.50　**7b.** $238.50　**8a.** $2560　**8b.** $34,560　**9a.** 50 spaces　**9b.** 5%
10a. 300 meters　**10b.** 4300 meters　　**11.** 12.5%　　**12.** 15%

Objective 6.2B

1. $7.80　**2.** $0.34　**3.** $10.88　**4.** 60%　**5a.** $13.60　**5b.** $47.60　**6a.** $19.80
6b. $64.80　**7a.** $0.60　**7b.** $1.69　**8a.** $9.10　**8b.** $35.10　**9.** $64.86　**10.** $44.64

Objective 6.2C

1. 15%　**2.** 30%　**3.** 12%　**4.** 15%　**5.** 81 employees　　**6.** $375
7a. 6 minutes　**7b.** 37.5%　**8a.** 49 orders　**8b.** 35%　**9a.** $17,100　**9b.** $267,900　**10a.** $63
10b. $357　**11.** 24%　**12.** 5%

Objective 6.2D

1. 36%　**2.** 15%　**3.** $30　**4.** $75　**5.** 20%　**6.** $4.80　**7a.** $0.60
7b. $1.80　**8a.** $9.90　**8b.** $45.10　**9a.** $4.20　**9b.** 12%　**10a.** $120　**10b.** 20%
11. $138　**12.** $39

Objective 6.3A

1. $1800　**2.** $8960　**3.** $99,200　**4.** $14,790　**5.** $6225　**6.** $5.40　**7a.** $714
7b. $117.25　**8a.** $23,400　**8b.** $1841.67　**9a.** $56,250　**9b.** $2187.50　**10a.** $3608　**10b.** $246

Objective 6.3B

1. $264.64　**2.** $84.42　**3.** $375.43　**4.** $161.86　**5.** $166.03　**6.** $6.74　**7.** $8.57
8. $6.69

Objective 6.3C

1. $3864.07　**2.** $1693.34　**3.** $24,488.64　**4.** $425,635.60　**5.** $44,578.50　**6.** $17,287.76　**7a.** $23,566.40
7b. $19,566.40　**8a.** $124,840,80　**9a.** $36,387.16　**9b.** $1826.22　**10a.** $65,544.80　**10b.** Yes

Objective 6.4A

1. $215,000　**2.** $180,000　**3.** $18,075　**4.** $12,000　**5.** $31,500　**6.** $36,000　**7.** $2000
8. $5400　**9a.** $30,000　**9b.** $120,000　**10a.** $8800　**10b.** $79,200

Objective 6.4B

1. $973.88　**2.** $2875.60　**3.** Yes　**4.** No　**5.** $63.75　**6.** $56.67　**7a.** $1140.54
7b. $900　**8a.** $2086.88　**8b.** $1800　**9.** $1401.40　**10.** $1560.78

Answers to Drill-and-Practice Pages

Objective 6.5A

1. $1020	**2.** No	**3.** $688.50	**4.** $442	**5.** $151.80	**6.** $201	**7a.** $286.60
7b. $2036.50	**8a.** $350	**8b.** $560	**9a.** $4800	**9b.** $19,200	**10.** $8925	

Objective 6.5B

1. $189.85	**2.** $250.47	**3.** $3920	**4.** $208	**5.** $0.14	**6.** $0.11	**7.** $3530
8. $74.80	**9a.** $5000	**9b.** $173.33	**10a.** $9000	**10b.** $255.00	**11.** $267.40	**12.** $190.80

Objective 6.6A

1. $236.40	**2.** $288	**3.** $3650	**4.** $2125	**5.** $48.50	**6.** $78	**7.** $451
8. $1800	**9.** $450	**10.** $80	**11a.** $29.20	**11b.** $350.40	**12a.** $320,000	**12b.** $38,400

Objective 6.7A

1. $444.95	**2.** $568.36	**3.** $3153.42	**4.** $2344.70	**5.** $567.42	**6.** $232.03	**7.** Yes
8. No	**9.** Yes	**10.** No				

Objective 6.7B

1. $495.06	**2.** $223.08	**3.** $325.34	**4.** $790.72	**5.** $1028.85	**6.** $721.72	**7.** $1197.44
8. $707.70	**9.** $1172.79	**10.** $1163.74				